Psychology 2e

An Introduction
for Health Professionals

Dedication

To Chris, Jordanne, Ben and Erin, without whom life would be soulless and uneventful. You never fail to make me smile and remind me what's important in life. Together, we create a tapestry of love, laughter and cherished moments that I hold close to my heart. I am blessed beyond measure to call you my family.

2e
Psychology
An Introduction
for Health Professionals

Deb O'Kane

RMN, ENB603, Grad Dip CN,
MN, Grad Cert Ed (Higher Ed)
BN Course Co-Ordinator
College of Nursing and Health Sciences,
Flinders University,
Adelaide, South Australia

ELSEVIER

ELSEVIER

Elsevier Australia. ACN 001 002 357
(a division of Reed International Books Australia Pty Ltd)
Tower 1, 475 Victoria Avenue, Chatswood, NSW 2067

This edition © 2024 Elsevier Australia. 1st edition © 2020 Elsevier Australia.

ISBN: 978-0-7295-4426-9

Notice

National Library of Australia Cataloguing-in-Publication Data

 A catalogue record for this book is available from the National Library of Australia

NATIONAL LIBRARY OF AUSTRALIA

Content Strategist: Melinda McEvoy
Content Project Manager: Kritika Kaushik
Edited by Matt Davies
Proofread by Tim Learner
Cover by Amy Buxton
Internal design by Georgette Hall
Index by Straive

Typeset by GW India

Printed in China by 1010 Printing International Ltd

Contents

Foreword

Health is fundamental to the wellbeing of individuals, families and communities. We live in an age of ever-increasing access to information about health, and greater expectations of individual participation and autonomy in knowledge exchange and decisions about health. This is coupled with an ever-ageing population and growing complexity of chronic conditions within global healthcare systems that struggle to keep up with this growing demand. The COVID-19 pandemic, in particular, has influenced how we view health and how health care is delivered. More than ever before, integrated multidisciplinary health care provision is proffered as one of the key solutions to this increasing complexity. Despite rapid technological and scientific advances, discoveries for improving health and treating health conditions, and increasing standards of living across communities, disparities in health status continue. Lifestyle risk factors continue to affect people across all spectrums in the community; consequently, supporting health behaviour change is an increasingly complex undertaking. Providing knowledge and expecting people to act in their own best interests for good health is no longer sufficient. Health professionals of the future will need new skills that embrace a more nuanced understanding of the human condition and also a broader understanding of the social and environmental contexts that shape health and human behaviour.

People make choices and decisions about their health or act in ways towards their health circumstances for a variety of reasons. There are many factors that can shape their perceptions and actions, their experiences of self-care and help-seeking behaviour. Some are within their control and others require an understanding of the social, political, cultural and wider context in which people live and interact within their community. Understanding this is the business of all health professionals who are providing support to people across health and social care systems, at whatever point of contact individuals have with those systems. This book helps to provide a useful introduction to health psychology, to bring an understanding of this field to healthcare students in ways that are easily accessible and relatable, and which place the experience of health by the person at the foreground.

The book is laid out in three main sections. The first section (Chapters 1–7) provides the building blocks for how we think about and understand health by engaging the reader step-by-step with the diversity of theoretical concepts underpinning health behaviour. The second section (Chapters 8–13) builds on these ideas and applies them to key issues for practice. The third section (chapter 14) provides application of psychology in healthcare practice. Chapter 1 introduces the reader to psychological theories and the interrelationship between psychological, biological and social influences on human behaviour. Chapter 2 focuses on how health professionals can use research to inform their everyday practice—to be competent consumers of research, thereby ensuring their actions have a clear evidence base. Chapters 3 and 4 explore health behaviour across the lifespan to help the reader understand the developmental trajectory in which health behaviours are shaped. Chapter 5 steps into the detail of understanding the diversity of how health is defined, the contribution of psychology to understandings of health, illness and health behaviours, and their interrelationships within the delivery of healthcare services. This chapter challenges the reader to think more deeply about the limits of biomedical dominance and theories about health. Chapter 6 examines the social context of behaviour and the important influence of social determinants for health. Chapter 7 provides clear descriptions and applications of the dominant psychological theories, models and approaches to explain health behaviours. This will help readers understand how they can support clients in behaviour change.

Chapter 8 is dedicated to the central role and skills of communication at an interpersonal and healthcare team level. It explores the role of power, professional boundaries and health literacy, and several other pertinent considerations for effective interactions to support health. Chapters 9, 10 and 11 are dedicated to examining the influence of stress, loss and pain on shaping health behaviour, exploring how these add complexity that requires health professionals to develop more advanced skills, and offering readers tangible tools for assessment and to support their work with these clients. Chapter 12 is dedicated to the relationship forged between the client and health professional, exploring the importance of partnership, engagement and understanding the diversity of expectations and experiences that each bring to the clinical encounter. Chapter 13 provides a detailed examination of the contribution of psychology to health promotion, integrating key concepts across prevention, social determinants and population approaches to health promotion. The book concludes with Chapter 14, which provides a comprehensive and valuable set of clinical case scenarios from the perspectives of several health professional disciplines, applying psychology in practice.

This is a collection that students can return to again and again during their training as health professionals. It provides a sound reference point for understanding this complex area of health care relevant to every health professional in their interactions with clients. Its strength is the rich collection of case studies and critical questions for reflection that are invaluable for emerging health professionals, and long into their later practice.

Sharon Lawn

Professor in the College of Medicine and Public Health
Flinders University, Adelaide, Australia

Chair and Executive Director
Lived Experience Australia Ltd

Welcome to the second edition of *Psychology: An Introduction for Health Professionals*.

In this updated edition, the book continues to fulfil its purpose of introducing healthcare students to the fundamental principles and theories of psychology in relation to health and health care. Additionally, it aims to provide a comprehensive understanding of the complex and interactive factors that influence health behaviours and outcomes.

One significant aspect of the second edition is its emphasis on contemporary issues and changes that have occurred in the field of psychology and health care in the past five years. The book incorporates updated research, new theories and current perspectives to reflect the evolving landscape of psychology and its applications in the healthcare domain. This ensures readers are exposed to the latest developments and insights in the field.

The book is supported by materials and resources using evidence-based research, references and clinical examples to ensure the content remains relevant to contemporary healthcare practice. Students can apply the material within the context of their own discipline and the health behaviours of the people they care for, their colleagues and themselves. It is written for, but is not limited to, undergraduate students of health including medicine, midwifery, nursing, nutrition, paramedicine, occupational therapy, speech pathology, physiotherapy and other allied health professions.

Unlike many health psychology textbooks, *Psychology: An Introduction for Health Professionals* examines individual personality and psychological theory in the social context of people's lives. This approach is taken because of the increasing awareness and abundant evidence that a person's behaviour is not only influenced by internal biological and psychological factors but also by external factors within the person's social and physical environment.

In keeping with the social determinant's framework, the book considers the social, political and cultural contexts of health care in Australia and New Zealand. Nevertheless, despite the theories and practices outlined in the book being situated in these two countries, they are also relevant to other countries and contexts.

The book also includes material that is not always found in undergraduate health psychology texts such as an introduction to psychological theory and healthcare research. Furthermore, to reflect the current interdisciplinary focus of tertiary healthcare education and practice, contributors to the book were recruited from and represent a range of healthcare disciplines.

By involving contributors from various healthcare disciplines who are currently engaged as health professionals or academics, the book can provide a well-rounded perspective on the applications of psychology in different healthcare contexts. This interdisciplinary approach promotes a comprehensive understanding of how psychological principles can be integrated into diverse healthcare settings and enhances collaboration among health professionals.

For ease of use and to support the understanding and application of theory to practice, the book has been divided into three sections. The first section outlines significant theoretical approaches to psychology that underpin the foundations of health behaviour. This consists of chapters 1–7. Section 2, chapters 8–13, identifies aspects of psychology that are relevant to healthcare practice and therefore covers the psychological aspects of specific health encounters, issues and interventions. The final section offers a wide range of case studies where the application of psychological perspectives can be applied. The chapter presents a range of discipline-specific case studies that allow a reader to place the theoretical concepts into the context of their own clinical practice. Throughout the book critical thinking questions, case studies and examples of research are included to encourage students to reflect on the application of theory to practice. Activities are provided for lecturers to use in the classroom.

Psychology: An Introduction for Health Professionals is intended to assist future health professionals to understand the diversity of human responses, particularly in relation to health behaviours, and to develop the knowledge, skills and disposition required to care for the patients and clients they will encounter in their chosen career. We trust that readers will find the content to be engaging, interesting and professionally relevant.

Deb O'Kane
June 2023

Deb O'Kane

Deb is an Associate Professor at Flinders University in South Australia with a diverse background in nursing and academia. She has worked in various areas of hospital-based care, community services and higher education that spans the United Kingdom and Australia. Her expertise lies in mental health and health psychology, and she is actively involved in coordinating and teaching undergraduate and postgraduate topics related to these fields.

One of Deb's primary interests is the mental health of children and young people. She has spent several years working as a clinician and educator in this area, gaining valuable experience and knowledge. Lifespan development and its impact on health and health choices are areas that particularly intrigue her. Deb recognises the importance of early intervention, person-centred care and collaborative practice, and she actively advocates for these principles.

Deb's dedication to improving health care extends beyond the classroom. She engages with service users, carers and healthcare providers to ensure their perspectives are incorporated into her work. By actively involving all stakeholders, Deb strives to promote the idea that health is a universal right and should be accessible to everyone.

Contributors and Reviewers

Contributors

Louise Baldwin PhD, MHSc(HProm), BEd(Sec), FHEA
School of Public Health and Social Work, Faculty of Health
Design Lab – Creative Industries, Education and Social Justice Faculty and Australian
Centre for Philanthropy and Nonprofit Studies – Faculty of Business and Law,
Queensland University of Technology, Brisbane, Australia
Founder and Director, Health and Social Change Australia (consultancy)
Global Vice President (Membership) International Union for Health Education and
Promotion (IUHPE)

Adam Gerace BPsych(Hons), PhD
Senior Lecturer and Head of Course – Positive Psychology, College of Psychology,
School of Health, Medical and Applied Sciences, CQUniversity, Adelaide, Australia

Debra O'Kane RMN, ENB603, GDipCN, MN, GCEd(Higher Ed)
BN Course Coordinator, College of Nursing and Health Sciences Flinders University,
Adelaide, Australia

Yyonne Parry RN, BA, MSHM, GCEd, PhD
School of Nursing and Midwifery, Flinders University, Adelaide, Australia

Ivanka Prichard PhD
College of Nursing and Health Sciences, Flinders University, Adelaide, Australia

Mat Prior MSpPhty, BPhty(Hons)
Clinical Teaching Specialist / Lecturer in Physiotherapy, College of Nursing and
Health Sciences, Flinders University, Bedford Park, Australia

Deb Rawlings BSN(Hons), MPH
Palliative Care, Flinders University, Adelaide, Australia

Gabrielle Rigney PhD
Psychology, Central Queensland University, Appleton Institute, Adelaide, Australia

Matt Sutton BPhty, MMuscskelSpPhty
College of Nursing and Health Sciences, Flinders University, Bedford Park, Australia

Eileen Willis BEd, MEd, PhD
College of Nursing and Health Sciences, Flinders University, Adelaide, Australia

Reviewers

David Arness PhD, BPsych(Hons)
Lecturer, School of Psychology, Western Sydney University, Parramatta, Australia

Daniel Degoey MClinChiro, BSc(Chiro), BClinPra(Paramed), FHEA
Lecturer, Paramedicine and Chiropractor, School of Nursing, Midwifery and Paramedicine, Faculty of Health Science, Australian Catholic University, Brisbane, Australia

Russell James PhD
Senior Lecturer, School of Nursing , University of Tasmania, Hobart, Australia

Kylie Kendrick MPH, GCParamed, BSci(Paramed)
Senior Lecturer, Faculty of Health Science, Australian Catholic University, Melbourne, Australia

PRE-PROPOSAL REVIEWERS

Ben Coyte
Lecturer, Paramedicine, Clinical Coordinator (Melbourne), National Specialised Learning Environments and Simulation Coordinator (Paramedicine), School of Nursing, Midwifery and Paramedicine, Faculty of Health Sciences, Australian Catholic University, Melbourne, Australia

Xanthe Glaw RN, CMHN, BN, GCMH, MNMH, MN(AppMan), PhD
Course Coordinator, Master of Health Administration, Academic Lecturer, School of Nursing, Midwifery and Paramedicine (NSW/ACT), Australian Catholic University, Sydney, Australia

Russell James BN, GDipN(MH), MN
Lecturer, Nursing, College of Health and Medicine, School of Nursing, University of Tasmania, Hobart, Australia

Acknowledgments

The writing of this book has truly been a collaborative effort, and I am deeply grateful to the many people who have contributed to its creation. It would be remiss of me not to begin by acknowledging the original author and editor of this book, Pat Barkway. This edition has evolved from her foundational work, and I am indebted to her for her contributions, knowledge, writing style and wisdom. Pat's belief in me to carry on her legacy as the author and editor of this book is something I deeply appreciate, and it has been an honour to follow in her footsteps.

I would like to express my heartfelt appreciation to all the contributors who generously volunteered their time and expertise to revise and update one or more chapters. Your willingness to share your insights and your patience with my countless queries have been invaluable. Your contributions have enriched this book and enhanced its relevance to readers. I am grateful for the depth of knowledge and expertise you have brought to the table.

I also want to extend my gratitude to the colleagues, patients, clients and students with whom I have had the privilege to work over the years. Your interactions, discussions and challenges throughout my career have played a significant role in shaping my thinking and deepening my understanding of psychological theory as it applies to real-life situations.

To the publishing team at Elsevier, I would like to commend your exceptional work in keeping this project on track. Your professionalism, dedication and attention to detail have been integral in bringing this book to fruition. I am grateful for your support throughout the publishing process.

I would also like to express my appreciation to the reviewers who provided critical and constructive feedback on the manuscript. Your insights and suggestions have been instrumental in improving the quality of this book.

Lastly, although it is impossible to name everyone individually, I want to sincerely thank my family, friends and colleagues who have shown interest in my work and provided unwavering support throughout the writing phase. Your encouragement, belief in me and understanding of the time and effort required to complete this book have meant the world to me. Your presence in my life has been a constant source of inspiration, and I am deeply grateful for your unwavering support.

To all those who have contributed to this book in one way or another, I offer my heartfelt thanks. Your collective efforts have made this book possible, and I am truly grateful for each and every one of you.

Section 1

Theoretical approaches to psychology in healthcare practice

Chapter 1

Psychology: an introduction

DEB O'KANE

Learning objectives

The material in this chapter will help you to:

- understand the psychological theories that provide explanations of human behaviour and personality
- describe and critique biomedical, psychological and sociological theories of human behaviour
- apply your knowledge of psychological theory to understand the behaviour of yourself and others
- describe how psychological theory informs interventions in healthcare practice
- explain the nature versus nurture debate
- understand the interrelationship between psychological, biological and social influences on human behaviour.

Key terms

- Psychological theories (5)
- Biomedical model of health (6)
- Psychoanalytic theory (7)
- Behavioural (9)
- Cognitive theory (12)
- Cognitive behavioural therapy (12)
- Humanistic psychology (15)
- Sociological theories (17)
- Eclectic/holistic approach (18)
- Nature versus nurture (21)

Introduction

Who are you? How have you come to be who you are? What influences how you think, feel and act? Are your personality and behaviour determined by your genetic makeup and biological events, by thoughts and feelings, by your experiences in the world, or by an interrelationship between some or all of these? Most of us, at one time or another, have thought about these questions. Through attempting to understand why humans behave as they do, a further question arises: Are human behaviour and personality determined by genetics and biology (nature) or shaped by one's upbringing, experiences and environmental factors (nurture)?

These questions have long engaged the interest and passion of philosophers, healers and health professionals and, in more recent times, psychologists and researchers. Psychology emerged as a discipline in its own right when the use of scientific methodologies were introduced to help understand human behaviour. Investigating these questions has resulted in various theories being proposed to explain typical and atypical thoughts, feelings and behaviours. These concepts—the theories that attempt to explain and provide understandings of behaviour—will be examined in this chapter.

Psychology

Psychology is a theoretical and applied discipline that emerged in the 19th century in Europe and North America from the established disciplines of physiology and philosophy. Its principal focus is the scientific study of behaviour. To achieve this, psychologists study how organisms (primarily humans but not exclusively) act, think, learn, perceive, feel, interact with others and understand themselves. Nevertheless, given that psychological theory originated in a Western context, caution is recommended when applying psychological theory to people from other cultures such as African, Asian, New Zealand Māori or Australian Aboriginal and Torres Strait Islander peoples.

The discipline of psychology focuses on behavioural responses (including affective and cognitive) to certain sets of conditions. Psychology is both a natural and a social science that attempts to determine the laws of nature at a cellular level (as in bioscientific enquiry) and also to explain human behaviour in individuals and groups. Within the discipline, professional psychologists practise in two broad areas: theoretical (research or academic) and applied (clinical practice or organisational psychology).

The major theoretical perspectives (also called paradigms) that attempt to explain and predict specific behaviours include psychoanalytic, behavioural (learning), cognitive and humanistic. At times these theories can be complementary, but at other times they can be contradictory. Finally, other theoretical perspectives that are outside the field of psychology are recognised for the role they play in influencing behaviour. These paradigms include the biomedical model and sociological theories.

Theories of personality and human behaviour

Psychological theories propose models to explain human behaviours. They emerged from curiosity about and philosophical enquiry into the human condition. The theories also place particular emphasis on identifying the causes of abnormal behaviour to develop models for understanding, preventing or treating health problems with a behavioural or lifestyle component such as physical activity or tobacco smoking. Explanations of human behaviour can be broadly divided into three paradigms:

- biomedical or biological/physical models
- psychological models, including personality, behavioural, cognitive, developmental and humanistic approaches
- sociological models.

Within these paradigms are several major viewpoints that offer a theory of personality development or an explanation of human behaviour:

- The *biomedical model* proposes that behaviour is influenced by physiology, with normal behaviour occurring when the body is in a state of equilibrium and abnormal behaviour being a consequence of physical pathology.

- *Psychoanalytic theory* asserts that behaviour is driven by unconscious processes and influenced by childhood/developmental conflicts that either have been resolved or remain unresolved.

- *Behavioural psychology* presents the view that behaviour is influenced by factors external to the individual. Behaviours are learned depending on whether they are rewarded (or not), by association with another event or by imitation.

- *Cognitive psychology* acknowledges the role of perception and thoughts about oneself, one's individual experience and the environment in influencing behaviour.

- *Humanistic psychology* focuses on developing a concept of self and the individual striving to achieve personal goals.

- *Developmental theories* propose that over time human development progresses through predictable stages of growth and development.

- *Sociological theories* shift the emphasis from the individual to the broader social forces that influence people. This model challenges the notion of individual pathology and acknowledges the responsibility of society for the health of its people.

- The *evolutionary approach* centres on the adaptation of a person (organism) to survive in its environment. The core idea is that behaviour, thoughts and feelings are best understood from the context of human evolvement, the process of natural selection and the continuation of genes to promote survival.

- *Sociocultural theories* look at how the behaviour and thinking of a person varies across diverse cultures (shaped by gender, ethnicity and religion) and how they interrelate and influence each other.

- The *eclectic approach* (also called holistic) draws on the theory and research of several paradigms to obtain an overall understanding or provide a more comprehensive explanation than would be achieved by using one theoretical model alone. For example, in clinical practice cognitive behavioural therapy is a frequently used counselling approach; in research a mixed-methods approach may be used.

Each of these seemingly disparate perspectives makes a substantial contribution to the understanding of how and why humans think, feel and behave as they do, thereby identifying opportunities for preventing and treating health problems with a behavioural component. Nevertheless, as a comprehensive theory of human behaviour, each also has major shortcomings, hence the practice of using an eclectic approach that applies more than one theory.

BIOMEDICAL MODEL

Also known as psychobiology or the neuroscience perspective, the **biomedical model of health** asserts that *normal* behaviour is a consequence of equilibrium within the body and that abnormal behaviour results from pathological bodily or brain function. This is not a new notion; in the 4th century BC the Greek physician Hippocrates attributed mental disorder to brain pathology. His ideas were overshadowed, however, when throughout the Dark Ages and later during the Renaissance, thinking and explanations shifted to witchcraft or demonic possession (Hooley et al. 2020; Kring & Johnson 2021). In the 19th century, a return to biophysical explanations accompanied the emergence of the public health movement.

In recent times, advances in technology have led to increased understanding of organic determinants of behaviour. Research and treatment have focused on four main areas:

- *Nervous system disorders, in particular neurotransmitter disturbance at the synaptic gap between neurons*—more than 50 neurotransmitters have been identified, four of which are implicated in mental illness. These are acetylcholine (Alzheimer's disease), dopamine (schizophrenia and mood disorders), noradrenaline (mood disorder) and serotonin (mood disorder).

- *Structural changes to the brain*—for example, following trauma or in degenerative disorders such as Huntington's disease.

- *Endocrine or gland dysfunction*—for example, hypothyroidism has a similar presentation to clinical depression, and hormonal changes are thought to contribute to postnatal depression.

- *Familial (genetic) transmission of mental illness*—family history is a possible risk factor for experiencing mental illness, although while some mental health disorders seem to share a common genetic risk factor and therefore are likely to run in a family, a shared genetic history alone is not enough (Hooley et al. 2020).

Although genetic studies show a correlation between having a close relative with a history of mental illness, there is not any mental health disorder with 100% genetic basis. Environmental factors play a significant role in developing a mental health issue despite the absence or presence of genetic elements. Research continues to grow in this area and is important because it supports the diathesis–stress hypothesis, a widely held explanation for developing a mental disorder that proposes that constitutional predisposition combined with environmental stress will lead to mental illness (Kring & Johnson 2021).

Critique of the biomedical model

Among treatments that emerge from the biomedical model are medications that alter the function, production and reabsorption of neurotransmitters in the synaptic gap. However, evidence that a particular intervention is an effective treatment is not proof of a causal link with the illness. For example, consider a person with type 1 (insulin-dependent) diabetes. Because this person lacks insulin to metabolise glucose, the condition is managed with regular insulin injections. However, the lack of insulin is a symptom of the disease, not the cause. Whatever caused the pancreas to stop producing insulin is not known, despite the treatment being effective. Similarly, with schizophrenia, the relationship between taking antipsychotic medications (which are dopamine antagonists), dopamine levels and symptom management is correlational, not causal. Therefore, although antipsychotic medication affects dopamine receptors and hence dopamine levels, and can be an effective treatment to manage the psychotic symptoms of schizophrenia, this does not provide evidence that elevated dopamine levels *cause* the disorder.

PSYCHOANALYTIC THEORY

Sigmund Freud developed the first psychological explanation of human behaviour—**psychoanalytic theory**—in the late 19th century. He placed strong emphasis on the role of unconscious processes (not in the conscious mind of the person) in determining human behaviour. Central tenets of the theory are that intrapsychic (generally unconscious) forces, developmental factors and family relationships determine human behaviour. According to psychoanalytic theory, normal development results when the person satisfactorily traverses each developmental stage and mental illness is seen as a consequence of fixation at a particular developmental stage or conflict that has not been resolved.

Sigmund Freud

Freud (1856–1939) was a neurologist who, in his clinical practice, saw a number of patients with sensory or neurological problems for which he was unable to identify a physiological cause. These patients were mainly middle-class Viennese women. It was from his work with these patients that Freud hypothesised that the cause of their illnesses was psychological. From this assumption he developed an explanation of personality development, which he called psychoanalytic theory. According to Freud the mind is composed of three forces:

1. *The id*—the primitive biological force comprising two basic drives: sexual and aggressive. The id operates on the pleasure principle and seeks to satisfy life-sustaining needs such as food, love and creativity, in addition to sexual gratification.
2. *The ego*—the cognitive component of personality that attempts to use realistic means (the reality principle) to achieve the desires of the id.
3. *The superego*—the internalised moral standards of the society in which one lives. It represents the person's ideal self and can be equated to a conscience.

Freud's theory proposed that personality development progresses through five stages throughout childhood. At each stage the child's behaviour is driven by the need to satisfy sexual and aggressive drives via the mouth, anus or genitals. Failure of the child to satisfy these needs at any one of the stages will result in psychological difficulties that are carried into adulthood. For example, unresolved issues at the oral stage can lead to dependency issues in adulthood; problems in the anal stage may lead to the child later developing obsessive-compulsive traits. Freud's stages of psychosexual development are:

1. *oral*—from birth to about 18 months, where the primary focus of the id is the mouth

2. *anal*—from approximately 18 months to 3 years, where libido shifts from the mouth to the anus and primary gratification is derived from expelling or retaining faeces

3. *phallic*—from approximately 3 to 6 years, where gratification of the id occurs through the genitals

4. *latent*—Freud proposed that from approximately 6 to 12 years the child goes through a latency phase in which sexual urges are dormant

5. *genital*—once the child passes through puberty, sexual urges re-emerge but now they are directed towards another person, not the self as they were at an earlier stage of development (Hooley et al. 2020; Kring & Johnson 2021).

Defence mechanisms

An important contribution of psychoanalytic theory to the understanding of behaviour has been identifying defence mechanisms and the role they play in mediating anxiety. Defence mechanisms were first described by Freud and later elaborated on by his daughter, Anna (Freud 1966). They are unconscious, protective processes whereby anxiety experienced by the ego is reduced. Repression is the primary defence mechanism and an unconscious process whereby unacceptable impulses/feelings/thoughts are barred from consciousness (e.g. memories of sexual abuse in childhood). Others include:

- regression—the avoidance of present difficulties by a reversion to an earlier, less mature way of dealing with the situation (e.g. a toilet-trained child who becomes incontinent following the birth of a sibling)

- denial—the blocking of painful information from consciousness (e.g. not accepting that a loss has occurred)

- projection—the denial of one's own unconscious impulses by attributing them to another person (e.g. when you dislike someone but believe it is the other person who does not like you)

- displacement—the transferring of emotion from the source to a substitute (e.g. a person who is unassertive in an interaction with a supervisor at work and 'kicks the cat' on arriving home).

Being aware of defence mechanisms and the role they play in behaviour can help health professionals to understand that a person's seemingly irrational actions may have an unconscious cause. For example, a child who regresses following a serious illness is not seeking attention but reverting to behaviours from a time when they felt safe.

Critique of psychoanalytic theory

Although the notions of unconscious motivations and defence mechanisms are helpful in interpreting behaviours, Freud's version of psychoanalytic theory has not been without its critics. Fellow psychoanalyst Erik Erikson disagreed with Freud's theory of psychosexual stages of development and proposed instead a psychosocial theory in which development occurs throughout the lifespan, not just through childhood as in Freud's model (e.g. Erikson 1963; Santrock 2021). (See Chapters 3 and 4 for more detail on developmental theories.)

The unconscious nature of Freud's concepts and stages renders them difficult to test and therefore there is little evidence to support Freudian theory. Feminists also object to Freud's interpretation of the psychological development of women, arguing that there is scant evidence to support the hypothesis that women view their bodies as inferior to men's because they do not have a penis (Kring & Johnson 2021). Nevertheless, despite these criticisms, psychoanalytic theory does provide plausible explanations for seemingly irrational behaviour.

BEHAVIOURAL PSYCHOLOGY

Behavioural psychology (also called behaviourism) is a school of psychological thought founded by JB Watson in the early 20th century. Its purpose was to objectively study observable human behaviour, as opposed to examining the mind, which was the prevalent psychological method at the time in Europe. The model proposes a scientific approach to the study of behaviour, a feature that behaviourists argue is lacking in psychoanalytic theory (and in humanistic psychology, which developed later).

Behaviourism opposes the introspective, structuralist approach of psychoanalysis and emphasises the importance of the environment in shaping behaviour. The focus is on observable behaviour and conditions that elicit and maintain the behaviour (classical conditioning) or factors that reinforce behaviour (operant conditioning) or vicarious learning through watching and imitating the behaviour of others (modelling).

Three basic assumptions underpin behavioural theory. These are that personality is determined by prior learning, that human behaviour is changeable throughout the lifespan and that changes in behaviour are generally caused by changes in the environment. The following people were prominent figures in the development of behavioural psychology.

Ivan Pavlov

Russian physiologist Ivan Pavlov (1849–1936) was the first to describe the relationship between stimulus and response. Pavlov demonstrated that a dog could learn to salivate (respond) to a non-food stimulus (a bell) if the stimulus was simultaneously presented with the food. His discovery became known as learning by association or classical conditioning. Phobias and fear, for example, can be explained by classical conditioning. See Table 1.1 for an explanation of how fear or phobia of a rabbit (an animal that is not normally feared) can develop.

Table 1.1		
CLASSICAL CONDITIONING OF FEAR		
Before conditioning		
Neutral stimulus Rabbit	No reaction	
During conditioning		
Neutral stimulus Rabbit	Unconditioned stimulus Loud noise	Unconditioned response Fear response
After conditioning		
Conditioned stimulus Rabbit	Conditioned response Fear of the rabbit	

◉ Critical thinking

- Consider how classical conditioning can explain why a patient receiving chemotherapy injections starts vomiting when the chemotherapy nurse enters the patient's room.
- Identify which of the following is the neutral stimulus, unconditioned stimulus, conditioned stimulus and conditioned response and enter them into the table below:
    - » nurse
    - » chemotherapy injection
    - » vomiting
    - » vomiting at the sight of the nurse.

Before conditioning		
Neutral stimulus	No reaction	
During conditioning		
Neutral stimulus	Unconditioned stimulus	Unconditioned response
After conditioning		
Conditioned stimulus	Conditioned response	

John B Watson

Watson (1878–1958), who is attributed as being the founder of behaviourism, changed the focus of psychology from the study of inner sensations to the study of observable behaviour. In his quest to make psychology a true science, Watson further developed

Pavlov's work on stimulus–response learning and experimented by manipulating stimulus conditions. In the classic 'Little Albert' experiment, Watson and his colleague Rayner (1920) conditioned a young child to fear a white rat by producing a loud noise at the same time that Albert touched the rat (which he initially did not fear). Albert's fear reaction also generalised to other furry objects such as a fur coat and a white rabbit.

Watch it on YouTube! *For a short video of the 'Little Albert' experiment see* http://www.youtube.com/watch?v=9hBfnXACsOI

Furthermore, Watson believed that abnormal behaviours were the result of earlier faulty conditioning and that reconditioning could modify these behaviours. His work heralded the introduction of psychological approaches to treat problem behaviours.

BF Skinner

Skinner (1904–1990) formulated the notion of instrumental or operant conditioning in which reinforcers (rewards) contribute to the probability of a response being either repeated or extinguished. Skinner believed that behaviour was the result of an interaction between the individual and the environment and because the environment was more readily amenable to change, this was the most appropriate place to intervene to bring about change. His research showed that by changing contingencies that were external to the person, behaviour could be altered. This is an underlying principle in interventions using an operant conditioning or 'learning by consequence' approach (Skinner 1953).

Critique of behavioural psychology

Behaviourism provided the first scientifically testable theories of human development, as well as plausible explanations of how behaviours are learned and, in the clinical arena, how conditions such as addictions, phobias and anxiety develop. Behavioural principles underpin many approaches to behaviour change (these are discussed more fully in Chapter 7). Behavioural explanations are less convincing, however, when applied to complex human emotions (e.g. compassion) or behaviours (e.g. risk taking), or the behaviours of a person with a medical condition like dementia. Furthermore, most behavioural research has been conducted on animals under laboratory conditions, so to extrapolate findings from this research to humans is mechanistic and does not allow for intrinsic human qualities like creativity or altruism. Finally, behavioural theory falls short in explaining the success of an individual brought up in an adverse environment or why a person whose environment is apparently healthy and advantaged engages in deviant or antisocial behaviour.

CASE STUDY: JASON

Three-year-old Jason was at the supermarket with his mother, Kate. He asked for a chocolate at the checkout and his mother said 'no'. Jason threw a tantrum, lay on the floor and started screaming. Kate was so embarrassed that she bought Jason a chocolate. The following week this scenario was repeated. Now Jason demands a chocolate every time he and his mother go shopping.

☀ Critical thinking

- Which behavioural theory explains Jason's behaviour?
- What can Kate do to stop Jason throwing tantrums at the supermarket?

COGNITIVE PSYCHOLOGY

Since the 1950s, interest in the cognitive or thinking processes involved in behavioural responses has expanded. **Cognitive theory** proposes that people actively interpret their environment and cognitively construct their world. Therefore, behaviour is a result of the interplay of external and internal events. External events are the stimuli and reinforcements that regulate behaviour, and internal events are one's perceptions and thoughts about oneself and the world, as well as one's behaviour in the world. In other words, how you think about a situation will influence how you behave in that situation.

Cognitive theories underpin many contemporary psychological therapies— for example, cognitive behavioural therapy, acceptance and commitment therapy, dialectical behaviour therapy and motivational interviewing. For instance, when **cognitive behavioural therapy** is applied to treat depression, the therapist helps the person to identify how the interaction of their thoughts, feelings and behaviours influence their current situation. The therapist assists the person to identify and challenge negative beliefs, emotions and unhelpful behaviours, and finds strategies to change these.

The following people are prominent figures in the development of cognitive psychology.

Albert Bandura

According to Bandura (1925–2021) it is not intrapsychic or environmental forces alone that influence behaviour. Rather, human behaviour results from the interaction of the environment with the individual's perception and thinking. Self-efficacy, or the belief that one can achieve a certain goal, is the critical component in achieving that goal. Bandura also proposed that consequences do not have to be directly experienced by the person for learning to occur—learning can occur vicariously through the process of modelling or learning by imitation (Bandura 2001, 2012, 2016).

Aaron T Beck

Problem behaviour, said Beck (1921–2021), results from cognitive distortions or faulty thinking that can occur automatically. It involves a process where our thoughts become biased resulting in inaccurate thinking (i.e. cognitive distortion), which in turn affects mood and daily living. For example, a depressed person will selectively choose information that maintains a gloomy perspective. Depression is experienced when one has a negative schema about oneself or one's situation. According to Beck, depression is a behavioural response to an attitude or cognition of hopelessness, as opposed to hopelessness being a symptom of depression. Anxiety, he said, is experienced when the person has a distorted anticipation of danger. Treatment within Beck's model involves changing the person's views about themselves and their life situation (Beck 1972; Beck et al. 2005; Whalley 2019).

Martin Seligman

Seligman (b. 1942) first proposed a theory to explain why a person learns to become helpless when they perceive they have no control over their situation or what is happening to them. The theory is called 'learned helplessness' and suggests that if a person experiences repeated adversity, and attempts to alleviate the situation are unsuccessful, eventually the person begins to believe nothing they do will change the outcome and so stop trying and behave in a helpless manner. Learned helplessness has been associated with issues such as low self-esteem, poor academic success and depression. Seligman later expanded his model to include learned optimism, a process of challenging negative cognitions to change from a position of passivity to one of control (Seligman 2011). He currently conducts research to investigate factors and circumstances that enable humans to *flourish*. Seligman's theoretical approach is called positive psychology (Seligman & Csikszentmihalyi 2014; Diener et al. 2018).

Critique of cognitive psychology

Cognitive theory is criticised as being unscientific (as are psychoanalytic and humanistic theories) because mental processes cannot be objectively observed and subjective reports are not necessarily reliable (Kring & Johnson 2021). Also, the insight that one's thinking is the cause of one's problems will not in itself bring about behaviour change.

Furthermore, contrary to the proposal that *cognitions influence emotions*, which in turn influence actions (a notion that underpins the cognitive approach), some psychologists propose that action needs to occur first, which in turn changes thinking and acts as an impetus for further behaviour. A prime example of this is when a student is waiting to become motivated to write their assignment or a person wants to start going to the gym. In these cases, changing the behaviour first—that is, taking action before the associated feeling (motivation) whether that be writing or going to the gym—can result in feeling more motivated (Kruglanski et al. 2015). These findings can be explained by the relational model of Ivey and colleagues (2022) in which thoughts, feelings and behaviour interact with each other and with meaning so that a change in any one part of the system may result in a change in other parts (see Fig. 1.1). So while cognition plays an integral part in behavioural outcomes, it may not necessarily be the initiating factor as proposed by cognitive theory. This is in contrast to the linear unidirectional explanation of cognitive psychology

Finally, the therapeutic techniques derived from cognitive (and cognitive behavioural) theory are practical and effective and can be self-administered by the client under the direction of a therapist. These therapies have an established record in changing problem behaviours such as phobias, obsessions and compulsions, and in stress management (Fordham et al. 2018). They also help in treating depression and schizophrenia, though whether the treatment result is more effective than other interventions is inconclusive (Laws et al. 2018).

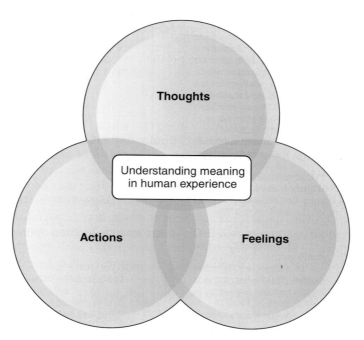

Figure 1.1 Meaning as the core of human experience and its relationship to feelings, thoughts and behaviours—*Meaning can drive action* Adapted from: Ivey et al. 2018

CASE STUDY: ANNA

Anna is a 30-year-old woman who has been experiencing panic attacks for 5 years since she was involved in a minor car accident on her way to work. She was driving her car when it clipped a cyclist, who fell off his bike but did not sustain significant injuries. When Anna arrived at work she experienced dizziness, palpitations and blurred vision and had to go home. The following day she caught the bus to work because she feared being involved in another accident. However, when she got to work the symptoms she experienced the day before returned. She left work and visited her GP, fearing that she was experiencing a heart attack. The GP reassured her that her heart was fine and explained that she was experiencing a panic attack. The GP advised her to take the rest of the week off work to relax. Anna felt safe at home and did not have any more panic symptoms.

But the following week Anna again experienced the panic symptoms at the bus stop on her way to work. She had to go home. Anna did not return to her job and resigned a month later. Anna has never experienced anxiety symptoms in her home. But she is so frightened of experiencing a panic attack in public that she no longer leaves home unless she is with her partner or someone else she trusts. Two years ago she was diagnosed with panic disorder.

Critical thinking

- Identify the factors that contributed to Anna developing panic disorder.
- Use behavioural/learning theories to explain how Anna's panic disorder developed.
- Identify Anna's thoughts that may be perpetuating the symptoms of the panic disorder.

HUMANISTIC PSYCHOLOGY

After becoming disenchanted with the psychological theories of the time, Charlotte Bühler, Abraham Maslow, Carl Rogers and their colleagues in the United States established the Association for Humanistic Psychology in 1962. **Humanistic psychology** has its intellectual and social roots in philosophical humanism and existentialism, which brought psychology back to a close relationship with philosophy (Bühler & Allen 1972; Rogers 1951). This school of psychology, which became known as the Third Force, arose in response to dissatisfaction with the mechanistic approach of psychoanalysis and behaviourism and the negative views that were implicit in both these theoretical perspectives.

Humanist psychologists objected to the determinism of the two prevailing theories: psychoanalysis, with its emphasis on unconscious drives; and behaviourism, which saw the environment as central in shaping behaviour. Humanistic psychology rejected the reductionism of explaining human behaviour, feelings, thinking and motivation merely in terms of psychological mechanisms or biological processes. It also opposed the mechanistic approach of behaviourism and psychoanalysis for the way in which they minimised human experience and qualities such as choice, creativity and spontaneity.

Humanistic psychologists focused on the intrinsic human qualities of the individual such as free will, altruism, self-esteem, freedom and self-actualisation—qualities that, they asserted, distinguished humans from other animals. Humanistic psychology therefore differed from its predecessors in its emphasis on the whole person, human emotions, experience and the meaning of experience, the creative potential of the individual, choice, self-realisation and self-actualisation. The theory also opposed dualistic (subject/object–mind/body splits), deterministic, reductionistic and mechanistic explanations of human behaviour.

The humanistic movement also reflected a historical trend in Western industrialised cultures at that time, namely an interest in the worth of the individual and the meaning of life and to be concerned about the rise of bureaucracy, the threat of nuclear and other war, the growing emphasis on scientific/positivist paradigms, alienation of the individual and the consequent loss of individual identity in mass society. This led to humanistic psychology being aligned with the philosophical school of existentialism, as well as being associated with the human potential movements of the 1960s and 1970s, the legacy of which can be seen today in individual and group counselling approaches. Humanistic psychology also played a part in the growing interest in qualitative research methods (see Chapter 2) that seek to understand the experience of the individual and the meaning of the experience, such as phenomenology. The following people were prominent figures in developing humanistic psychology.

Charlotte Bühler

Bühler (1893–1974) distinguished her theory from Freudian psychoanalysis with the thesis that development was lifelong, goals were personally selected and that the individual was searching for meaning in life beyond their own existence. She maintained that self-fulfilment was the key to human development and that this was achieved by living constructively, establishing a personal value system, setting goals and reviewing progress to thereby realise one's potential. Throughout the lifespan, according to Bühler, people strive to achieve four basic human tendencies, which are to:

1. satisfy one's need for sex, love and recognition
2. engage in self-limiting adaptation in order to fit in, belong and feel secure
3. express oneself through creative achievements
4. uphold and restore order so as to be true to one's values and conscience (Bühler 1971; Bühler & Allen 1972).

Abraham Maslow

As a frequently cited author in healthcare literature, Maslow (1908–1970) is renowned for his theory of human needs. Maslow, like Bühler and Rogers, premised his theory on the notion that human beings are intrinsically good and that human behaviour is motivated by a drive for self-actualisation or fulfilment. Maslow (1968) identifies three categories of human need:

1. fundamental needs
    -   physiological (hunger, thirst and sex)
    -   safety (security and freedom from danger)
2. psychological needs
    -   belongingness and love (connection with others, to be accepted and to belong)
    -   self-esteem (to achieve, be competent, gain approval and recognition)
3. self-actualisation needs
    -   to achieve one's innate potential (Maslow 1968; Santrock 2021).

Typically, Maslow's needs are represented in a hierarchical pyramid with fundamental needs at the base of the triangle and self-actualisation at the top, although Maslow did not describe his model in this way, nor did he suggest that progression through the hierarchy was in one direction (i.e. ascending) as his model is often depicted. For example, one may have a positive sense of self (self-esteem needs met) but be vulnerable regarding safety needs during a natural disaster like a tsunami.

Critique of humanistic psychology

Intuitively, humanistic psychology appeals as a positive, optimistic view of humankind with its focus on personal growth, not disorder. However, this can also be a criticism in that, as a theory, humanistic psychology is naïve and incomplete. If humans are driven by a need to achieve their best and to live harmoniously with others as Bühler, Rogers and Maslow suggest, how does this account for disturbed states like depression or antisocial behaviour like assault? Humanistic concepts can be difficult to define objectively, thereby posing a challenge for scientific investigation of the theory. Finally, there is little recognition of unconscious drives in explaining behaviour, which limits the ability of the theory to contribute to an understanding of abnormal, deviant or antisocial behaviour.

Developmental theories

Developmental theories, which provide a stage model of predictable human development, are discussed in detail in Chapters 3 and 4.

SOCIOLOGICAL THEORIES

Sociological and psychological theories differ in that **sociological theories** do not seek explanations for individual behaviour; rather, they examine societal factors for their influence on the behaviour of its members (see Chapter 6). Sociologists propose that the origin of behaviour (both normal and abnormal) lies not in the individual's mind but in the broader social forces of the society in which the person lives. For example, demographic factors such as age, gender and socioeconomic status can influence patterns of health. The application of sociological theories in health helps draw attention to the social dimensions of health and wellbeing that can alleviate inequality. Three main sociological perspectives in health and illness include structural functionalism, conflict theory and symbolic interactionist theory.

A functionalist perspective highlights the need for good health and health care in order for a society to function. The conflict approach examines inequality between the quality of health and healthcare delivery in society, and the symbolic interactionist perspective argues that health and illness is a social construct (i.e. defined by society) (Weitz 2020).

Critique of sociological models

Sociological models identify social determinants of health (Huda et al. 2018; World Health Organization 2022), vulnerable populations and health inequities (Naidoo & Wills 2022), which can inform health promotion initiatives as well as identify biases that influence diagnosis and treatment. But it is important to note that although social determinants are associated with better or poorer health outcomes, the relationships are correlational and cannot be assumed to be in themselves causative. Nevertheless, the contribution of population statistics and social demographic data is significant. By identifying social determinants that are associated with protective factors for mental health and risk factors for mental illness, for example, potential areas for prevention and intervention are thereby identified.

EVOLUTIONARY APPROACH

Evolutionary psychology mainly focuses on the effects of evolution in shaping the mind and associated behaviour by adapting to the environment. As a biologically informed approach, proponents of evolutionary psychology aim to explain internal or neural psychological mechanisms such as behaviour, cognitive processes and emotions as a means of adapting to challenging situations and solving problems by using innate instincts that have been passed down from ancestors via a process of natural selection that allowed them to thrive, survive and reproduce.

Critique of the evolutionary approach

One of the most common critiques of the evolutionary approach is its lack of testability reinforced by vague and unproven assumptions, meaning the theory is not falsifiable. There is also an assumption that all adaptation and evolution occurs in an homogeneous environment, whereas human evolution is more likely to occur in varied and multiple environments.

SOCIOCULTURAL THEORY

Theorists based in the sociocultural perspective of psychology study how human behaviour is influenced by society and the cultural environment. Both directly and indirectly, individual psychological growth is guided by other people such as social groups or people deemed better skilled than us. More information on sociocultural theory can be found in Chapter 3.

ECLECTIC APPROACH

An **eclectic/holistic approach** is used in both psychological research and clinical practice. For example, initially Seligman's theory of learned helplessness (to explain depression) was underpinned by cognitive principles (Seligman 1974). However, as Seligman broadened his theory to seek explanations for *happiness and wellbeing* and *flourishing* to establish a branch of psychology, which he called positive psychology (Seligman & Csikszentmihalyi 2014), he integrated theoretical principles from cognitive psychology (e.g. focus on strengths, setting of achievable goals), humanistic psychology (e.g. the seeking of meaning) and sociology (e.g. the importance of relationships and one's social network). The premise of holistic psychology is that people are seen as a whole rather than individual components. While not a specific school of psychology, it nevertheless informs practice in healthcare settings. Biomedical and psychological interventions are frequently used concurrently to achieve better outcomes, as shown in the following *Research focus*.

Research focus

Source: Armenta et al. 2019

OVERVIEW

When faced with painful procedures such as blood taking, injections and cryotherapy, children with dermatological conditions can often refuse these treatments due to acute distress, anxiety and fear. Since such procedures are associated with pain, avoidance can become a key issue. Avoidance of such medical procedures can result in failure to receive a definitive diagnosis or unsatisfactory treatment options to address the dermatological health issue (Page 1996).

Cont... ▶

Various options have been implemented to reduce a child's anxiety, with more recent evidence exploring the efficacy of psychological interventions for reducing distress.

In this review, the authors present the use of cognitive behavioural therapy, a psychological intervention often used in health issues such as depression, to help alleviate the anxiety experienced in children when undergoing medical procedures. Factors such as the language used when informing the child or young person of a procedure, when to inform them (immediately before or allow time for mental preparedness), where the procedure will occur and who will be present are also relevant in reducing distress.

KEY POINTS

- Anticipation of pain associated with a procedure will result in a high level of experienced pain.
- A cognitive behavioural therapy approach educates people to recognise patterns of distorted thinking and supports the principle that if the central belief (resulting from the distorted thinking) can be altered, this in turn will change behaviour.
- Consideration for how and when the procedure is communicated as well as where it is implemented is important.
- There are other promising psychological strategies such as distraction and relaxation techniques that can be implemented to minimise distress and anxiety for children and young people.
- Strategies used should be age-appropriate and be person-centred to ensure the child feels they have some control and voice in the situation.

Incorporation of both psychological and physical strategies has proven to ease the fear, anxiety and distress in children and therefore improve adherence to painful procedures.

Critical thinking

- What does this research contribute to our understanding of psychological tools for improving adherence to painful procedures?
- How can this research influence clinical practice?

Personality theories and explanations of human behaviour

Table 1.2 outlines the key features of the major biomedical, psychological and sociological theories that propose explanations of human behaviour. These theories inform our understanding of others and ourselves and underpin interventions for health promotion, health behaviour change and treatments for mental illness.

Table 1.2

PERSONALITY THEORIES AND EXPLANATIONS OF HUMAN BEHAVIOUR

	Focus	Stage theory	Motivation	Individual control	Development explanation	Intervention
Biomedical	Physiological homeostasis/pathology	No	Physiological homeostasis	Internal Biological	Genetics Biological homeostasis/pathology	Medication Physical treatments
Psychoanalytic	Unconscious processes	Yes; e.g. Freud, Erikson	Internal drives Seek pleasure	Internal Psychological	Stage progression Ego development	Psychoanalysis Insight therapy
Behavioural	Learning Environment	No; e.g. Pavlov, Skinner	Seek reinforcement Avoid punishment	External Psychological	Behaviours learned through reinforcement, association or observation	Learn new behaviours Extinguish unwanted behaviour
Cognitive	Thinking Perception	Some no; e.g. Seligman, Bandura Some developmental; e.g. Piaget	Thoughts and beliefs	Internal Psychological	Thoughts and beliefs influence feelings and behaviour	Cognitive restructuring/therapy including cognitive behavioural therapy, dialectical behavioural therapy
Humanistic	Self-concept Self-actualisation	No; e.g. Maslow, Rogers	Meet needs Set goals Self-actualisation	Internal Psychological	Seek meaning Achieve goals Accomplishments	Find meaning or set achievable goals Client-centred therapy
Sociological	Social determinants Power Inequities	No; e.g. Durkheim, Marmot, Szasz	Social influences Power	External Social	Societal determinants influence health outcomes Notion of mental illness challenged	Social justice Economic and political reform

Student activity

1. Before the tutorial, divide students into three groups. Ask students to bring to the tutorial articles that report on biomedical, psychological or combined (eclectic) approaches to managing one of the following health problems:

   ▪ pain
   ▪ chronic fatigue syndrome
   ▪ anxiety.

2. Identify and discuss the key findings of the research.
3. Identify and discuss how theory informs the intervention.
4. Relate the discussion to the students' clinical practice experiences.

Personality and behaviour: nature versus nurture

Who or what is responsible for personality and human development: heredity or the environment? Philosophers have long debated this issue, though scientific interest is more recent, dating from the work of Galton. Galton was a 19th-century British pioneer in the study of personality differences and is reportedly credited with proposing the immortal phrase '**nature versus nurture**' (Gottesman 1997; Plomin et al. 2014). The ensuing debate resulted in a proliferation of philosophical discussion about, and scientific investigation into, the effects of biological phenomena and inheritance (nature) and a person's environment and experiences in the world (nurture).

THEORETICAL PERSPECTIVES ON NATURE VERSUS NURTURE

The theories discussed in this chapter place varied emphasis on whether hereditary or environmental factors play a more important role in personality development, human behaviour and mental illness. Behavioural and cognitive psychology advocate for the environment and factors external to the individual being more influential, as does the sociological perspective, though for different reasons. The biomedical model argues for a nature explanation, while psychoanalytic theory and humanistic psychology acknowledge the contribution of both. The psychoanalytic concept of the id, for instance, is biological but it interacts with the environment in personality development. In humanistic psychology the need to achieve one's potential is considered to be innate, but the eventual outcome is influenced by the person's experiences in the world.

NATURE OR NURTURE?

There is an abundance of evidence to support an interactive explanation of nature and nurture rather than the answer being found in the either/or proposal (Badcock 2015; Seligman & Csikszentmihalyi 2014). Despite this, some commentators and theorists continue to advocate for the relative importance of one over the other, notably exponents of the biomedical model for nature and behaviourism for nurture.

Evidence to support a genetic or nature position can be found in family, twin and adoptee studies. Research over the past 20 years shows that human behaviour, personality and mental illness do have a genetic component (Gottesman 1997; Scolnick 2017). Findings from studies into the heritability of intelligence quotient (IQ) offer the most convincing nature evidence. An American, British and Swedish study of 240 octogenarian twins found the heritability of IQ to be 62% (Gottesman 1997). In the Colorado Adoption Project a correlation was found between the IQ of adopted adolescents and their birth parents, but no relationship was found between the IQ of adopted adolescents and their adoptive parents. The researchers concluded that the environment in which the young person was reared had little impact on cognitive ability.

In the case of schizophrenia, however, heredity accounts for less than 50% of the predictability of the disorder. And while first-degree relatives of a person with schizophrenia have a greater risk of developing the disorder than the general population, that genetic risk is only 1 to 10% (Scolnick 2017). It is clearly evident, therefore, that factors in addition to one's genetic inheritance influence whether the disorder manifests. Genetic inheritance is only a partial influence, with the environment accounting for the rest.

Gottesman's research assumes that siblings reared together share the same environment. Caution is recommended in presuming this because different siblings in the same family do not necessarily experience exactly the same environment. Siblings do share many experiences, such as the same parents, social class and home environment, but other experiences are unique to the individual and not shared by siblings. This non-shared environment can include such experiences as birth trauma, illness and different schooling. Significantly, it appears that it is the non-shared environment that accounts for most of the environmental influence on a child's personality and mood (Santrock 2021) and that behaviour is a result of the interplay between the inherited characteristics and the environment rather than either/or.

A person's personality does not develop without a genetic inheritance, nor can it develop in the absence of influences from experience and the environment. How, then, can the nature versus nurture debate be resolved? Gestalt psychology, founded by Fritz Perls (1893–1970) in the 1960s, comprises humanistic and existentialist elements and offers a model for understanding the nature versus nurture debate—that is, to view personality development as a gestalt. There is no exact English equivalent for this German term, but it loosely translates as 'a meaningful, organised whole' that is more than the sum of its parts (Perls et al. 1973, p. 16). Consider a cake, for example: flour, eggs, milk and sugar are its basic ingredients, but the product or gestalt bears no resemblance to any of the original ingredients. Yet each of the ingredients is vital to the final product, as is the process of cooking. Leave out the sugar and it will not taste like a cake; omit the heating process and it will not have the texture of a cake.

Considering human personality development as a gestalt means that neither nature nor nurture can be considered in isolation from the other. The process of their interaction and the context in which they interact are significant. Attributing a relative value of one over the other serves no purpose. Both nature and nurture are vital, inseparable, interdependent components of personality and human development that also influence human behaviour and health outcomes.

Student activity

1. For this activity, students should:
   - stand at the front of the class
   - move to the left if you think personality and human behaviour is most influenced by nature (genetics, biology); move to the right if you think personality and human behaviour is most influenced by nurture (learning and experiences in the world)
   - pair up with a student holding the opposite view and explain your view to your partner.
2. Repeat this activity regarding your views about whether you think personality and human behaviour are:
   - constantly changing or essentially unchanging
   - influenced by past (history and experiences) or future (goals and aspirations) events
   - personal decisions (own values and ambitions) or social influences (family and societal values).
3. Reflection questions for the class:
   - What did you learn from this activity?
   - What was surprising about this activity?
   - What are the implications for:
     - » working with other health professionals who hold different explanatory views from your own?
     - » caring for patients who hold different explanatory views from your own?

Chapter summary

The theoretical perspectives discussed in this chapter provide complementary, overlapping and, at times, contradictory theories of human behaviour and personality development. Yet despite individual theories providing plausible explanations for specific human behaviours, no theory alone explains all human behaviour or a single behaviour in all circumstances. Also, the theories must be used cautiously when being applied to people from non-Western cultures.

Some psychological theories offer a nature explanation, others a nurture explanation, and yet others incorporate both. Even when a specific theory provides convincing evidence to support a nature or nurture explanation, such evidence is generally correlational and therefore cannot be considered causative. Consequently, in seeking to identify factors that influence personality development and human behaviour, it is evident that the answer will not be found in asking the nature or nurture question; rather, in investigating *how the nature is nurtured*.

In conclusion, although psychological theories do have limitations, they nonetheless provide insightful understandings of human behaviour and explanations of personality in many contexts. These theories can be used by health professionals to understand the motivations and behaviours of the people they care for and to plan appropriate interventions and care. Furthermore, humans are biological beings who exist in a social context, therefore psychological theories must be applied within a biopsychosocial framework that also acknowledges these other influences.

KEY POINTS

- Psychology is the scientific study of behaviour—particularly, but not exclusively, the study of human behaviour.
- Psychological theories offer competing and, at times, complementary explanations for human behaviour.
- Psychological theories are effective in explaining specific behaviours in specific circumstances but have limitations for global explanations for human behaviour.
- Psychological theory underpins therapeutic interventions in healthcare practice.
- Often human behaviour can be best understood by using an eclectic/holistic approach—that is, by taking into consideration biomedical, psychological and sociological factors (a biopsychosocial approach).

Further reading

Bandura, A., 2016. The power of observational learning through social modelling. In: Stenberg, R., Fiske, S., Foss, D. (Eds.), 2016. Scientists Making a Difference: One Hundred Eminent Behavioral and Brain Scientists Talk About Their Most Important Contributions. Cambridge University Press, Cambridge, (Chapter 50).

Carducci, B., 2015. The Psychology of Personality: Viewpoints, Research and Application, 3rd edn. Wiley-Blackwell, New York.

Diener, E., Seligman, M., Choi, H., et al., 2018. Happiest people revisited. Perspectives on Psychological Sciences, 13(2), 176–178.

Germov, J. (Ed.), 2018. Second Opinion: an Introduction to Health Sociology, 6th edn. Oxford University Press, Melbourne.

Kring, A., Johnson, S., Davison, G., et al., 2017. Abnormal Psychology: The Science and Treatment of Psychological Disorders, 13th edn. Wiley, New York.

Moore, D. S. 2015. The Developing Genome: An Introduction to Behavioral Epigenetics. New York: Oxford University Press.

Weblinks

Types of Psychological Theories by Kendra Cherry

www.verywellmind.com/what-is-a-theory-2795970

This article provides an overview of the major psychological and developmental theories and discusses how they are used to understand human behaviour.

American Psychological Association

www.apa.org

This website contains useful information about psychology topics, publications and resources.

Authentic Happiness

www.authentichappiness.sas.upenn.edu

This website contains information about positive psychology, which focuses on the empirical study of wellbeing, positive emotions and strengths-based research.

Australian Psychological Society

www.psychology.org.au

The Australian Psychological Society is the peak professional association for psychologists in Australia. The society's website contains information relevant to psychologists and health professionals and provides academic resources, publications and community information.

New Zealand Psychological Society

www.psychology.org.nz

The New Zealand Psychological Society is the premier professional association for psychologists in New Zealand. The society's website contains information about the society, membership, services and publications, as well as acting as a gateway to psychology in New Zealand.

References

Armenta, A.M., Jaquez, S.D., Levy, M.L., et al., 2019. Use of psychologic strategies to reduce pain and anxiety related to dermatology procedures. Pediatric Dermatology. 36, 416–417.

Badcock, C.R., 2015. Nature-Nurture Controversy, History of. In: James D. Wright (editor-in-chief), International Encyclopedia of the Social & Behavioral Sciences, 2nd edn, Vol 16. Oxford: Elsevier. pp. 340–344.

Bandura, A., 2001. Social cognitive theory. Annual Review of Psychology 52, 1–26.

Bandura, A., 2012. Social cognitive theory, Ch 17. In: van Lange, P., Kruglanski, A., Tory Higgins, E. (Eds.), Handbook of Theories of Social Psychology, vol. 1. Sage, London.

Bandura, A., 2016. The power of observational learning through social modelling, Ch 50. In: Stenberg, R., Fiske, S., Foss, D. (Eds.), Scientists Making a Difference: One Hundred Eminent Behavioral and Brain Scientists Talk About Their Most Important Contributions. Cambridge University Press, Cambridge.

Beck, A., 1972. Depression: Causes and Treatment. University of Pennsylvania Press, Philadelphia.

Beck, A., Emery, G., Greenberg, R.L., 2005. Anxiety Disorders and Phobias: a Cognitive Perspective. Basic Books, New York.

Bühler, C. 1971. Basic theoretical concepts of humanistic psychology. American Psychologist, 26(4), 378–386.

Bühler, C., Allen, M., 1972. Introduction to Humanistic Psychology. Brooks/Cole, California.

Diener, E., Seligman, M., Choi, H., et al., 2018. Happiest people revisited. Perspectives on Psychological Sciences, 13(2), 176–178.

Erikson, E., 1963. Childhood and Society, 2nd edn. WW Norton, New York.

Fordham B., Sugavanam T., Hopewell S., et al., 2018. Effectiveness of cognitive–behavioural therapy: a protocol for an overview of systematic reviews and meta-analyses. BMJ Open; 8:e025761. doi: 10.1136/bmjopen-2018-025761

Freud, A., 1966. The Ego and the Mechanisms of Defence. International Universities Press, New York.

Gottesman, I.I., 1997. Twins: en route to QTLs for cognition. Science 277 (5318), 1522–1523.

Hooley, K., Butcher, J., Nock, M., et al., 2020. Abnormal Psychology, 18th edn. Pearson, Boston.

Huda, T., Hayes, A., Dibley, M., 2018. Examining horizontal inequity and social determinants of inequality in facility delivery services in three South Asian countries. Journal of Global Health 8 (1). Available: www.ncbi.nlm.nih.gov/pmc/articles/PMC6008508/. (Accessed 20 August 2018).

Ivey, A., Ivey, M., Zalaquett, C., 2022. Intentional Interviewing and Counselling: Facilitating Client Development in a Multicultural Society, 10th edn. Cengage Learning, US.

Kring, A., Johnson, S., 2021. Abnormal Psychology: The Science and Treatment of Psychological Disorders, 15th edn. Wiley, New York.

Kruglanski, A., Chernikova, M., & Kopetz, C., 2015. Motivation science. In: R. Scott & S. Kosslyn (Eds.), Emerging Trends in the Social and Behavioural Sciences. New York: Wiley.

Laws, K., Darlington, N., Kondel, T., et al., 2018. Cognitive behavioural therapy for schizophrenia—outcomes for functioning, distress and quality of life: a meta-analysis. BMC Psychology 6 (32), Available: https://bmcpsychology.biomedcentral.com/articles/10.1186/s40359-018-0243-2#Abs1. (Accessed 11 September 2018).

Maslow, A., 1968. Towards a Psychology of Being. Van Nostrand, New Jersey.

Naidoo, J., Wills, J., 2022. Foundations for Health Promotion, 5th edn. Elsevier, Australia.

Page, A.C., 1996. Blood-injury-injection fears in medical practice. Medical Journal of Australia, 164(3), 189.

Perls, F., Hefferline, R., Goodman, P., 1973. Gestalt Therapy Now: Experiment and Growth in the Human Personality. Pelican, London.

Plomin, R., Shakeshaft, N., McMillan, A., et al., 2014. Nature, nurture and expertise. Intelligence 45, 46–59. Available: https://www.sciencedirect.com/science/article/pii/S0160289613000810?via%3Dihub (Accessed March 2022).

Rogers, C., 1951. Client-Centered Therapy. Houghton Mifflin, Boston.

Santrock, J., 2021. Life-Span Development, 18th edn. McGraw-Hill, New York.

Scolnick, E., 2017. The path to new therapies for schizophrenia and bipolar illness. The FASEB Journal 31 (4), 1254–1259. Available: www.fasebj.org/doi/pdf/10.1096/fj.201700028. (Accessed 28 August 2018).

Seligman, M., 1974. Depression and learned helplessness. In: Friedman, J., Katz, M. (Eds.), The Psychology of Depression: Theory and Research. Winston-Wiley, Washington.

Seligman, M., 2011. Learned Optimism. Random House, Sydney.

Seligman, M., Csikszentmihalyi, M., 2014. Positive Psychology: An Introduction, Flow and Foundations of Positive Psychology. Springer, pp. 279–298. Available: https://link.springer.com/chapter/10.1007%2F978-94-017-9088-8_18. (Accessed 28 August 2018).

Skinner, B.F., 1953. Science and Human Behaviour. Macmillan, New York.

Watson, J., Rayner, R., 1920. Conditioned emotional reactions. Journal of Experimental Psychology 3 (1), 1–14.

Weitz, R. 2020. The sociology of health, illness and health care. A critical approach. 8th edn. Cengage Learning, US.

Whalley, M.G. 2019. Unhelpful thinking styles: cognitive distortions in CBT. Psychology Tools. Available: https://www.psychologytools.com/articles/unhelpful-thinking-styles-cognitive-distortions-in-cbt/. (Accessed 7 January 2022)

World Health Organization (WHO), 2022. Social Determinants of Health. Available: https://www.who.int/health-topics/social-determinants-of-health#tab=tab_1 (Accessed 10 January 2022).

Chapter 2
Research-informed practice

ADAM GERACE

Learning objectives

The material in this chapter will help you to:

- distinguish between and describe various research paradigms used in psychology and health research
- understand how research shapes healthcare practice
- describe the role of health professionals as research consumers
- critically appraise research reports and draw conclusions appropriate for practice
- describe the ethics of research participation and the advocacy role played by health professionals.

Key terms

- Quantitative research (32)
- Statistical significance (32)
- Validity (32)
- Reliability (32)
- Clinical significance (32)
- Randomised controlled trial (RCT) (33)
- Informed consent (33)
- Qualitative research (35)
- Thematic analysis (35)
- Reflexivity (36)
- Triangulation (39)
- Research consumer (41)

Cont... ▶

- Refereed journal (41)
- Evidence-based healthcare (49)
- Beneficence (51)
- Research ethics (51)

Introduction

This chapter examines how psychological and health research findings influence healthcare practice and provides an overview of research paradigms, methodologies and methods. It is not within the scope of this chapter to provide a detailed account of *how* to conduct research. This is covered in more depth elsewhere in your course and in specific research textbooks. Rather, this chapter focuses on how research findings influence healthcare practice and how health professionals can use research in their day-to-day clinical practice and, thereby, be competent *consumers of research* (Whitehead et al. 2020). Being a competent consumer of research involves knowing how to access, critique and use research findings to inform your everyday work. Finally, the role of health professionals in the ethical conduct of research is addressed.

Healthcare research: an overview

Research is a process of enquiry that aims to develop new knowledge or to expand existing knowledge. In the health arena, research findings are used to:

- identify the health needs of populations
- test and choose appropriate interventions and treatments for illness and health problems
- plan and implement intervention strategies for illness prevention and health promotion
- evaluate programs and interventions
- assist with resource allocation.

Research can be either basic or applied (Bentley et al. 2015; Cozby & Bates 2020). *Basic* research aims to develop new theory and/or knowledge, while *applied* research examines the application of knowledge in certain circumstances. A study of the factors that influence someone's decision to follow or disregard a recommended health treatment, for example, is basic research; a randomised controlled trial testing a new drug to treat cancer is an example of applied research.

A further important distinction between research studies is whether they are experimental, observational, interpretive or critical (Cozby & Bates 2020; Holloway & Galvin 2017). Experimental studies use quantitative methods and are a powerful research method because people (participants) can be allocated to receive an exposure of interest, such as a new treatment or healthcare practice, or an intervention, such as allergen avoidance or dietary advice. In such studies, researchers investigate how varying exposure to an *independent variable*—such as whether participants are exposed to a new drug (treatment group) or are given a placebo (control group)—affects a particular outcome (a *dependent variable*) such as improving illness symptoms. Experimental designs can also allow researchers to statistically account for other variables (e.g. age) that may have a relationship with the dependent variable and, in doing so, can assess the unique effects of the main independent variable of interest—in this case, the new drug. Therefore, the level of evidence obtained is high.

Observational research, also called descriptive studies, uses either quantitative (e.g. census) or qualitative (e.g. ethnography) methods. Descriptive studies are less powerful for measuring associations; nevertheless, they are a valuable method for:

- measuring the effects of non-modifiable risk factors such as age or gender
- measuring the effects of exposures to which people cannot be ethically randomised, such as environmental tobacco smoke
- understanding human experience and social issues.

Interpretive and critical approaches are located within the qualitative research paradigm and aim to describe, explore and seek understanding of human and social phenomena. Interpretative research focuses on understanding or creating meaning, while critical research has the added goal of bringing about social and political change.

Research paradigms

Various methods can be used to conduct research, and the choice of method is driven by the methodology. Methodologies, also referred to as paradigms, are the theoretical and philosophical positions that underpin the research approach. They are a broad framework of perception, understanding and beliefs within which theory and practice operate.

There are two main research paradigms: quantitative and qualitative. The *quantitative* research paradigm is scientific and positivist and seeks objective answers to a research question. It assumes that an objective answer to the question exists. The *qualitative* research paradigm is interpretative and critical and seeks greater meaning and understanding of the issue under investigation. It acknowledges the subjective nature of human experience. When designing a study, researchers often make use of *either* the quantitative or qualitative research paradigm. However, mixed-methods research—where the researchers use data collection methods informed by both quantitative and qualitative paradigms—are increasingly common in health research (Halcomb 2021). Such approaches are considered in more detail later in this chapter when the method of triangulation is discussed.

QUANTITATIVE RESEARCH

Quantitative research is steeped in conventional scientific tradition. It involves collecting data that are quantifiable and measurable and, therefore, can be analysed and interpreted numerically. It takes a positivist philosophical position and is underpinned by the view that reality is objective, measurable and separate from the researcher. In this way, quantitative research follows the scientific tradition of objective observation, prediction and testing of causal or correlational relationships (Norman & Eva 2019).

Quantitative research generally involves extensive data collection and, thereby, seeks a *broad* understanding to enable explanations and predictions to be made. Hypotheses can either be supported or rejected by applying statistical tests of significance to the data. Traditionally, the p value (probability value), a measure of **statistical significance**, has been used in quantitative research to accept or reject the *null hypothesis* (i.e. that no relationship or link exists between factors). That is, if the calculated p value is below a certain threshold (typically less than 0.05), researchers have confidence that the result is not due to chance. However, the p value is influenced by factors such as sample size, which affects the power of the study to find differences if they exist, as well as the **validity** and **reliability** of measurement instruments. Given problems associated with p values, a prominent group of authors called for the threshold for significance to be lowered from $p < 0.05$ to $p < 0.005$ when new relationships are tested (Benjamin et al. 2018). A small number of journals that publish scientific research have gone even further, with editors making the decision not to publish p values and other tests of statistical significance (e.g. Trafimow & Marks 2015).

Rather than focusing on statistical significance, researchers and consumers of health research often focus on **clinical significance**—that is, whether changes or observed effects are meaningful for those with illness, even if not meeting traditional tests of statistical significance. Clinical significance involves assessing the 'change in an outcome score that is considered "important" or "worthwhile" by the practitioner or the patient and/or would result in a change in patient management' (Page 2014, p. 729). In order to assess clinical significance, researchers and consumers of research need to consider the validity and reliability of studies, the sample size and measures of the magnitude and nature of observed relationships (e.g. effect sizes and confidence intervals; Page 2014).

The data collected in quantitative research can be: *nominal*, when the data distinguish categories (like male/female); *ordinal*, when the data distinguish between levels and allow ranking like never, sometimes, always (often reflected in 5-point and 7-point Likert-type response scales); or *ratio* or *interval*, when the data measure numbers like how many cigarettes smoked per day or reaction time (these are ratio data as they have a zero point) or temperature (interval data because, while also numeric, there is no zero point) (Cozby & Bates 2020). Examples of quantitative methods include experiments (e.g. randomised controlled trials, questionnaires and surveys), structured interviews and census collection.

Quantitative research designs include: *experimental*, which attempt to show that one thing causes another and involves randomly assigning participants to different conditions (e.g. experimental/treatment versus control group); *quasi-experimental*, which is an experimental design but does not have random allocation to the control group or an experimental group; non-experimental designs such as *descriptive*, which summarise and describe a set of measurements; and *correlational*, which explore the relationship between variables (Cozby & Bates 2020; Pelham & Blanton 2019).

Focus on quantitative research: randomised controlled trials

In **randomised controlled trials (RCTs)** with human subjects, participants agree to enrol by providing their **informed consent**, where the research is explained to the person (including possible risks and benefits) and the person makes a voluntary decision to be involved. Participants are then randomly allocated to the experimental (receive the intervention) or control (do not receive the intervention) group. Depending on the type of study, the control group may receive a placebo intervention, current best practice (e.g. treatment 'as usual') or receive another treatment. Placebo interventions are usually only used when a new treatment method is being assessed and, for this reason, placebo-controlled trials usually have a small sample size because they are seen as an intermediary step in the process of showing the efficacy of a new treatment.

RCTs provide the highest level of evidence because the random allocation of participants to study groups minimises the influences of selection bias, of known and unknown confounders and of prognostic factors such as participant characteristics on the study results. Blinding (not informing the participants and/or the research team about which participants are in which group) can also reduce the effects of other biases.

The inclusion criteria are an important issue in RCTs. In trials to measure the effectiveness of a treatment or intervention, participants who have an identified health problem are enrolled. However, in interventions designed to prevent an illness or condition from developing, participants who are 'at risk' are enrolled before the illness or condition has developed. Although RCTs provide the most scientifically rigorous research method available, they are often difficult to conduct, and low response rates may reduce the generalisability of the results. Table 2.1 summarises the strengths and weaknesses of RCTs.

Table 2.1

STRENGTHS AND WEAKNESSES OF RCT

Strengths	Weaknesses
Provide a high level of evidence	Selection bias may be an issue if potential participants have treatment preferences
Confounders, prognostic factors and exposures are balanced between groups	Follow-up bias may be influential if control group participants selectively drop out because they are receiving a placebo or existing treatment
Allocation, reporting and observer bias can be controlled by blinding	Low participation rates may reduce the generalisability of the results
Willingness to participate does not influence group allocation	Long-term outcomes may not be measured

The following *Research focus* is from a scholarly refereed journal (scholarly referred journals are described later in this chapter). It reports the findings of an RCT. The article shows some of the challenges in conducting studies with patients in real-world settings and will help you to consider the ways in which research can be used to implement programs in your own practice.

Research focus

Source: Fure et al. 2021

ABSTRACT

Background

Returning to work is often a primary rehabilitation goal after a traumatic brain injury (TBI). However, the evidence base for treatment options for returning to work and stable work maintenance remains scarce.

Objective

This study aimed to examine the effect of a combined cognitive and vocational intervention on work-related outcomes after a mild-to-moderate TBI.

Methods

In this study, the researchers compared 6 months of a combined compensatory cognitive training and supported employment (CCT-SE) intervention with 6 months of treatment as usual (TAU) in an RCT to examine the effect on time to return to work, work percentage, hours worked per week and work stability. Eligible patients were those with mild-to-moderate TBI who were employed ≥ 50% at the time of injury, 18 to 60 years old and sick-listed ≥ 50% at 8 to 12 weeks after injury due to post-concussion symptoms, assessed by the Rivermead Post Concussion Symptoms Questionnaire. Both treatments were provided at Oslo University Hospital, and follow-ups were conducted at 3, 6 and 12 months after inclusion.

Results

The study included 116 people, 60 randomised to CCT-SE and 56 to TAU. The groups did not differ in characteristics at the 12-month follow-up. Overall, a high proportion had returned to work at 12 months (CCT-SE, 90%; TAU, 84%, $p = 0.40$), and all except three were stably employed after the return to work. However, a significantly higher proportion of participants in the CCT-SE than TAU group had returned to stable employment at 3 months (81% vs 60%, $p = 0.02$).

Conclusion

These results suggest that the CCT-SE intervention might help patients with mild-to-moderate TBI who are still sick-listed 8 to 12 weeks after injury in an earlier return to stable employment. However, the results should be replicated and a cost-benefit analysis performed before concluding.

◉ Critical thinking

- What might be the difficulties in conducting RCTs of people with health conditions such as a traumatic brain injury?
- How might health professionals working with people with a traumatic brain injury use the research findings?
- How can familiarity with the theoretical concepts of health psychology help you to understand the research findings?

QUALITATIVE RESEARCH

Qualitative research proposes that there is no objective reality, as assumed by the quantitative positivist paradigm. It is a constructivist approach in which people construct meaning and interpretation of reality from their own experiences. Nevertheless, like quantitative studies, qualitative research uses a range of methodologies and methods that help us explore different phenomena, meaning and experience.

In qualitative research, data are collected from observation and interview within a population and describe the range of responses, as well as variation between responses. Narrative data are collected as opposed to numerical data in qualitative research and, thereby, a *depth* of understanding about the issue under investigation is provided in contrast to the *breadth* of understanding sought in quantitative research.

Qualitative methodologies include the following:

- *Symbolic interactionism* aims to understand how people make meaning of their environment through social interaction processes (Handberg et al. 2015; for an example see Handberg et al. 2018).

- *Phenomenology* aims to understand the experiences of a phenomenon (Creswell & Poth 2018; for an example see Dagyaran et al. 2021).

- *Ethnography* aims to understand societies, cultures or institutions, with the researcher observing and interacting with particular groups (Madden 2017; for an example, see Dawson et al. 2021).

- *Grounded theory* aims to develop theory based on collected data in an inductive and iterative process (Charmaz 2014; for an example, see Andrews et al. 2020).

Methods for collecting data in a qualitative study include (but are not limited to) focus groups, unstructured or semi-structured interviews, participant observation, ethnography, case studies and document analysis.

In qualitative studies, the approach chosen (e.g. grounded theory, phenomenology) determines the way in which collected data is analysed, with each methodology having guidelines and procedures for how to approach the analysis (Whitehead et al. 2020). However, a qualitative approach to data *analysis* that is popular in health disciplines is **thematic analysis**, which Virginia Braun and Victoria Clarke (2022), who are experts in thematic analysis, describe as 'a method for developing, analysing and interpreting patterns across a qualitative dataset, which involves systematic processes of data coding to develop themes' (p. 4). Thematic analysis is seen as a *method* (way of doing things) rather than a methodology (way of seeing things) and can be used as a data analysis tool with studies that are underpinned by different theoretical frameworks (Clarke & Braun 2013, 2014). Thematic analysis can take a deductive or a 'top down' approach, where the analysis is driven by theory, or an inductive or 'bottom up' approach, which is more data-driven (Braun & Clarke 2021).

Braun and Clarke (2022) now refer to their approach as *reflexive thematic analysis*. This is to highlight the importance of a researcher reflecting on how their own assumptions, values and choices affect all stages of the research process and the practices that they employ, such as how they code and interpret data. Such **reflexivity**—that is, reflection and awareness of how personal values, methods chosen and underlying approach (e.g. philosophical underpinnings of a paradigm) influence knowledge production—is particularly important in qualitative research, and such reflections are often documented during data collection (through a journal) and when writing up findings for publication. Consideration of any biases or underlying values that may influence the research process should also be a part of quantitative research, although this is not usually as explicitly stated in publications.

An aspect that health researchers need to consider as part of this reflexivity is whether they are an 'insider' and belong to the same group as the people they are researching or if they are more of an 'outsider' (Braun & Clarke 2022). An example of an 'insider' might be a researcher who has a background as a nurse and is interviewing nurses about a particular practice, while an 'outsider' might be someone from a non-nursing background conducting such a study.

While it is not within the scope of this chapter, like other qualitative approaches, there are guides for conducting thematic analysis such as Braun and Clarke's (2006, 2021) influential six-phase approach which involves: (1) data familiarisation; (2) data coding; (3) theme generation; (4) theme development and review; (5) theme refining, defining and naming; and (6) writing up the findings.

Focus on qualitative research: phenomenology

Phenomenology began as a philosophical mode of enquiry in continental Europe around the turn of the 20th century. Its founder is the German philosopher Edmund Husserl (1859–1938). Throughout the latter part of the 20th century and early 21st century, phenomenology was adapted as an approach in health research enquiry, particularly by nurse researchers (Dowling 2007). The goal of phenomenological health research is to understand a human or social issue by examining the human experience of the phenomenon under investigation, whereas the goal of philosophical phenomenology is to examine the phenomenon itself (Aspers 2010; Crotty 1996; Flood 2010).

Consequently, phenomenology is both a philosophy and a research method. As a philosophy, it is interested in the person's perception of a phenomenon—that is, the subjective understanding of the meaning of the phenomenon being investigated, such as the phenomenon of sadness. As a research approach, phenomenology is interested in understanding the human (or lived) experience of a particular phenomenon, such as what it is like to be sad. It is the latter form of phenomenology that is prevalent in the health research literature. This type of phenomenological research generally takes the form of interviewing participants, analysing the data and developing themes from which conclusions and recommendations are drawn.

Controversy surrounds phenomenology as a method in health research. Crotty (1996) refers to the study of the lived experience as 'new' phenomenology, arguing that this differs from philosophical phenomenology because it attempts to draw objective conclusions from subjective data. Paley (2005) is also critical of phenomenological health research, stating that in attempting to make sense of subjective data, nurse researchers draw objective conclusions and in doing so 'mimic science' in assuming that an objective reality exists.

Aspers (2010), however, does not see a problem with there being two approaches. While distinguishing *philosophical* phenomenology from what this researcher calls *empirical* phenomenology, Aspers describes the two approaches as having different purposes. Philosophical phenomenology seeks to understand the phenomenon itself, while empirical phenomenology is interested in the social meaning of the person's experience of the phenomenon. Finlay (2010) also observes that a variety of research methods and techniques are conducted under the banner of phenomenology. Finlay argues that rather than debating the difference in approaches, the important issue for researchers should be to be clear about which philosophical and research traditions they are using and why. Nevertheless, despite the methodological debate surrounding phenomenological health research, phenomenological studies contribute to the body of knowledge about people's experiences of health and illness issues and thereby can influence healthcare practices. In fact, van Manen (2014) uses the term *phenomenology of practice* for research in nursing, medicine, psychology, education and other helping professions that 'reflects *on* and *in* practice, and prepares for practice' (p. 15).

Interpretative phenomenological analysis, which was developed by Jonathan Smith, is an approach that has been used in health psychology to examine people's lived experiences of health-related phenomena. Interpretative phenomenological analysis attempts to obtain an account of an experience from the perspective of the person while acknowledging the interpretive process that the researcher undertakes when engaging with the research data (Smith et al. 2022). That is, through the research process, 'participants are trying to make sense of their world; [and] the researcher is trying to make sense of the participants trying to make sense of their world' (Smith & Osborn 2015, p. 26). The approach is one that has been used to address diverse health-related research topics from the perspectives of patients, caregivers and health professionals. Studies using the approach have included investigations of patients' experiences of living with chronic pain (Marikar Bawa et al. 2021), sexual difficulties related to medication use (O'Mullan et al. 2019) and co-existing mental health and medical conditions (Ware et al. 2015). The method has been used to examine the experiences of those who care for loved ones with health conditions (Judd et al. 2019), the perspectives of health professionals caring for people with particular physical and mental health conditions (McMullan 2018) as well as health professionals' work experiences, such as during the COVID-19 pandemic (McGlinchey et al. 2021). The approach has also been used to address the processes involved in people enacting behaviour change (e.g. Finlay & Elander 2018). Such research can help health professionals to understand, predict and intervene (change) to facilitate positive health behaviours.

Research focus

Source: van Heijningen & Underhill 2022

ABSTRACT

Study design

Qualitative research design using interpretative phenomenological analysis to interpret users' experiences with digital prostheses.

Background

Digital prostheses are rarely used, and little is known about the experiences of traumatic finger amputees with digital prostheses. When advising patients about digital prostheses, it is crucial for professionals to understand users' experiences of wearing a digital prosthesis and the meaning attached to it.

Purpose of study

The aim of this study was to explore and understand users' experiences of wearing a digital prosthesis in daily functioning.

Methods

Individual semi-structured interviews were conducted, recorded and transcribed. The written interview texts were analysed following interpretative phenomenological analysis guidelines.

Results

Four participants were interviewed. They experienced the prostheses as valuable additions to their daily functioning. Three themes relating to wearing and using digital prostheses emerged from in-depth analysis of the data: how the prosthesis helped them to regain a 'grip' on life; reduced overload on unaffected side; and restored body image.

Conclusions

This study provides a deeper understanding of the experiences of people with digital amputations who use prostheses. Most importantly, that a prosthesis is of crucial importance for participants to be able to act independently and autonomously as well as to participate in family, work and social environments. This insight will help practitioners when considering the most appropriate digital prosthesis to meet their client's goals.

◉ Critical thinking

- Why do you think a phenomenological approach is useful in examining the experiences of people using particular devices such as digital prostheses?

- Based on the findings of this study and psychological concepts covered within this book, what advice would you give to health professionals working with clients with prostheses? Why?

QUANTITATIVE OR QUALITATIVE?

In the planning phase of an investigation, a decision is made early in the research process about which methods or methodology to use (namely, quantitative or qualitative) or whether to use multiple methods or methodologies—that is, *triangulation*. Choosing a method is best addressed by considering the question to be investigated and the methodology that best informs the research question. For example, if a researcher wants to investigate the *incidence* of asthma in the community, then epidemiological (quantitative) data will provide that information. However, if the researcher wants to know about the *experiences* of people living with asthma, then a semi-structured interview or focus group is an appropriate (qualitative) method for data collection. Table 2.2 summarises the similarities and differences between quantitative and qualitative research.

TRIANGULATION

Triangulation, or the use of mixed methods and/or methodologies in psychological and social research, is a process whereby various forms of data are collected from different sources. Triangulation provides a comprehensive explanation of a phenomenon, reduces effects of bias of individual methods and enables better understanding (Denzin 2017; Torrance 2012, 2017). For example, a researcher

Table 2.2		
TYPES OF RESEARCH		
	Quantitative	Qualitative
Methodology	Scientific Positivist	Philosophical Sociological Postmodern
Purpose	Explanation Prediction Objective truth	Interpretive Critical Subjective understanding
Methods	Experimental Measurement Statistical analysis	Interview Observation Narrative analysis
Sample size	Usually large	Usually small
Research evaluation	Reliability Validity Correlation	Rigour Credibility Auditability
Ethics	Beneficence, not harm Informed consent Confidentiality Right to withdraw from research Merit and integrity of the research	

observing healthcare providers on a hospital unit by: (1) standing near the nurses' station; (2) observing via security cameras; and (3) asking staff to self-report practices would likely lead to a more complex or nuanced picture of unit routines and practices.

Triangulation may be applied to one or more of the following: methodology, method, data and/or investigator. It can use both quantitative and qualitative paradigms and methods for data collection, such as by obtaining data from key informant interviews (qualitative) and questionnaires (quantitative). For example, a study by McCaughan and colleagues (2018) assessed the effectiveness of a 9-week psychosocial program for men with prostate cancer and their partners. This study measured change in the men and their partners subsequent to the intervention on factors such as self-efficacy and quality of life using quantitative questionnaires and scales. However, a study of this type could also use semi-structured interviews with these participants to elicit perceptions of changes in these factors from the perspectives of participants.

Triangulation can also include collecting data using different methods within the same research paradigm—for example, focus group and participant observation, which are both qualitative. To use the example of men with prostate cancer and their partners, participants in such a program could take part in focus groups with other members of the trial, and researchers may also observe the men and their partners engaging in activities and conversation to collect data on quality of relationships where one partner has become ill.

Collecting data from various sources enables researchers to corroborate their findings, or not. For example, obtaining reports of food choices or adherence to home rehabilitation exercises from the patient versus their partner may lead to complementary or contradictory reports. If both quantitative and qualitative methods are used, a broad *and* deep understanding of the issue is obtained. For example, in determining the needs of parents who have a child with a disability, a researcher could interview key informants (qualitative research) and use this data to design a questionnaire to canvass the opinions of a wider selection of the target population (quantitative research). In a study undertaken in Australia, researchers investigated nurses' perceptions about the practices of seclusion and restraint with both a survey completed by more than 500 participants (quantitative research) and a series of focus groups (qualitative research) to delve in greater depth into some of the topics covered in the survey (Gerace & Muir-Cochrane 2019; Muir-Cochrane et al. 2018).

In summary, the question of whether to use quantitative or qualitative methods to conduct research relates not to what the better method is but to what is the more *appropriate* method for providing the information sought. If identifying the magnitude—or the extent—of an issue is sought or a hypothesis is to be tested, then quantitative methods are required. On the other hand, if the researcher is concerned with understanding human experience from an informant's perspective, then a qualitative method is called for. Furthermore, by using both quantitative and qualitative methods—as in triangulation—researchers can obtain a greater understanding of the research question under investigation.

Health professionals as consumers of research

Although health professionals may not *conduct* research in their day-to-day work, all will use research findings on a daily basis. Whitehead and colleagues (2020) refer to this as being a consumer of research. Being a **research consumer** requires health professionals to understand and use research evidence in clinical practice. Specifically, this means being able to:

- access contemporary research reports about an area of intended healthcare practice
- analyse and critique research findings and conclusions
- underpin clinical practice with an evidence base—that is, articulate the evidence base for clinical practices
- know the processes required to translate research findings into new clinical practices
- know the processes required to change clinical practices that are not supported by contemporary evidence
- observe ethical issues of research participation (and advocate on behalf of participants if required).

Accessing research findings

The findings of research studies need to be disseminated before they can influence practice. Research studies are published in a number of ways including: as an article in a refereed journal; as an article in a non-refereed journal; as a monograph; as a conference presentation or poster; as a report on an internet specialist website; or in the popular media, including newspapers, radio, television and the internet.

Where a research report is published can be indicative of the degree of confidence the reader can place in the claims made by the researcher. For example, the conclusions drawn by the author of an article published in a scholarly refereed journal can be accepted with more confidence than claims posted on a news-based website or reported in a daily newspaper.

REFEREED JOURNALS

Articles submitted to a **refereed journal** undergo peer review before being accepted for publication. This involves a process of subjecting the author's work to scholarly review and scrutiny by experts in the field of study. Experts assess and comment on factors such as the appropriateness of the methodology and methods used, statistical tests employed and conclusions reached (Rowley & Sbaffi 2018). However, the quality of the peer review process is influenced by factors such as the extent to which editors choose appropriate reviewers who have enough expertise and experience with the topic area or methodology. A drawback of disseminating research findings through the peer review process is that it can take months or even years for an article to be accepted by a scholarly journal, thereby delaying the time taken for the research findings to influence practice. But most journals tend to now be available online, meaning that research, once accepted by a journal, can be made available more quickly than in traditional print-only formats.

Original studies

For an article reporting on research findings, the peer review process aims to ensure the research design is sound and ethical, and that the conclusions drawn and claims made by the authors can be substantiated by the process and results presented. Articles reporting original studies describe and discuss the researcher rationale for conducting the study including:

- research questions and hypotheses
- methodology and methods chosen to investigate the issue
- analyses conducted with appropriate statistical or other analyses reported
- discussion of the study findings and implications
- any identified limitations in study design.

SYSTEMATIC REVIEWS

A systematic review of the literature identifies a single question and examines all the published quality literature (e.g. original studies) that relates to the question. They are commonly used to examine cause and effect and clinical effectiveness studies (Whitehead et al. 2020)—for example, to identify risk factors for cancer or to ascertain the most effective drug treatment for osteoarthritis. In the health field, systematic reviews provide the highest level of evidence.

Cochrane is the most widely known publisher of systematic reviews. The organisation aims to provide independent evidence to inform healthcare decision making. Cochrane publishes reviews investigating:

- the effects of health or social care interventions, with a focus on bringing together the results of RCTs
- the ability of diagnostic tests to detect the presence or absence of a condition or illness
- the prognosis for people with specific conditions or illnesses
- the methodologies used in particular studies (e.g. RCTs) so the ways in which studies are conducted can be improved.

Cochrane also publishes overviews of previous systematic reviews that deal with similar topics. This allows health professionals to get an overall picture of often-complex topics in an accessible form (Chandler et al. 2022). This is useful, particularly for research consumers so they can get across an important clinical topic using the best available evidence.

For researchers conducting systematic reviews, it is important to have a well-defined research question. In health research, questions are often framed using the PICO acronym as a framework, with the question including the population (the P), the intervention being examined (the I), the comparison group or control condition (the C) and the outcome (the O) we are interested in.

In assessing systematic reviews, Hagger (2012) suggests that the features of a 'good' review article are that it:

- is *original*—makes a unique contribution to the literature and field of study

- *advances thinking and knowledge*—challenges previous ideas and contributes to new and existing understandings of the issue

- is *theory-based*—takes into consideration what has gone before and uses current thinking and evidence to develop new ideas

- is *evidence-based*—takes into consideration previous research findings when developing new ideas

- is *accurate, comprehensive and rigorous*—uses the highest methodological standards when conducting the review and includes all important studies in the field or *provides justification for their exclusion*

- *provides recommendations for future research*—is diligent in generating new questions to be addressed and fosters future research enquiry and empirical work

- *stimulates debate*—values scholarly debate between researchers and theorists on key questions related to theory, research and practice.

OTHER PUBLICATIONS

Research findings can also be disseminated through conference presentations and posters. Conference presentations often report on recently completed research that has not yet been published in a peer-reviewed journal article, or may report on practice initiatives by health professionals, which the authors may or may not choose to publish subsequently. Conference presentations and posters undergo some form of peer review (usually a submitted abstract is sent out for review by the conference scientific committee, but sometimes a full article is required) with regard to methodological and interpretive soundness and, hence, the audience can place greater confidence in the conclusions drawn by the researchers.

Another source of research reports is the popular media that, in the main, are not peer-reviewed. Included in this category are newspaper articles, radio and television programs and the internet. Less confidence can be placed in the reliability, validity and credibility of claims made in such reports if they have not undergone the scrutiny of professional review or are not written by and involve the participation of experts in the area.

Government departments and non-government organisations frequently publish reports as a monograph, which is a small book or treatise on a particular subject. Governments, academics and organisations also publish reports and policies in hard copy and on the internet in what has become known as the 'grey literature'. The credibility of these reports is influenced by who the author is and who published it. Non-refereed journals and newsletters, such as those published by professional organisations, are another source for research reports or updates. However, as these publications have not been subjected to the scrutiny of review by experts, they do not carry the same authority as a report published in a refereed scholarly journal.

Nevertheless, they can be informative and a discerning reader can critically evaluate the conclusions drawn by the authors just as they also would for a refereed article.

Access to research information by the general public has increased exponentially in recent years, principally through the internet but also through current affairs programs on television and from the print media. Many patients now research their conditions on the internet before visiting their GP. Although this enables patients to be more informed about their condition and treatment options, it is important to stress that any information sourced from the popular media must be critically assessed before being accepted as valid. Health professionals, as research consumers, have an important role to play in answering questions that patients may have from conducting their own research using such sources.

To conclude, before accepting claims made by researchers, the responsibility rests with readers to critically appraise the veracity of those claims, regardless of whether the research findings are peer assessed or not, but particularly if they are not.

Analysis and critique of research reports

In analysing and critiquing research articles and reviews, some considerations apply to both quantitative and qualitative studies, such as assessing to what extent ethical principles were upheld during the research process. There are also separate questions to be asked due to the different approaches of the two paradigms regarding research design, data collection, analysis, interpretation and conclusions drawn. The questions in Boxes 2.1 and 2.2 (adapted from Whitehead 2020) provide a template for critically appraising quantitative and qualitative research reports.

Research focus

Source: Cohen et al. 2021

ABSTRACT

Purpose
  To study how young adult college students are managing their health behaviours and risks related to spreading COVID-19.

Methods
  The researchers created a national cohort of full-time college students in late April 2020 ($n = 707$) and conducted a follow-up survey with participants in July 2020 ($n = 543$). Participants reported COVID-19-related health risk behaviours and COVID-19 symptoms, and also responded to an open-ended prompt about how the COVID-19 pandemic has affected their lives. Quantitative data were analysed in Stata and a content analysis helped identify themes in the qualitative data.

Results
  For most health protective behaviours (e.g. frequent handwashing, social distancing), participants were less compliant in the northern summer of

Cont... ▶

2020 than in the spring of 2020, with the exception of face mask use, which increased. In each month of the first half of 2020, only approximately half of participants with any symptoms that could indicate COVID-19 stayed home exclusively while symptomatic (there was no meaningful change from pre-pandemic or over the course of the pandemic). In qualitative data, the participants who had gone to bars or clubs at least twice within a 4-week period in the summer reported being bored and/or isolated, stressed and/ or taking pandemic safety measures seriously.

Conclusions

These findings suggest multiple areas for intervention including harm reduction and risk management education approaches for the students who went to bars and clubs, and creating policies and programs to better incentivise young people with symptoms to stay home exclusively while symptomatic.

Student activity

1. In small groups, obtain the complete article from the Science Direct database for Cohen and colleagues 2021 study and assess it using the critical review of quantitative studies guidelines in Box 2.1. Alternatively, find another peer-reviewed article that reports on a quantitative study and assess it using the critical review of quantitative studies guidelines in Box 2.1.
2. How might health professionals in your discipline use these findings to work with young people?
3. How can the research findings be understood in light of theories of development in Chapters 3 and 4?
4. How can the research findings help identify areas for health prevention, promotion and education?

Box 2.1 Critical review of quantitative studies

Article details	Record author name(s), publication date, article title and journal details. Is the article published in a scholarly journal and has it been through a peer-review process? Is the title consistent with the stated aim of the study? Is the abstract a succinct summary of the study, its findings and its recommendations?
Research background and literature review	Are the reasons for conducting the study stated? Does the literature review demonstrate a need for the study by examining previous work and identifying gaps in knowledge?

Cont... ▶

Box 2.1 Critical review of quantitative studies—cont'd

Aim of the study	What is the research question? Are hypotheses clearly stated?
Method	What is the study design? Is it appropriate for the hypothesis or research question under investigation? Is the data collection process (including participant recruitment) and method (e.g. questionnaire) clearly described? Are the validity and reliability of instruments used discussed? What statistical tests are used? Were they descriptive, correlational or inferential? Are the statistical tests used appropriate for the question/issue under investigation?
Findings	Was the hypothesis confirmed/refuted? Are the findings statistically significant? Have the findings been interpreted in relation to the research question and aims? Were there any unexpected findings?
Significance of findings	What is the significance of the findings? Why are they important? To whom are they important? What are the implications of the findings for clinical practice? What are the implications of the findings for further research?
Limitations/rigour	Are the limitations of the study reported? Is the sample size sufficient for the statistical tests used in the study? Can the findings be generalised, or are they limited to the population studied? Is there a conflict of interest (e.g. who funded the study)? Is enough detail provided to allow the study to be replicated?
Conclusion	Can the conclusion logically be drawn from the data analysis and findings? Is the conclusion related to the findings and the stated aim of the study? Do the recommendations regarding clinical practice or future research logically follow from the analysis of the findings? Did the study provide new insights or a different perspective on the issue?

Adapted from Whitehead 2020.

Research focus

Source: Ray et al. 2021

ABSTRACT

Background

Experiencing complications in pregnancy is stressful for women and can affect fetal and maternal outcomes. Supportive encounters with health professionals can reduce the worry women experience. Further research is needed to understand women's perspectives on communicating with healthcare providers about their concerns.

Aim

This study explored women's experiences of receiving information about pregnancy complications from healthcare providers and their interactions with multiple professionals and services during pregnancy.

Methods

This was a qualitative interpretive study. Semi-structured interviews were conducted with 20 women experiencing pregnancy complications recruited from antenatal services at two hospitals in Sydney. Inductive thematic analysis was used to analyse the data.

Findings

Women had a range of reactions to their diagnoses including concern for their baby, for themselves and for their labour. Most women reported that communication with healthcare providers was distressing, that they were not listened to and that staff used insensitive, abrupt language. Women were also distressed by delays in education, receiving contradictory information and having to repeatedly share their stories with different health professionals. In some cases, this damaged the therapeutic relationship and reduced trust towards healthcare providers. Midwives were generally preferred over doctors because they had a more woman-centred approach.

Conclusion

To improve women's experiences of care for pregnancy complications, it is critical to improve the communication skills of maternity service providers. Women's need for information, resources and support can best be provided by continuity of care with a named health professional—for example, a midwife working within an integrated multidisciplinary antenatal service model.

Student activity

1. In small groups, obtain the complete article from the Science Direct database for Ray and colleagues 2021 study and assess it using the critical review of qualitative studies guidelines in Box 2.2. Alternatively, find another peer-reviewed article that reports on a qualitative study and assess it using the critical review of qualitative studies guidelines in Box 2.2.
2. How might health professionals in your discipline use these findings to work with women who are pregnant?
3. Discuss how issues such as 'breaking bad news' are important for health practitioners to understand when undertaking research in practice. How will these research findings support changes in practice?

Box 2.2 Critical review of qualitative studies

Article details	Record the author's name(s), publication date, article title and journal details. Is the article published in a scholarly journal and has it been through a peer-review process? Is the title consistent with the stated aim of the study? Is the abstract a succinct summary of the study, its findings and its recommendations?
Research background and literature review	Are the reasons for conducting the study stated? Does the literature review demonstrate a need for the study by examining previous work and identifying gaps in knowledge?
Aim of the study	What is the purpose of the study? What is the issue or phenomenon under investigation?
Method	What is the study design? Is it appropriate for the issue under investigation? Is the data collection process, including participant recruitment, ethics and method (e.g. interviews, focus groups), clearly described? Is the theoretical framework and the process used for data analysis clearly described? Is the data analysis method appropriate for the question/issue under investigation? Does the researcher discuss their own values, potential biases and assumptions, and how these have been managed?

Box 2.2 Critical review of qualitative studies—cont'd

Findings	Is the phenomenon sufficiently identified? Have the findings been interpreted in relation to the research question and aims? Is a new theory developed or are the findings related to existing theory?
Significance of findings	What is the significance of the findings? Why are they important? To whom are they important? What are the implications of the findings for clinical practice? What are the implications of the findings for further research?
Limitations/rigour	Are the limitations of the study reported? Can the findings be generalised, or are they limited to the population studied? Is there a conflict of interest (e.g. an unequal power relationship between participants and the interviewer)? Is enough detail provided to allow the study to be replicated?
Conclusion	Can the conclusion logically be drawn from the data analysis? Is the conclusion related to the findings and the stated aim of the study? Do the recommendations about clinical practice or future research logically follow from the analysis of the findings? Did the study provide new insights or a different perspective on the issue?

Adapted from Whitehead 2020.

Evidence-based healthcare

Evidence-based healthcare, sometimes referred to more generally as evidence-based practice, is premised on the notion that every clinical intervention needs to be supported by findings from contemporary research. In theory, this means that health professionals will use effective practices, question practices that lack supporting evidence and cease practices that are harmful (Greenhalgh 2014, 2018). While quantitative evidence is often privileged in the health disciplines (a criticism of evidence-based practice), qualitative studies allow researchers and health professionals to ascertain the perceptions, attitudes and experiences of people regarding their health and illness (Hoffman et al. 2017). In addition, for many areas of practice, RCTs may be limited or non-existent, meaning that evidence to inform clinical decision making is needed from qualitative and other types of quantitative studies.

Health professionals whose practice is underpinned by an evidence base can better articulate a treatment rationale and refer to the research findings that support particular interventions. They can keep themselves up to date by regularly accessing the relevant quality literature in their area of practice or specialty. Importantly, practitioners will have the skills to evaluate research findings and, where relevant, translate these into new practices, or stop using practices that are not supported by contemporary evidence. Nevertheless, despite the rhetoric surrounding evidence-based best practice, barriers exist that prevent the transfer of identified best practice guidelines into everyday clinical care. Such barriers include resistance from health professionals as well as structural barriers within organisations (Avorn & Fischer 2010; Morrison et al. 2019).

Research conducted by Forsner and colleagues (2010) examining the barriers and facilitators to implementing clinical guidelines in psychiatry found there were three categories of barriers and facilitators to implementing clinical practice change: organisational resources; health professionals' individual characteristics; and perceptions of guidelines and implementation strategies. The researchers also found differences between the practitioners in the implementation team and the staff at the clinics, including concern about control over clinical practice, beliefs about evidence-based practice and suspicions about financial motives for introducing the guidelines. The researchers concluded that new guidelines could be better adopted if staff at the local level were able to actively participate in the implementation process and if the barriers were addressed at the organisational and individual levels.

Earlier research by Grol and Wensing (2004) examined the implementation of guidelines for diabetes care and found there were three categories of barriers to implementing clinical practice change: individual, social and organisational/economic.

Individual factors included:

- *cognitive*—decision-making processes and risk–benefit analysis
- *educational*—learning styles
- *attitudinal*—perceived behavioural control, self-efficacy
- *motivational*—the individual's motivational stages and barriers.

Social factors included:

- *social learning*—role models
- *social network and influence*—values and culture
- *patient influence*—patient expectations and behaviour
- *leadership*—style, power and the leader's commitment.

Organisational and economic factors included:

- *innovativeness of the organisation*—specialisation, decentralisation and professionalism

- *quality management*—culture and leadership
- *complexity*—interaction between system parts
- *organisational learning*—capacity and arrangements for ongoing learning
- *economic*—rewards and incentives for change or maintaining the status quo.

The authors concluded that although the research identifies a range of factors that pose barriers to clinical practice change, the findings do not specify which of the factors are the most influential, nor in which circumstances they might have the most influence. Regardless, the findings are important because they highlight the complexity involved in bringing about change in clinical practice—even when there is evidence to support the change. Also, the findings identify areas for future research to explore these contributing factors further. Some proposed ways to reduce the *research–practice gap* include: encouraging partnerships between researchers and clinicians to explore clinically relevant topics; involving clinical staff or health professionals in all stages of a research project to encourage uptake in the clinical setting; and valuing the expertise and unique perspectives of both researchers, who are experts in research design, and clinicians, who understand the clinical environment in which they work (Denvall & Skillmark 2021; Huston et al. 2018).

In summary, research provides the evidence on which best practice can be based. However, although health professionals are responsible for ensuring their practice makes use of the available evidence, the responsibility for this does not rest with individual health professionals alone because the transfer of the research findings into clinical practice change is complex, political and influenced by social and organisational factors. Evidence-based practice, therefore, is not and cannot be merely an individual health professional's responsibility.

Research ethics in healthcare practice

Throughout the world, research conducted on humans must conform to ethical codes or guidelines. The primary ethical consideration of any research involving humans is that of **beneficence**, or the principle that on balance the potential good resulting from research participation must outweigh the potential harm.

Ethical codes and guidelines are intended to protect the rights of vulnerable people. The first code of medical ethics, the Nuremburg code, was developed subsequent to the Nuremburg tribunal that investigated the human rights violations of the medical experiments carried out by doctors in Germany during World War II. In 1964, the World Medical Association adopted an international code of medical ethics, based on the Nuremburg code, which became known as the *Declaration of Helsinki*. The Helsinki declaration, which has been updated several times since the original document, is a statement of ethical principles that provides guidance to physicians and other participants in medical research involving human subjects (World Medical Association 2013) and is the foundation on which worldwide codes of health **research ethics** are based.

AUSTRALIAN AND NEW ZEALAND CODES OF ETHICS

The body that oversees the ethical conduct of research involving human subjects in Australia is the National Health and Medical Research Council (NHMRC), and in New Zealand it is the Health Research Council of New Zealand (HRC). Both councils have developed guidelines for the ethical conduct of research involving human subjects, namely the NHMRC *National Statement on Ethical Conduct in Human Research* (NHMRC et al. 2018) in Australia, and the HRC *Research Ethics Guidelines* (2021) in New Zealand.

In 2007 (and updated in 2018) the NHMRC, Australian Research Council and the Australian Vice-Chancellors' Committee released the *National Statement on Ethical Conduct in Human Research*, which contains Australia's primary guidelines for ethically conducting research involving human participants. The purpose of the statement is to promote ethical human research, ensure participants are accorded respect and protection and foster research that benefits the community. The statement is based on four values that the design and conduct of all research involving human participants must follow. The central theme of these values is respect for all human beings, and beneficence is the value that underpins the other three. The values are:

- *respect for human beings*—the research takes into account the welfare, beliefs, customs and cultural heritage of research participants
- *research merit and integrity*—the research is justified by the potential benefits it has to individuals, communities and/or knowledge generation, has been conceptualised and designed based on the literature and sound design principles, and is conducted with appropriate resources and personnel
- *justice*—the inclusion (who is allowed to participate) and exclusion (who is not allowed to participate) criteria for participation and recruitment of participants is fair and does not place unfair burden on individuals or groups; and for those who do participate, that benefits of participation are fairly distributed and participants are not exploited
- *beneficence*—the benefits of the research justify the risks to participants and/ or the community, and researchers are mindful of the welfare of participants and aim to minimise risk of their harm or discomfort (NHMRC et al. 2018).

RESEARCH WITH INDIGENOUS PEOPLE AND PEOPLE FROM CULTURALLY DIVERSE BACKGROUNDS

Following a history of colonisation and injustice, the ethics of health research involving Indigenous people are complex (Baum 2016). Hence, further issues need to be considered for research that includes Indigenous people. Therefore, as well as heeding the ethical principles outlined in the *Research Ethics Guidelines*, New Zealand researchers, for example, must also take into consideration additional issues for Māori participants developed by the HRC (2010, 2021). The council directs that all research proposals involving Māori must observe the principles of the *Treaty of Waitangi* and incorporate this in the proceedings and processes of ethics committees. Particularly relevant are the principles of:

- *partnership*—working together with iwi, hapū, whanau and Māori communities to ensure Māori individual and collective rights are respected and protected

- *participation*—involving Māori in the design, governance, management, implementation and analysis of research, especially research involving Māori

- *protection*—actively protecting Māori individual and collective rights, Māori data, Māori culture, cultural concepts, values, norms, practices and language in the research process (HRC 2010, 2021).

Australia, too, has developed guidelines for research with Indigenous people. The NHMRC has published the guideline, *Ethical Conduct in Research with Aboriginal and Torres Strait Islander Peoples and Communities: Guidelines for Researchers and Stakeholders* (NHMRC 2018). Six core overlapping values that should underpin research are proposed. The central or core value is spirit and integrity. This involves respect for the connection to and continuity of connection that Aboriginal and Torres Strait Islander people have to their culture and identity, as well as researchers engaging in honourable behaviours when interacting with Aboriginal and Torres Strait Islander communities and stakeholders. This core value is reflected in the other five values:

- *cultural continuity*—engaging with Aboriginal and Torres Strait Islander people and involving community members in the research in a way that includes individuals and communities in consultation and respects the sharing of information

- *equity*—establishing partnerships between the researchers and those individuals and communities who are participating, such as involvement in all parts of the research process and considering the best methods of communication (e.g. first language being used in information sheets)

- *reciprocity*—considering the potential benefit of the research to Aboriginal and Torres Strait Islander people by considering community priorities and needs

- *respect*—respecting the welfare and rights of Aboriginal and Torres Strait Islander people (e.g. ensuring informed consent) and including participant and community involvement in decision making around the research, such as through research agreements

- *responsibility*—ensuring research is conducted in a way that benefits outweigh careful consideration of potential risks, and that researchers are accountable to individuals and communities in their conduct of research.

Researchers conducting research with Indigenous people need to closely consider these principles, as well as other guidelines such as the *Keeping Research on Track* (NHMRC 2018) and the Australian Institute of Aboriginal and Torres Strait Islander Studies (2020) *Code of Ethics for Aboriginal and Torres Strait Islander Research*.

Ethical guidelines in Australia and New Zealand also provide guidance for researchers working with people from culturally diverse backgrounds, who are those members of the community who were born overseas and/or speak languages other than English (Sawrikar & Katz 2008). For example, the NHMRC *National Statement on Ethical Conduct in Human Research* (NHMRC et al. 2018) states that researchers need to consider and respect the customs, cultural heritage and cultural sensitivities of people and communities who take part in their studies. These factors are important at all stages of the research process including recruitment, obtaining informed consent, using appropriate methods and measures during the study, and how data is stored once the study is completed.

An important consideration for health professionals working with Indigenous people or people from culturally diverse backgrounds is the extent to which research findings can be generalised to their patients if study participants were not from these groups. People from Indigenous and culturally diverse backgrounds are often underrepresented in studies in health and medicine owing to factors such as:

- concerns from both potential participants and researchers about the ability to understand the nature of the study and to provide informed consent
- researchers not having enough funding to employ translators
- fear and mistrust of research processes (George et al. 2014; Woodward-Kron et al. 2016).

Without studies available to health professionals (research consumers) that take a culturally embedded perspective that examines the ways in which culture and other contextual factors influence a person's behaviour (Englar-Carlson & Smart 2014; Pedrotti et al. 2021), professionals may lack the knowledge to provide individualised and culturally sensitive care (Tucker et al. 2013). Culturally sensitive healthcare is care that 'effectively responds to the attitudes, feelings and circumstances of people that share common identifying characteristics' such as a particular ethnicity, language or religious belief, and care that 'patients perceive as being concordant with their cultural values and beliefs' (Tucker et al. 2013, p. 63).

Researchers therefore need to consider ways in which they can increase the participation of Indigenous and culturally diverse people in research studies (and ensure their involvement is ethical and culturally sensitive), and research consumers should always consider the extent to which available literature is applicable to the people and groups they work with.

HEALTH PROFESSIONALS AS PATIENT ADVOCATES

Health professionals may engage in research that focuses on generating knowledge about a phenomenon, such as understanding children's lived experiences of grief, or they may engage in projects that are more specific to their workplaces and practice, such as service evaluations and audits. Service evaluations examine particular services or practices within a workplace, focusing on outcomes such as patient experiences, while audits compare practice against particular benchmarks (Illing 2014; Twycross & Shorten 2014).

As well as conducting research, health professionals also engage in health research either as participants or because the patients they care for are participants in other studies. For example, in some research, the researchers ask health professionals to what extent they think certain patients would be able to provide informed consent to participate in a research study. Consequently, it is crucial that health professionals are aware of the 'rights' of research participants, including themselves (Whitehead et al. 2020).

In caring for patients who are research participants, a health professional's role includes ensuring that: the patient fully understands what they are consenting to (informed consent); the rule of beneficence applies; the patient's anonymity, privacy and dignity is respected; and the patient is aware that they can withdraw from the research at any time. At times, this may involve acting as an advocate for the patient such as providing extra information to the patient or explaining the patient's right to not take part in the research if they don't want to.

Extreme examples of the need to advocate on behalf of patients include the 1980s RCT of cervical cancer conducted at the National Women's Hospital in Auckland in which conventional cancer treatment was withheld from some participants in the study without their consent (Paul 1988; Skegg 2011); and the United States army-sponsored AIDS research in Thailand in the 1990s that tracked the natural course of vertical transmission of HIV in children born to sero-positive mothers. The infants were not given the antiretroviral drug zidovudine (AZT), despite the drug being proven effective in reducing vertical HIV transmission in American and French studies. Thirty-seven children in the Thai study contracted the HIV virus (Hassani 2005; Robb et al. 1998). Similar controversy surrounded trials of AZT in Africa in the 1990s, in which control groups were given a placebo, despite the results of other trials that convincingly demonstrated the effectiveness of antiretroviral drug treatment, thereby making a control group unethical (Brewster 2011). Haire (2011) further argues that the debate that ensued following the exposure of the antiretroviral drug trials in developing countries was important because it highlighted the need for health equity and access to care to redress health disparities. Researchers, Haire argues, have a duty of care and a moral responsibility to ensure treatments for the diseases under investigation must be made available to the populations participating in the study, regardless of where they live.

These examples are from previous decades, and certainly since then there has been increased focus on ethical conduct in research. However, researchers do continue to face complex ethical issues when doing real-world applied research into the effects of potentially life-saving treatments. For example, during the early vaccination trials for COVID-19, ethicists and researchers grappled with whether it was ethical to assign participants to a control group if we know a vaccine is efficacious or if this means control participants are denied a potentially life-saving vaccine (Han et al. 2020; Wendler et al. 2020). Those considering such issues highlight the importance of ensuring participants are fully aware of what they are being asked to do, including risks and potential benefits, and can provide informed consent.

In summary, codes of ethics and ethical research guidelines serve the purpose of protecting participants in health research. It is the responsibility of health professionals to ensure they adhere to these principles, such as ensuring participants understand fully what they are being asked to do, and that they take action on behalf of themselves or the patient in their care should the health professional become aware that this is not the case.

Student activity

In United States army research, reported by Robb and colleagues (1998) and Praphan (1998), the researchers argued that AZT was not deemed standard treatment in Thailand for people at risk of contracting HIV (although it was at that time in Western countries) and therefore it was not unethical to withhold the drug from infants born to HIV-positive mothers. Brewster (2011), reporting on African antiretroviral drug trials, disagrees, arguing that once an intervention is proven to be effective, it is unethical to include a placebo group in drug trials.

1. Debate the ethics of researchers withholding a known effective treatment because it is not a standard treatment in the country where the research is conducted.

2. Do you agree or disagree with Haire's view that researchers have a duty of care and a moral responsibility to provide treatment for the disease under investigation to participants of the study, regardless of where they live, or the cost of the treatment?

3. Explain your reasons for this view.

CASE STUDY: JACK

Jack is 75 years old and was diagnosed with sporadic Alzheimer's disease 3 years ago. He lives at home with support from his elderly wife, Margaret. He has been asked if he is willing to be a participant in a dementia study exploring people's experience of cognitive decline being undertaken at a local hospital. Margaret has reservations about Jack's ability to provide informed consent, but Jack is keen to be involved. Jack tells his wife that he thinks his participation may help others with the disease.

Critical thinking

- Identify the issues in this case study regarding the ethical principles of research merit and integrity, justice, beneficence and respect.

- Can a person with mild cognitive impairment or in the early stages of Alzheimer's disease give informed consent? What about someone with advanced dementia?

- If yes, in what circumstances? Do you think the risks and benefits to Jack's participation would be different if the study was a qualitative investigation of people's experiences with dementia versus an RCT of a new drug?

- If no, what are the implications for research involving people with cognitive impairment?
- One approach to research with people with cognitive impairment involves a proxy (e.g. spouse) providing consent for the person to participate, with the person indicating 'assent' or lack of objection to being involved in the research (Black et al. 2013). Based on ethical principles outlined by the NHMRC or HRC, what is your view of this recommendation?
- How might you as a future health professional go about ascertaining whether a person with cognitive impairment can take part in your study or the study of another health professional?
- What *advice* would you give Jack's wife if you were caring for Jack as a future health professional?

You can read more about specific ethical considerations when conducting research involving participants with a cognitive impairment, intellectual disability or a mental illness in section 4 of the *National Statement on Ethical Conduct in Human Research* (NHMRC et al. 2018), as well as in a study investigating participants and proxy decision-makers' perspectives of participation in dementia research (Black et al. 2013).

Chapter summary

In this chapter, the two major research paradigms—quantitative and qualitative—were presented. Differences between and similarities of the two approaches were highlighted and the conclusion drawn that the selection of a particular research paradigm is influenced not by the intrinsic merits of either a positivist or a critical approach but by the question under investigation and the best way to seek an answer to that question.

The importance of research in the everyday practice of psychologists and health professionals was emphasised, including the notion that research provides the evidence on which all healthcare practice should be based. The complexities of translating research findings into practice were recognised and the role of health professionals as research consumers was emphasised. Finally, the important role played by health professionals in the ethical conduct of research was highlighted.

KEY POINTS

- Research is fundamental to the clinical practice of health professionals because it provides the evidence on which healthcare practice is based.
- Skills as a research consumer are essential in healthcare practice.
- Research findings can identify healthcare practices that are effective and efficient, thereby identifying 'best practice'.
- Research findings can identify healthcare practices that are not effective or efficient and thereby provide evidence to facilitate change.
- Health professionals play a key role in the ethical conduct of research and as advocates for their patients.

Further reading

Hoffman, T., Bennett, S., Del Mar, C., 2017. Evidence-Based Practice Across the Health Professions, 3rd edn. Elsevier, Sydney.

Watson, R., McKenna, H., Cowman, S., et al. 2008. Nursing Research: Designs and Methods. Churchill Livingstone, Edinburgh.

Whitehead, D., Ferguson, C., LoBondio-Wood, G., et al., 2020. Nursing and Midwifery Research: Methods and Appraisal for Evidence-Based Practice, 6th edn. Elsevier, Sydney.

Weblinks

Cochrane Library

www.cochranelibrary.com/

The Cochrane Library contains high-quality, independent evidence that can inform healthcare decision making. It includes reliable evidence from Cochrane and other systematic reviews, clinical trials and more. It includes the combined results of the world's best medical research studies, which are recognised as the gold standard in evidence-based healthcare.

Joanna Briggs Institute

www.joannabriggs.org

The Joanna Briggs Institute is an international not-for-profit research and development organisation specialising in evidence-based resources for health professionals in nursing, midwifery, medicine and allied health. The institute is a recognised global leader in evidence-based healthcare.

National Health and Medical Research Council

www.nhmrc.gov.au

The NHMRC is Australia's peak body for health and medical research, health advice and ethics in healthcare and in health and medical research.

Health Research Council of New Zealand/Te Kaunihera Rangahau Hauora o Aotearoa

www.hrc.govt.nz

This is the New Zealand Government's main funding agency for health research. Its mission is to benefit New Zealand through health research, with the goal of improving health for all.

Science Direct

www.sciencedirect.com

Science Direct is operated by the publisher Elsevier. It is one of the world's largest collections of published scientific research, including health and social sciences.

References

Andrews, H., Tierney, S., Seers, K., 2020. Needing permission: the experience of self-care and self-compassion in nursing: a constructivist grounded theory study. International Journal of Nursing Studies, 101, 103436.

Aspers, P., 2010. Empirical phenomenology: a qualitative research approach (The Cologne Seminars). Indo-Pacific Journal of Phenomenology 9 (2), 1–12.

Australian Institute of Aboriginal and Torres Strait Islander Studies, 2020. AIATSIS Code of Ethics for Aboriginal and Torres Strait Islander Research. AIATSIS, Canberra. Available: https://aiatsis.gov.au/research/ethical-research (Accessed 23 March 2022).

Avorn, J., Fischer, M., 2010. Bench to behaviour: translating comparative effectiveness research into improved clinical practice. Health Affairs 29 (10), 1891–1900.

Baum, F., 2016. The New Public Health, 4th edn. Oxford University Press, Melbourne.

Benjamin, D.J., Berger, J.O., Johannesson, M., et al. 2018. Redefine statistical significance. Nature Human Behaviour 2 (1), 6–10.

Bentley, P.J., Gulbrandsen, M., Kyvik, S., 2015. The relationship between basic and applied research in universities. Higher Education 70 (4), 689–709.

Black, B.S., Wechsler, M., Fogarty, L., 2013. Decision making for participation in dementia research. The American Journal of Geriatric Psychiatry 21 (4), 355–363.

Braun, V., Clarke, V., 2006. Using thematic analysis in psychology. Qualitative Research in Psychology 3 (2), 77–101.

Braun, V., Clarke, V., 2021. One size fits all? What counts as quality practice in (reflexive) thematic analysis? Qualitative Research in Psychology, 18 (3), 328–352.

Braun, V., Clarke, V., 2022. Thematic Analysis: A Practical Guide. Sage, London.

Brewster, D., 2011. Science and ethics of human immunodeficiency virus/acquired immunodeficiency syndrome controversies in Africa. Journal of Paediatrics and Child Health 47 (9), 646–655.

Chandler J., Cumpston M., Thomas J., et al. 2022. Chapter I: Introduction. In: Higgins J. P. T., Thomas J., Chandler J., et al. (eds.), Cochrane Handbook for Systematic Reviews of Interventions, version 6.3. Available: www.training.cochrane.org/handbook (accessed 23 March 2022).

Charmaz, K., 2014. Constructing Grounded Theory, 2nd edn. Sage, London.

Clarke, V., Braun, V., 2013. Teaching thematic analysis: overcoming challenges and developing strategies for effective learning. The Psychologist 26 (2), 120–123.

Clarke, V., Braun, V., 2014. Thematic analysis. In: Michalos, A.C. (Ed.), Encyclopedia of Quality of Life and Well-Being Research. Springer, Dordrecht, pp. 6626–6628.

Cozby, P.C., Bates, S.C., 2020. Methods in Behavioral Research, 14th edn. McGraw-Hill Education, New York.

Creswell, J.W., Poth, C.N., 2018. Qualitative Inquiry & Research Design: Choosing Among Five Approaches, 4th edn. Sage, Thousand Oaks.

Crotty, M., 1996. Phenomenology and Nursing Research. Churchill Livingstone, Melbourne.

Dagyaran, I., Olesen, C.M., Brix, L.D., 2021. Patient-experienced quality during postoperative pain management – a phenomenological-hermeneutic study. Journal of PeriAnesthesia Nursing, https://doi.org/10.1016/j.jopan.2021.09.007.

Dawson, S., Muir-Cochrane, E., Simpson, A., et al. 2021. Community treatment orders and care planning: How is engagement and decision-making enacted? Health Expectations, 24 (5), 1859–1867.

Denvall, V., Skillmark, M., 2021. Bridge over troubled water: closing the research–practice gap in social work. The British Journal of Social Work 51 (7), 2722–2739.

Denzin, N., 2017. The Research Act: A Theoretical Introduction to Sociological Methods. Routledge, Oxford.

Dowling, M., 2007. From Husserl to van Manen: a review of different phenomenological approaches. International Journal of Nursing Studies 44 (1), 131–142.

Englar-Carlson, M., Smart, R., 2014. Positive psychology and gender. In: Pedrotti, J.T., Edwards, L.M. (Eds.), Perspectives on the Intersection of Multiculturalism and Positive Psychology. Springer, Dordrecht, pp. 125–141.

Finlay, K.A., Elander, J., 2018. Developing successful social support: an interpretative phenomenological analysis of mechanisms and processes in a chronic pain support group. Psychology & Health 33 (7), 846–871.

Finlay, L., 2010. Debating phenomenological research methods. Phenomenology and Practice 3 (1), 6–25.

Flood, A., 2010. Understanding phenomenology. Nurse Researcher 17 (2), 7–25.

Forsner, T., Hansson, J., Brommels, M., et al., 2010. Implementing clinical guidelines in psychiatry: a qualitative study of perceived facilitators and barriers. BMC Psychiatry 10 (8), 1–20.

Fure, S.C.R., Howe, E.I., Andelic, N., et al., 2021. Cognitive and vocational rehabilitation after mild-to-moderate traumatic brain injury: a randomised controlled trial. Annals of Physical and Rehabilitation Medicine, 64(5), 101538.

George, S., Duran, N., Norris, K., 2014. A systematic review of barriers and facilitators to minority research participation among African Americans, Latinos, Asian Americans, and Pacific Islanders. American Journal of Public Health 104 (2), e16–e31.

Gerace, A., Muir-Cochrane, E., 2019. Perceptions of nurses working with psychiatric consumers regarding the elimination of seclusion and restraint in psychiatric inpatient settings and emergency departments: an Australian survey. International Journal of Mental Health Nursing 28 (1), 209–225.

Greenhalgh, T., 2014. How to Read a Paper: The Basics of Evidence-Based Medicine, 5th edn. Wiley, Chichester.

Greenhalgh, T., 2018. How to Implement Evidence-Based Healthcare. Wiley, Hoboken.

Grol, R., Wensing, M., 2004. What drives change? Barriers to and incentives for achieving evidence-based practice. The Medical Journal of Australia 180 (6 Suppl), s57–s60.

Hagger, M., 2012. What makes a 'good' review article? Some reflections and recommendations. Health Psychology Review 6 (2), 141–146.

Haire, B., 2011. Because we can: clashes of perspective over researcher obligations in the failed PrEP trials. Developing World Bioethics 11 (2), 63–74.

Halcomb, E., 2021. Research in nursing. In: Daly, J., Jackson, D. (Eds.), Contexts of Nursing: An Introduction. Elsevier, Chatswood, pp. 105–118.

Han, Z., Wang, J., Zhang, K., et al., 2020. The ethic of COVID-19 clinical trials: new considerations in a controversial area. Integrative Medicine Review, 9 (3), 100425.

Handberg, C., Thorne, S., Maribo, T., 2018. When a policy decision meets practice realities: the case of cancer survivorship care and rehabilitation needs assessment. European Journal of Oncology Nursing 33, 70–77.

Handberg, C., Thorne, S., Midtgaard, J., et al., 2015. Revisiting symbolic interactionism as a theoretical framework beyond the grounded theory tradition. Qualitative Health Research 25 (8), 1023–1032.

Hassani, B., 2005. Trials by fire: the case of unethical clinical trials in the countries of the south. University of Toronto Medical Journal 82 (3), 212–216.

Health Research Council of New Zealand (HRC), 2010. Guidelines for Researchers on Health Research Involving Māori, version 2. HRC, Auckland.

Health Research Council of New Zealand (HRC), 2021. Research Ethics Guidelines. HRC, Auckland.

Hoffman, T., Bennett, S., Del Mar, C., 2017. Evidence-Based Practice Across the Health Professions, 3rd edn. Elsevier, Sydney.

Holloway, I., Galvin, K., 2017. Qualitative Research in Nursing and Healthcare, 4th edn. Wiley, Chichester.

Huston, C.L., Phillips, B., Jeffries, P., et al., 2018. The academic-practice gap: strategies for an enduring problem. Nursing Forum. 53 (1), 27–34.

Illing, J., 2014. Thinking about research: theoretical perspectives, ethics and scholarship. In: Swanwick, T. (Ed.), Understanding Medical Education: Evidence, Theory and Practice, 2nd edn. Wiley, Chichester, pp. 331–347.

Judd, R., Guy, H., Howard, R.A., 2019. Caring for a dying partner: the male experience. Journal of Palliative Care 34 (1), 5–11.

Madden, R., 2017. Being Ethnographic: A Guide to the Theory and Practice of Ethnography, 2nd edn. Sage, London.

Marikar Bawa, F.L., Sutton, J.W., Mercer, S.W., et al., 2021. "I'm empowered to look after myself"—Mindfulness as a way to manage chronic pain: an interpretative phenomenological analysis of participant experiences in Scotland. Social Science & Medicine, 281, 114073.

McCaughan, E., Curran, C., Northouse, L., et al., 2018. Evaluating a psychosocial intervention for men with prostate cancer and their partners: outcomes and lessons learned from a randomized controlled trial. Applied Nursing Research 40, 143–151.

McGlinchey, E., Hitch, C., Butter, S., et al., 2021. Understanding the lived experiences of healthcare professionals during the COVID-19 pandemic: an interpretative phenomenological analysis. European Journal of Psychotraumatology, 12 (1). 1904700.

McMullan, E., Gupta, A., Collins, S.C., 2018. Experiences of mental health nursing staff working with voice hearers in an acute setting: an interpretive phenomenological approach. Journal of Psychiatric and Mental Health Nursing 25 (3), 157–166.

Morrison, V., Bennett, P., Butow, P., et al. 2019. Introduction to Health Psychology in Australia, 3rd edn. Pearson Education, Sydney.

Muir-Cochrane, E., O'Kane, D., Oster, C., 2018. Fear and blame in mental health nurses' accounts of restrictive practices: implications for the elimination of seclusion and restraint. International Journal of Mental Health Nursing 27 (5), 1511–1521.

National Health and Medical Research Council (NHMRC), 2018. Keeping research on track II: a companion document to ethical conduct in research with Aboriginal and Torres Strait Islander Peoples and communities: guidelines for researchers and stakeholders. Commonwealth of Australia, Canberra. Available: https://www.nhmrc.gov.au/about-us/resources/keeping-research-track-ii. (Accessed 23 March 2022).

National Health and Medical Research Council, Australian Research Council, Australian Vice-Chancellors' Committee, 2018. National Statement on Ethical Conduct in Human Research, 2007 (updated 23 March 2022). NHMRC, Canberra.

Norman, G., Eva, K.W., 2019. Quantitative research methods in medical education. In: Swanwick, T., Forrest, K., O'Brien, B.C. (Eds.), Understanding Medical Education: Evidence, Theory, and Practice, 3rd edn. Wiley-Blackwell, Hoboken, NJ, pp. 405-425.

O'Mullan, C., Doherty, M., Coates, R., et al., 2019. Using interpretative phenomenological analysis (IPA) to provide insight into female sexual difficulties. Sexual and Relationship Therapy 34 (1), 75–86.

Page, P., 2014. Beyond statistical significance: clinical interpretation of rehabilitation research literature. International Journal of Sports Physical Therapy 9 (5), 726–736.

Paley, J., 2005. Phenomenology as rhetoric. Nursing Inquiry 12 (2), 106–116.

Paul, C., 1988. The New Zealand Cervical Cancer Study: could it happen again? British Medical Journal 297 (6647), 533–539.

Pedrotti, J.T., Edwards, L.M., Lopez, S.J., 2021. Positive psychology within a cultural context. In: Snyder, C.R., Lopez, S.J., Edwards, L.M., et al. (Eds.), The Oxford Handbook of Positive Psychology, 3rd edn. Oxford University Press, New York, pp. 59–70.

Pelham, B., Blanton, H., 2019. Conducting Research in Psychology: Measuring the Weight of Smoke, 5th edn. Sage, Thousand Oaks, CA.

Praphan, P., 1998. Ethical issues in studies in Thailand of the vertical transmission of HIV. The New England Journal of Medicine 338 (12), 834–835.

Ray, A.E., Jeffrey, K.N., Nair, P.H., et al., 2021. "You're a 'high-risk' customer": a qualitative study of women's experiences of receiving information from health professionals regarding health problems or complications in pregnancy. Women and Birth, 35 (5), e477–e486.

Robb, M., Khambaroong, C., Nelson, K., 1998. Studies in Thailand of the vertical transmission of HIV. The New England Journal of Medicine 338 (12), 843–844.

Rowley, J., Sbaffi, L., 2018. Academics' attitudes towards peer review in scholarly journals and the effect of role and discipline. Journal of Information Science 44 (5), 644–657.

Sawrikar, P., Katz, I., 2008. Enhancing family and relationship service accessibility and delivery to culturally and linguistically diverse families in Australia. Australian Institute of Family Studies, Melbourne.

Skegg, P., 2011. A fortunate experiment? New Zealand's experience with a legislated code of rights. Medical Law Review 19 (2), 235–266.

Smith, J.A., Flowers, P., Larkin, M., 2022. Interpretative Phenomenological Analysis: Theory, Method and Research, 2nd edn. Sage, London.

Smith, J.A., Osborn, M., 2015. Interpretative phenomenological analysis. In: Smith, J.A. (Ed.), Qualitative Psychology: A Practical Guide to Research Methods, 3rd edn. Sage, London.

Torrance, H., 2012. Triangulation, respondent validation, and democratic participation in mixed methods research. Journal of Mixed Methods Research 6 (2), 111–123.

Torrance, H., 2017. Be careful what you wish for: data entanglements in qualitative research, policy, and neoliberal governance. In: Denzin, N.K., Giardina, M.D. (Eds.), Qualitative Inquiry in Neoliberal Times. Routledge, New York, pp. 73–84.

Trafimow, D., Marks, M., 2015. Editorial. Basic and Applied Social Psychology 37 (1), 1–2.

Tucker, C.M., Arthur, T.M., Roncoroni, J., et al., 2013. Patient-centered, culturally sensitive health care. American Journal of Lifestyle Medicine 9 (1), 63–77.

Twycross, A., Shorten, A., 2014. Service evaluation, audit and research: what is the difference? Evidence-Based Nursing 17 (3), 65–66.

van Heijningen, V.G., Underhill, A., 2022. User experiences of digital prostheses in daily functioning in people with an amputation of thumb or finger. Journal of Hand Therapy 35 (2), 289–298.

van Manen, M., 2014. Phenomenology of Practice: Meaning-Giving Methods in Phenomenological Research and Writing. Routledge, New York.

Ware, K., Davies, J., Rowse, G., et al., 2015. The experience of hepatitis C treatment for people with a history of mental health problems: an interpretative phenomenological analysis. Journal of Health Psychology 20 (7), 990–1001.

Wendler, D., Ochoa, J., Millum, J., et al., 2020. COVID-19 vaccine trial ethics once we have efficacious vaccines. Science, 370 (6522), 1277–1279.

Whitehead, D., 2020. Critically searching and reviewing the research literature. In: Whitehead, D., Ferguson, C., LoBondio-Wood, G., et al., 2020. Nursing and Midwifery Research: Methods and Appraisal for Evidence-based Practice, 6th edn. Elsevier, Sydney, pp. 55–80.

Whitehead, D., Ferguson, C., LoBondio-Wood, G., et al., 2020. Nursing and Midwifery Research: Methods and Appraisal for Evidence-based Practice, 6th edn. Elsevier, Sydney.

Woodward-Kron, R., Highson, J., Parker, A., et al., 2016. Culturally and linguistically diverse populations in medical research: perceptions and experiences of older Italians, their families, ethics administrators and researchers. Journal of Public Health Research 5 (1), 667.

World Medical Association, 2013. World Medical Association Declaration of Helsinki—Ethical principles for medical research involving human subjects. Available: www.wma.net/policies-post/wma-declaration-of-helsinki-ethical-principles-for-medical-research-involving-human-subjects/ (accessed 23 March 2022).

Chapter 3

Lifespan: the early years (birth to adolescence)

DEB O'KANE

Learning objectives

The material in this chapter will help you to:

- describe some of the major developmental changes of infants, children and adolescents
- describe and critique a selection of key theories related to child development (Freud, Skinner, Piaget, Vygotsky, Erikson)
- describe parenting styles and the influences on parenting
- discuss how health professionals can adapt their practice when working with children at different ages.

Key terms

- Developmental theories (66)
- Psychoanalytic theory (69)
- Behavioural theory (69)
- Cognitive development (71)
- Sociocultural approach (74)
- Lifespan development (76)
- Parenting (79)
- Attachment theory (81)

Introduction

According to the World Health Organization (2018), the period of early childhood is one of the most critical phases for healthy development throughout life. One could start then by asking the fundamental question: 'Do all children have the same opportunity for good health?' As more research comes to light, we know that childhood can influence a range of health and social outcomes in later life. Therefore, to understand health behaviour in adults it's helpful to first understand the biological, psychological and social factors that may interact in a person's life across the lifespan. Numerous theories and stage models have been proposed to describe the years of life from birth to adolescence (e.g. Erikson 1959, 1963; Freud 1917; Piaget 1952, 1954, 1962; Vygotsky 1978), but rather than learn these exhaustively, it is more important to understand the broad changes that can be seen across these years. These observable changes are important for health professionals to consider when working with children.

Clearly, there are many changes taking place as a child develops including physical, emotional, cognitive, social and psychological changes. All these changes ('developments') occur within historical and cultural contexts that can also influence development. While this may seem obvious, it was not that long ago that children were seen as 'little adults', with the same cognitive, emotional and psychological abilities of adults, although without all the physical abilities (Aries 1962). If we were to compare a 2-year-old child with a 12-year-old child, we would find enormous differences in almost everything about their life situation and their behaviour. It is these differences and the changes in activities and processes that occur throughout childhood and adolescence that theorists have attempted to describe and explain by proposing theories to explain the patterns that have been observed. How these theorists have attempted to do this has varied because they have focused on different aspects of development.

Child development is a substantial field in its own right, with entire books dedicated to the subject. For the purpose of this chapter, the focus is on the social and psychological aspects of development rather than the biological or physical development of children. Discussion is primarily focused in the Western world, but comparing the significant similarities and differences in developing countries should also be considered in the context of global health.

Exploring **developmental theories** in relation to a child or young person's emotions, cognitive and social growth will support you in understanding aspects of behaviour, particularly health behaviour, reactions and decision making when working with children, adults and communities. Linking the theoretical perspectives to your own discipline will in turn inform your practice and enable you to offer appropriate and contemporary healthcare.

Stages, ages and milestones of development

Developmental milestones are a useful guide to parents, caregivers, educators and health professionals to gauge a child's development. Milestones can indicate whether a child is developing within a 'normal' range, although it is also important to acknowledge that deviations from these milestones do not necessarily mean there is anything wrong. Take, for example, speech and language development. While talking among toddlers varies greatly, it would be important to explore why a toddler might not be talking by 24 months and to rule out physical causes such as hearing difficulties. It also helps to examine their social circumstances; for instance, the toddler may be part of a large family where other family members continually speak on the child's behalf. There are many well-developed milestone charts that health professionals use to help understand children's development. You may find different charts or ways of presenting milestones more useful than others. It is worthwhile exploring the differences between them and determining which ones work best for you in practice.

Student activity

Before reading about the various theories of child development, sit down in groups and pool your knowledge from everyday life about what children can accomplish. Try dividing your collective experience into categories of:

- birth to 2 years old
- 2–5 years old
- 5–10 years old
- 10–15 years old.

Exercise 1
Consider your own experiences with children and identify for each age group:

- what children can accomplish (what they can do at this age)
- what children cannot accomplish (what they can't do at this age)
- what main patterns and activities change as children get older
- what triggers or brings about the changes
- in what ways children rely on others around them to do what they do.

Consider areas such as physical changes of the body, physical skills or behaviours, thinking and talking (cognitive) skills, social skills and emotional skills. Outline the changing patterns you have observed.

Exercise 2
Think again about each age group and discuss the following.

- What are the main health challenges at this age?
- What healthy and unhealthy patterns might children have at this age?
- What health knowledge or discussions about health would this age group have?
- From where would children get this health knowledge?
- Who would usually take responsibility for the child's health at this age?

Theorising about development

Having completed the *Student activity*, you are hopefully devising your own ideas and theories about what changes occur between these age groups. There are many ways to categorise theories: reductionistic, mediational, deterministic, essentialistic, causal, contextual, explanative or descriptive. A *reductionistic theory*, or *reductionism*, is a theory in which complex things are reduced or understood in terms of basic, simplified elements. For example, risk-taking behaviour among adolescents would be understood in terms of brain development in a reductionistic theory. Specifically, research has shown that the prefrontal cortex, which is the site of higher order cognitive functioning (i.e. the ability to think things through), is not yet fully developed in adolescents (Qu et al. 2018).

A *mediational theory* is similar to reductionism, but the key element in mediationism is that a behaviour or concept is *mediated* by something else. Using again the example of adolescent risk taking, a mediationist would say that brain development *mediates* risk-taking behaviour. For example, an adolescent who is sleeping excessively, lacks interest in things they used to enjoy and spends a lot of time alone might be considered as depressed, such that depression is then the mediator of these behaviours. This is an important distinction because it influences how we then go about intervening or what we do to change the behaviour. Do we change the sleeping, lack of interest, the time spent alone or the depression?

Determinism is a theoretical approach in which the behaviour we see is determined by past history: history of relationships (e.g. parental relationships in the case of Freud) or the history of consequences of behaviours (in the case of the behaviourism of BF Skinner, discussed later). Using the above risk-taking example, behaviour may be explained in a deterministic way by referring to the history of consequences of behaviour, specifically that risk-taking behaviour has been positively reinforced, perhaps by getting attention. In contrast, *essentialism* views characteristics of groups (e.g. groups based on ethnicity, gender or age) as fixed or unchangeable; therefore, risk taking by adolescents would be seen as an *essential quality* or characteristic among adolescents that is not changeable or influenced by context.

Causal and *contextual* theorising can be understood by contrasting them. Causal theories look to understand exactly what it is that *causes* what we observe, while a contextual theory looks to understand the *contexts* in which those behaviours emerge. Again, for adolescent risk-taking behaviour, we could say that brain development causes risk taking or, contextually, that risk-taking behaviour is more likely to occur in groups of youth in unsupervised situations, for example.

Finally, *explanative* or *descriptive* theories can also be understood by contrasting them. They are similar to causal and contextual theorising, with an explanative theory similar to causal explanations and descriptive theories similar to contextual explanations. Using the depression example, we could refer to physiological deficits (e.g. low serotonin levels) to *explain* why an adolescent is depressed, or we could *describe* the contexts (especially social ones) in which depressive behaviours are more or less likely to occur, such as a lack of social support.

There are a number of theoretical approaches associated with lifespan development, and although many theorists today merge theories rather than relying exclusively on one or the other, in this chapter we will refer to only one major difference between theories: whether changes that arise with age are explained by something *within* the person and their body (reductionism, mediationism, essentialism) or by forces *outside* the person (contextualism or determinism). This distinction will help to understand what the original theorists observed and were trying to explain.

DEVELOPMENTAL THEORISTS

Sigmund Freud is probably best known for his theories of psychoanalysis, but he also developed a theory of psychosexual development where he suggested certain key events that occurred in childhood *determined* behaviour patterns later in life. He believed the pattern in which these events transpired and the manner in which parents managed them contributed to the kind of person they would become as an adult. For instance, learning to control eating, drinking and defecating ('potty training'), learning about genitals and societal rules of appropriate and inappropriate behaviour and learning about family control were the most important factors contributing to healthy personality development. Specifically, Freud suggested five stages of psychosocial development—oral, anal, phallic, latency and genital—and that issues arising in any of these stages leads to various behaviour and personality traits later in life. If one used the psychosexual stages to describe an adult who overeats or smokes, for example, the behaviour would be explained by having had unmet needs in the oral stage of their development.

Freud's theorising about adult behaviour was actually quite revolutionary at that time. While the particulars of his theories have not been supported with rigorous research and found to be largely inaccurate, there is no doubt they have had a huge impact on Western society. Consider the popularised use of phrases like 'anal retentive' to label someone with obsessive qualities or even the use of 'Freudian slip' to describe verbal faux pas usually with sexual connotations. As we will see later in this and the following chapter, Erik Erikson also followed through with this **psychoanalytic theory** but made the social dimension much larger than just the family circle.

Burrhus Frederick Skinner (1938, 1957, 1969) was a famous psychologist. He found that changing minute details of an animal's environment or context (primarily its cage and the lights and switches in its cage) could control how the animal behaved. Skinner's **behavioural theory**, known as *radical behaviourism*, asserts that behaviour does not depend on internal processes but occurs as a natural result of things happening in the environment. For example, rats that had to press a lever (behaviour) more than once to get food (consequence) when a light was on (antecedent or stimuli) would persist in pressing the lever longer when the food supply was stopped compared with those rats that received food on every press they made. Therefore, simply put, the consequences of the rat's behaviour increased or decreased the probability it would repeat the behaviour in the future. By working on these basic concepts of antecedents (environments, contexts or stimuli), behaviour and consequences (what happens when a behaviour occurs), Skinner proposed that small and not easily observed changes in an animal's environment could shape and make a difference to its behaviour. Figure 3.1 illustrates how antecedents (or the environment/context) can influence behaviour that then leads to a consequence. These consequences contribute to both changing the environment and changing behaviour in a circular pattern.

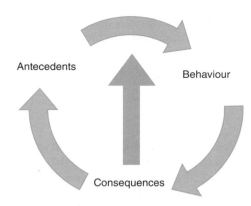

Figure 3.1 How antecedents (or the environment) can influence behaviour, leading to consequences

These observations led Skinner to advocate a theory that almost all behaviour was determined or controlled by factors in the environment rather than something that seemed to be 'stored' inside the body or was 'made into your personality' (i.e. Freud's approach or mediationism). Skinner found he could change the environment for his animals and watch their behaviour change subtly and in precise and predictable ways. This means that for any behaviour changes observed, we need to examine the environment or context very carefully to see what might be controlling the behaviour.

When applying this to humans, the principle of 'consequence'—usually in the form of rewards and punishments—is not a new concept. It is these positive and negative reinforcements in the environment that shape a person's behaviour. See Chapter 7 for more information on Skinner.

Opinions on Skinner's theory are divided. One perspective claims environmental factors do not apply to humans since we often complete actions despite nothing in the environment having changed, whereas others argue we are not looking hard enough and they have likely occurred at an earlier point in time. According to Skinner, it would be possible (although often very difficult) to discover environmental changes contribute to all human behaviour. Yet while there is no doubt Skinner helped shape our understanding of how the environment can influence behaviour, his theory denies the role of genetics and cognitive science; therefore, researchers continue to explore how genetic predispositions may also play an important role in a child's development.

Jean Piaget (1952, 1954, 1962) was the most famous psychologist to consider how children think (cognition) and speak (language). In contrast to Skinner, he was not looking for environmental influences but was more interested in theoretical ideas of 'information processing' centres and 'cognitive processes' in the brain. Piaget spent a lot of time observing behaviour, particularly by participating in thinking games with children, which contributed to his theories. Regardless of the theory or issue under consideration, understanding children requires spending a lot of time systematically observing and participating with them.

Table 3.1		
PIAGET'S STAGES OF COGNITIVE DEVELOPMENT		
Approx. age	Stage	Description
Birth–2 years	Sensorimotor	An infant understands the world through senses (sensory) and movement (motor)
2–7 years	Preoperational	A child begins to use words and symbols to make sense of the world
7–11 years	Concrete operational	Reason is used to logically make sense of concrete events in the world and to classify objects
11–15 years through adulthood	Formal operational	Reasoning becomes more abstract, logical and idealistic

Piaget observed that children of different ages think in very different ways from each other. What he saw was not a continuum of thinking from simple to complex but a set of stages (see Table 3.1 for a summary). For example, he observed that very young children did not seem to be able to think in terms of causality—that one event can cause another event. It was not that the children had different causes for the same event but, rather, they did not seem to be able to think in terms of causes at all. He surmised that causality was *not thinkable* below a certain age. Piaget observed that older children start to explain what caused events, naming events and objects that might have caused something else and trying to justify the way things occurred the way they did.

These observations led Piaget to argue for a stage model in which children learn more and more complex ways of thinking whereby they are not able to think in one level until they have achieved the level before that in the sequence. He also argued that once a certain stage of thinking was reached, this had consequences for what the child could accomplish and would lead to new ways of communicating or thinking. For example, once a child could think in terms of causality, then they could think in terms of making excuses and getting themselves out of trouble. 'I only did it because Giles told me to' requires a level of causal thinking before it can be thought at all.

While Piaget described a number of stages and substages of **cognitive development**, we focus here on the broader overall changes he described and not the complex details of each stage. Table 3.1 lists the basic stages, the approximate ages associated with those stages and a brief description. The first broad stage Piaget called *sensorimotor* because children at this age think, as it were, through their senses and their physical movements. Something like, 'If I can't see it, taste it or touch it then it does not exist and I cannot think it!' Children explore and learn only what they physically interact with through their senses. At this stage, children cannot 'think' about a cat being somewhere else if it is not in front of them, or they are not touching it, or they do not have its tail in their mouth.

At the *preoperational* stage, children begin to attribute words to the things around them and use those words, but this stage is 'pre' operational, with 'operational' referring to 'logic'. This is not just being able to reliably say a sound when something is there because even very young children can say 'caaa' when a cat is presented. It is the beginning of 'representing' things by words so the child can also say 'caaa' when the cat's box is there or 'caaa' when a parent gets the cat's food out of the cupboard.

One interesting thing Piaget found for children at an early age was that if, say, a cat was hidden under a blanket, the child would act as if the cat had gone for good and was no longer in existence—'out of sight, out of mind'. However, as a child developed, they began to look under the blanket for the cat—that is, the object has permanence even if it cannot be seen. Piaget called this developmental aspect *object permanence*. Around the same time children would also begin using the word 'caaa' in the preoperational sense explained above.

From this preoperational stage of beginning to 'see things that are not immediately there' and being able to talk about things not in front of them, children then develop the ability to reason and to classify and code. In the *concrete operational* stage, children begin to use logical forms of reasoning (note that there are several main systems of logic, not just one) and to classify things into groups based on characteristics. However, these processes are only for concrete things and events, such as 'my trucks' or 'Gracie got an ice-cream, why can't I have one?' rather than anything more abstract.

The ability to complete complex tasks or abstract ways of thinking arise in the *formal operational* stage in which abstract thinking is possible and can be used in reasoning and logical processes. Piaget, as well as other child development researchers, devised a number of tests to determine development at this stage, and it is not so much the resolution to these tests that is important but how children come up with the resolution. For example, to combine a yellow solution with a blue solution to create a green solution, a child in the concrete operational stage may, through trial and error, mix the solutions together. However, a child in the formal operational stage may use logic to come up with the answer before using trial and error.

Typically, the ages associated with these stages are: *sensorimotor* 0–2 years, *preoperational* 2–7 years, *concrete operational* 7–11 years and *formal operational* 11–adulthood. However, these have been found to vary depending on the education system and the context of the child and, indeed, not everyone may reach every stage. What is important is that vast changes are taking place in the very way children think and talk about things, and this is what Piaget observed and attempted to formally describe. (Box 3.1 has more information on how children talk about health.) Piaget treated the stages he saw as changes in internal information processing or the 'structure' of cognition. Because a key criticism of

Piaget was his disregard for environmental influences and the assumption that all children will reach all stages as they mature, later theorists spent more time in those same situations but focused on how the children's social interactions influenced the 'individual cognitive' abilities (Bruner 1973). As we will see, Vygotsky, Bruner and others showed there was a 'social scaffold' that supported 'cognitive' development.

Box 3.1 Children talking about health

It is worth learning about the limitations of children's talk and thinking since we often attribute too much logic to what children say. Children can talk as if they are saying complicated and wise things, but they often have no real conception of the meaning or consequences.

This might be keywords they have picked up before they really know how to use them. As an example, a doctor might ask if the child has 'constipation' and the child knows the word means something and answers either yes or no. Further questioning will show whether or not the child actually knows the meaning of constipation. You can even ask fictitious concepts to check out how likely the child will answer something when they are not sure: 'And have you been feeling soppid pains?'

Once the child gets to an *operational* stage in Piaget's framework, another problem occurs. In those stages (and into adulthood) the words become more abstract and disconnected from any sort of reality. While this is good, for example, in that we can talk about a cat without it being present, the problem when talking about health is that what a child says can be determined by social influences as much as the so-called reality of what is being talked about. So the answer to a question such as whether there has been constipation, even if understood properly, is now subject to a variety of influences. In the extreme, imagine the child answering that question in front of a group of peers, or their parents, or just alone with a doctor. Regardless of the truth, we would get strategically different answers even if the answers are all basically saying yes: 'Sort of ...', 'Just a little', 'A little but it was quickly over', 'Not really', or 'Would that be normal?'

So when working with children at early ages, health professionals need to be very careful about how and when questions are asked, in the earlier case because the child might respond quite happily without really knowing the answer, and in the latter case because of extraneous but strong influences over what they say since it is no longer fully determined by concrete objects.

In all cases, the best strategy for health professionals is to ask questions more than once in very different ways, and ask in different contexts if that seems to be a problem.

CASE STUDY: SOPHIE

Four-year-old Sophie is brought to the clinic by her mother after being referred by her GP for a cyst under her right eyebrow that has been there for about 4 months. The referral letter indicates Sophie's anxiety in attending medical appointments and the GP and nurses' inability to examine the cyst as a result (she kicks and screams when approached). When the mother and Sophie are called in to see the specialist, he addresses the mother and asks her to tell him about why they are there. While the mother explains about the cyst, Sophie begins to get upset. He tries to look at the cyst, telling the mother to hold Sophie still, and Sophie's discomfort escalates, such that he cannot examine her. The specialist tells the mother that she will need to reschedule the appointment and 'have a talk' with Sophie about how to behave when she comes to see the doctor. The specialist has not looked at the cyst above Sophie's eye, nor has he communicated with Sophie during the consultation.

Critical thinking

- Consider:
  - » Sophie's age and her social and emotional development, and how the social, emotional and cognitive domains influence her behaviour
  - » the contextual factors that may influence the mother and how she does or does not respond in the situation.
- What factors are influencing the specialist and his behaviour?
- How might you approach working with Sophie and her mother in a consultation that considers the social, emotional and cognitive elements?
- Are there other factors that influence the people in this scenario?

Lev Vygotsky (1978), a Russian theorist in the late 1920s, was the first of a series of theorists who, like Skinner, explored the environmental or external factors that control the changes that appeared to occur 'within' the child. Often perceived as a **sociocultural approach** to development, Vygotsky emphasised the pivotal role that families and cultural groups play in the context of relationships, learning and development. He suggested the internal cognitive changes and stages in human development depend on hidden environmental factors that are difficult to observe since they are based in the social relationships experienced by the child.

Also known as a constructivist theory, the idea was that the 'mind' and the 'cognitive processes' were in fact controlled by social factors that were very subtle, hence not easy to see unless you observed closely and over a long period. According to this line of thinking, the mind is not inside the body but, rather, it is a name for processes of social interaction that cannot be directly seen and that occur over time.

Vygotsky did not theorise about children 'having' or 'possessing' skills (whether physical or cognitive), nor did he talk or theorise about children learning to think in 'stages' set apart from their social interactions, conversations, modelling and other social experiences. Instead, Vygotsky wrote about how children think and learn in the context of development, especially in the social context—that is, their interactions with others. This idea of considering the social influences on what seem to be purely 'internal' thinking events has been developed in various ways. For example, some researchers have looked for patterns in social relationship thinking and explored how social support, encouragement and training can facilitate cognitive thinking, particularly in education and learning.

Vygotsky's ideas often become clearer to people in the context of his notion of zone of proximal development (ZPD). Rather than conceiving of children reaching new stages of cognition because of changes taking place inside them somewhere, Vygotsky proposed that the changes occur within interactions with other people, through processes of imitation, cooperation, support, guidance and enrichment. If children act totally alone then there are many things they cannot do and cannot easily learn to do—this is the lower limit to the ZPD. If children act with other people in concert, or with support, they can do a lot of things by accepting the other person's responsibility and help—this is the upper limit of the ZPD.

Therefore, there are skills children learn through others and, perhaps, when they are not present, they can no longer do those skills. For example, a child may learn how to turn on the computer and open the program to play their favourite game when she is with her older brother and in response to his prompting, but later she may not be able to recall all the necessary steps to play the game when he is not there. Eventually, as people get older, they can do more without other people's direct involvement. But this Vygotskian way of thinking means that skills are not absolute, all-or-none possessions that once gained cannot be lost. We lose skills as well as develop them and we have a variable set of skills that we sometimes have and sometimes do not have.

We can apply these ideas to children and physical activity, and how behaviour can change depending on the people the children are with and the contexts. For example, learning to ride a bike may develop with help from parents or older siblings. Riding without training wheels may start with someone holding onto the seat and letting go when the rider is not aware, but this skill may depend on the presence of others until the skill refines. Eventually, riding a bike may develop into very complex skills such as riding with friends at a bike park. But, after not riding a bike for a long time, a child would not be able to go straight back to the bike park and perform all the tricks again. Even though we may be able to ride a bike even after a long period of not riding one, some of the finer skills would require practice to relearn.

The Vygotskian answer to the question of 'What cognitive stage is that child up to?' is: 'Well, it depends on who that child has been interacting with and has been supported by. By themselves they might not be showing too many thinking skills, but when interacting with a parent or a favourite carer or teacher they might show remarkable cognitive prowess.' In essence, the answer is in the environment (social environment), not inside the child, though critics have gone on to challenge this assumption. How does this embrace an individual's capability or motivational level to rise above their social circumstances or take into account a child's learning ability or style of learning? Despite Vygotsky being one of the first to consider the broader social historical context of development, there are still questions that require further exploration.

As a health professional working in a shifting society, it is useful to consider the influence of environment, relationships and daily interactions of children. One only has to consider the use of online social media platforms to see how relationships between people are changing, adapting and developing. What this means for child development is still in its infancy, with more research emerging examining how Vygotsky's co-constructed knowledge can be fostered by online interactions through social media applications such as Twitter, Facebook and Snapchat (Chatham 2021).

Some recent approaches to describing human development have set similar ideas within *multidimensional* approaches. This means that human biology, social factors, psychological factors, spirituality, structural issues and culture are all considered when trying to understand human development (Harms 2020). Some call these approaches biopsychosocial models, ecological approaches or contextual approaches. What they all try to encapsulate is that human development is obviously made up of lots of changes, that most of the determinants of these changes are difficult to observe easily and that the changes all involve the body, the environment and the social world. Psychologists do not yet know how these elements might all fit together, but these approaches suggest that all these elements are necessary ingredients.

OVERALL DEVELOPMENT

Much of the theorising and research discussed in this chapter revolves around the development of thinking and social relationships. Others have characterised the whole development sequence through the use of stages. Sometimes this is called **lifespan development** (e.g. Santrock 2021). In this regard it is worth looking at the model of Erik Erikson, since he also proposed a very different and interesting stage theory of development.

Instead of proposing a series of stages that all people purportedly travel through, Erikson suggested a series of life conflicts, tasks or issues that are dealt with at different ages. These conflicts can result in good outcomes or poor outcomes depending on the environment and the history of the individual. He proposed eight stages from infancy through to late adulthood (60 years old and beyond). Only the first five that are relevant to childhood development are discussed in this chapter, but all the stages are included in Table 3.2 because they will be considered in Chapter 4.

Notice that this sequence includes development relevant to family social relationships, cognitive development and friendship. This was shown through the ideas of Vygotsky and others, where being able to function successfully in social relationships is a prerequisite for any 'cognitive' or 'mind' development. Therefore, working in normal relations will facilitate the ZPD and lead to improvement in all theories that have been discussed in this chapter.

According to Erikson, the main hurdle during infancy is to develop a basic sense of trust in people and the world, rather than to develop a general mistrust. He proposed that an optimal social environment or context would result in a person who will generally trust that their needs will be met and have confidence in themselves and the world they are in. In a social environment where an infant's needs are not met,

Table 3.2

ERIKSON'S DEVELOPMENTAL STAGES

Erikson's stages	Developmental stage (age)
Trust versus mistrust	Infancy (first year)
Autonomy versus shame and doubt	Late infancy (years 1–3)
Initiative versus guilt	Early childhood (years 3–5)
Industry versus inferiority	Middle and late childhood (years 6 to puberty)
Identity versus identity confusion	Adolescence (years 10–20)
Intimacy versus isolation	Early adulthood (20s, 30s)
Generativity versus stagnation	Middle adulthood (40s, 50s)
Integrity versus despair	Late adulthood (60s onwards)

Erikson believed this child would develop to generally mistrust the world and the people around them and therefore not be willing to risk events with other people. This would mean that opportunities would be lost. It is not so much mistrusting that is the problem but the opportunities for further development that get restricted if a basic trust in people and the world is not present.

Later in infancy and toddlerhood, the task is for the child to begin acting independently and to rely less on parents and others. This was characterised as a conflict between autonomy and shame or doubt, but the same thing can apply without those latter terms. A child who is too dependent might not develop self-doubt or shame, especially considering they are aged under 3 years at this point, but they still have not managed an important skill in the context of their future development; shame and doubt could develop as a consequence.

Similar comments apply to the stage in early childhood. The basic idea is that the child needs to have a context in which they can show initiative and start events by themselves. They need to get up in the morning, sometimes get food without asking or being told to, and need to initiate games and peer interaction. If this does not occur for the child, once again, numerous cognitive and social opportunities for further skill development will be missed. Though, as mentioned, we do not necessarily have to agree that the lack of initiative necessarily leads to guilt. A child might not even be aware or be able to verbalise what is going on if this contextual skill development is missed. But the basic process is still important and necessary for further development.

Erikson's fourth life task is developing 'industry', meaning that things get done. The child can execute tasks. This includes all the cognitive, logical, social and other skills discussed in this chapter. Inability to do this is characterised as inferiority but, once again, we might temper this and say that children might grow up with different ideas of what they can and cannot do. Certainly in some circumstances this would lead to what is called a sense of inferiority but not in all cases. Some might accept (unwittingly) that this is just how things are and others might feel 'safer' not attempting everything.

Finally, adolescence is said to be characterised by developing a sense of identity or a sense of identity confusion. This can have a couple of meanings. First, it can refer to the ways we learn to talk about ourselves to ourselves and others and what talk we can get away with. Are others agreeable with how we talk about who we think we are and what we can do? Second, it can mean a sense of taking on more adult-like roles and responsibilities and whether we do a good job—what special and unique things can I do and take responsibility for? Basically, how we talk about ourselves is related to whether we are good at doing these jobs and taking on responsibility.

There is no denying Erikson's theory offers a consistent and helpful framework to consider what is happening developmentally for people; however, it is largely based on interpretations and speculation. By critically examining his work, you will see it lacks detail in the developmental aspects of emotion and cognition, it does not account for cultural differences in the timing of development, and the generalisation of each stage means there is a shortage of explicit detail. For instance, can a person change their identity through self-reflection or rediscovering themselves? What happens to a person when they are in crisis and unable to resolve it? Can a person become resilient? These and many more questions mean that while useful to you as a health professional, the framework must also be considered as a guiding framework rather than scientific evidence.

SUMMARY OF DEVELOPMENTAL THEORIES

Key theorists have all spent extensive time observing behaviour or interacting with people; their theories were attempts to describe systematically the changes in development that they had observed, however biased or selective we might now view these to be. Some theorists emphasised that changes resulted from environmental changes, some from internal cognitive changes or biology, and others tried to meld these two perspectives together. Perhaps the most useful approaches consider social influences as the key to understanding developmental changes because these are things that are observable or can change.

Major influences on developmental changes

There are obvious key events and people that influence children as they grow older. There is growing evidence that childhood experiences in both the prenatal and the postnatal periods can affect later life. Well-documented factors that can compromise healthy development include:

- children exposed to environments that lack nurturing, care and affection
- parental maltreatment
- poor social networks

- early life adversity

- socioeconomic disadvantage

- poverty.

All these factors place children at more risk of health issues, poor health outcomes and even mortality in adulthood (Levine 2017; Moore et al. 2017). Historically, aspects of child development have been explored once the child is born, but more recently, a body of knowledge has emerged highlighting the importance of good prenatal care, suggesting a strong link between the biological and neurological development of a child in utero and the daily environmental conditions a mother experiences (Kim et al. 2018; Lu et al. 2021).

The field of epigenetics is fast becoming an area of interest for researchers, neuroscientists and psychologists for this very reason. Epigenetics is the study of changes that occur at a molecular and cellular level principally related to changes in gene regulation. While epigenetic modification is part of a natural process, research is finding that genetic coding in a person can be influenced by several factors such as age, diet, lifestyle, environment and stress (Lopez et al. 2021). For instance, Kim (2018) points out that the mother's experience and their environment during the peri-conceptual period and throughout pregnancy can have a direct impact on the outcome of a child's development later in life. Such influences can in fact change not only individual health outcomes but that of their descendants too.

It is also worth mentioning that social support or the lack of support in a child's environment—whether it is practical, emotional or financial—has without doubt implications for development and future health status, as does education and the exposure to the huge array of media and smart technology in a child's world.

THE FAMILY ENVIRONMENT

Children are exposed to a variety of environments, people and communities, and this exposure affects how they develop. It is often assumed that parents comprise a major determinant of children's development. Freud, Skinner and ecological approaches would all suggest that parents are a major influence in the child's environment and surely influence development. However, there are two limitations to the view that parents are a major determinant of children's development.

First, parent-centred life for children is not globally universal or even within countries. For many children, parents are busy working and children spend more time with extended family or with others in their wider community. The image in Western, English-speaking communities is a family unit that comprises one or two parents and their children in a house (i.e. the 'nuclear' family); however, this is a somewhat narrow perspective in today's contemporary and changing society. Take, for example, those children who live with other relatives or whose family consists of members with no biological connection to each other. What about those children who attend boarding school and see their parents only in school holidays or at weekends? Regardless of these changes to the family, and specifically the influence of **parenting**, this continues to be a key area in child development, health and wellbeing (Baxter 2016; OECD 2020) and remains the focus of research. Whatever the findings, parents may have different impacts in the hugely diverse range of family and community settings (see Box 3.2).

Box 3.2 So, what makes good parenting?

This is a vexing question that does not have one answer. Different groups of people, communities and societies have different expectations of children that shape how they are raised. In Western countries such as Australia, New Zealand, the United Kingdom and the United States, independence from others and a strong education are often perceived as overriding concerns, whereas elsewhere, community spirit and cooperation may be more valued. Most would agree, however, that parenting not only consists of demonstrating love in a parent–child relationship but to also incorporate limits that allow the child to remain physically and emotionally safe and secure and provide them with opportunities to learn and develop.

Developmental psychologists usually refer to four styles of parenting. These are based on the degree to which parents control their child's behaviour, and how responsive they are to the child's needs (Baumrind 1967; Maccoby & Martin 1983). The *indulgent* or *permissive* parent accepts what a child does without making any attempt to control the child, whereas the *neglectful* or *uninvolved* parenting, while similarly not controlling the child's behaviour, in fact demonstrates little involvement in the child's life. *Authoritarian* parenting is often described as rejecting or being unresponsive to the child while at the same time attempting to control what they do. Finally, the *authoritative* parent is both accepting and responsive while trying to control the child and protect them from mistakes. The last approach could be argued as the one of choice in the context of a Western society, though it may not apply to all populations. For instance, parenting in China is often perceived as harsh, strict and 'authoritarian' yet often results in children being high achievers compared with authoritarian parenting in Western countries that has been associated with poor academic success (Smetana 2017). Similarly, Lee and colleagues (2014) describe some aspects of authoritative parenting as having protective factors, particularly if the child and parents live in a very harsh and risky environment or neighbourhood.

More recently, 'domain-specific' parenting models have begun to emerge that explore parental behaviour in certain 'domains'. These models recognise parents as flexible in their approach and who can change their response and practice depending on the situation. This is achieved by interpreting the needs of the child and adapting their own response to ensure the need is met, therefore using a range of parenting styles depending on what is required at the time (Smetana 2017). Despite the progress made in this area, there are still questions that have not been adequately addressed, namely the developmental outcome of children who have two parents with differing parenting styles or how children interpret and apply different meanings to parenting styles and, importantly in health, how parenting styles affect health behaviour and outcomes such as exercise, sleep and diet (Power et al. 2013).

Second, not everyone is unanimous in declaring parents a major influence. In the late 1990s Judith Rich Harris proposed it is a cultural myth that parents alone are responsible for the way children turn out as adults, and in fact have little impact on their development (Harris 2011).

Harris considered several lines of research to explore the case for parents having little or no influence on their children. For example, while twin studies show that twins reared apart are more different than those raised together (suggesting that the environmental factors such as parents are highly influential), it was pointed out that even identical twins reared together in the same home with the same parents are different in many ways. News stories have focused on a few examples of twins amazingly liking or doing similar things that are unusual despite being reared apart, such as both wearing rubber bands on their wrists or reading magazines from back to front, but these cases are not common over the whole population (Segal et al. 2021). This suggests that environmental factors including groups, peers and friendships play a greater role in developmental changes, rather than the home environment of the parents (Harris 2011; Polderman et al. 2015). Nonetheless, showing whether a behaviour is primarily due to genetics or to the environment is not a simple dichotomous question and no methodology is straightforward, meaning the quality of the research examining the role of parents in a child's development can be questionable. Many of the research methods have been found to be flawed or with limitations. For example, although research may show results claiming a child is influenced by peers, it takes a special research methodology to determine whether that peer influence was moderated by the parents as a key social agent in the first place. It could be that a child is influenced by peers at school but that the context for being influenced in such a way was produced by the parents (Collado et al. 2017). Similarly, other research suggests that parents can influence this selection of peers from the onset. For example, a parent may tell a child, 'Only play with the nice children when you get to school', or they may influence friend selection through their own networks such as by only inviting children of parents that they know over to play. This then proposes there can still be a parental influence on the child even if the child seems to be influenced by their friends, since the parents are facilitating or inhibiting the child's receptivity to peer influence, or at least to certain types of peers. A child could be influenced by a peer at school, but the parental influence on friend selection might have encouraged their child to make friends with just that sort of peer.

PARENTING AND ATTACHMENT THEORY

With an increasing diversity of family composition and parenting roles, particularly in developed Western countries, there has been greater attention to the role of 'mothering' in society and in families. Early theorists such as John Bowlby emphasised that mothers are of crucial importance to children and developed his original **attachment theory**. Similar to Freud, Bowlby believed that early experiences in childhood influenced later behaviour and that mothers are of special importance to raising healthy and happy children by providing a secure base from which the child feels safe to go and explore their world (Bowlby 1969, p. 194). Mary Ainsworth and colleagues (1978) built on Bowlby's work by depicting three major patterns of attachment depending on the primary caregiver's ability to respond appropriately to the child (secure, ambivalent and avoidant), with a fourth later identified—disorganised (Main & Soloman 1986). These attachment relationships in turn are deemed to influence later social connections, relationships and behaviour in life despite the growing body of evidence supporting the role of culture, education, social class and personality as strong predictors of outcomes in later life.

While the early attachment of children to parents and others is not disputed, attachment no longer refers solely to mothers and their children. As society evolves, the relational and logistical work of child rearing may or may not involve only women as mothers. Take, for example, single fathers, relatives or same-sex couples raising children. While a lay view may exist that these 'non-traditional' parenting arrangements are problematic, a recent study on children being raised by gay or lesbian couples found very few differences from heterosexual couples (Farr 2017). Yet, regardless of this, there are some who continue to argue that the role of motherhood is unique for women (Doucet 2018).

One other aspect of parenting and family composition worthy of consideration is that of adoption and fostering. While it is easy to presume this is only for those children considered 'at risk' or for families unable to raise children, in many countries adoption and fostering has always been a common event, with children being raised by kin (with full knowledge of their origin) within very healthy contexts. This is common, for example, in both traditional and contemporary Māori social relations. This customary Māori practice is known as whāngai (Claiborne & Drewery 2014; New Zealand Government 2020). For instance, a woman might ask her sister if she would raise one of her children, and this can be arranged even before the child is born. These arrangements can be made for a wide range of reasons. For example, it may be that the adopting sister has had problems conceiving and therefore would like a child. In other cases, the adopting sister might already have a family but still be asked to raise a child, maybe because of her parenting skills or knowledge of traditional tribal customs. This sort of adoption process can be seen as another way of facilitating and maintaining bonds and relationships between people in kin-based communities.

One important element in this fostering scenario is that the context involves a kin-based community in which everyone spends time together and is close (even if conflict occurs regularly). This means that the child would know his or her 'biological' parents and see them regularly, which is unlike how adoption was conducted until very recently in most Western systems—where the child was made anonymous and the 'biological' parents' names were kept secret. There are numerous examples of kin-adoption or fostering and reports of this from all corners of the world, mainly where extended or kin-based families remain intact (Hegar & Scannapieco 2017).

Overall, how health professionals manage the diversity of children, parenting and relationships in practice can have a significant impact on health care and cannot be underestimated. A child's development is influenced by genetics, parents, families, peers, communities and the environment in which they live, and while not always clear, these different contexts can produce different outcomes. Figure 3.2 clearly shows the relationship between these factors and childhood development. Early life contexts not only contribute significantly to health outcomes but to the development of health and health issues and the effectiveness of healthcare interventions. Healthcare services will be much more effective when health professionals are informed with even a basic understanding of these contexts and complexities of their clients.

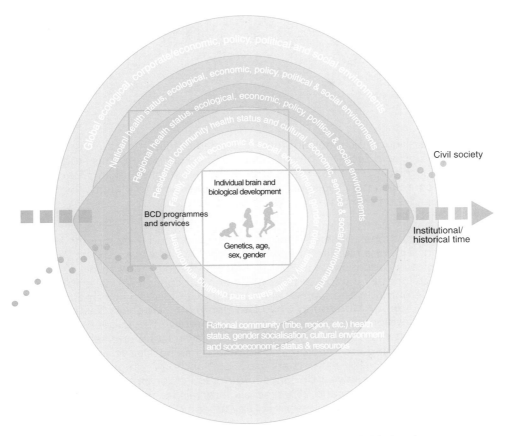

Figure 3.2 Total environment assessment model for early child development.
Source: Siddiqi et al. 2007

Student activity

Discuss the following within your class.

1. How would you define a 'disadvantaged' child?
2. What is the relationship between early childhood disadvantage and health issues in adulthood?
3. What areas should be focused on to promote healthy child development, health and wellbeing from individual, local, national and global perspectives?
4. How can health professionals work together to promote healthy childhood development?

Research focus

Source: Ertem et al. 2017

ABSTRACT

Background

Knowledge about typical development is fundamentally important for understanding and promoting child health and development. This study aimed to ascertain when healthy children in four culturally and linguistically different countries attain developmental milestones and to identify similarities and differences across sexes and countries.

Methods

In this cross-sectional, observational study, children aged 0–42 months and their caregivers were recruited between March 2011 and May 2015 at 22 health clinics in Argentina, India, South Africa and Turkey. The study excluded children with a low birthweight, perinatal complications, chronic illness, undernutrition or anaemia, and children with missing health data. Using the *Guide for Monitoring Child Development*, caregivers described their child's development in seven domains: expressive language, receptive language, gross motor skills, fine motor skills, play, relating and self-help. Clinicians examining the children also completed a checklist about the child's health status. The researchers used logit and probit regression models based on the lowest deviance information criterion to generate Bayesian point estimates and 95% credible intervals for the 50th percentile ages of attainment of 106 milestones. They assessed the significance of differences between sexes and countries using predefined criteria and regions of practical equivalence.

Findings

Of 10,246 children recruited, 4,949 children (48.3%) were included in the healthy subsample. For the 106 milestones assessed, the median age of attainment was equivalent for 102 (96%) milestones across sexes and 81 (76%) milestones across the four countries. Across countries, median ages of attainment were equivalent for all play milestones, 20 (77%) of 26 expressive language milestones, 10 (67%) of 15 receptive language milestones, 9 (82%) of 11 fine motor milestones, 14 (88%) of 16 gross motor milestones and 8 (73%) of 11 relating milestones. However, across the four countries the median age of attainment was equivalent for only 2 (22%) of 9 milestones in the self-help domain.

Interpretation

The ages of attainment of developmental milestones in healthy children, and the similarities and differences across sexes and country samples, might help in developing international tools to guide policy, service delivery and intervention research, particularly in low- and middle-income countries.

Critical thinking

- According to this research, if children attain their developmental milestones at a similar age across sexes and countries in their first year, when does the influence of culture and ethnicity begin to make a difference to a child's development?

- The research found that when a difference in attainment of milestones occurred, it was often associated with the timing of children's exposure to experiences. What do you think the researchers mean by this? Why might this make a difference to a child's development?

- How can comparing child development between populations guide health policy and service delivery?

THE SOCIAL ENVIRONMENT

In relation to peer influence, research methods can be limited in their ability to provide clear answers to what seem easy questions such as: 'How do peers influence children?' As suggested earlier, peers are a strong force, though not as influential as some have argued, and it is often difficult to tease out parental influence on choosing peers in the first place (Collado et al. 2017).

But how might peer influence actually function in reality? A common view is that 'peer pressure' forces teenagers belonging to a group to do everything done by that group. People commonly say that teenagers all dress the same and do the same things because of peer pressure (a causal theory). A child gets into a group and then that group pressures them to do the same things such as wear the same clothes, listen to the same music or imbibe the same alcohol, drugs and tobacco. However, this view may be too simplistic.

As discussed earlier, the way people view the influences from family, friends and communities is changing, and new ways of thinking about these issues are emerging. Research exploring the role of adolescent groups on smoking, drinking, drug use and, more recently, digital media (Beal 2022; Bukowski et al. 2018; Sumter et al. 2016) challenge the common view that groups of peers pressure children into behaviours they would not do otherwise, but, more importantly, they expand our notions and see 'peer pressure' as one social strategy among others. Peer influence is bi-directional (i.e. peers influence each other), and these influences can be both positive and negative. Also, as adolescents get older, resistance to negative peer influence increases, and girls have been found to be more resistant to peer influence than boys (Sumter et al. 2016).

Participation in groups is multifaceted, so it is important not to oversimplify this complexity and make assumptions based on misleading information. There are four points to consider in relation to research in this area. The first is that peer pressure is not necessarily negative. Prosocial behaviour can also be a result of peer influence and in fact can prove beneficial in potentially reducing risk-taking behaviour rather than increasing it (Hoorn et al. 2016). Second, research suggests that people overestimate the similarity among group members, especially groups other than their own. This is clearly part of the illusion that it is peer pressure that contributes to the behaviour of adolescents. Peers within groups are quite aware of small differences within their group, and outsiders (e.g. parents) may not be able to identify those differences. Third, it is in parents' best interests to portray their own children as innocent victims of peer pressure, rather than believe that their children actually self-select into groups. The final consideration is that far from adolescents being compliant in a group of peers that pressure them to take risks, some young people possess resilience, self-confidence and social skills that make it highly unlikely to be easily pressured into anything they don't want.

As suggested earlier, it is not that children become involved in groups that then pressure them in various ways but, rather, for a multitude of reasons (including parental influence) children *participate* in certain groups, get *expelled* from certain groups or are *selected* into groups. So it is the selection into and out of groups that makes a group similar or homogeneous rather than pressure within a group for all the members to be similar. The links between parents, peers and influences on a child's development are very convoluted and complex and therefore simple generalisations are not useful.

Critical thinking

- To what extent is peer pressure the reason why children engage in behaviours they otherwise may not have engaged in?
- Describe the main influences on children's development.
- What sorts of contexts or situations may lead to different influences having a greater or lesser impact? For example, when might parents have a greater influence than school?

EDUCATION AND SCHOOLING

In this section, we consider the influence of education on children's development. First, we have seen that peers at school are one major influence on development, whatever the causal pathways. When children do not go to school, there might be less influence from non-related peers. Schooling in Western societies creates many opportunities for peer social influence and pressure that do not exist in other groups around the world.

Second, education is not the same as schooling, and in many communities, children are educated out of school more than in school. For example, families educate their children explicitly (even if informally) in and around the home and social environment. This might be in activities that are useful for the community and ritual activities, as well as reading, writing and mathematics. Some families do not attempt to educate children except in a moral sense; they leave education to the schools. And in some cases, even moral education is left to the schools (as in religious or other private schools that may teach 'values'). Some parents, however, explicitly teach children, sometimes formally, in home schooling or through travel and life experiences.

The third point is that researchers who have studied children's cognitive or thinking development outside of the school setting may not show the full impact of the explicit education of children in how to think, count and so on. Many children, by the age of 3 or 4 years, are engaged in an education program aimed at facilitating or developing their abilities. Clearly, what is taught in kindergartens and schools will be a major influence on children. Discovering how children develop requires a perusal of formal schooling, as well as any peer or informal family education.

Chapter summary

In this chapter, several theories of human development have been explored, with an emphasis on understanding the key features of these theories. Theorists have attempted to explain the behaviours they observed in children and adolescents that were inexplicable or interesting.

Some of the main influences on development have been discussed and the relative weights of those influences critically examined. Critical thinking has been encouraged about influences that are often taken for granted, such as the influence of peers or parents on children's development. We also discussed the diversity of parenting practices and the complexities of peer influence, schooling and education. There is no doubt that health has its roots in early childhood. With both nature and nurture playing an important role in a child's development, the quality of environments, relationships and education become central in shaping development and promoting success and better health outcomes in adult life, which is one of the many reasons governments are encouraged to invest in early childhood for the future economy of a country and the provision of health services (WHO 2018).

KEY POINTS

- Theories of human development are influenced by the life contexts of the people developing the theories.
- Family, friends and school all influence child development.
- Parenting styles are diverse and can be influenced by context and history.
- Healthcare practice can benefit from knowledge and understanding of the influences and issues of childhood and adolescence.
- Although developmental theories provide useful models for understanding human development, they are not universally applicable.

Further reading

Bornstein, M.H., Rothenberg, W.A., Lansford, J.E., et al., 2021. Child development in low- and middle-income countries. Pediatrics, 148(5):e2021053180.

Cure Kids. 2020. State of Child Health in Aotearoa New Zealand. Auckland: Cure Kids; 2020. Available: www.curekids.org.nz (accessed 8 March 2022)

Evans, G.W. 2021. The physical context of child development. Current Directions in Psychological Science, 30(1), 41–48.

Frosch, C.A., Schoppe-Sullivan, S.J., O'Banion, D.D. 2021. Parenting and child development: a relational health perspective. American Journal of Lifestyle Medicine, 15(1), 45–59.

Jeong, J., Franchett, E.E., Ramos de Oliveira, C.V., et al., 2021. Parenting interventions to promote early child development in the first three years of life: a global systematic review and meta-analysis. PLoS Medicine, 18(5):e1003602.

Office of the Children's Commissioner, Oranga Tamariki. 2019. What makes a good life? Children and young people's views on wellbeing. Wellington: Office of the Children's Commissioner and Oranga Tamariki. Available: https:// www.occ.org.nz/publications/reports/what-makes-agood-life/ (accessed 8 March 2022)

PwC Global, 2019. Action Required: The Urgency of Solving for Social Determinants of Health. Available: https://www.pwc.com/sdoh (accessed 9 March 2022)

Strong Foundations Collaboration. 2019. The first thousand days: A case for investment. PricewaterhouseCoopers.

World Health Organization, 2020. Improving Early Childhood Development Guidelines. World Health Organization, Geneva. Available: https://www.who.int/publications/i/item/97892400020986 (accessed 9 March 2022)

Weblinks

Australian Early Development Census

www.aedc.gov.au

This is a website for anyone interested in early childhood development and covers several key developmental domains related to later health and wellbeing such as physical health, cognitive skills and social competence.

Dunedin Multidisciplinary Health and Development Research Unit at the University of Otago

dunedinstudy.otago.ac.nz

This site provides information on research conducted in the Dunedin Multidisciplinary Health and Development Research Unit including one of the largest ever longitudinal studies on human development, which has been going for nearly 40 years.

Healthdirect

www.healthdirect.gov.au

The HealthDirect website from the Australian Government is a useful website for finding information about a wide range of health issues. Search for 'developmental milestones' to access topic pages relevant to baby and child development.

Ministry of Health (New Zealand) Child Health Section

www.health.govt.nz/our-work/life-stages/child-health

The child health section of the New Zealand Ministry of Health website provides information on a range of services offered in New Zealand relevant to child health, as well as links to publications.

Raising Children Network

www.raisingchildren.net.au

The Raising Children Network is a web resource for parents that is supported by the Australian Government and provides a wide range of useful materials and information about raising children and links to services and support.

Centers for Disease Control and Prevention

www.cdc.gov/ncbddd/actearly/milestones

The Centers for Disease Control and Prevention website supported by the US Department of Health and Human Services includes an interactive milestones chart for parents as well as other developmental information for a range of age groups from the National Center on Birth Defects and Developmental Disabilities.

References

Ainsworth, M.D.S., Blehar, M.C., Waters, E., et al., 1978. Patterns of Attachment: A Psychological Study of the Strange Situation. Erlbaum, Hillsdale, NJ.

Aries, P., 1962. Centuries of Childhood. Vintage Books, New York.

Baumrind, D., 1967. Child care practices anteceding three patterns of preschool behavior. Genetic Psychology Monographs 75, 43–88.

Baxter, J., 2016. The modern Australian family (Facts Sheet). Australian Institute of Family Studies, Melbourne.

Beal, J.A., (2022). Impact of social media on adolescents. MCN: The American Journal of Maternal/Child Nursing, 47(2), 108.

Bowlby, J., 1969. Attachment and Loss. Attachment 1. Basic Books, New York.

Bruner, J.S., 1973. Beyond the Information Given: Studies in the Psychology of Knowing. Norton, New York.

Bukowski, W.M., Laursen, B., Rubin, K.H. (Eds.), 2018. Handbook of Peer Interactions, Relationships, and Groups. Guilford Press, New York.

Chatham, D., 2021. Advancing Online Course Design and Pedagogy for the 21st Century Learning Environment. IGI Global.

Claiborne, L., Drewery, W., 2014. Human Development: Family, Place, Culture, 2nd edn. McGraw-Hill Education, Sydney.

Collado, S., Staats, H., Sancho, P., 2017. Normative influences on adolescents' self-reported pro-environmental behaviors: the role of parents and friends. Environment and Behavior. Available: http://journals.sagepub.com/doi/pdf/10.1177/0013916517744591. (Accessed 8 May 2018).

Doucet, A., 2018. Do Men Mother? Fatherhood, Care, and Domestic Responsibility, 2nd edn. University of Toronto Press, Toronto.

Erikson, E.H., 1959. Identity and the Lifecycle—Selected Papers 1959. International University Press, New York.

Erikson, E.H., 1963. Childhood and Society. Norton, New York.

Ertem, I.O., Krishnamurthy, V., Mulaudzi, M.C., et al., 2017. Similarities and differences in child development from birth to age 3 years by sex and across four countries: a cross-sectional, observational study. Lancet Glob Health, 6, e279–e291.

Farr, R.H. 2017. Does parental sexual orientation matter? A longitudinal follow-up of adoptive families with school-age children. Developmental Psychology, 53(2), 252–264.

Freud, S., 1917. A General Introduction to Psychoanalysis. Washington Square Press, New York.

Harms, L., 2020. Understanding Human Development. 3rd edn. Oxford University Press, Melbourne.

Harris, J.R., 2011. The Nurture Assumption. Why Children Turn Out the Way They Do, 2nd edn. eBook. Simon & Schuster., NY.

Hegar, R.L., Scannapieco, M., 2017. Foster care to kinship adoption: the road less traveled. Adoption Quarterly 20 (1), 83–97.

Hoorn, J., Dijk, E., Meuwese, R., et al., 2016. Peer influence on prosocial behavior in adolescence. Journal of Research on Adolescence 26, 90–100.

Kim, M., Lee, S., Bae, S.H., et al., 2018. Socioeconomic status can affect pregnancy outcomes and complications, even with a universal healthcare system. International Journal for Equity in Health 17, 2.

Lee, E.H., Zhou, Q., Ly, J., et al., 2014. Neighborhood characteristics, parenting styles, and children's behavioral problems in Chinese American immigrant families. Cultural Diversity & Ethnic Minority Psychology 20, 202–212.

Levine, C., 2017. Psychological buffers against poor health: the role of the socioeconomic environment. Current Opinion in Psychology 18, 137–140.

Lopez, M., Ruiz, M.O., Rovnaghi, C.R., et al., 2021. The social ecology of childhood and early life adversity. Pediatr Res. 89 (2), 353–367.

Lu, Y.C., Kapse, K., Andersen, N., et al., 2021. Association between socioeconomic status and in utero fetal brain development. JAMA Network Open 1, 4 (3).

Maccoby, E.E., Martin, J., 1983. Socialization in the context of the family: parent-child interaction. In: Hetherington, E.M. (Ed.), Handbook of Child Psychology: Socialization, Personality, and Social Development. Wiley, New York.

Main, M., Solomon, J., 1986. Discovery of an insecure-disorganized/disoriented attachment pattern. In: Brazelton, T.B., Yogman, M.W. (Eds.), Affective Development in Infancy. Ablex Publishing, Westport, CT, pp. 95–124.

Moore, T.G., Arefadib, N., Deery, A., et al., 2017. The first thousand days: An evidence paper—summary. Parkville, Victoria: Centre for Community Child Health, Murdoch Children's Research Institute.

New Zealand Government, 2020. Adoption and fostering. Whāngai. Available: https://www.govt.nz/browse/family-and-whanau/adoption-and-fostering/whangai/. (Accessed 8 May 2022).

OECD. 2020. Early Learning and Child Well-being: A Study of Five-year-Olds in England, Estonia, and the United States, OECD Publishing, Paris

Piaget, J., 1952. The Origins of Intelligence in Children (M. Cook, Trans.). International Universities Press, New York.

Piaget, J., 1954. The Construction of Reality in the Child. Basic Books, New York.

Piaget, J., 1962. Play, Dreams and Imitation. WW Norton, New York.

Polderman, T.J.C., Benyamin, B., de Leeuw, C.A., et al., 2015. Meta-analysis of the heritability of human traits based on fifty years of twin studies. Nature Genetics 47, 702–709.

Power, T.G., Sleddens, E.F.C., Berge, J., et al., 2013. Contemporary research on parenting: conceptual, methodological, and translational issues. Childhood Obesity 9 (Suppl. 1), 87–94.

Qu, Y., Pomerantz, E.M., McCormick, E., et al., 2018. Youth's conceptions of adolescence predict longitudinal changes in prefrontal cortex activation and risk taking during adolescence. Child Development. 89 (3), 773–783.

Santrock, J., 2021. Life-Span Development, 18th edn. McGraw-Hill, New York.

Segal, N.L., Niculae, F.J., Becker, E.N., et al., 2021. Reared-apart/reared-together Chinese twins and virtual twins: Evolving research program and general intelligence findings. Journal of Experimental Child Psychology, 207, Article 105106.

Siddiqi, A., Irwin, L., Hertzman, C., 2007. Total Environment Assessment Model for Early Child Development: Evidence Report for the World Health Organization's Commission on the Social Determinants of Health. World Health Organization, Geneva.

Skinner, B.F., 1938. The Behavior of Organisms. Appleton-Century-Crofts, New York.

Skinner, B.F., 1957. Verbal Behavior. Appleton-Century-Crofts, New York.

Skinner, B.F., 1969. Contingencies of Reinforcement: A Theoretical Analysis. Prentice Hall, Englewood Cliffs.

Smetana, J.G., 2017. Current research on parenting styles, dimensions, and beliefs. Current Opinion in Psychology 15, 19–25.

Sumter, S.R., Bokhorst, C.L., Westenberg, P.M., 2016. Resistance and Conformity. In: Levesque R. (eds) Encyclopedia of Adolescence. Springer, Cham, Switzerland.

Vygotsky, L.S., 1978. Mind in Society: The Development of Higher Psychological Functions. Harvard University Press, Cambridge.

World Health Organization, 2018. Nurturing care for early childhood development: a framework for helping children survive and thrive to transform health and human potential. World Health Organization, Geneva.

Chapter 4

Lifespan: middle and later years (adulthood to ageing)

DEB O'KANE

Learning objectives

The material in this chapter will help you to:

■ describe the major developmental theories relevant from adolescence to late adulthood
■ discuss the diversity of partner selection, marriage and family structures
■ discuss the complexities of employment, career and lifestyle during adulthood and the implications of these for health
■ identify the common issues of ageing in the context of health.

Key terms

■ Chronological age (94)
■ Biological age (94)
■ Psychosocial ageing (102)
■ Milestones of adulthood (103)
■ Healthy ageing (113)
■ Chronic illness (114)
■ Spirituality (116)

Introduction

In this chapter we examine theories of adulthood and ageing in the context of health psychology. The period from emerging adulthood to the end of life spans a huge part of human experience, with a wide range of events taking place. While it is not possible to review all the health psychology material relevant to adulthood in one chapter, a range of issues relevant to adulthood will be covered and this will, perhaps, inspire you to seek out more information on related topics. The purpose is to give you a developmental perspective when confronting issues in your healthcare practice.

A common practice among researchers and theorists is to partition adulthood into stages or milestones, even though these might not apply universally. The broad stages of early, middle and late adulthood show major differences in physical, social, emotional and cognitive abilities, as well as circumstances. Theorists have observed quantum changes in how people behave across these periods. Also, theorists have more recently been discussing the transition from adolescence to adulthood, referring to this stage as *emerging adulthood* and arguing for it to be included in contemporary models of human development (Arnett 2000, 2018; Arnett et al. 2011; Hochberg & Konner 2020). It is helpful to explore all lifespan development within the context of economic, political, sociocultural factors in a contemporary society since this in turn can result in changes to adult circumstances. For example, to establish a career or save to buy their first house, young adults may find they live at home with their parents longer than they have in the past when economic circumstances were more favourable.

In this chapter, we will focus on adulthood as the time in a person's life in which they have taken on greater responsibility, whether through employment, marriage or partnership, having children or living away from primary caregivers. The times at which these events occur varies substantially in different people's lives, and it is therefore essential to have an understanding of the various conceptions of age, such as chronological, psychological, social and biological.

Chronological age, or the number of years since someone was born, becomes important during emerging adulthood for a number of legal issues, such as being able to drive, vote or have certain jobs, or to get access to healthcare benefits. Chronological age, however, does not necessarily correlate with *psychological age*, which relates to a person's ability to adapt to various circumstances compared with others who might be the same chronological age. Psychological age also differs from *social age*, or the social roles and expectations relative to chronological age. While someone might be functioning at an advanced social age (relative to their chronological age), this does not necessarily imply that they are also advanced psychologically, although these tend to be related.

Biological age, or the age in terms of physical health and development, is yet another conception of age. For example, while a 14-year-old female may biologically be capable of motherhood, the social role of motherhood is often considered more appropriate for women in their 20s or 30s in Western societies (social age). Similarly, at the other end of the spectrum are the wide differences between older people of various chronological ages and biological ages. For example, a 60-year-old may participate in competitive athletics and be healthier than many 40-year-olds, but both these differ from a 60-year-old who has been diagnosed with dementia and has had double knee replacements.

Chronological age is the concept that is almost exclusively used in healthcare practice, but it has many limitations, and health professionals need to be careful about basing health judgements on this alone. Because of the extreme variability in the health of older people, some have argued that health care should not be related to chronological age but should be relevant to need, health conditions or biological age. For example, because policies relate to health care relevant to specific chronological ages (e.g. various cancer screening programs are only available for certain age groups), those who do not 'fit' in this conception (e.g. residents from refugee backgrounds or Aboriginal and Torres Strait Islander Australians with chronic conditions) can miss out on important care (see, for example, the case study about Jane on page 110).

Theories

The theories of human development usually outline various stages of life pinned to chronological ages. However, others have argued that imposing chronological age on human development is imprecise at best (Hendry & Kloep 2002; Kloep et al. 2009, 2016) and can be demeaning, or even damaging, at worst. We will consider some of the stage theories while also bringing in other views of what occurs during human development. In this section we will review Erikson's theory and will then explore Kohlberg's theory of moral judgement, Hendry and Kloep's lifespan model of developmental challenge and Bronfenbrenner's ecological theory, before moving on to explore a few of the key theories of ageing.

ERIKSON'S THEORY

Erik Erikson is probably the most well known developmental psychologist whose psychosocial lifespan theory extends into adulthood. Other theorists such as Havighurst (1972) and Gould (1978) used his work to further elaborate other facets of development such as physical maturation, learning and personal identity or, as in the case of Robert Peck, expanded the final stage of Erikson's theory to include tasks specific to old age (Rogers 2019). Unlike in the past, when theorists such as Freud and Piaget only extended their theories to puberty—that is, Freud's 'genital stage' and around age 11 in Piaget's 'stage of formal operations' (see Chapter 3)—Erikson and those previously mentioned agreed that developmental tasks continue throughout life and do not stop once a person reaches maturity. In Erikson's theory, each stage provides an opportunity for the person to resolve an innate personal conflict known as a 'crisis', which in turn identifies their strengths and attributes before moving to the next stage. The three main stages relevant to adulthood are the stages of intimacy versus isolation, generativity versus stagnation and integrity versus despair (Erikson 1950, 1982; Erikson & Erikson 1997) (see Chapter 3, Table 3.2). The stage of *intimacy versus isolation* is characterised by either the seeking of companionship and intimate love with another person or becoming emotionally isolated and fearing rejection or disappointment. This stage is usually said to occur during early adulthood and is often associated with the chronological ages of 18–24 years. In terms of healthcare practice, health professionals who recognise that people at this stage may be struggling to come to terms with intimacy issues and those multiple factors that contribute to isolation can serve a very useful role in helping clients to successfully resolve this stage. For example, linking clients with support services, community organisations or self-help programs and groups can go a long way in preventing issues that could become more serious if left unrecognised and reinforce their isolation. This is supported by evidence of the relationship between social isolation and mental disorders such as schizophrenia (e.g. Wang et al. 2017) and that most mental disorders occur before age 25 (McGorry et al. 2022).

Middle adulthood, according to Erikson, is characterised by a contribution to the next generation, usually through work or employment or having a family (i.e. *generativity*) or by becoming socially inactive (i.e. *stagnation*). One of the limitations of applying Erikson's theory is that it can be interpreted as an either/or dichotomy; whereas, in reality, adults may find that in some aspects of their lives they have been generative but in other aspects have a sense of stagnation. Take, for example, a woman who is highly successful in her career but who never had children. While she may have a strong sense of generativity in her career, she may have regrets for not having had children (being stagnant in that area), although we must not assume that someone who has not had children would have regrets. However, it is also usually not this simple. For example, many families also contribute to their siblings' families rather than have their own families, and this could be considered either generativity or stagnation, depending on how the person sees it. It is therefore important to consider diversity in developing and understanding these concepts and the importance of considering assumptions that might be made around these concepts. Always check with clients about their own understanding of where they are at in life.

Finally, in Erikson's theory, older adults make sense of their lives either as having *integrity* (i.e. being meaningful) or they may *despair* about the things that they did not achieve or accomplish in life. Health professionals can serve an important role in assisting clients to develop a sense of integrity rather than despair, particularly when working with people who are chronically ill or those nearing the end of their life.

While Erikson's theory stimulated considerable debate in the fields of adulthood and ageing, chiefly being one of the first to articulate lifelong development, it is not without its critics. Similar to other developmental stage models, little empirical evidence exists to suggest adults progress through discrete stages of development and in fact some argue adulthood is more likely to be characterised by stability rather than ongoing changes (McCrae & Costa 2015).

KOHLBERG'S THEORY

Kohlberg's theory of moral reasoning (1976, 1981, 1984) included three levels and six stages, roughly from age 4 to adulthood (see Table 4.1). Level I, or preconventional morality, includes stages 1 (orientation towards punishment and obedience) and 2 (individualism and exchange). Level II, or conventional morality, generally relates to

Table 4.1
KOHLBERG'S THEORY OF MORAL REASONING

	Level I: preconventional
Stage 1	Punishment and obedience
Stage 2	Individualism and exchange
	Level II: conventional
Stage 3	Maintaining mutual relations and approval of others
Stage 4	Social concern and conscience or maintaining the social order
	Level III: postconventional
Stage 5	Social contract or individual rights and democratically accepted law
Stage 6	Morality of universal ethical principles
Stage 7	The cosmic stage: able to see impact of actions on the greater world

children aged 10–13 and includes stages 3 (maintaining mutual relations and approval of others) and 4 (social concern and conscience or maintaining the social order). Level III, or postconventional morality, includes stages 5 (social contract or individual rights and democratically accepted law) and 6 (morality of universal ethical principles). Stages 5 and 6 are most relevant to adulthood and health care, although Kohlberg suggested that some people never enter these stages. In stage 5, people are rational and can be thoughtful and critical of laws and legal issues but inevitably will conform to laws and human rights as morally ideal. In stage 6, however, universal ethical principles will outweigh legal concerns in a moral dilemma. Kohlberg also later included a stage 7 (the cosmic stage) in which people would be able to see the impact of their action on the greater world, rather than only their immediate world (Kohlberg & Ryncarz 1990).

In terms of health care, the relevance of Kohlberg's theory is obvious. There are many moral and ethical dilemmas that health professionals regularly contend with, and resolving these dilemmas will partly depend on where a person is at in terms of these stages and *how* the dilemmas are resolved. But it is perhaps too restrictive to view these as internal stages of moral development. Dealing with moral dilemmas regularly and the social and structural systems in place to facilitate this, such as the quality of debates with co-workers or the policies in place surrounding moral dilemmas, will influence the resolutions of these dilemmas. Take, for example, the issue of euthanasia or, for a less contentious issue, the use of a medication that has serious side effects. Kohlberg's theory would suggest that how you think about these issues can differ with a more or less developed sense of moral reasoning. Therefore, health professionals need to consider all forms of reasoning and not just believe there is only one right or wrong answer to euthanasia or medication.

Health professionals will not only benefit from understanding Kohlberg's theorising in their own practice, but consideration of Kohlberg's stages in respect of clients will help in how they interact and behave towards people in general. For example, issues of violence, drug abuse and even parenting can be understood better by considering the stages of moral development. Health professionals should be aware that their clients may think about these issues very differently from their own perspective and consequently influence how the health professional relates to and understands their client.

Carol Gilligan is a theorist who argued that human development theories (especially Kohlberg's) are male-dominated and do not adequately account for development as it relates to girls and women (Gilligan 1982). In her research with pregnant women contemplating abortion, she found that conflicts with responsibility to self and to others related to moral development for women that is not adequately addressed in Kohlberg's theory. Overall, Gilligan found that morality for women relates to the ethics of care (i.e. care-based morality) rather than justice-based morality and that these differences between men and women should not be minimised (Gilligan & Farnsworth 1995). Kohlberg never opposed Gilligan's relational theory of female morality and saw it as complementary to his own.

OTHERS' THEORIES

Though there are still strong advocates for a stage approach to lifespan development, with theorists such as Jeffrey Arnett continuing to argue for new stages such as 'emerging adulthood' addressing young people between the ages of 18 and 25 (Arnett 2000, 2018; Arnett et al. 2011; Arnett et al. 2014), limitations to these classic theories have led to the need for theories that are more contextual and not so limited to Western notions of individuality and chronological age. Theorists such as Kloep and Hendry insist stage theories should be eliminated completely, contending that individual transitions and human change occur throughout life as part of a process rather than a stage (Arnett et al. 2011) and therefore more recent theories to be studied include the ecological approach of Urie Bronfenbrenner (1979, 2004), Paul Baltes' lifespan perspective (Baltes 1987, 2000; Baltes et al. 2006) and the lifespan model of developmental challenge (Hendry & Kloep 2002; Kloep et al. 2009).

Bronfenbrenner's (1979, 2004) theory considers individual development in a wider social context that includes micro (e.g. family and work), meso (the interactions between the person's social connections, e.g. your mother interacting with your partner), exo (the social connections that the person's social connections have, e.g. your partner's work colleagues) and macro systems (e.g. religion and politics). Bronfenbrenner's system, also called a 'bioecological' system, is multidirectional in that it is not only the social systems that impact on the individual but that the individual also impacts on those systems (see Fig. 4.1). You will notice that this model is very similar to the total environment assessment model for early child development outlined in the previous chapter (Fig. 3.2, Siddiqi et al. 2007), whereby policymakers are beginning to recognise and understand how a person's environment impacts on

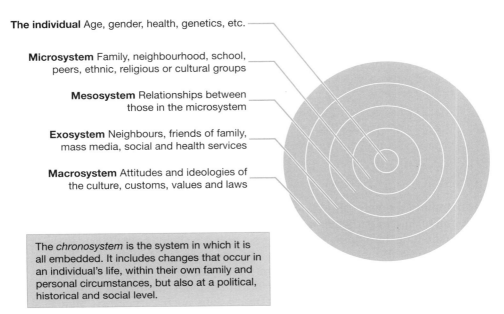

The individual Age, gender, health, genetics, etc.

Microsystem Family, neighbourhood, school, peers, ethnic, religious or cultural groups

Mesosystem Relationships between those in the microsystem

Exosystem Neighbours, friends of family, mass media, social and health services

Macrosystem Attitudes and ideologies of the culture, customs, values and laws

The *chronosystem* is the system in which it is all embedded. It includes changes that occur in an individual's life, within their own family and personal circumstances, but also at a political, historical and social level.

Figure 4.1 Bronfenbrenner's model of human development (based on Urie Bronfenbrenner's 1979 model)

their growth and development throughout life and are therefore using ecological models to inform and advance future health practice. As Hendry and Kloep (2002) clearly state, 'Development is not something that just "happens" to the individual person but an interactive, dynamic process that involves all the system levels of a society'.

CASE STUDY

You are a healthcare worker in the emergency department of a major metropolitan hospital. A mother and father come in with their 18-month-old daughter, who has had severe diarrhoea and vomiting for the past 4 days. You find out that the mother and daughter are new arrivals and have just flown in from a small African country. The vomiting and diarrhoea started during the flight. The father is a postgraduate student at a local university, and it is unclear who is responsible for the cost of the health care. Despite that, the baby is rushed in to see a paediatrician. The baby is severely dehydrated, and the staff attempt to insert a line for a drip, but the dehydration combined with the baby's dark skin is making it difficult to find a vein. You notice that even though the baby is crying, the mother keeps going to the back of the room to sit in a chair with her head in her hands. You ask if the couple have other children and the father tells you no. After some time, you ask if the baby has been this sick before and the mother tells you that they had another baby who died at 1 year of age from diarrhoea, just before they fell pregnant with this baby.

⚙. Critical thinking

- Consider Bronfenbrenner's model of human development and identify the socioeconomic issues you would need to consider as a health professional in this situation.
- What might you need to know about Africa (broadly) to care for this family?
- What social, developmental and psychological issues might you need to consider during your further treatment of the baby and family?

An important theorist most known for his multidisciplinary approach to human development, and in particular his work on successful ageing, is Paul Baltes. Baltes identified lifelong development as having seven key principles. Notably his first principle is to assert that development is a lifelong process. He goes on to suggest development does not decline with age but changes and adapts to meet the new challenges faced with older age. He puts forward that development is both multidimensional and multidirectional. 'Dimensions' such as cognitive, biological, emotional and social factors may all have a part to play in a person's development, whereas multidirectional indicates developmental outcomes are not achieved by following one pathway but can occur in a number of different ways (Baltes 1987). We have only to consider a person experiencing diabetes or heart disease to recognise the interplay between diet, environmental factors and heredity.

According to Baltes, individualised development has both losses and gains, and as such we learn to navigate and regulate the outcomes by the choices we make. This is called self-regulation. Even with self-regulation, for some people, cultural, biological or economic influences can alter their developmental pathway. One of the key principles of Baltes's theory is therefore the concept of plasticity. Plasticity within human development refers to a person's ability to be able to modify, adapt or change their behaviour (Baltes 1987). Examples of this in health care would be a client with an amputation of an upper body limb learning to function and compensate with their non-dominant limb.

As previously discussed, development does not happen in isolation. We live in a world influenced by the environment in which we grow. Baltes recognises this when he identifies context and history as one of his key principles in lifelong development. Identifying sociocultural conditions such as family values, environment and societal norms, and acknowledging how this is embedded in a history that has evolved over time, will impact on individual development (Baltes 1987). For instance, a 10-year-old girl living in the Aboriginal Anangu Pitjantjatjara Yankunytjatjara lands is likely to develop significantly differently from the same girl living in a metropolitan area of Australia. Educational differences, housing, appropriate health care and nutrition have already been identified as considerable barriers to effective population health outcomes by the Australian Government (Holland 2018).

Baltes (1987) was a firm believer that lifelong development must come from a multidisciplinary perspective. One discipline alone cannot express all aspects of development, yet with the contribution of many disciplines such as medicine, research and psychology, knowledge can be integrated to form a clearer picture of human development from conception to death. This fits well in health care. Working with clients and considering all aspects of lifelong development from a multidisciplinary team perspective reflects contemporary health practice.

Lifespan perspectives, or lifespan theories, of human development consider development across the full lifespan and suggest that to fully understand someone's development, one needs to consider how life events influence development. The lifespan perspective also considers important social and political factors that have an impact on development such as policies affecting Aboriginal and Torres Strait Islander peoples, Māori populations of New Zealand or economic conditions (such as the global financial crisis). Marion Kloep and Leo Hendry proposed such a lifespan model of developmental challenge (Hendry & Kloep 2002; Kloep et al. 2009). In their model, the concepts of challenges, resources, stagnation and decay feature prominently (2002). Basically, in this model, people have 'potential resources', and these resources influence how an individual will respond to various challenges ('potential tasks') that will occur throughout life. Resources include a person's biology, social resources, skills, self-efficacy and structural resources. An interesting feature of this model is the relationship between task demands (whether there are many or few) and the availability of resources and how they relate to feelings of anxiety or security, and whether the task is then a risk, a challenge or routine. If tasks are often routine and the resources exceed the task, then stagnation can result. Also, if there are not enough resources and the tasks are risky, then decay can result.

Take, for example, a person who is overworked with high family demands but on a low income. Over time, the resource pool will deplete, and the person's development risks 'decay'. Success, in this model, is 'development', and development can contribute more resources to the pool. However, people can be in a state of 'dynamic security' in which their resource pool is full and there are not many challenges. This is not necessarily an ideal situation because boredom can ensue. It is in this way that the model is also interesting, in that individuals are active players through their seeking or not seeking challenges to continue their development. If people do not seek out a challenge they may then be in a state of 'contented stagnation'. On the contrary, 'unhappy stagnation' occurs when there are no challenges but the person does not have the resources to seek them out.

Kloep and Hendry's lifespan model of developmental challenge (Fig. 4.2) is useful for health professionals because it reflects the complex realities of people's lives that we observe in real situations. Health professionals are in a position where they may see people experiencing a challenge (e.g. a health condition or an accident) and can determine whether people and their families have the resources to successfully develop through the challenge. From a client's perspective, a health professional who helps them identify these factors will contribute to improved outcomes, from both the healthcare situation and more holistically for the client.

THEORIES OF AGEING

As already established, historically, human development largely focused on child development, and it is only over the last century researchers have started to challenge that these developmental models do not extend to adults. From this, concepts such as

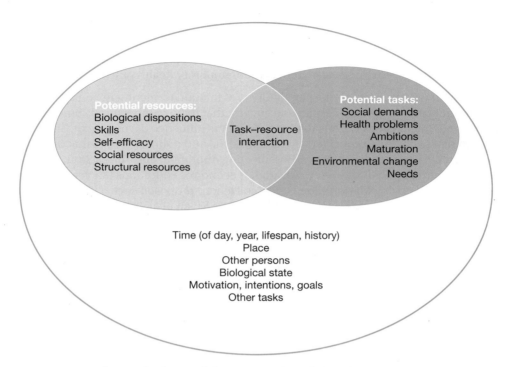

Figure 4.2 Hendry and Kloep's lifespan model of developmental challenge
Depiction of the relationship between potential resources, potential tasks and the context. Source: Hendry & Kloep 2002

continuity of development became questions to be further investigated within the context of lifelong development and, more recently, ageing.

There are several theories attempting to explain what transpires physically to our bodies over time. Theories that focus largely on the body and the process of ageing rather than personal, social or cultural aspects predominantly originate from a biomedical perspective and fall into two distinct categories. One proposes ageing is genetically programmed similar to that in child development, while the other suggests ageing is caused by an accumulation of damage and deterioration as a result of environmental factors such as 'wear and tear' of cells and tissues (Goldsmith 2020). In health psychology, while the aforementioned theories are important, we are interested in the psychosocial context of ageing, an area that is often overlooked despite the many ageing theories.

Psychosocial theories of ageing

A number of theories have emerged in the area of **psychosocial ageing**. Some of the better known include Havighurst's activity theory (1961), the disengagement theory created by Cumming and Henry (1961), the continuity theory (Atchley 1989) and more recently the socioemotional selectivity theory by Carstensen and colleagues (1999), and the theory of gerotranscendence (Tornstam 1989, 1996). These theories have been summarised in Table 4.2. One common theme found in each theory is that ageing does not simply refer to the passing of time but encompasses much more than this.

Table 4.2	
PSYCHOSOCIAL THEORIES OF AGEING—SUMMARY	
Theory of ageing	Summary
Activity theory	Strong relationship between the level of activity and life satisfaction. Engagement in social activities enhances life satisfaction, increasing a positive self-concept that in turns helps adjust to changes in later life.
Continuity theory	Existing behaviours, relationships and activities from earlier years are maintained for positive ageing. Adaptive choices are made to align and preserve connections with previous experience for internal (personality, values, beliefs) or external structures (activities, relationships).
Disengagement theory	A voluntary separation/disengagement from people, society and roles. Family expect less from the older generation, and the ageing individual is less emotionally invested in the younger generation. Life satisfaction and self-worth is maintained through inner reflection.
Socioemotional selectivity theory	The older person spends more time on relationships and activities that are rewarding, in the pursuit of emotional satisfaction as they become aware there is less time to waste.
Gerotranscendence theory	A variant of disengagement theory with a more selective choice in activities and social roles. Increased connection to spirituality and the universe with redefined perceptions of life and decreased fear of death.

When considering all that can occur alongside the process of biological ageing, the term 'gerontology' is often heard in healthcare practice. Gerontology draws attention to the 'normal' process of ageing and its implications within a social, physical, cultural and psychological context, unlike the field of geriatrics, which is based on illness, treatment and how we as health professionals can better care for older adults. Exploring changes in behaviour, social roles, relationships, cultural expectations and other effects of the ageing process can influence how society views ageing from a wider perspective. In turn, this can influence the policy agenda, which is often referred to as 'healthy' or 'successful' ageing by supporting health professionals in the care and treatment of older adults. See later in the chapter for more on healthy ageing.

Milestones of adulthood

So far in this chapter we have examined theories of lifespan development in adulthood and ageing. We will now look at adulthood from the perspective of the main **milestones of adulthood** and the complexities associated with these. As already mentioned, some argue that the distinct stage of 'emerging adult' be introduced between adolescence and adulthood, but others would reason that it is not a universal stage of development and is in fact found only in industrialised countries (Arnett 2022). There are, however, some common milestones attributed to adulthood including marriage, partnership and family; parenting and caregiving; employment and career development; lifestyle; the development of chronic or other illness during adulthood; dying, death and bereavement; and spirituality and wellbeing.

MARRIAGE, PARTNERSHIP AND FAMILY

Being in a close relationship with another person through marriage, a civil union or co-habitation is perhaps one of the most significant milestones of human life. With around 50% of the adult population currently married, and certainly many more in other forms of close and lasting relationships, and a variety of health and legal implications for those who are married or not, it is certainly an important topic for health professionals. Marriage and civil unions are also currently a highly politically charged topic worldwide. Although some countries now have legalised civil unions (i.e. a legally recognised relationship between people of either the same or opposite sex), same-sex relationships are not legally recognised in many countries. In New Zealand, same-sex marriage was legalised in 2013, whereas in Australia an amendment to the *Marriage Act 1961* came into effect in 2017 allowing same-sex couples to be legally married (Australian Government Attorney-General's Department 2017). In 2020 same-sex marriages represented 3.7% of registered marriages within Australia (Australian Bureau of Statistics [ABS] 2021b), with the national population census indicating 46,800 same-sex couples living in Australia and 10,484 of these documented as same-sex couple families (ABS 2017). While these figures do not provide a complete picture of same-sex relationships, they certainly reflect a significant increase in numbers from previous statistical information. This is possibly due to the growing number of people willing to identify themselves as being in a same-sex relationship.

With the huge religious and cultural global diversity, mate selection, marriage, partnership and family are correspondingly diverse (Cohen 2018). We might think that differences in marriage fall into distinct categories of 'love marriages' or 'arranged marriages', or we may have our own ideas about what it is that makes up a family. These ideas are strongly influenced by our own family, the media and other social influences.

According to census data from Australia and New Zealand, family is defined as two or more people related by blood, marriage (including de facto partnerships), adoption, step-relationships or fostering, with one person being at least 15 years of age, and who usually live in the same household (ABS 2021a). Families are further defined as consisting of couple families with and without children, one-parent families, step-families and blended families (Qu & Weston 2013; Stats NZ 2020a). The concept of family is therefore now considered dynamic, with increasing diversity and a significant move away from the very Western conception of a 'nuclear' family. In that definition, for example, 'family' who do not live in the same household are not considered part of that family unit. However, how families perceive themselves can differ quite drastically. For instance, siblings, grandparents and adult children living away from home may still consider each other as 'family' despite not living in the same household. The relevance of the 'household' may have different meanings for different people and groups. For some people, companion animals are very much considered to be part of the 'family', though they would not be included in official records or documentation. Furthermore, how families are conceptualised in different cultural groups can challenge this notion of family. Placing such defined boundaries on Indigenous communities, for example, does not reflect an accurate description of family members living under one roof where kinship networks mean there is an often-changing composition, with family members frequently moving between households (Qu 2020b; Qu & Weston 2013). When practising as a health professional, it helps to identify who the family members are by asking the client and not presuming you already know. Remember, family can be defined in many different ways, whether by residence, descent or choice.

Marriage is generally considered to be a permanent and legally recognised arrangement between two people that includes both a sexual and an economic relationship with mutual rights and obligations. An *endogamous* marriage is one where the partners are from the same group (like Italians marrying other Italians or Jewish people marrying other Jewish people), and an *exogamous* marriage is one in which the partners are from differing groups (like a Catholic marrying a Muslim or someone from Iraq marrying someone from France). For example, for some Australian Aboriginal groups it is important to marry outside of one's 'skin group' and to marry someone from certain other skin groups only.

While only *monogamous* marriages are legal in Australia and New Zealand (i.e. only have one husband or wife), it is perhaps useful to know that this is not the case in all countries around the world. And with increasing migration from non-Western countries, health professionals should be aware of other types of marriage arrangements. For example, *polygamy*, or marriage to multiple spouses, is desirable in many Islamic countries and communities, where it is acceptable and even expected for men to have up to four wives (also called *polygyny*), but this arrangement is illegal in Australia. Less common are *polyandrous* marriages where a woman has more than one husband at the same time. Perhaps more common in Australia and New Zealand is *serial monogamy*, or successive marriages that may be short- or long-term.

There are also various notions of relatives that are important for health professionals to recognise. For example, *consanguineal kin* are people who are related by blood, ancestry or descent, and *affinal kin* are people who are related by marriage. In-laws and their relatives are therefore affinal kin. *Adopted kin* are family created through adoption, and *fictive kin* are those who you might consider to be related to you, like calling your best friend your sister or a family friend your 'aunt'.

Figures 4.3 and 4.4 illustrate only two of the many ways that relationships in a family can be construed. Figure 4.3 shows the *Euro kinship* pattern, while Figure 4.4 illustrates the *Dravidian kinship* pattern. The Euro kinship pattern is common in Western groups, while the Dravidian system is found in South India and in some Aboriginal and Oceanic groups. These are only two kinship patterns, and there are a number of other ways in which relationships between blood and marriage can be understood. However, in Australia and New Zealand, the Dravidian and Euro patterns are perhaps most common.

In Euro kinship, siblings are called brothers and sisters and offspring from the brothers and sisters of one's mother and father are called cousins. The brothers and sisters of one's mother and father are not distinguished and are referred to as aunts or

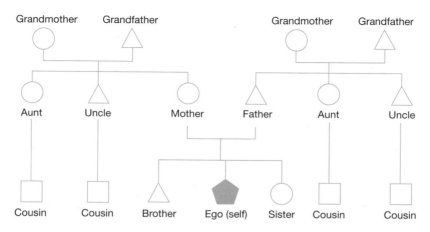

Figure 4.3 Euro kinship Source: Dousset 2011

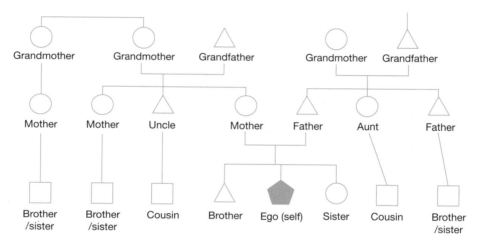

Figure 4.4 Dravidian or Australian Aboriginal kinship Source: Dousset 2011

uncles, based on gender. Similarly, the parents of one's parents are referred to as grandmother or grandfather, again, depending on gender.

In Dravidian kinship, on the other hand, a person can have multiple mothers and fathers and sisters and brothers who are outside the immediate family unit. For example, the sister of one's mother is also called mother and the daughter or son of that mother is called a brother or sister. In terms of parenting (discussed next), this kinship pattern can be very useful. For example, if a teenage boy whose biological father is not available is getting into trouble, then another 'father' may be called upon to offer guidance. In terms of health care, a mother's sister may take children to healthcare appointments in her role as another mother. Another characteristic in Aboriginal kinship systems is 'avoidance relationships', which is the avoidance of, or not interacting with, certain relatives out of respect. For example, a man and his mother-in-law constitutes an avoidance relationship.

Critical thinking

- Is development in adulthood related to chronological age or to life experiences? Or is it related to both? Take, as your examples, a 60-year-old with small children and a 35-year-old with teenagers.
- How can an understanding of different kinship patterns influence healthcare practice?

Overall, the number of marriages per year, and the marriage rate, has decreased over time (ABS 2021b; Stats NZ 2020a). Age at marriage has been steadily increasing, and living together before getting married (i.e. cohabitating) is now a common practice (ABS 2017; Stats NZ 2020a). Being part of a committed relationship, whether married or de facto, plays an important part in a person's overall health and wellbeing (Aldwin et al. 2017). For example, people who are in a relationship appear to have a lower mortality rate and a longer life expectancy than those who are single (Chiu 2019). This is supported by several studies that found married people were overall (except in bodyweight) healthier than people who were not married (Stavrova 2019). This better health includes being less likely to suffer various conditions such as headaches or back pain, as well as healthier lifestyle factors such as not smoking, not drinking alcohol or not being physically inactive. Married men, however, were more likely to be overweight, which might lend some credibility to the old saying that the best way to a man's heart is through his stomach! Interestingly, the patterns did not hold for people who are divorced or separated despite the years they may have been part of a couple. It should also be noted that although the research clearly shows being in a long-term relationship often equates to better health, it is based on the presumption that the relationship is a happy one and therefore the quality of the relationship is central to the impact on health outcomes (Stavrova 2019).

DIVORCE AND FAMILY BREAKDOWN

Divorce and family breakdown—like marriage, partnership and having a family—are major milestones in adult development if they occur and can have both positive and negative consequences. These effects depend on the social contexts and consequences of the divorce or family breakdown. For example, divorce with children involved can be very complicated, but the outcomes largely depend on how these complications are managed (Brand et al. 2019). While there is a large body of research showing negative health consequences from divorce, staying in violent marriages or in highly dysfunctional relationships may be more harmful (Palmtag 2022). Whether those involved marry again is another consideration in the interpretation of the health consequences of divorce. When working in health care with people who have divorced or separated from long-term partners, or children of parents who have divorced, it is important to get a full contextual picture of the family situation before making assumptions about the health and social effects.

Student activity

In small groups, discuss your knowledge and experience with marriage, partnership, civil unions and divorce.

1. How did you or your parents commit to a long-term relationship? Think about how you or they met or were introduced to each other. What sort of ceremonies and social events took place related to commitment in the relationship?
2. What are the dating or partner selection experiences in your family or culture?
3. Discuss similarities and differences with others in the group.

PARENTING, CAREGIVING AND RECONCEPTUALISING CHILDREN

Data shows that the number of children in an Australian or New Zealand family is slowly declining, with people choosing to have fewer children or no children. On average in Australia, a family includes 1.9 children, whereas in New Zealand it is 2.1, with the mother most likely to be between 30 and 34 years old when she has her first child (GBD 2017 Population and Fertility Collaborators 2018; Qu 2020a). Although this can contribute to a static and narrow view of families in Australia and New Zealand, the reality is that family composition, parenting and divorce are highly diverse and change drastically over time. Take, for example, sole-parent households, blended families, teenage parents, same-sex parents, fostering, adoption and grandparents taking responsibility for bringing up their grandchildren. Becoming a parent or the caregiver of children is a major milestone of adulthood, challenging identity and social roles. In fact, being a parent or carer of children changes almost everything a person does and can do.

As discussed in Chapter 3, parenting is an important contributor to children's development, but it is highly complex and diverse. One of the complexities of parenting relates to the different ways of parenting or interacting with children. Most research has been conducted in Western countries, with corresponding biases in terms of what is considered to be 'good parenting', as well as how parenting styles are represented.

For example, as discussed in Chapter 3 (see Box 3.2) one popular version of parenting includes four dimensions: authoritative, indulgent, neglectful and authoritarian (Baumrind 1991; Baumrind et al. 2010). Although authoritative parenting is generally considered a preferable parenting style in the Western world, there are communities and contexts in which this parenting style would be considered inappropriate. Consider a context in which the environment is socially or physically dangerous, such as a socially and economically depressed locale with high rates of violence. In this context, authoritative parenting might not be beneficial and authoritarian parenting might have better health and social outcomes for children. Similarly, in a context in which being educated is the most important and useful goal and the environment is less risky, then authoritative or even indulgent parenting may be preferable.

Another issue related to parenting style is the way a society or parents view children. In some contexts, children are viewed as an economic resource for parents because they can gain employment and bring money into the household, or they can work around the house and thereby relieve the parents for employment purposes, or they will marry into another family and attract wealth. In some contexts, babies may be considered dispensable, particularly those countries with poor access to quality antenatal and postnatal health care and poverty conditions. In contexts with greater social and economic stability, such as in the West, children may be viewed more idealistically and seen as people in themselves rather than as a resource for the family.

Several studies have explored gender preference and family size preference in developing areas such as India and South Asia, finding several interesting things. First, those who were more economically disadvantaged reported wanting more children than those who were better off. From a Western perspective this seems irrational because those with less money and fewer resources should want fewer children. However, the social logic is quite clear when children are considered as resources: those who are economically more disadvantaged have greater benefits with more children because they attract more resources than they use. Second, gender preference of wanting boys rather than girls identified that boys are deemed stronger and able to help out more in daily work, they could inherit the property, provide security against risks and provide for the parents in their old age (Roberts & Montgomery 2016). All of these are to do with economic resources. So, while the United Nations is attempting to ban child labour across the world by 2025, others contend this notion by arguing that in some cultures allowing children to work is positive, beneficial and necessary for those from a disadvantaged socioeconomic climate to have any chance in improving their lives. Most concerning is the number of countries identified in the last few years showing a significant increase in child labour. This is closely linked with coronavirus, poverty and unemployment, whereby families see little alternative than to send their children to work in order to survive (International Labour Office and United Nations Children's Fund 2021).

Importantly, when children are considered a resource, parenting patterns will be very different from when children are not seen in that way. Advising people in different social and economic contexts to reduce the number of children they have because of the problems associated with the increasing world population, while good-intentioned, may inadvertently result in compromising their standard of living and social and economic resources. The values that are derived in one social and economic context can be harmful when applied in a different context.

In greater socially and economically advantaged contexts, having fewer children has greater advantages and benefits, especially in relation to education and the cost of education, particularly in many Western countries. Having fewer children provides for a greater share of the resources because of the way resources are allocated or structured in Western societies. Therefore, having fewer children and educating them better has the same social logic spelled out by developing countries where people have more children. Both are built within a particular social and economic context.

Health professionals are often in the position to observe family dynamics and interactions between caregivers and children, and it is important to recognise and not be critical of dynamics that may seem unusual or different from one's own way of doing things. Family relationships and how children are viewed within the family depends heavily on the context, milieu or culture in which people have been raised, and it is these factors that may not be easily accessible to health professionals. Figure 4.5 offers a framework to reflect key areas required for a family to achieve wellbeing.

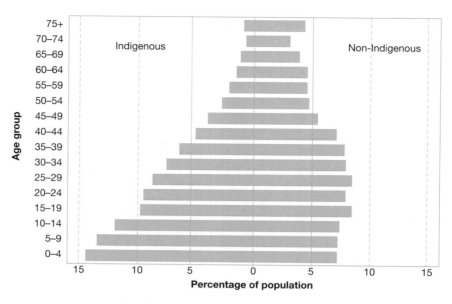

Figure 4.5 Family wellbeing framework Source: Superu 2015

CASE STUDY: JANE

Jane is a community health worker who conducts education sessions for a group of elderly refugee women from East Africa. Before starting the education sessions Jane found out that life expectancy for the countries where the women are from is less than 50 years and that, roughly, there is only one health professional for every 100,000 people. Jane also knows that all the women are Muslim and that she may need to be sensitive to issues of modesty. Jane organises a session about breast and cervical cancer screening. On the night of the session, when Jane introduces the speaker and the topic, many of the women say they do not get cancer in Africa and that it is a Western disease.

Student activity

Discuss the following in small groups.

1. Considering what Jane knows about health care and life expectancy in East Africa. How might she approach discussing the issue of cancer screening with the women?

2. How might an understanding of human development be influenced by differences in life expectancy for different population groups or for migrants or refugees from countries with very different life expectancies from the new country of residence?

EMPLOYMENT, CAREER AND LIFESTYLE

Employment and careers are obviously important to our life stages, but research shows that the nature of career development has changed over time (Warren et al. 2020). Although parents or grandparents may have been employed in the same place for their entire adult life, many people today make substantial career changes throughout their working life. Again, while most Australians and New Zealanders will finish high school and then go on to either trades training or university before moving into a career, there is a substantial minority who will not navigate such a clear path to employment opportunities and career options.

In Australia, Census data show that the percentage of families with children with both parents employed has gradually increased, with a parallel decline in the percentage of stay-at-home mums (Warren et al. 2020). This being said, there remains a division of labour between genders in that men rarely change their work hours on the arrival of children, and despite the small increase of stay-at-home fathers in the past few years the percentage remains very low in comparison with women who either stay home or work part-time when small children are part of the family (Baxter 2018).

The employment status of parents is related to the age of dependent children in the household (ABS 2017). For example, as children get older, there is a higher proportion of parents employed. Although there are a number of economic benefits for families when the caregivers are employed, this also means there are many children in homes where the only parent is working. Many social and health effects can stem these arrangements, and they are not necessarily all positive.

'Being employed' is a major aim of adulthood and has a number of health benefits, particularly if employed in a role with job satisfaction, good working conditions and security. It supports financial stability, helps purchase nutritious food, offers access to medical care and provides adequate housing, all of which support a healthier lifestyle. Equally, being unemployed or being employed in the wrong job or in poor-quality employment can have a negative impact on health. This is clearly demonstrated with the recent coronavirus pandemic, where many people suffered a loss of livelihood. Although other factors were at play, the disconnection of social belonging, isolation, loss of a role and the stress of a reduced income and the inability to pay bills links closely with higher stress levels and an increase of people experiencing psychological distress and stress-related diseases such as high blood pressure and heart disease (Wilson & Finch 2021). *Underemployment* is when someone is employed at a level lower than their qualifications or skills. *Overemployment*, in contrast, is the employment of someone in a position that requires greater skills or knowledge than the person has. Both of these conditions can be stressful and have an adverse impact on health. Also, poor work environments and high-risk jobs can make employment more problematic than beneficial.

One frequently explored area when looking at major milestones in life is that of retirement and its effect on health. Contradictory results from research make it difficult to say with certainty whether retirement has a negative or positive outcome on a person's health (Yeung & Zhou 2017). Historically, assumptions have been made that since retirement is a major life transition, it inevitably affects both physical and psychological wellbeing, but that may not always be the case. While Xue and colleagues (2018) found retirement to have a negative impact on cognitive functioning such as the ability to recall names, places and other verbal information, other cognitive functions were largely unaffected. Szabo and colleagues (2017) similarly concluded that retirement is beneficial to those with existing health issues and limited resources but shows no health advantage for those already healthy and financially stable. In fact, there is strong evidence to suggest that mental health improves once retired despite conflicting data to suggest high rates of depression and anxiety in older people. Maybe the key message for health professionals is to acknowledge the individual circumstances and variables for each person and consider how these may interrelate towards the overall health outcomes for a person. One such variable is a person's established lifestyle patterns.

Lifestyle patterns largely develop during early adulthood along with the development of social circles, employment, education and family (married or not, having children or not). Lifestyle patterns that develop during early adulthood—such as smoking, alcohol or other drug consumption; religious or spiritual activity; physical activity; and dietary habits—reveal their impacts in middle adulthood. Lifestyle, in health psychology, has largely been a concept relevant to individuals and research, and intervention in this area has largely focused on individual behaviour change. However, lifestyle is inextricably linked with social conditions, economic circumstances such as employment, place of residence and the larger community.

Student activity

1. Before coming to class, have a discussion with a parent, aunt, uncle, grandparent or an 'elder' who you are close to about their lifetime lifestyle experiences. Consider the following questions in your discussion. Bring these responses to discuss in a small group.
    - What sort of things do you do to relax?
    - Do you do anything for exercise, physical activity or leisure (sports, walking, gardening, housework, etc.)?
    - What sort of things did you do for exercise, physical activity or leisure when you were in your 20s? 30s? 40s? 50s? (as appropriate)
    - Would you say that your lifestyle/leisure activities have changed much in your life? If so, what would you say contributed to those changes? If not, what things do you think contributed to maintaining your lifestyle behaviours or what things might have been barriers to changing or doing things differently?
2. In small groups discuss the following:
    - Did your discussion with your interviewee change your ideas about how you think about lifestyle and what is 'good' and 'bad' (e.g. what is exercise or physical activity and how your interviewee changed in their life with respect to these activities), especially for older people?
    - Did you learn anything in your interview that you didn't know before? What did you learn and what impact has that had on you? If you didn't learn anything new, was there anything interesting or noteworthy about your conversation with this person?

Healthy ageing

The World Health Organization (WHO) defines **healthy ageing** as 'the process of developing and maintaining the functional ability that enables wellbeing in older age' (WHO 2020a); therefore, with a growing population (particularly in the over-65 age group), health services, health professionals and industry stakeholders are adapting and considering how to best support people to age well. Healthy ageing is often synonymous with other concepts such as successful ageing, productive ageing or positive ageing, all of which have been developed in response to the changing demographic of populations worldwide. For instance, the Australian Institute of Health and Welfare (AIHW) (2018) predicts that 8.7 million Australians will be aged 65 or older in 2056, and national population projections in New Zealand indicate between 1.36 and 1.51 million people aged 65-plus by 2048 (Stats NZ 2020b).

Such terms used to describe people in later life are not without criticism. They imply that a person who gets sick or who can no longer mobilise or is unable to engage in social activities for whatever reason is unsuccessful in ageing, hence more recently the concept of 'optimal ageing' has been coined to acknowledge that in spite of medical issues, a person can still function across cognitive, physical, emotional and spiritual domains (Aldwin et al. 2017).

Regardless of our growing older population, the reality remains that older adults continue to face discrimination and marginalisation, and are frequently perceived as a burden on family, society and health services. This is in part due to people being classified by their age rather than as an individual with distinct and varied needs. Such negative stereotypes and misconceptions do nothing to support ageing as a positive process and in fact deny the many significant roles older people play that contribute to society. For instance, it is well known that older adults provide the majority of informal care for their ill partner/spouse (often with little or no support), assist families by offering flexible child care and make up a large amount of the voluntary workforce (AIHW 2017; Bom et al. 2019).

In response to this, the past 10 years have seen an increase in literature and policy reform to enable the model of healthy ageing to become part of a person's life development. Health services and non-government services have deliberately changed their focus of ageing from the biomedical model of disease and treatment to one of promoting engagement, healthy lifestyle choices, good mental health, cognitive wellbeing and disease prevention.

This is not to ignore the many challenges older people face. While not inevitable in old age, health issues appear to increase, often to a point that can be disabling and life-threatening. Of course, health-related values and health behaviours are often ingrained by this age and more difficult to change, leading to further challenges for health professionals. Research has found several factors that compound this issue. Limited health literacy (see Chapter 8), not wanting to ask for help, being unaware of available services and polypharmacy are commonly identified barriers for accessing appropriate care and support in old age.

Research focus

Source: Jopp et al. 2017

ABSTRACT

Objectives

Having a role model of successful ageing may contribute to views on ageing. This research investigated the nature and correlates of young, middle-aged and older adults' successful ageing role models.

Method

In the study, 151 people aged 18–99 were asked whether they had a role model of successful ageing and, if so, the reasons for their choice. Open-ended answers were coded for recurring themes. Views on ageing and attitudes towards own ageing were assessed with questionnaires.

Results

Eighty-five per cent of participants indicated at least one role model. Most mentioned role models from their family, including parents and grandparents. Role models were gender matched. Most frequent reasons for model choices were health, activities and social resources. Mediation analyses confirmed that family role models were associated with more reasons for role model choice, which in turn was associated with less negative views on ageing. Furthermore, the effect of reasons on attitudes towards own ageing was mediated by negative views on ageing.

Discussion

Young, middle-aged and older adults have role models for successful ageing. Links between role model features and views on ageing suggest that role models may be useful in promoting successful ageing.

Critical thinking

- When you think about successful ageing, do you have a certain person in mind?
- What is it about that person that makes you believe they are ageing well?
- How can choosing a successful ageing role model help in developing a plan for one's own ageing?
- Consider how the research can challenge harmful stereotypes. How is this research useful for health professionals?

CHRONIC ILLNESS AND OTHER HEALTH ISSUES

Chronic illness, disability and other health issues increasingly become a part of life as people age. Health psychology has also gained an increasing role in chronic and other illnesses because of the growing recognition of behavioural and social factors contributing to these conditions. For example, in 2020 ischaemic heart disease, cerebrovascular disease and dementia and Alzheimer's disease were the top three underlying leading causes of death in Australia (ABS 2020). In New Zealand, cancer, ischaemic heart disease and cerebrovascular disease were the leading causes of death in 2019 (Ministry of Health 2021). This aligns globally with ischaemic heart disease being responsible for most deaths worldwide (WHO 2020b).

For health professionals, these statistics suggest that illnesses are more common, partly because people are living longer. But, more importantly, as people age and certain illnesses become more prevalent, people will increasingly need care and specialised processes and equipment. For example, there has been an increase in the need for dialysis machines for kidney disease stemming from diabetes. Therefore, not only are there more people with various illnesses but people need to travel to access specialised equipment and care, and their final years may be involved with hospitals rather than living close to families. For more on chronic conditions, refer to Chapter 12.

DEATH, DYING AND BEREAVEMENT

The topics of death, dying and bereavement are often addressed in the context of older people, but obviously they can affect people of all ages. They are discussed here because death, dying and bereavement become more likely as people grow older and therefore are a major part of human development for adults. Death, dying and bereavement may affect people differently depending on many factors such as the contexts of the death (e.g. whether by an accident or after a long illness), the family and support situation available (to both the person who dies and those who love or have cared for them) and economic circumstances. Chapter 10 on loss also provides more information on death, dying and bereavement, but for the purpose of this chapter let us consider how such a life event can affect a person and their health.

Research on the health outcomes of bereavement suggest there are several risk factors that increase vulnerability to problems with bereavement. Death of a spouse, in terms of stressfulness of life events, ranks as the most stressful experience that people have, with widowhood recognised as one of the most difficult to experience (Phyo et al. 2022). Grieving after someone dies is normal and, indeed, not grieving, especially if the death was of a close family member or friend, would be seen as problematic. Reactions to bereavement are generally classified according to affective (emotional), cognitive (thought-based), behavioural, physiologic-somatic and immunological/endocrine changes. Adjusting to a different lifestyle can have a detrimental impact on a person's health. No longer having a regular routine or familiar prompts for preparing food, eating, sleeping and hygiene can result in a decline in such daily living activities. Overall, bereavement requires a person to adjust emotionally and physically, which as a result can increase physical and mental ill health as well as the incidence of seeking health care (Stahl et al. 2017).

As with research on other topics relevant to health psychology (e.g. trauma and stress), it should not be surprising that research in bereavement is also exploring the positive aspects of grief and challenging previously held notions. For example, Waugh and colleagues (2018) looked at posttraumatic growth following the death of a child bereavement and Heilman (2018) looked at the diversity of the grief experience, particularly the positive dimensions, following the 9/11 attacks on the World Trade Center in New York.

CASE STUDY: ARI

Ari is a 70-year-old male living in a rural area of Towai, New Zealand. While having plenty of fresh air, peace and quiet, and experiencing less violence and crime in contrast with the nearest metropolitan area, he experiences higher costs of food, fuel and transportation, has difficulty meeting friends to engage in social activities, and faces challenges to access adequate health services without travelling vast distances. Recently Ari has been diagnosed with angina. This is causing exertional chest pain, shortness of breath and reduced physical capacity, resulting in Ari handing over the overall management of the family's cattle farm to his son.

Critical thinking

- How might the loss of managing the family farm impact on Ari socially, psychologically and physically?
- Other than the challenges already identified in the case study, what other challenges might Ari experience as he ages living in a rural area?
- What can be implemented to help Ari experience optimal ageing?
- How might knowledge of rural areas in your country contribute to your practice? Consider if you are working in an urban centre and have clients from rural or remote areas. What might you need to consider in your treatment?

SPIRITUALITY AND WELLBEING

The massive growth in literature and research relating to **spirituality** and religion and their relevance to wellbeing and health is testament to the importance of these topics for contemporary health professionals. During adulthood, religious or spiritual development can change dramatically depending on many factors such as social groups that one is involved with, employment situations and major life events (especially traumatic ones). Also, beliefs and practices may change more than once; this is known as 'religious mobility' or 'religious switching'. For example, someone may become involved in a new church through the invitation of someone at work, but then, perhaps after moving to a new town, may find that their church attendance ceases, but they start other activities such as joining a social running group.

Overall, research generally finds that religiosity or **spirituality** contribute to improved wellbeing and can contribute to health improvements and healing from illnesses (Koenig et al. 2012; Wachelder et al. 2016). Spirituality, while once (and still often) synonymous and used interchangeably with 'religion' and organised religious practices (e.g. Catholicism, Islamism and Buddhism), has become a field of study on its own, encompassing both secular and religious practices. In this sense the definition continues to develop, now incorporating concepts such as being socially connected to others, having a purpose in life, attaching hope and meaning to life, and being at peace with oneself (Koenig et al. 2012). The problem can arise when the definition becomes too broad, attempts to encompass too much and in turn becomes a word health professionals use but are unsure quite what it means or how to go about meeting the spirituality needs of a person. To avoid confusion and to recognise the positive role spirituality can play in a person's health, La Cour and Hvidt (2010) described the three domains of secular, spiritual and existential orientations in terms of meaning-making in relation to health and illness. They consider the three domains in relation to knowing (cognition), doing (practice) and being (importance), providing a useful tool to extract some of the complexities of these important topics. For example, using this framework, researchers can tease out some of the relationships between religion and health such as the social supports often associated with some religious practices (e.g. going to church) or the influence of meditation or prayer activities on health.

Given the importance of links between religion or spirituality and health, health professionals may find it very beneficial for clients to have their religious or spiritual needs considered, particularly in acute care or end-of-life contexts. For example, a recovering alcoholic undergoing inpatient cancer treatment may find it helpful for healthcare staff to assist with finding a local 12-step recovery meeting. Twelve-step recovery groups are based on spiritual principles and belief in a 'higher power' to relieve one of their addictions. Health professionals may also recommend, when appropriate, that clients explore religion or spirituality as part of their healing processes.

Chapter summary

This chapter explored various stage theories in adult developmental psychology, including those of Erikson, Kohlberg, Bronfenbrenner, Hendry and Kloep, and Baltes. Theories of ageing and lifespan milestones, such as marriage and employment, were explored and the relevance of these to healthcare practice discussed. All of these theories and ideas can be critiqued and exceptions made to the stages or theories. While stages and generalisations about adulthood and ageing can be made, it is important to consider different circumstances at different ages and how people of various ages in differing situations might be affected. It is not possible to determine exactly how people will behave at different times of their lives, but learning how to identify differences and to expect these differences will improve the appropriateness of healthcare practice.

For example, knowing that a client in your health clinic is 21 years old provides very different health expectations compared with knowing that a client is 50 or 80 years old. However, expectations and treatment would differ greatly for a single 21-year-old client who grew up in urban Australia compared with a 21-year-old client with three children and recently arrived from the Middle East. Theories about developmental stages of adulthood can provide a guide to understanding clients but cannot predict exactly the lived human experience.

Developing an understanding of developmental (st)ages depends at least partly on personal experience, in addition to experience with others to understand the diversity of people's lives. With so much diversity, asking your clients about their contexts, circumstances, milestones and stages of life will go far in ensuring the health care provided is appropriate and relevant.

KEY POINTS

- The lived experiences of adulthood are amazingly diverse in Australia and New Zealand relative to socioeconomic status, ethnicities, disabilities, genders, geographic locations and types of religions and spiritualities.
- Understanding the diversity of adult lives can improve healthcare practice and outcomes.
- Although developmental theories provide useful models for understanding human development, they are not always universally applicable.

Further reading

Barry, C.M., Madsen, S.D., DeGrace, A., 2016. Growing up with a little help from their friends in emerging adulthood. In: Arnett, J.J. (Ed.), Oxford Handbook of Emerging Adulthood. Oxford University Press, Oxford, England, pp. 215–229.

Burman, E., 2016. Deconstructing Developmental Psychology, 3rd edn. Routledge., London.

Feldman, R.S., 2020. Development Across the Lifespan, 9th edn. Pearson, Sydney.

Padilla-Walker, L.M., Nelson, L.J., 2017. Flourishing in Emerging Adulthood: Positive Development During the Third Decade of Life. Oxford University Press, New York.

Robinson, O. 2020. Development through adulthood. 2nd edn. Bloomsbury, London.

Swihart, D.L., Yarrarapu, S.N.S., Martin, R.L., 2021. Cultural Religious Competence in Clinical Practice. StatPearls Publishing, Treasure Island.

Weblinks

Australian Indigenous Health*InfoNet*

www.healthinfonet.ecu.edu.au

The Australian Indigenous Health*InfoNet* is an innovative web resource that makes knowledge and information on Indigenous health easily accessible to inform practice and policy.

Australian Institute of Family Studies

www.aifs.gov.au

The Australian Institute of Family Studies provides bibliographies on a range of topics of interest to health psychology and lifespan development including: separation and divorce; grandparents; and Indigenous families.

Australian Institute of Health and Welfare

www.aihw.gov.au

The Australian Institute of Health and Welfare website provides an extensive range of publications and information relevant to material covered in this chapter. See, for example, Australia's Health 2008, Chapter 6 'Health across the life stages'.

Ministry of Health Manatū Hauora

www.health.govt.nz/

The Ministry of Health Manatū Hauora website is the principle adviser in all aspects of health and disability in New Zealand. It offers a range of resources including publications, the latest information on health topics and links to health services.

Stats NZ Tatauranga Aotearoa

www.stats.govt.nz/

This is an excellent website to access data sets on population groups, the economy, society and health.

Strengthening Families / Whakapiripiri Nga Whānau

www.strengtheningfamilies.govt.nz/about-strengthening-families/

This website provides information for families to achieve health, social and education outcomes.

References

Aldwin, C.M., Igarashi, H., Gilmer, D.F., et al., 2017. Health, Illness, and Optimal Aging: Biological and Psychosocial Perspectives, 3rd edn. Springer Publishing Company, New York.

Arnett, J.J., 2022. Emerging adulthood. In: R. Biswas-Diener & E. Diener (Eds), Noba Textbook Series: Psychology. DEF publishers, Champaign, IL. Available: http://noba.to/3vtfyajs (Accessed 9 March 2022)

Arnett, J.J., 2000. Emerging adulthood: a theory of development from the late teens through the twenties. The American Psychologist 55, 469–480.

Arnett, J.J., 2018. Adolescence and Emerging Adulthood: A Cultural Approach, 6th edn. Pearson Higher Education, New Jersey.

Arnett, J.J., Kloep, M., Hendry, L.B., et al. (Eds.), 2011. Debating Emerging Adulthood: Stage or Process? Oxford, New York.

Arnett, J.J., Zukauskiene, R., Sugimura, K., 2014. The new life stage of emerging adulthood at ages 18-29 years: implications for mental health. The Lancet Psychiatry 1 (7).

Atchley, R.C., 1989. A continuity theory of normal aging. The Gerontologist 29, 183–190.

Australian Bureau of Statistics, 2020. Causes of death, Australia 2020. Available: https://www.abs.gov.au/statistics/health/causes-death/causes-death-australia/2020#:~:text=cause%20of%20death.-,In%202020%3A,and%20Chronic%20lower%20respiratory%20diseases)%20. (Accessed 9 March 2022).

Australian Bureau of Statistics, 2021b. Marriages and Divorces Australia. Available: https://www.abs.gov.au/statistics/people/people-and-communities/marriages-and-divorces-australia/latest-release (Accessed 10 March 2022)

Australian Bureau of Statistics. 2017. Census of population and housing. Stories from the Census 2016. Available: www.abs.gov.au/ausstats/abs@.nsf/Lookup/by%20Subject/2071.0~2016~Main%20Features~Same-Sex%20Couples~85. (Accessed 11 March 2022).

Australian Bureau of Statistics. 2021a. Census of population and housing. Census Dictionary. Available: https://www.abs.gov.au/census/guide-census-data/census-dictionary/2021/glossary/f#:~:text=A%20family%20is%20defined%20by,resident%20in%20the%20same%20household. (Accessed 10 March 2022)

Australian Government Attorney-General's Department, 2017. Marriage equality in Australia. Canberra. Available: www.ag.gov.au/marriageequality. (Accessed 9 March 2022).

Australian Institute of Health and Welfare (AIHW), 2018. Older people at a glance (web report). AIHW, Canberra. Available: www.aihw.gov.au/reports/older-people/older-australia-at-a-glance/contents/summary. (Accessed 8 March 2022).

Australian Institute of Health and Welfare, 2017. Australia's welfare 2017. Canberra. Available: www.aihw.gov.au/reports/australias-welfare/australias-welfare-2017/contents/table-of-contents. (Accessed 8 March 2022).

Baltes, P.B., 1987. Theoretical propositions of life-span developmental psychology: on the dynamics between growth and decline. Developmental Psychology 23 (5), 611–626.

Baltes, P.B., 2000. Life-span developmental theory. In: Kazdin, A. (Ed.), Encyclopedia of Psychology. American Psychological Association & Oxford University Press, Washington DC & New York.

Baltes, P.B., Lindenberger, U., Staudinger, U.M., 2006. Lifespan theory in developmental psychology. In: Damon, W., Lerner, R.M. (Eds.), Handbook of Child Psychology, vol. 1, 6th edn. Theoretical models of human development. Wiley, New York, pp. 569–664.

Baumrind, D., 1991. The influence of parenting style on adolescent competence and substance use. The Journal of Early Adolescence 11 (1), 56–95.

Baumrind, D., Larzelere, R.E., Owens, E.B., 2010. Effects of preschool parents' power assertive patterns and practices on adolescent development. Parenting: Science and Practice 10, 157–201.

Baxter, J., 2018. Stay-at-home Fathers in Australia. (Research Report). Australian Institute of Family Studies. Melbourne.

Bom, J., Bakx, P., Schut, F., van Doorslaer, E., 2019. The impact of informal caregiving for older adults on the health of various types of caregivers: a systematic review. The Gerontologist, 59(5), e629–e642.

Brand, J.E., Moore, R., Song, X., et al., 2019. Parental divorce is not uniformly disruptive to children's educational attainment. Proceedings of the National Academy of Sciences of the United States of America. 116 (15), 7266–7271.

Bronfenbrenner, U. (Ed.), 2004. Making Human Beings Human: Bioecological Perspectives on Human Development. Sage, Thousand Oaks.

Bronfenbrenner, U., 1979. The Ecology of Human Development. Harvard University Press, Cambridge.

Carstensen, L., Isaacowitz, D., Charles, S., 1999. Taking time seriously. A theory of socioemotional selectivity. The American Psychologist 54 (3), 165–181.

Chiu C.T., 2019. Living arrangements and disability-free life expectancy in the United States. PloS One.;14(2)

Cohen, P.N., 2018. The Family: Diversity, Inequality, and Social Change, 2nd edn. W.W. Norton & Company, New York.

Cumming, E., Henry, W.E., 1961. Growing Old: The Process of Disengagement. Basic Books, New York.

Dousset, L., 2011. Australian Aboriginal Kinship: An Introductory Handbook with Particular Emphasis on the Western Desert. pacific-credo Publications, Marseille.

Erikson, E.H., 1950. Childhood and Society. WW Norton, New York.

Erikson, E.H., 1982. The Life Cycle Completed. WW Norton, New York.

Erikson, E.H., Erikson, J.M., 1997. The Life Cycle Completed. WW Norton, New York.

GBD 2017 Population and Fertility Collaborators. 2018. Population and fertility by age and sex for 195 countries and territories, 1950–2017: a systematic analysis for the Global Burden of Disease Study 2017. Lancet, 392 (10159). pp. 1923–1994.

Gilligan, C., 1982. A Different Voice: Psychological Theory and Women's Development. Harvard University Press, Cambridge.

Gilligan, C., Farnsworth, L., 1995. A new voice for psychology. In: Chester, P., Rothblum, E.D., Cold, E. (Eds.), Feminist Foremothers in Women's Studies, Psychology, Mental Health. Harrington Park Press, Binghamton.

Goldsmith, T., 2020. Introduction to Biological Aging Theory, 2nd edn – Rev 2, Azinet Press, Maryland.

Gould, R.L., 1978. Transformations: Growth and Change in Adult Life. Simon & Schuster, Oxford, UK.

Havighurst, R.J., 1961. Successful aging. The Gerontologist 1 (1), 8–13.

Havighurst, R.J., 1972. Developmental Tasks and Education. McKay Company, New York.

Heilman, S.C. (Ed.), 2018. Death, Bereavement and Mourning. Transaction, New Brunswick.

Hendry, L.B., Kloep, M., 2002. Lifespan Development: Resources, Challenges and Risks. Thomson, Australia.

Hochberg, Z.E., Konner, M., 2020. Emerging adulthood, a pre-adult life-history stage. Front Endocrinol (Lausanne). Jan 14;10, 918.

Holland, C., 2018. A ten-year review: the closing the gap strategy and recommendations for reset. The Close the Gap Campaign Steering Committee, Canberra.

International Labour Office and United Nations Children's Fund. 2021. Child Labour: Global estimates 2020, trends and the road forward, ILO and UNICEF, New York. License: CC BY 4.0.

Jopp, D.S., Jung, S., Damarin, A.K,. et al., 2017. Who is your successful aging role model? Journals of Gerontology, Series B: Psychological Sciences and Social Sciences 72 (2), 237–247.

Kloep, M., Hendry, L., Saunders, D., 2009. A new perspective on human development. Conference of the International Journal of Arts and Sciences 1 (6), 332–343.

Kloep, M., Hendry, L.B., Taylor, R., et al., 2016. Development from Adolescence to Early Adulthood: A Dynamic Systemic Approach to Transitions and Transformations. Psychology Press, Hove, UK.

Koenig, H.G., King, D.E., Carson, V.B., 2012. Handbook of Religion and Health. 2nd edn. Oxford, Auckland.

Kohlberg, L., 1976. Moral stages and moralization: the cognitive developmental approach. In: Lickona, T. (Ed.), Moral Development and Behaviour: Theory, Research and Social Issues. Holt, New York, pp. 33–35.

Kohlberg, L., 1981. Essays on Moral Development, vol. 1. The Philosophy of Moral Development. Harper & Row, New York.

Kohlberg, L., 1984. Essays on Moral Development, vol. 2. The Psychology of Moral Development: Moral Stages, Their Nature and Validation. Harper & Row, New York.

Kohlberg, L., Ryncarz, R.A., 1990. Beyond justice reasoning: moral development and consideration of a seventh stage. In: Alexander, C.N., Langer, E.J. (Eds.), Higher Stages of Human Development. Oxford University Press, New York, pp. 191–207.

La Cour, P., Hvidt, N.C., 2010. Research on meaning-making and health in secular society: secular, spiritual and religious existential orientations. Social Science and Medicine 71 (7), 1292–1299.

McCrae, R.R., Costa, P., 2015. Personality in Adulthood: a Five Factor Theory Perspective, 2nd edn. Guilford Press, New York.

McGorry, P. D., Mei, C., Chanen, A., et al., 2022. Designing and scaling up integrated youth mental health care. World Psychiatry, 21(1), 61–76.

Ministry of Health. 2021. Mortality Web Tool. Wellington, New Zealand.

Palmtag, E.L., 2022. Like ripples on a pond: The long-term consequences of parental separation and conflicts in childhood on adult children's self-rated health. SSM – Population Health, 18, 101100.

Phyo, A.Z., Gonzalez-Chica, D.A., Stocks, N.P., et al., 2022. Impact of economic factors, social health and stressful life events on physical health-related quality of life trajectories in older Australians. Qual Life Res. 31 (5), 1321–1333.

Qu, L., 2020a. Families then and now: Having Children. Australian Institute of Family Studies, Melbourne Available: https://aifs.gov.au/publications/having-children (accessed 10 March 2022)

Qu, L., 2020b. Families then and now: Households and families. Research Report. Australian Institute of Family Studies, Melbourne Available: https://aifs.gov.au/publications/households-and-families (accessed 10 March 2022)

Qu, L., Weston, R., 2013. Australian Households and Families (Australian Family Trends No. 4). Australian Institute of Family Studies, Melbourne. Available: https://aifs.gov.au/publications/Australian-households-and-families (accessed 10 March 2022)

Roberts, L.R., Montgomery, S.B., 2016. India's distorted sex ratio: dire consequences for girls. Journal of Christian Nursing. 33 (1), E7–E15.

Rogers, A., 2019. Human Behavior in the Social Environment: Perspectives on Development and the Life Course, 5th edn. Routledge, New York.

Siddiqi, A., Irwin, L., Hertzman, C., 2007. Total Environment Assessment Model for Early Child Development: Evidence Report for the World Health Organization's Commission on the Social Determinants of Health. World Health Organization, Geneva.

Stahl, S.T., Emanuel, J., Albert, S.M., et al., 2017. Design and rationale for a technology-based healthy lifestyle intervention in older adults grieving the loss of a spouse. Contemporary Clinical Trials Communications 8, 99–105.

Stats NZ Tatauranga Aotearoa. 2020a. Families and households in the 2018 Census: Data sources, family coding, and data quality. Available: www.stats.govt.nz. (Accessed 10 March 2022).

Stats NZ Tatauranga Aotearoa. 2020b. National population projections 2020–2073. Available: https://www.stats.govt.nz/information-releases/national-population-projections-2020base2073#:~:text=the%20population%20aged%2065%2B%20 (0.79,1.61%E2%80%932.22%20million%20in%202073 (accessed 10 March 2022)

Stavrova, O., 2019. Having a happy spouse is associated with lowered risk of mortality. Psychological Science. 30 (5), 798–803.

Superu 2015. At a Glance: Frameworks to measure family and whānau wellbeing. Social Policy Evaluation and Research Unit, New Zealand Government, Auckland.

Szabo, A., Allen, J., Stephens, C., et al., 2017. Does physical functioning decline after retirement? A longitudinal investigation from 2006 to 2016. Innovation in Aging 1 (1), 579.

Tornstam, L., 1989. Gerotranscendence – a reformulation of the disengagement theory. Aging Clinical and Experimental Research 1, 55–63.

Tornstam, L., 1996. Gerotranscendence – a theory about maturing into old age. Journal of Aging and Identity 1, 37–50.

Wachelder, E.M., Moulaert, V., van Heugten, C., et al., 2016. Dealing with a life changing event: the influence of spirituality and coping style on quality of life after survival of a cardiac arrest or myocardial infarction. Resuscitation 109, 81–86.

Wang, J., Lloyd-Evans, B., Giacco, D., et al., 2017. Social isolation in mental health: a conceptual and methodological review. Social Psychiatry and Psychiatric Epidemiology 52 (12), 1451–1461.

Warren, D., Qu, L., Baxter, J., 2020. Families then and now: How we worked. Research Report. Australian Institute of Family Studies, Melbourne Available: https://aifs.gov.au/publications/how-we-worked (accessed 10 March 2022)

Waugh, A., Kiemle, G., Slade, P., 2018. What aspects of post-traumatic growth are experienced by bereaved parents? A systematic review. European Journal of Psychotraumatology 9 (1).

Wilson, H., Finch, D., 2021. Unemployment and mental health. The Health Foundation; Available: https://www.health.org.uk/publications/long-reads/unemployment-and-mental-health (Accessed 10 March 2022)

World Health Organization. 2020a. Healthy Aging and Functional ability. WHO, Geneva.

World Health Organization. 2020b. The top ten causes of death. WHO, Geneva.

Xue, B., Cadar, D., Fleischmann, M., et al., 2018. Effect of retirement on cognitive function: the Whitehall II cohort study. European Journal of Epidemiology 33 (10), 989–1001.

Yeung, D.Y., & Zhou, X., 2017. Planning for retirement: longitudinal effect on retirement resources and post-retirement well-being. Frontiers in Psychology, 8, 1300.

Chapter 5

Health and health psychology

GABRIELLE RIGNEY

Learning objectives

The material in this chapter will help you to:

- understand the complex dynamics of the concept of health
- understand the role of health psychology in healthcare practice
- describe the biomedical model of health and illness
- describe the biopsychosocial model of health and illness
- explain the contribution of psychology and, in particular, health psychology to understandings of health, illness and health behaviours
- analyse and critique the interrelationship between biological, psychological and social factors in health and illness behaviours and in the delivery of healthcare services.

Key terms

- Health (126)
- Biomedical model of health (127)
- Social determinants of health (128)
- Biopsychosocial model of health (131)
- Health psychology (136)
- Health behaviours (137)

Introduction

In this chapter health is presented as a dynamic concept that is constantly changing, multidimensional and influenced by factors that are both internal and external to the individual. The biomedical (also called bioscience) model of health and illness, which dominated healthcare delivery up until the middle of the 20th century and perpetuates the notion of a mind–body split, is examined and critiqued. Finally, it will be argued that the biopsychosocial model, which uses research evidence, theory and clinical practices from a range of health disciplines including bioscience, psychology and sociology offers a more comprehensive explanation for health behaviours and health outcomes than is provided by the biomedical model alone. In particular, health psychology (a branch of psychology) is examined for the contribution it makes to understandings of human behaviour in relation to health and illness and thereby to the clinical practice of not only psychologists but of all health professionals.

Psychological theories offer complementary and, at times, contradictory views of human behaviour that reflect different assumptions about the nature of individuals and how they should be studied. These varying theoretical perspectives include bioscientific, psychoanalytic, behavioural (or learning), cognitive and humanistic theories. These explanations are described in detail in Chapter 1 and underpin the approaches used in health psychology. You will discover that each theoretical position offers a different perspective on human behaviour, and each may provide useful explanations in specific situations. Nevertheless, none provides a universal explanation of behaviour that applies to all people in all situations.

What is health?

Health is a construct that can be defined in both broad and narrow terms. Narrow interpretations are provided by the biomedical model, which emphasises the presence or absence of disease, pathogens and/or symptoms. A broader interpretation is provided by the biopsychosocial approach, which proposes that health is influenced by a complex interaction of biological, psychological and social factors. See Table 5.1 for sociological, psychological and biomedical factors that influence health.

Also, health can be examined both objectively and subjectively. Objective measures such as an x-ray or scan can indicate health or illness, while a person's subjective interpretation will report whether they feel healthy or ill, but there may be no correlation between the two. For example, a person may report feeling healthy but have dangerously high blood pressure, or another person may report pain for which physical pathology cannot be identified. Therefore, given the range of criteria and the different perceptions that can influence a definition of health, it is not surprising that there is no one simple measure. Rather, health and wellbeing result from a complex interplay between physical, psychological, social and environmental factors (Australian Institute of Health and Welfare [AIHW] 2021b).

Table 5.1		
HEALTH MODELS AND THEIR INFLUENCE		
Biomedical	Psychological	Sociological
Pathogens	Thoughts	Social
Genetics	Feelings	Cultural
Biochemical	Behaviours	Ethnicity
Hormonal	Unconscious drives	Economics
Injury	Learning	Politics
Environment	Environment	Environment

Furthermore, health can have different meanings for the general public or laypeople than it does for health professionals. Three consistent themes arise in research into laypeople's understanding of the concept of health. They are: health is not being ill; health is a prerequisite for life's functions; and health involves both physical and mental wellbeing (Baum 2015). Baum suggests that these lay definitions have more in common with the World Health Organization's (WHO) definition of health (more than the absence of disease) than biomedical interpretations do.

BIOMEDICAL MODEL

Throughout history, explanations for illness have included somatic imbalance, demonology, witchcraft and environmental pathogens. In Western-industrialised countries up until the middle of the 20th century, health was generally viewed as the absence of disease, and illness was seen as a pathological state. With the emergence of the public health movement in the 19th century, the biomedical approach (also called the medical model) rose to prominence and dominated Western medicine for more than 200 years. The **biomedical model of health** proposes organic, pathological theories to explain and treat illness. Essentially, this approach is an illness-based model with the underpinning assumption that illness and disease are caused by disequilibrium in the body that is brought about by one or more of the following:

- biological pathogens such as a viral or bacterial infection
- trauma or injury such as an acquired brain injury
- a biochemical imbalance in the body such as hypothyroidism or diabetes
- degenerative processes such as arthritis or dementia.

From the 19th century, public health strategies using a biomedical approach such as sanitation and mass vaccinations have achieved a worldwide reduction in many communicable diseases like polio and pneumonia and an increase in life expectancy (Goldman 2018). In the 20th century, the discovery of antibiotics, chemotherapy drugs, anti-hypertensive agents and psychotropic medications and the development of sophisticated surgical techniques such as organ transplantation have enabled previously life-threatening diseases and conditions to be treated and, in many instances, cured.

However, by the latter half of the 20th century it became apparent that the *treatment* era of the previous decades did not live up to the expectations of the scientific or wider community. In Western countries, for example, diseases related to lifestyle (e.g. diabetes and cardiovascular disease) now pose a greater threat to health than that of infectious diseases. Also, with treating infectious diseases, some bacterial strains have developed resistance to antibiotics (e.g. methicillin-resistant *Staphylococcus aureus*), and for many cancers neither a cure nor preventive vaccination has been discovered. In the main, many cancer prevention and chronic illness management strategies are related to lifestyle and the environment, such as ceasing cigarette smoking, using sun protection, being physically active, eating a healthy diet and maintaining weight within the healthy range.

In the mental illness field, the unwanted side effects of antipsychotic drugs are often problematic and can contribute to non-adherence to treatment—for example, the rapid and sustained weight gain and iatrogenic diabetes mellitus experienced by some patients taking atypical antipsychotic medication to treat schizophrenia (Musil et al. 2015; Raben et al. 2018). Such consequences of treatment present a challenge to patients and health professionals for the relative cost–benefit of the treatment. For patients, the unwanted social and health consequences may interfere with adherence to the recommended treatment. For health professionals, there is the ethical dilemma of encouraging adherence to a treatment for one health condition such as schizophrenia that carries a high risk that the patient will develop another serious health condition such as metabolic syndrome or type 2 diabetes.

Challenges to an exclusive biomedical approach

Initially, the biomedical model held great promise to improve the health of individuals and communities. Scientific research in the 20th century led to discovering medications that could cure, or eliminate, many diseases. Sulfur drugs—developed in the 1930s—and other antibiotics revolutionised how we treat infection. In the mental health field, the first antipsychotic medication (chlorpromazine) was introduced in 1950. At the time it was lauded as a breakthrough in treating schizophrenia because of its ability to reduce disruptive behaviour (Meadows et al. 2020). Patients who would have been in straitjackets and lived out their lives in a mental institution could now be discharged and returned to live in the community.

However, by the middle of the 20th century concerns were mounting about the cost escalation of scientific, technological medicine; worldwide there was recognition of the need for sustainable environments. It was also evident, particularly in Western countries, that the diseases that threatened communities were no longer infectious and acute but were chronic and related to lifestyle. For example, the health conditions that now carry the greatest burden of disease are cancer, cardiovascular disease, mental and substance use disorders, musculoskeletal conditions and injuries (AIHW 2021b).

Challenges to the biomedical model as the *exclusive* framework for understanding health and to structure the delivery of healthcare services began to emerge from the middle of the 20th century. The major criticism has been that an exclusive biomedical approach fails to consider the contribution of the **social determinants of health**—that is, the broader psychological, sociological, political, economic and environmental factors that influence health and illness. Furthermore, social determinants are now considered the major contributor to health inequities (AIHW 2021d). Another criticism of an exclusively biomedical approach is that health resources are directed to costly curative services rather than to health promotion or illness prevention. According to Baum (2015), more research is required into exactly how and which economic factors affect health, and how improved health and health equity can be achieved through social, educational and housing interventions.

Earlier questioning of the dominance of the biomedical model by policymakers, commentators and clinicians coincided with the United Nations establishing WHO in the 1940s. WHO was given the brief to work towards 'the attainment by all peoples of the highest possible level of health' and in 1946 the organisation released its then groundbreaking definition of health:

Health is a state of complete physical, mental and social wellbeing and not merely the absence of disease or infirmity.

(WHO 1946)

This definition was developed in response to the changing healthcare needs of populations. The WHO explanation contested the efficacy of the prevailing biomedical view of health at the time by recognising the contribution of not only physical factors to health and illness but social and psychological factors as well. WHO's broadening of the definition of health signalled the introduction of what became known as the biopsychosocial approach in which the contribution of individual, lifestyle and social factors to health outcomes is acknowledged. It also laid the foundation for the emergence in the 1970s of the primary healthcare / new public health movement.

Nevertheless, while the WHO definition of health is a comprehensive one, it has its limitations. The use of the word 'complete' is problematic. Is it possible to be completely healthy in all areas identified (physical, mental and social) and at all times? And if this is not possible, does it necessarily follow that a person who has one health issue is unhealthy? Consider, for example, a person with a well-managed chronic illness (asthma) or a disability (vision impairment) who is otherwise in good health. If you asked either of these two people to rate their health, do you think they would describe themselves as unhealthy? They probably wouldn't. When asthma is managed by medication and vision impairment corrected by glasses, the person does not experience limitations from the health issue. Therefore, in seeking a comprehensive definition of health other factors must be considered including the person's sense of control of and satisfaction with their health and life.

Furthermore, there are demonstrated links between income and health outcomes; that is, that poor people have worse health outcomes regarding morbidity and mortality than people who are wealthy. This occurs both within and between countries (WHO 2022). For example, in a study conducted in the United States, Chetty and colleagues (2016) found a gap in life expectancy of 14.6 years for men and 10.1 years for women between people in the lowest and highest income groups. And Indigenous populations worldwide have greater rates of diabetes than the general population (Harris et al. 2017). Furthermore, while life expectancy in New Zealand is 81.75 years, it is only 60.77 years in Sierra Leone (Stats NZ Tatauranga Aotearoa 2021; WHO 2019). WHO recognised the importance of addressing income inequities to improve health and stated in the *Closing the Gap in a Generation* report that 'higher levels of better coordinated aid and debt relief, applied to poverty reduction through a social determinants of health framework, are a matter both of life and death and of global justice' (WHO 2008, p. 130). Further to this, the first two of the eight United Nations Millennium Development Goals (MDGs) were to eradicate extreme poverty and hunger, and to achieve universal primary school education by 2015 (WHO 2018). Although the MDGs were not fully met, and some commentators would say they were overly ambitious, there were significant advancements made that continue through the pursuit of the Sustainable Development Goals (United Nations 2022), which expands the original goals from 8 to 17. See Table 5.2 for the United Nations' Sustainable Development Goals.

Increased longevity in Western countries over the past two centuries is attributed not only to advances in medical treatments but also to public health initiatives and population-level interventions such as access to safe water and sanitation, programs to address global road safety, tobacco control and vaccination programs for preventable diseases (United Nations 2022). In fact, the biggest increase in life expectancy that occurred in the first half of the 20th century is attributed mainly to public health initiatives and population-focused interventions, not advances in

Table 5.2

UNITED NATIONS SUSTAINABLE DEVELOPMENT GOALS

1. No poverty
2. Zero hunger
3. Good health and well being
4. Quality education
5. Gender equality
6. Clean water and sanitation
7. Affordable and clean energy
8. Decent work and economic growth
9. Industry innovation and infrastructure
10. Reduced inequality
11. Sustainable cities and communities
12. Responsible consumption and production
13. Climate action
14. Life below water
15. Life on land
16. Peace, justice and strong institutions
17. Partnerships for the goals

Source: From Sustainable Development Goals. Available: www.un.org/sustainabledevelopment/sustainable-development-goals/ (accessed 24 February 2022) © 2022 United Nations. Reprinted with the permission of the United Nations.

medical science (Marmot 2020). In 2019–20 the Australian Government and private providers spent only $3,591 million of its $202.5 billion health budget on public health activities for whole populations or population groups (AIHW 2022a). This was an increase of ~$505 million on public health activities from the 2018–19 financial year, largely attributed to the COVID-19 pandemic (e.g. health promotion campaigns to educate about social distancing and hand hygiene; AIHW 2022a). However, these figures highlight that the vast majority of the public and private health budget was allocated to treatment interventions, services for illness and injury, and administration and research, yet the evidence suggests that this is not the most effective allocation of financial resources to achieve the best health outcomes for individuals and populations (Marmot 2020).

In summary, the biomedical model holds the view that health outcomes are influenced by physiology, with health occurring when the body is in a state of equilibrium and illness being a consequence of physical pathology or disequilibrium. The approach is limited as a theory to explain and understand health and the provision of healthcare services because it is a one-dimensional model that fails to consider the complex interplay of other factors—namely, psychological and social factors that interact with biological factors and affect health.

BIOPSYCHOSOCIAL MODEL

As discussed, the philosophy that underpins the **biopsychosocial model of health** is that health or illness results from a complex interplay between biological, psychological and social factors. The model emerged in the 1970s in response to realisations about the limitations of the biomedical model in a changing world.

The notion of an alternative to the biomedical model was first proposed by Engel (1977) and quickly gained momentum among health professionals and policymakers. The biopsychosocial model is holistic in approach and thereby avoids the mind–body split inherent in the biomedical model. A further outcome of this approach is recognising the contribution allied health professionals make to health care and the emergence of the multidisciplinary team as a mechanism for providing health services.

Health priorities

Priority areas and targeted conditions are major health issues identified by the Australian Department of Health for focused attention because they contribute significantly to the burden of illness and injury. The department's priority areas are: dementia, obesity, arthritis and musculoskeletal conditions, asthma, diabetes, mental health, injury prevention and control, cardiovascular health and cancer control—all of which have complex aetiology including lifestyle, biological, psychological and social factors (Primary Health Network for country South Australia 2022). COVID-19 has most recently been added as the 10th priority area. The New Zealand government health priorities for 2021–2025 focus on the COVID-19 response, health and disability system reform, improving child wellbeing, improving mental health, improving wellbeing through preventative measures, creating a strong and equitable public health system, providing better primary health care and ensuring a financially sustainable health system (New Zealand Ministry of Health 2021). In addressing these health problems, the holistic nature of the biopsychosocial model offers greater opportunity to improve health outcomes than a biomedical approach alone because the biopsychosocial approach addresses more than just the symptoms of the condition.

Nevertheless, despite the intrinsic appeal of the biopsychosocial model, some critics argue that, generally, social issues are not sufficiently addressed in policy or practice (Fisher et al. 2016). Using another approach—primary healthcare / new public health that operates from a biopsychosocial framework *and* has a strong emphasis on social, economic and political issues that impact on health—is proposed as a way to overcome this shortcoming.

PRIMARY HEALTHCARE / NEW PUBLIC HEALTH

The emergence of the primary healthcare / new public health movement in the 1970s coincided with the growing awareness that psychological and social influences as well as physical and biological factors influenced health outcomes for individuals and communities. It was formally endorsed as a mechanism to achieve 'Health for all by the year 2000' at the 1978 WHO conference in the Declaration of Alma-Ata in the former Soviet Union. The declaration was the culmination of a WHO–UNICEF-sponsored conference at which representatives from 134 nations endorsed the declaration with the philosophical principles of: social justice; equity; access; empowerment; self-determination; political action; health promotion and illness prevention; collaboration between consumers, practitioners, countries, governments and those responsible for health; and striving for world peace.

Worldwide policymakers, health professionals and communities were increasingly looking beyond the biomedical model for answers to health problems (Baum 2015). In 1981 Lalonde, the then Canadian Minister of National Health and Welfare, described four general determinants of health that he called human biology, environment, lifestyle and healthcare organisation. Supporting a shift from a biomedical approach to a broader approach acknowledging biopsychosocial factors, Lalonde stated:

There can be no doubt that the traditional view of equating the level of health in Canada with the availability of physicians and hospitals is inadequate. Marvellous though healthcare services are in Canada in comparison with many other countries, there is little doubt that future improvements in the level of health of Canadians lie mainly in improving the environment, moderating self-imposed risks and adding to our knowledge of human biology.

(Lalonde 1981, p. 18)

In 1986, 8 years after the Alma-Ata declaration, the first WHO International Conference on Health Promotion was held in Ottawa, Canada. Conference participants developed an action framework of five strategies (the Ottawa Charter) to achieve 'health for all' (Table 5.3). These five strategies have become the cornerstone of the primary healthcare / new public health movement, and the charter continues to be a robust, insightful and useful document in contemporary healthcare policy and practice (Nutbeam et al. 2021; Thompson et al. 2018). Nevertheless, some commentators argue that health policy alone is insufficient to achieve health equity and social justice, and that a 'health in all policies' (e.g. education, welfare, housing) approach is needed to redress health inequities (Lawless et al. 2018).

Table 5.3

ACTIONS OF THE OTTAWA CHARTER FOR HEALTH PROMOTION

Ottawa Charter strategy	Action
Build healthy public policy	Direct policymakers to be aware of the health consequences of their decisions and to develop socially responsible policy
Create supportive environments	Generate living and working conditions that are safe, stimulating, satisfying and enjoyable
Strengthen community action	Empower communities and enable ownership and control of their own endeavours and destinies
Develop personal skills	Support personal and social development through providing information, education for health and enhancing life skills
Reorient health services	Share responsibility for health promotion in health services among individuals, community groups, health professionals, health service institutions and government

HEALTH OF AUSTRALIANS AND NEW ZEALANDERS

When compared with other countries, the health of Australians and New Zealanders ranks highly. They are rated among the top 10 developed countries in the world across a range of significant indicators. Life expectancy is ranked among that of the top nations in the world. See Table 5.4 for life expectancies for selected countries.

In addition, Australians born in the 21st century can expect to live 30 years longer than their ancestors born in the 19th century and 13 years longer than ancestors born in the 20th century. That is, a male born in 1890 had a life expectancy of 51.1 years, whereas a male born in 2019 has a life expectancy of 80.9 years (see Table 5.5).

Student activity

1. Examine the international life expectancy statistics in Table 5.4.
   - What do these statistics tell us?
   - What are the implications of this?
2. Before coming to class, select three countries (each with a short, medium and long life expectancy) and research the health issues in these three countries.
   - Identify the health priorities or significant health issues of the three countries.
   - Discuss and critique these health issues and priorities in class.
   - Identify biomedical, psychological and sociological contributors to these health issues.

Table 5.4

LIFE EXPECTANCY IN SELECTED COUNTRIES, 2018

Selected countries	Life expectancy at birth
Japan	84.26
Switzerland	83.56
Spain	83.5
Italy	83.4
Iceland	82.9
Israel	82.9
Australia	82.8
New Zealand	81.75
United Kingdom	81.4
United States	78.5
China	77.43
New Zealand Māori	75.25
Indigenous Australians	73.6
Indonesia	71.31
India	70.79
Sierra Leone	60.77

Compiled from: Australian Institute of Health and Welfare 2021c, Stats NZ Tatauranga Aotearoa 2021, World Health Organization 2019.

Table 5.5

AUSTRALIAN LIFE EXPECTANCY (YEARS) AT DIFFERENT AGES, 1881–1890, 1960–1962, 2013–2015 AND 2017–2019

Age	Males				Females			
	1881–1890	1960–1962	2013–2015	2017–2019	1881–1890	1960–1962	2013–2015	2017–2019
Birth	51.1	67.9	80.7	80.9	54.8	74.2	84.5	85.0

Cont... ▶

Table 5.5

AUSTRALIAN LIFE EXPECTANCY (YEARS) AT DIFFERENT AGES, 1881–1890, 1960–1962, 2013–2015 AND 2017–2019—cont'd

	Males				Females			
25 years	63.9	70.8	81.1	81.6	66.7	76.3	85.1	85.5
65 years	76.3	77.5	84.5	85.0	77.8	80.7	87.3	87.7
85 years	88.8	89.1	91.2	91.4	89.1	89.8	92.2	92.6

Source: Australian Institute of Health and Welfare 2021c

Student activity

1. Compare the life expectancy statistics for Australia in 1881–1890, 1960–1962, 2013–2015 and 2017–2019 in Table 5.5.
   - What do these statistics tell us?
   - Identify factors that have contributed to increased life expectancy in Australia.
2. It is predicted that the current generation of young Australians will be the first to not outlive their parents.
   - Identify factors that have led commentators to make this claim.

TWENTY-FIRST CENTURY HEALTH CHALLENGES

Regardless of the gains made in longevity over the past 100 years in Australia and New Zealand, there are some disturbing trends in the health statistics of these two nations. Life expectancy for Indigenous Australians was lower than the national average—8.6 years for men and 7.8 years for women (AIHW 2021c). While this gap has reduced since 2005–07, the AIHW cautions that the decrease is more likely to be due to a change in how the Australian Bureau of Statistics (ABS) collects statistics rather than an actual increase in Indigenous life expectancy. Also, while the discrepancy is not as great in New Zealand as it is in Australia, Māori life expectancy is 6.5 years less than the New Zealand average (Stats NZ Tatauranga Aotearoa 2021). Furthermore, Indigenous Australians not only die younger than the national average, they also experience significantly more ill health and disability than other Australians (AIHW 2021b). Australia's health report for 2020 stated that Indigenous Australians are more likely to experience a burden of disease 2.3 times the rate of non-Indigenous Australians (AIHW 2021b, p. 555).

Also of concern is cardiovascular disease which, in Australia, is the leading cause of death (25% of all deaths in 2019) and one of the leading causes of disability (6.9% of the population). And while mortality figures for most health conditions, including coronary heart disease, stroke, colon cancer and infant mortality, have improved over the past 25 years in Australia, the mortality figures have worsened for some other illnesses, such as diabetes, chronic obstructive pulmonary disease and accidental falls (AIHW 2021b). Finally, Australia has the unenviable 'honour' of having higher rates of obesity than the OECD average (AIHW 2021b). That puts these Australians at increased risk for lifestyle health conditions such as high cholesterol, hypertension, heart disease and some cancers.

The COVID-19 pandemic has resulted in many direct and indirect health effects, with new challenges continually arising (e.g. emergence of new variants). Direct health effects include total case numbers, illnesses and deaths from COVID-19, whereas indirect health outcomes include adverse effects on the mental health of populations and health service changes. Cancer screening and services were affected globally. For example, breast screening in Australia declined from 75,000 tests in April 2018 to just 1,100 tests in April 2020 (AIHW 2021a). In New Zealand, where an elimination strategy to COVID-19 was pursued, there were initial downturns in service access during the national shutdown in March and April 2020; however, the impact on cancer services returned to pre-pandemic levels in subsequent months (Gurney et al. 2021). Another important change in health services in both Australia and New Zealand was that GPs were able to continue patient consultations with the uptake of telehealth arrangements and electronic prescriptions for virtual care (New Zealand Ministry of Health 2022). Two key social determinants affected by the pandemic include loss of income through increased unemployment and underemployment rates, as well as increases in family and domestic violence and child abuse and neglect during COVID-19 restrictions (AIHW 2022b). The impacts of the COVID-19 pandemic are likely to affect our lives and be a significant health challenge for several years to come.

FRAMEWORK FOR HEALTH

In conclusion, finding a universally applicable definition of health is challenging because health is a dynamic concept influenced by a complex range of factors that interact with and influence each other. Therefore, rather than pursuing an all-encompassing definition of health, a more useful approach is to use a *framework* for understanding health, such as the one developed by the AIHW (Fig. 5.1) that identifies individual, societal and environmental influences on health and the interrelationship between these factors.

What is health psychology?

Health psychology arose as a branch of psychology in the 1970s during the emergence of the biopsychosocial model and the primary healthcare / new public health movement. Influential in the development of health psychology was the changing health needs of populations, mounting dissatisfaction with the biomedical model and concerns about the escalating costs of a medically oriented healthcare system. This was alongside the growing realisation of the role psychological, social and lifestyle factors play in health and illness. Also, chronic illnesses were replacing acute illnesses as posing the greatest burden of disease to individuals, communities and healthcare resources. The prevailing view at this time was that individuals were primarily responsible for their own health and that health outcomes were a consequence of the individual's lifestyle choices (Jancey et al. 2016).

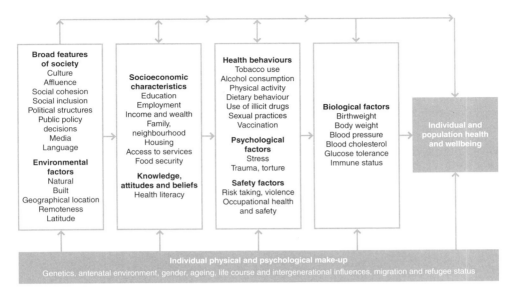

Figure 5.1 Framework for determinants of health Source: Australian Institute of Health and Welfare 2021b

In 1980 Matarazzo provided a definition of health psychology that stated that health psychology was an:

... aggregate of the specific educational, scientific and professional contributions of the discipline of psychology to the promotion and maintenance of health, the prevention and treatment of illness, the identification of etiologic and diagnostic correlates of health, illness and related dysfunction and the improvement of the healthcare system and health policy formation.

(Matarazzo 1980, p. 815)

This definition specified the scope of health psychology, which was to:

- study the psychological aspects of how people engage in behaviours that maintain health and minimise health risks
- study how thoughts, feelings and personal qualities influence health behaviours and lifestyle choices
- study how thoughts, feelings and personal qualities influence responses to stress, pain, loss and chronic illness
- study how people recognise and respond to illness and how they decide to seek, start and complete treatment (or not)
- identify health promotion and illness prevention strategies and early intervention opportunities.

Contemporary critical health psychologists, however, question the moral and ethical stance of the psychological approaches to health that emerged in the 1970s and 1980s that blamed individuals (victim blaming) for their **health behaviours** such as smoking or eating unhealthy food, and avoided addressing the social and environmental factors that affected the health of vulnerable people (Jancey et al. 2016). In the 21st century there is now abundant evidence that social determinants play a major role in health outcomes (Baum 2015; WHO 2022). Hence, contemporary critical health psychologists place increasing importance on the contexts in which individuals live their lives and advise that social, political and economic forces must be taken into consideration when exploring explanations of health behaviours (Goldman 2018; Jancey et al. 2016; Marmot 2020). As Murray (2014, p. 215) observed, health psychology 'was prefigured by sustained debate within social and applied psychology about the nature of psychology and its role in society'.

In summary, health psychology seeks understanding for human health behaviours within the psychosocial, economic and political contexts in which people live in order to: identify ways of maintaining positive health behaviours; identify strategies to assist people to avoid or modify negative health behaviours; and assist people to maintain new health behaviours. This not only enables individuals to achieve, maintain or improve health but it is important for wider society in that it can improve the health of its citizens and reduce the human and resource cost of illness.

HEALTH PSYCHOLOGY AS A CAREER

Health psychology is a specialised branch of psychology and has two career pathways: theoretical (research) and applied (clinical practice). Research psychologists develop and test theories and evaluate interventions, while clinical psychologists work in a range of healthcare settings as members of multidisciplinary teams or as private practitioners. Entry to both these career pathways requires a specialist postgraduate qualification in psychology. According to the Australian Psychological Society, health psychologists specialise in understanding how psychological and behavioural factors interact with the physical systems of the body and social factors to influence health and illness. Health promotion (prevention of illness and promotion of healthy lifestyles) and clinical health (application of psychology to illness assessment, intervention and recovery) are the two main areas in which health psychologists practise (Australian Psychological Society 2022).

Health psychology for health professionals

Health psychology contributes to the education and practice of *all* health professionals. Theory and research from health psychology is a fundamental component in courses that prepare practitioners for all the healthcare professions including nursing, nutrition, medicine, occupational therapy, social work, speech pathology, paramedicine, physiotherapy and podiatry. Health professionals use knowledge and research findings from health psychology to understand the health behaviours of their patients and to plan treatment interventions, rehabilitation and recovery programs, illness prevention and health education and promotion programs.

Understanding health behaviours

Behaviours that promote health have long been known. For example, in 1983 Berkman and Breslow identified seven health practices that their research demonstrated could significantly reduce a person's risk of dying at any age:

1. sleeping 7–8 hours per day
2. eating breakfast

3. rarely eating between meals
4. being roughly appropriate weight for height
5. not smoking
6. drinking alcohol in moderation or not at all
7. engaging in physical activity regularly (Berkman & Breslow 1983).

These practices continue to be relevant in the 21st century. During the early stages of the COVID-19 pandemic in April and May of 2020, the large changes to society through lockdowns and restrictions resulted in changes to health risk factors including diet, physical activity and alcohol consumption (AIHW 2021a). These health risk factors are known to contribute significantly to disease burden in Australia (AIHW 2021b).

Critical thinking

- Keep a diary for a week in which you record whether or not you observe the health behaviours identified by Berkman and Breslow.
- Identify your reasons for following or not following these health behaviours.

INFLUENCES ON HEALTH BEHAVIOURS

Psychological approaches to understanding health include: examinations of personality factors; perceptions and beliefs about personal control and the individual; and social and environmental factors that reinforce behaviours.

PERSONALITY

The psychological theories of personality that have particular relevance to the field of health psychology are the behavioural and cognitive models. Behavioural psychologists stress the role of learning, reinforcement and modelling in initiating and maintaining behaviours, while cognitivists argue that behaviours are influenced by the individual's beliefs and perceptions about themselves, events or circumstances. Also, personality traits and dispositions that predict behaviour have been identified.

Personality types

The first description of a personality style that was purported to influence health was the type A personality, which was described by two American cardiologists who observed personality characteristics in their patients that they believed predisposed these patients to the risk of cardiovascular disease (Friedman & Rosenman 1959, 1974). People with type A personality were considered to be competitive, impatient, time-conscious, hostile, unable to relax and had rapid, loud speech. Type B people were described as relaxed, quieter and less hurried than type As. While these categorisations have intuitive appeal, it appears that the distinctions cannot predict risk for coronary heart disease, and that the hostility component of the type A personality is the greater predictor of cardiac risk (Piña et al. 2018).

Nevertheless, interest has been reignited recently in researching personality as a risk factor in the long-term prognosis of cardiac patients. With the introduction of the distressed personality type or type D, Denollet (2005, 2017) described people who simultaneously experience high levels of negative affectivity (or mood) and high levels of social inhibition. What this suggests is that when people with type D personality experience negative emotions, they inhibit the expression of these emotions in social interactions. Furthermore, negative affectivity, which includes depression, anxiety and social inhibition, each of which are associated with type D personality, have been found to be independent predictors of cardiac events (Kupper & Denollet 2018; Pluijmers & Denollet, 2017). Interestingly, Suls (2018) conducted a narrative review of studies that had simultaneously tested three negative affective dispositions—anger, anxiety and depression—as risk factors for cardiac outcomes. The focus of this review was to recognise the overlap among these dispositions and evaluate the findings from when they have been tested together. Results suggested that anxiety and depression play independent roles in cardiac risk, but the verdict for anger/hostility was unclear. This indicates that anger/hostility may emerge as important only when other negative effects have not been measured, but more research is needed. This does suggest, however, that experiencing a variety of negative emotions may be important for determining cardiac risk. Denollet's research suggests it is not just the presence of negative emotions that may pose a risk factor for cardiac disease but also how that person copes with their negative emotions. The following research conducted by Wu and colleagues (2015) suggests a way of mediating the influence of negative affectivity on medication compliance, thereby enhancing cardiac outcomes.

Research focus

Source: Wu et al. 2015

ABSTRACT

Background
Type D personality is associated with medication non-adherence. Both type D personality and non-adherence are predictors of poor outcomes. Self-efficacy, which is modifiable, is also associated with medication adherence.

Objectives
To determine the relationships among type D personality, self-efficacy and medication adherence in 84 heart failure patients.

Methods
Self-efficacy, type D personality, medication adherence, demographic and clinical data were collected. Hierarchical linear regression was used.

Results
Type D patients were more likely to have lower self-efficacy ($p = 0.023$) and medication non-adherence ($p = 0.027$) than non-type D patients. Low self-efficacy was associated with medication non-adherence ($p < 0.001$). Type D personality didn't predict medication adherence after entering self-efficacy in the model ($p = 0.422$), demonstrating mediation.

Cont... ▶

Conclusions
Self-efficacy mediates the relationship between type D personality and medication adherence. Developing and applying interventions to enhance self-efficacy may help to sever the link between type D personality and poor outcomes.

Critical thinking

- Wu and colleagues (2015) suggest that enhancing self-efficacy (also see the section 'Personal control') may improve medication adherence. Discuss the association between self-efficacy and medication adherence.
- What strategies would you implement to encourage self-efficacy in patients with type D personality?
- Identify other health-enhancing behaviours that may be increased by improving self-efficacy.

Resilience

Resilience is another personality trait that is linked to health outcomes. The word itself has a Latin derivation and means to spring or bounce back. In psychology, resilience refers to a personality trait that can withstand and overcome adversity, tragedy, trauma, threats or significant sources of stress (American Psychological Association 2022). See also Chapter 9.

Resilience was first described by Garmezy (1987) who, while researching risk factors for schizophrenia, observed that some children seemed to be thriving despite living in high-risk situations such as having a drug-dependent parent. Garmezy then shifted his research focus to examine what enabled such children to be successful, despite the adversity in which they lived. Subsequent research supports Garmezy's observation that resilient children are emotionally mature—that is, they possess high self-esteem and self-confidence, have the capacity to make and maintain friendships with peers, have the ability to gain the support of adults, are trusting, have a sense of purpose, possess a set of values and beliefs and have an 'internal locus of control' (Garmezy 1987).

Contemporary definitions of resilience include that it consists of individual and social components, and that it is mediated by protective and vulnerability factors and the person's ability to adapt their emotions and to use social skills and resources when faced with adversity (Luthar 2017; Manjula & Srivastava 2022). Importantly, recognising the contribution of both the individual's personality traits and the role of wider society means that a person's ability to respond to negative events can be enhanced by intervening at the social level. By mobilising social resources, the person's ability to respond to and manage challenging experiences and events will be improved.

PERSONAL CONTROL

Beliefs about who or what is responsible for behaviours differ between individuals. There are many psychological concepts that attempt to explain these differences. Two of them are locus of control and self-efficacy.

Locus of control

LOC is an attribution style that was identified by Rotter in his social learning theory (Rotter 1966). It refers to a person's belief as to whether outcomes or events in their life are brought about by themselves (internal LOC), by powerful others or are random (external LOC). The model predicts that a person with an 'internal' explanatory style will assume responsibility for whatever happens to them, crediting their own efforts when they are successful and citing insufficient effort for failure.

Wallston and colleagues (1978) applied Rotter's LOC theory to health and developed an instrument called the 'multidimensional health locus of control scale' (health LOC). In the health LOC model, the 'external' explanatory style of Rotter's LOC model is expanded to describe people whose explanatory style was either that health outcomes were the result of chance or were under the control of powerful others (doctors or other people). Wallston's three dimensions of control in relation to health are: internal health LOC, chance health LOC and powerful others health LOC (Wallston 2005, 2022). The model predicts that if a person believes they can control their health (internal attribution) then they will behave in ways that are health enhancing. Alternatively, if a person has an external attribution style (chance or powerful other) they will be less likely to take responsibility for managing their health.

Student activity

Jordan is a 35-year-old overweight man who has recently been diagnosed with type 2 (non-insulin-dependent) diabetes.

1. In pairs identify and discuss likely health behaviours in relation to managing Jordan's diabetes for each of Wallston's multidimensional health LOC explanatory models.

Health LOC	Cognitions and beliefs	Predicted health behaviours
Internal	I will be able to control my diabetes if I am given enough information about the condition and its treatment.	
Powerful others	The doctor knows more about this condition than me. I will follow the medical advice.	
Chance	My father had diabetes, so it's probably hereditary. Nothing I do can change that.	

Cont... ▶

2. Identify possible cognitions/beliefs and consequent health behaviours for 48-year-old Sandy, who has smoked for 30 years and has been advised to quit smoking following a bout of bronchitis.

Health LOC	Cognitions and beliefs	Predicted health behaviours
Internal		
Powerful others		
Chance		

Student activity

1. Complete Wallston's (2022) Multidimensional Health Locus of Control Form A (available at https://nursing.vanderbilt.edu/projects/wallstonk) before coming to class.
2. Identify and reflect on your highest score. What would be the implications of this if you had a health problem?
3. Bring your results to your class.
4. In small groups, complete the following:
   - Compare and discuss your own perspective with the perspective of others.
   - Consider the implications of caring for a patient when their perspective is different from your own.

Self-efficacy

The concept of self-efficacy was first described by Bandura (1977) and refers to a person's perceived ability to perform a certain task or achieve a specific goal in a situation. Like health LOC, self-efficacy stresses the importance of the person's perceptions and beliefs about their personal control in a particular circumstance. However, self-efficacy also considers the expectation the person has about the consequences of action taken or not taken. For example, 'What will happen if I take no action?' (situation outcome expectancy); 'What will happen if I change my behaviour?' (action outcome expectancy); and 'Am I capable of changing my behaviour to achieve the goal?' (efficacy expectancy).

The theory speculates that a person's level of confidence in their ability to succeed in a certain situation will influence whether the person engages in activities that will facilitate either success or failure. For example, when approaching an exam, a student with a high level of self-efficacy who believes they can pass the exam would engage in behaviours that lead to success such as managing their time to incorporate study, whereas a student who does not believe they can pass is likely to engage in behaviours that bring about failure such as procrastinating and avoiding preparing for the exam. Finally, while self-efficacy is considered a personality trait, it is amenable to modification through cognitive behavioural therapy and other psychological interventions (Merluzzi et al. 2019).

Nevertheless, caution is advised in assuming that personality traits, resilience, internal LOC, high self-efficacy and an optimistic outlook are ideal in all circumstances. Consider the circumstance where the outcome cannot be controlled such as recurrence of cancer following a period of remission. The person who initially believed they could control their illness would have their belief seriously challenged by the recurrence and be vulnerable to depression according to Seligman's learned helplessness theory (Seligman 1994). Harris, the founder of acceptance and commitment therapy, argues that it is unrealistic to always be optimistic and seek happiness, advocating an approach that includes self-acceptance and compassion (Harris 2018).

Research focus

Source: Tan et al. 2021

ABSTRACT

Background

The successful management of hypertension requires sustained engagement in self-care behaviour such as adhering to medication regimens and diet. Bandura's social cognitive theory suggests that self-efficacy is a major determinant of engagement in self-care behaviour. Self-efficacy refers to a person's belief in their capacity to execute behaviours necessary to produce specific performance attainments. This systematic review of observational studies aims to summarise and evaluate the quality of evidence available to support the association between self-efficacy and engagement in self-care behaviour in hypertension.

Methods

Searches were performed of the Pubmed, MEDLINE, CINAHL and OpenSIGLE databases from database inception to January 2020. Reference lists and individual journals were also hand searched. Observational studies in English quantifying self-efficacy and self-care behaviour in hypertensive adults were included. The quality of included articles was assessed with the National Institute of Health Quality Assessment Tool for observational studies.

Results

The literature search identified 102 studies, of which 22 met the inclusion criteria for full-text review. There were 21 studies reporting that higher self-efficacy was associated with engagement in self-care behaviours including

Cont... ▶

medication adherence ($n=9$), physical activity ($n=2$) and dietary changes ($n=1$). Of these, 12 studies were rated as 'good' on the quality assessment tool and 10 were 'fair'. A common limitation in these studies was a lack of objectivity due to their reliance on self-reporting of engagement in self-care behaviour.

Conclusion

The review suggests an association between self-efficacy and self-care. However, the evidence supporting this association is of low to medium quality and is limited by heterogeneity. Research findings suggest the need for further well-designed interventional studies to investigate this association.

Critical thinking

Tan et al. (2021) reported that there is an association between self-efficacy and self-care behaviours in those with hypertension. Identify and discuss strategies to enhance self-care behaviours such as exercise and diet for patients who have lower self-efficacy.

CASE STUDY: KARA

Kara is a 21-year-old third-year behavioural science student at a metropolitan university. She plans to pursue a career in sports psychology and work with elite athletes after completing her studies. Kara's health and fitness priorities are that she eats a healthy diet and trains three times a week at her local surf lifesaving club where she is a member of the current state champion surfboat team. Nevertheless, each weekend when she goes out with her friends Kara binge drinks to the point of not remembering what she did the night before. She brushes off her friends' concerns about her drinking and argues that the safe drinking limit for women is two standard drinks per day and therefore she is only having her weekly quota if she has 14 drinks in one night.

Student activity

Read the case study above and revisit Chapter 1. Discuss the following in small groups.

1. What is your response to Kara's logic?
2. Reflect on how her engagement in healthy behaviours can be explained by:
   - classical conditioning (learning by association)
   - operant conditioning (learning reward or avoidance of an adverse outcome)
   - modelling (observational/vicarious learning).
3. Reflect on how her engagement in unhealthy behaviours can be explained by:
   - classical conditioning
   - operant conditioning
   - modelling.

Social influences on health

Social influences on health are briefly identified here and are discussed in more detail in Chapter 6. Demographic data demonstrate health inequities for:

- *SES*—lower income is correlated with poorer health and higher smoking rates (Hobkirk et al. 2018; AIHW 2021b)
- *age*—the most pressing chronic health issue for people aged 15–44 years is mental and behavioural conditions, while it is arthritis for those aged over 65 years (AIHW 2021b)
- *gender*—Australian and New Zealand women's life expectancy is almost 5 years greater than that of men's (AIHW 2021c; Stats NZ Tatauranga Aotearoa 2021)
- *ethnicity*—Pacific Islanders have disproportionate rates of obesity and diabetes compared with the rest of the world, regardless of whether they are living in their home country or have emigrated (Hawley & McGarvey 2015).

Population groups considered at risk because of social inequities include people from lower socioeconomic backgrounds, unemployed people, Indigenous people, people living in rural and remote areas, prisoners, refugees and people with mental illness (AIHW 2021b). Interestingly, in Australia migrant populations experience better health than the overall population when they arrive in the country, but this advantage declines over time (Smith 2015).

Critical thinking

- List reasons why you think new migrant populations experience better health than the wider Australian population.
- List reasons why you think the health of migrant populations declines over time.

SOCIAL DETERMINANTS

WHO, in its publication *Social Determinants of Health: The Solid Facts* (Marmot & Wilkinson 2006), identified 10 key social and political factors that influence health. These different but interrelated social determinants of health are the social gradient, stress, early life, social exclusion, work, unemployment, social support, addiction, food and transport. The authors stated that the publication of *Social Determinants of Health* was intended to 'ensure that policy—at all levels in government, public and private institutions, workplaces and the community—takes proper account of the wider responsibility for creating opportunities for health' (Marmot & Wilkinson 2006, p. 7).

Subsequently, WHO established the Commission on Social Determinants of Health to examine and collate evidence on what could be done to bring about health equity and to foster a global movement to achieve it (WHO 2008). In the commission's *Closing the Gap in a Generation* report, the commissioners called on governments worldwide to reduce health inequities through policy and programs that engage key sectors of the community, such as economic development, transport and education, and to include health in all policies because *health* policies and programs alone cannot achieve health equity or social justice (Lawless 2018). And furthermore, research conducted by Huda and colleagues (2018) has demonstrated that tackling the social determinants of health can enhance better access to healthcare services for poorer people, which is also consistent with the WHO's Sustainable Development Goals (WHO 2015).

CROSS-CULTURAL INFLUENCES

Culture can be defined as the history, values, beliefs, language, practices, dress and customs that are shared by a group of people and that influences the behaviour of the members (Germov & Poole 2019). Commonly, culture is equated with ethnicity, but this is a limited interpretation; other cultural groupings also exist based on shared understandings. For example, the phrase 'right hander' has different meanings for a surfer, a boxer or a schoolteacher. And, despite commonalities that define a culture, it cannot be assumed that all members of one culture necessarily share identical worldviews on any or all issues (Clendon & Munns 2018).

Different interpretations of health and explanations for illness exist between cultures that are *individualistic* (i.e. a society in which the smallest socioeconomic unit is the individual and independence is valued) and cultures that are *collectivist* (i.e. a society in which the smallest socioeconomic unit is the family and human interdependence is valued). Individualism is a cultural pattern mainly found in developed Western countries and is 'chiefly concerned with protecting the autonomy of individuals against obligation imposed by the state, family and community' (Kato & Sleeboom-Faulkener 2011, p. 509). Individualist cultures attribute responsibility for health to the individual. Collectivist cultures, on the other hand, recognise the role of the extended family and community in all aspects of life. Members are 'usually characterized by a sense of emotional, moral, economic, social and political commitment to their collective' (Haj-Yahia 2011, p. 333). For example, traditional Māori beliefs are that four domains influence health: physical, spiritual, family and mental (New Zealand Ministry of Health 2017).

Also, it is important to recognise that, in the main, psychological theories of behaviour were developed in Western Europe and the United States, which are individualistic cultures. Consequently, caution must be exercised when applying these psychological theories derived from research conducted in individualist societies to people from collectivist societies such as Australian Aboriginal and Torres Strait Islander peoples or New Zealand Māori, and the immigrant populations of the two countries.

Chapter summary

This chapter provides an overview of the many factors that influence health and health outcomes. In particular, the contribution that health psychology makes to understanding and managing health and illness is presented. While this branch of psychology generally focuses on understanding individual behaviour and the factors that influence health outcomes, the dynamic nature of health is acknowledged, particularly the social context in which individuals live. Health psychology, therefore, is located within the biopsychosocial framework—a model that recognises the interdependence and interrelationships between biological, psychological, social and political factors in understanding and managing health and illness.

KEY POINTS

- Health and health outcomes are influenced by a complex interaction of biological, psychological, social and political factors.
- Health psychology proposes theories that attempt to explain why people engage in behaviours that maintain, enhance or threaten their health.
- A person's thoughts, feelings and personal qualities can influence health behaviours and lifestyle choices.
- Understanding these influences enables health professionals to assist clients to engage in behaviours that maintain or enhance health and to cease behaviours that pose health risks.

Further reading

Australian Institute of Health and Welfare (AIHW), 2020. Australia's health 2020. AIHW, Canberra. Available: https://www.aihw.gov.au/reports-data/australias-health

Baum, F., 2015. The New Public Health, 4th edn. Oxford University Press, Melbourne.

Clendon, J., Munns, A., 2018. Community Health and Wellness: Primary Health Care in Practice, 5th edn. Elsevier, Sydney.

Jancey, J., Barnett, L., Smith, J., et al., 2016. We need a comprehensive approach to health promotion. Health Promotion Journal of Australia 27 (1). Available: https://on-linelibrary.wiley.com/doi/full/10.1071/HEv27n1_ED. (Accessed 18 March 2022).

United Nations, 2022. Sustainable Development Goals. Available: www.un.org/sustain-abledevelopment/sustainable-development-goals/. (Accessed 14 March 2022).

Weblinks

American Psychological Association

www.apa.org/topics/resilience

The American Psychological Association provides general information about resilience and focuses on how the individual can develop and use a personal strategy to enhance resilience.

Australian Institute of Health and Welfare

www.aihw.gov.au

The Australian Institute of Health and Welfare is Australia's national agency for health and welfare statistics and information.

Australian Psychological Society

www.psychology.org.au

The Australian Psychological Society is dedicated to advancing the discipline and profession for the benefits of members and the community.

New Zealand Ministry of Health

www.health.govt.nz/publication/annual-update-key-results-2019-20-new-zealand-health-survey

This page provides a link to the annual update of key results for the 2019 to 2020 New Zealand Health Survey.

The Social Report/Te pūrongo oranga tangata

http://socialreport.msd.govt.nz

The Social Report/Te pūrongo oranga tangata 2016 provides an overview of the current state of New Zealand's health and the likely trends in the future.

References

Amer, F.A., Mohamed, M.S., Elbur, A.I., et al., 2018. Influence of self-efficacy management on adherence to self-care activities and treatment outcome among diabetes mellitus type 2. Pharmacy Practice (Granada), 16 (4).

American Psychological Association, 2022. Building your resilience. Available: www.apa.org/topics/resilience. (Accessed 20 March 2022).

Australian Institute of Health and Welfare (AIHW), 2021a. The first year of COVID-19 in Australia: direct and indirect health effects. Canberra

Australian Institute of Health and Welfare (AIHW), 2021b. Australia's health 2020. AIHW, Canberra. Available: https://www.aihw.gov.au/reports-data/australias-health (Accessed 10 March 2022).

Australian Institute of Health and Welfare (AIHW), 2022a. Total Health Expenditure https://www.aihw.gov.au/reports/health-welfare-expenditure/health-expenditure-australia-2019-20/contents/main-visualisations/overview (Accessed 20 April 2022).

Australian Institute of Health and Welfare (AIHW), 2022b. COVID-19 https://www.aihw.gov.au/covid-19 (Accessed 10 April 2022)

Australian Institute of Health and Welfare, 2021c. Deaths: life expectancy. Available: www.aihw.gov.au/reports/life-expectancy-death/deaths/contents/life-expectancy#data. (Accessed 20 March 2022).

Australian Institute of Health and Welfare, 2021d, Social determinants. Available: www.aihw.gov.au/reports-statistics/behaviours-risk-factors/social-determinants/about. (Accessed 20 March 2022).

Australian Psychological Society, 2022. Health psychologists. Available: https://psychology.org.au/psychology/about-psychology/types-of-psychologists/health-psychology. (Accessed 12 March 2022).

Bandura, A., 1977. Self-efficacy: towards a unifying theory of behaviour change. Psychological Review 84, 191–215.

Baum, F., 2015. The New Public Health, third ed. Oxford University Press, South Melbourne.

Berkman, L., Breslow, L., 1983. Health and Ways of Living: The Alameda County Study. Oxford University Press, New York.

Chetty, R., Stepner, M., Abraham, S., et al., 2016. The association between income and life expectancy in the United States, 2001–2014. Journal of the American Medical Association, 315 (16), 1750–1766.

Clendon, J., Munns, A., 2018. Community Health and Wellness: Primary Health Care in Practice, 6th edn. Elsevier, Sydney.

Denollet, J., 2005. DS14: standard assessment of negative affectivity, social inhibition and type D personality. Psychosomatic Medicine 67, 89–97.

Denollet, J., 2017. Type D personality as a predictor of poor health outcomes in patients with cardiovascular disease. Netherlands Heart Journal 25 (4), 286–287.

Engel, G., 1977. The need for a new medical model: a challenge for bio-medicine. Science 196, 129–135.

Fisher, M., Baum, F., MacDougall, C., et al., 2016. To what extent do Australian health policy documents address social determinants of health and health equity? Journal of Social Policy 45 (3), 535–564.

Friedman, M., Rosenman, R., 1959. Association of specific overt behavior pattern with blood and cardiovascular findings; blood cholesterol level, blood clotting time, incidence of arcus senilis, and clinical coronary artery disease. Journal of the American Medical Association 169 (12), 1286–1296.

Friedman, M., Rosenman, R., 1974. Type A Behavior and Your Heart. Knopf, New York.

Garmezy, N., 1987. Stress, competence and development: continuities in the study of schizophrenic adults, children vulnerable to psychopathology and the search for stress-resistant children. American Journal of Orthopsychiatry 57 (2), 159–174.

Germov, J., Poole, M., 2019. Public Sociology: An Introduction to Australian Society, fourth ed. Allen & Unwin, Sydney.

Goldman, L., 2018. Three stages of health encounters over 8000 human generations and how they inform future public health. American Journal of Public Health 108 (1), 60–62.

Gurney, J.K., Millar, E., Dunn, A., et al., 2021. The impact of the COVID-19 pandemic on cancer diagnosis and service access in New Zealand – a country pursuing COVID-19 elimination. The Lancet Regional Health-Western Pacific, 10, p. 100127.

Haj-Yahia, M., 2011. Contextualising interventions with battered women in collectivist societies: issues and controversies. Aggression and Violent Behavior 16, 331–339.

Harris, R., 2018. ACT Questions and Answers: A Practitioner's Guide to 150 Sticking Points in Acceptance Commitment Therapy. New Harbinger Publications, Oakland.

Harris, S., Tompkins, J., TeHiwi, B., 2017. Call to action: a new path for improving diabetes care for Indigenous peoples, a global view. Diabetes Research and Clinical Practice 123, 120–133.

Hawley, N.L., McGarvey, S.T., 2015. Obesity and Diabetes in Pacific Islanders: the current burden and the need for urgent action. Current Diabetes Reports 15 (29).

Hobkirk, A., Krebs, N., Muscat, J., 2018. Income as a moderator of psychological stress and nicotine dependence among adult smokers. Addictive Behaviours 84, 215–223.

Huda, T., Hayes, A., Dibley, M., 2018. Examining horizontal inequity and social determinants of inequality in facility delivery services in three South Asian countries. Journal of Global Health 8 (1). Available: www.ncbi.nlm.nih.gov/pmc/articles/PMC6008508/. (Accessed 18 March 2022).

Jancey, J., Barnett, L., Smith, J., et al., 2016. We need a comprehensive approach to health promotion. Health Promotion Journal of Australia 27 (1). Available: https://onlinelibrary.wiley.com/doi/full/10.1071/HEv27n1_ED. 18 March 2022, Online.

Kato, M., Sleeboom-Faulkener, M., 2011. Dichotomies of collectivism and individualism in bioethics: selective abortion debates and issues of self-determinism in Japan and 'the West'. Social Science & Medicine 73, 507–514.

Kupper, N., Denollet, J., 2018. Type D personality as a risk factor in coronary heart disease: a review of current evidence. Current Cardiology Reports, 20 (11), 1–8.

Lalonde, M., 1981. A New Perspective on the Health of Canadians: A Working Document. Ministry of National Health and Welfare, Ottawa.

Lawless, A., Baum, F., Delaney-Crowe, T., et al., 2018. Developing a framework for a pro-gema theory-based approach to evaluating policy processes and outcomes: health in all policies in South Australia. Health Policy and Management 7 (6), 510–521.

Luthar, S., 2017. Resilience in development: a synthesis of research across five decades, Ch. 20. In: Cicchetti, D., Cohen, D. (Eds.), 2015. Developmental Psychopathology: Volume Three: Risk, Disorder and Adaptation. Wiley Online Library. Available: https://onlinelibrary.wiley.com/doi/abs/10.1002/9780470939406.ch20. (Accessed 18 March 2022).

Manjula, M., & Srivastava, A., 2022. Resilience: Concepts, Approaches, Indicators, and Interventions for Sustainability of Positive Mental Health. In Handbook of Health and Well-Being (pp. 607–636). Springer, Singapore.

Marmot, M., 2020. Health equity in England: the Marmot review 10 years on. BMJ, 368.

Marmot, M., Wilkinson, R., 2006. Social Determinants of Health: The Solid Facts, third ed. World Health Organization, Geneva.

Matarazzo, J., 1980. Behavioral health and behavioral medicine: frontiers for a new health psychology. American Psychologist 35, 807–817.

Meadows, G., Farhall, J., Fossey, E., et al., 2020. Mental Health in Australia: Collaborative Community Practice, 4th edn. Oxford University Press, South Melbourne.

Merluzzi, T. V., Pustejovsky, J. E., Philip, E. J., et al., 2019. Interventions to enhance self-efficacy in cancer patients: A meta-analysis of randomized controlled trials. Psycho-Oncology 28 (9), 1781–1790.

Murray, M., 2014. Social history of health psychology: contexts and textbooks. Health Psychology Review 8 (2), 215–237. Available: www.tandfonline.com/doi/full/10.1080/17437199.2012.701058. (Accessed 18 March 2022).

Musil, R., Obermeier, M., Russ, P., et al., 2015. Weight gain and antipsychotics: a drug safety review. Expert Opinion Drug Safety. 14 (1), 73–96.

New Zealand Ministry of Health, 2017. Māori health models – Te Whare Tapa Wha. Available: www.health.govt.nz/our-work/populations/maori-health/maori-health-models/maori-health-models-te-whare-tapa-wha. (Accessed 19 March 2022).

New Zealand Ministry of Health, 2022. Telehealth and online tools. Available: https://www.health.govt.nz/covid-19-novel-coronavirus/covid-19-information-health-professionals/telehealth-and-online-tools https://www.health.govt.nz/covid-19-novel-coronavirus/covid-19-information-health-professionals/telehealth-and-online-tools (Accessed 24 June 2022)

New Zealand Ministry of Health, 2021. Strategic Intentions 2021 to 2025. Wellington: Ministry of Health.

Nutbeam, D., Corbin, J.H., Lin, V., 2021. The continuing evolution of health promotion. Health Promotion International, 36(Supplement_1), pp.i1–i3.

Piña, I.L., Di Palo, K.E., Ventura, H.O., 2018. Psychopharmacology and cardiovascular disease. Journal of the American College of Cardiology, 71(20), 2346–2359.

Pluijmers, E., Denollet, J., 2017. Type D personality as a predictor of poor health outcomes in patients with cardiovascular disease. Netherlands Heart Journal 25 (4), 286–287.

Primary Health Network for country South Australia 2022. National Health Priority Areas. https://www.countrysaphn.com.au/community/national-health-priority-areas/ (Accessed 18 March 2022).

Raben, A.T., Marshe, V.S., Chintoh, A., et al., 2018. The complex relationship between antipsychotic-induced weight gain and therapeutic benefits: a systematic review and implications for treatment. Frontiers in Neuroscience, 11, 741.

Rotter, J.B., 1966. Generalized expectancies for internal versus external control of reinforcement. Psychological Monographs 80, 234–240.

Seligman, M., 1994. Learned Optimism. Random House, Sydney.

Smith, L., 2015. The health outcomes of migrants: a literature review. Migration Council Australia. Available: https://ranzcog.edu.au/RANZCOG_SITE/media/RANZCOG-MEDIA/About/NWHS/Resources/The-health-outcomes-of-migrants.pdf (Accessed 20 March 2022).

Stats NZ Tatauranga Aotearoa, 2021. National and subnational period life tables: 2017–2019. Available: https://www.stats.govt.nz/information-releases/national-and-subnational-period-life-tables-2017-2019 (Accessed 20 March 2022).

Suls, J., 2018. Toxic affect: Are anger, anxiety, and depression independent risk factors for cardiovascular disease? Emotion Review, 10(1), 6–17.

Tan, F.C.J.H., Oka, P., Dambha-Miller, H., Tan, N.C., 2021. The association between self-efficacy and self-care in essential hypertension: a systematic review. BMC Family Practice, 22, 1–12.

Thompson, S.R., Watson, M.C., Tilford, S., 2018. The Ottawa Charter 30 years on: still an important standard for health promotion. International Journal of Health Promotion and Education, 56(2), 73–84.

United Nations, 2022. Sustainable Development Goals. Available: www.un.org/sustainable-development/sustainable-development-goals/. (Accessed 18 March 2022).

Wallston, K., 2005. The validity of the multidimensional health locus of control scales. Journal of Health Psychology 10 (5), 623–631.

Wallston, K., 2022. Multidimensional health locus of control (MHLC) scales. Available: https://nursing.vanderbilt.edu/projects/wallstonk/index.php. (Accessed April 2022).

Wallston, K., Wallston, B., DeVellis, R., 1978. Development of multidimensional health locus of control (MHLOC) scales. Health Education Monographs 6, 160–170.

World Health Organization (WHO), 1946. WHO Constitution. WHO, New York.

World Health Organization (WHO), 2008. Closing the Gap in a Generation: Health Equity Through Action on the Social Determinants of Health. WHO, Geneva. Available: https://www.who.int/publications/i/item/WHO-IER-CSDH-08.1 18 March 2022 Online.

World Health Organization (WHO), 2015. Health in 2015: from MDGs to SDGs. Available: https://www.who.int/data/gho/publications/mdgs-sdgs. (Accessed 18 March 2022).

World Health Organization (WHO), 2018. Millennium Development Goals (MDGs). Available: www.who.int/topics/millennium_development_goals/about/en/. (Accessed 18 March 2022).

World Health Organization (WHO), 2019. Life expectancy at birth (years). Available: https://www.who.int/data/gho/data/indicators/indicator-details/GHO/life-expectancy-at-birth-(years) (Accessed 20 March 2022)

World Health Organization (WHO), 2022. Social determinants of health. Available: https://www.who.int/health-topics/social-determinants-of-health#tab=tab_1. (Accessed 15 March 2022).

Wu, J., Song, K., Moser, D., 2015. Type D personality, self-efficacy, and medication adherence in patients with heart failure – mediation analysis. Heart and Lung. 44(4) 276–281.

Chapter 6

The social context of behaviour

YVONNE PARRY & EILEEN WILLIS

Learning objectives

The material in this chapter will help you to:

- describe the social model and the social determinants of health
- understand the history and evidence leading to a social model of health as a counter to the biomedical model of health
- evaluate the social justice argument in support of a social model of health and the implications for government policy
- examine the relationship between the social model of health, intersectorial policy and health promotion actions as a way of understanding the relationship between the social determinants of health and psychological and behavioural explanations of health.

Key terms

- Social gradient (157)
- Social model of health (157)
- Behavioural model of health (158)
- Social determinants of health (159)

Introduction

In Chapter 5 it was argued that the biomedical model of health was inadequate in explaining the patterns of mortality and morbidity for populations and individuals. A biopsychosocial model of health was proposed and a brief outline of the social determinants of health presented. This chapter takes the 'social' aspects of the biopsychosocial model of health and examines the evidence, debates and theories that argue that illness and disease for individuals, populations and nations is not simply a matter of germs and viruses (biomedical) or individual psychology and behaviour (biopsychological) but a complex interaction between the social system of a given society and the individual (biopsychosocial) and their particular genetic inheritance (biomedical).

Traditionally there has been a stand-off between biomedical, biopsychological and social models of health. This stand-off is counterproductive and contrary to the evidence. Over the past five decades particular population groups within affluent nations have failed to make the promised biomedical and health promotion gains (World Health Organization [WHO] 2018a). Evidence of this has been obtained from long-term studies of health differences between sections of society in developed nations (WHO 2018a). Comparisons of health outcomes between nations have shown that although baseline improvements in life expectancy, infant mortality and death from childhood injury have occurred in countries such as the United Kingdom (UK), Australia, New Zealand and the United States (US), there are marked differences in health status between individuals in these countries, as well as marked differences between countries (Australian Institute of Health and Welfare 2020a; Pickett & Wilkinson 2015).

These differences appear to be the result of life chances and the kind of social institutions and welfare policies a country has and how these policies are actioned. For example, in Scandinavian countries, while the gains in health have mirrored those in the UK, Australia, New Zealand and the US, the population as a whole has made further health gains as the percentage of people on low incomes is lower than in English-speaking countries. This is best explained through the kinds of social policies in Scandinavia. For example, OECD data shows that for 2020, infant mortality (deaths per 1,000 live births) in the US was 5.7, the UK (3.7), New Zealand (4.7), Australia (3.3) Sweden (2.1) and Norway (2.0) (Organisation of Economic Co-operation and Development 2021). One hypothesis is that despite high taxation and a lucrative welfare state, citizens have a high level of trust in government, which means there is little free-riding and a strong sense of wellbeing (Holmberg 2020; Svendsen & Svendsen 2014).

The social model of health and the social determinants of health

There are two major components to a social model of health. First, health and illness are seen to be partly attributed to the social circumstances of individuals and populations. These social circumstances include their level of income in absolute terms and relative to other people in the population—hence the policy term 'Closing the gap'—in their education, employment, gender, culture and status. Epidemiological evidence provides clear proof of differences in health status between individuals based on these factors. For instance, research on the **social gradient** (one of the social determinants of health) explains how the perception of one's social position can be a predeterminant of a chronic stress response that may create long-term physical and psychological illness (Mirowsky & Ross 2017).

The second aspect of the social model of health suggests that the health of individuals and populations is influenced by the social, economic, political and welfare policies of a country. This includes policies covering taxation, welfare payments eligibility, public services such as health and education, and employment opportunities. A **social model of health** means governments need to focus on policy at all levels, not just health. This is referred to as intersectorial collaboration across policy portfolios or a 'whole-of-government approach', or 'health in all policies' (Australian Institute of Health and Welfare 2020a; WHO 2022).

Figure 6.1 illustrates the complex and multifaceted view of health portrayed by the social view of health. It incorporates the social, cultural, community, familial and economic circumstances that influence and determine health status.

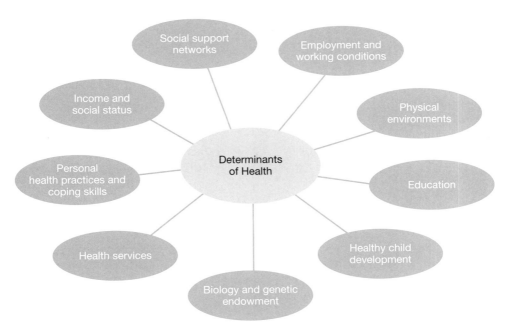

Figure 6.1 Social view of health Source: Government of Canada 2013

THE IMPLICATIONS OF THE SOCIAL MODEL

The implications of taking a social model approach to health means that rather than focusing solely on the individual's behaviour or their biological or genetic attributes, the focus shifts onto the attributes of society such as the level of wealth, differences in income, poverty and government policies dealing with these inequalities. This differs from the biomedical model, which defines illness as a condition of the individual who may now have a disease or injury. It also differs from the biopsychological or **behavioural model of health**, which suggests many illnesses result from the interaction between physical factors and the behaviour of individuals, with the responsibility for treatment resting solely with the individual. The case study below outlines some of the social factors that have an impact on health status for disadvantaged people.

CASE STUDY: INDIGENOUS RENAL DISEASE

Thelma is a senior artist living in one of the communities on the Anangu Pitjantjatjara Yankunytjatjara Lands in the north of South Australia. She has renal disease. Her older sister, who also had renal disease, had to relocate to Adelaide when she needed dialysis. This was very difficult for her and the family. Thelma will be able to stay in her community because in 2018 the federal government announced funding for dialysis in remote communities and this is being managed by the Purple House (Davidson 2018). Thelma is one of the key artists in the Anangu Pitjantjatjara Yankunytjatjara Lands, so being able to stay in her community means she can continue to paint. It will also allow her to supplement her pension and feed her five grandchildren. The art centre will not lose a valuable artist who contributes to the painting of country and to the centre's profits.

The high rates of renal disease among Aboriginal people is concerning. We could say that Thelma has not taken proper care of her diet, and has been too sedentary, or that as an Aboriginal person she has a genetic propensity to renal failure (Kowal & Anderson 2012). This form of blaming the person does not address other underlying causes of ill health.

The social model would assert that the cost of food in remote communities is high, and the availability of fresh fruit and vegetables erratic, leading Thelma to eat food with a high fat, sugar and carbohydrate content (dense highly calorific foods store for longer and travel better). It should also be pointed out that Thelma lives in a house with 10 other people and does not have a fridge (too expensive and the fluctuating electricity supply damages electrical equipment) or functioning stove. In the past the store at her community was not well stocked, and prices were high given the poor roads and long distance travelled. However, more recently, the community has signed up to the Mai Wiru service, so she and her family now have access to fresh fruit and vegetables.

Despite this Thelma is geographically disadvantaged and does not have the same life chances as someone living in the city close to shops and cheap supermarkets.

The solution lies in the community devising strategies to help people buy whitegoods but also in government policy legislating equal access to healthy food options and employment.

■ Note recent government policy that has extended Medicare rebates for dialysis. This will enable Thelma to stay in her community, continue to paint and support her grandchildren.

■ Mai Wiru is an Aboriginal community-controlled organisation that argues it supports a social model of health. If you would like to know more about the issue of healthy food in remote communities, try this web page for an understanding of intersectorial policy: www.maiwiru.org.au/home.

■ If you were the remote area health professional in this community, what would you see as essential care for Thelma?

A SOCIAL MODEL OF HEALTH IDENTIFIES THE SOCIAL DETERMINANTS OF HEALTH

The factors that make up the social model of health are known as the **social determinants of health** (SDH) (WHO 2022). These SDH explain the differences in health outcomes between individuals and populations. Each social determinant of health describes a set of circumstances that influences a particular health outcome. The SDH listed in Figure 6.2 were developed 30 years ago by Dahlgren and Whitehead

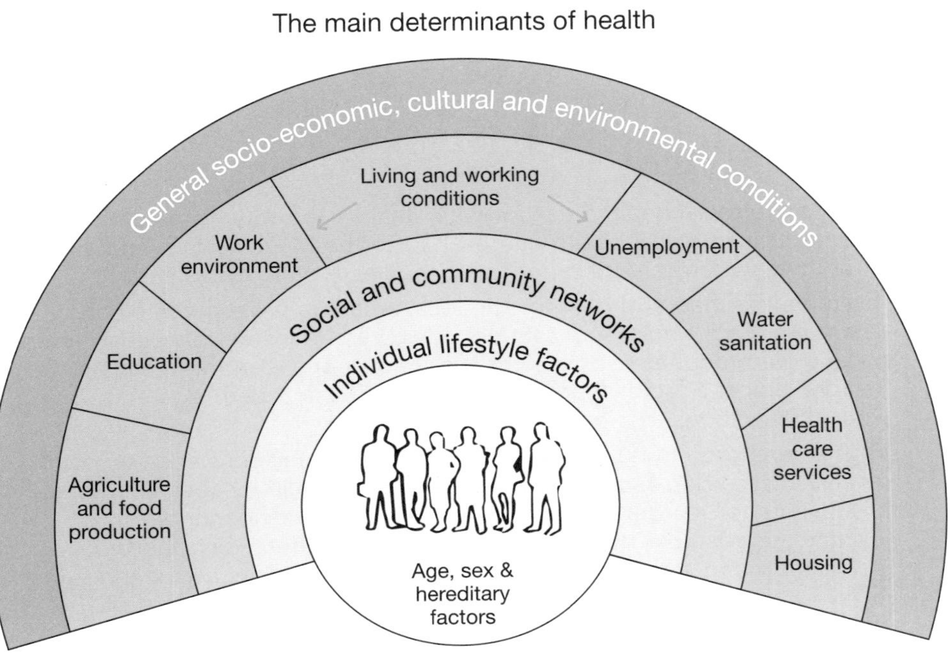

The main determinants of health

Figure 6.2 The social determinants of health

(1991). In their model, there are four layers of influence: individual lifestyle factors followed by three layers of social determinants. The first or outer layer includes the socioeconomic, cultural and environmental conditions; the second layer includes agriculture and food production, education, the work environment, unemployment, sanitation and water supplies, healthcare services and housing. Dahlgren and Whitehead add a third layer that suggests social networks also affect health outcomes. It is not until the fourth layer that the individual and their behaviours are listed. This diagram is not simply a listing of features in a society. The authors suggest that the outer layers determine the health of its members and that each layer shapes the next inner layer, including behaviour.

These two authors have published a recent paper reminding us that the model encompasses whole-of-population SDH (Dahlgren & Whitehead 2021). They suggest one way of dealing with inequality is to employ the framework provided by Diderichsen and colleagues (2001). This framework examines four mechanisms of inequality: differences in power and access to resources; exposure to risks; vulnerability; and differences in the consequences of being sick (Dahlgren & Whitehead 2021). For example, they cite research that shows differences in the impact of COVID-19 on various populations. The worldwide lockdowns and regulations governing COVID-19 were at the population level, so everyone had to abide by them. However, socioeconomic and ethnic status made a difference to the outcomes across the world. For example, in the UK many people from low socioeconomic or ethnic groups had greater exposure to the virus because they were in service jobs that prevented them from working at home, or the industry they were in closed down. So, the risk level was higher for them. They also experienced more complications because of pre-existing comorbidities or compromised immune systems.

Student activity
Australian students

1. Access the social health atlas for your state or territory (https://phidu. torrens.edu.au/social-health-atlases). Go to the Maps section and click on your state or territory for quintiles of socioeconomic status.

2. Examine the map and data for the local area you have chosen. For example, the SA map and data provides a comparison between different local government areas. Note the differences between the areas on two factors. Select a factor that highlights the SDH and be prepared to bring your observations to a tutorial.

3. Pick an area from the Quintiles link (https://phidu.torrens.edu.au/social-health-atlases/data#social-health-atlases-of-australia-by-socioeconomic-disadvantage-of-area) and compare the levels of socioeconomic disadvantage across two SDH from the spreadsheet. Bring these comparisons to class. Discuss why there are differences across the same SDH. Explore together in class the impact of the SDH on mental wellbeing.

1. Prior to your class, go to the Health Quality dashboard (https://www.hqsc. govt.nz/our-programmes/health-quality-evaluation/projects/quality-dashboards/dashboard-of-health-system-quality/he). Examine the various determinants of health. Be prepared to come to class with information on these determinants.

The history and formation of the social determinants of health

The acknowledgment of the importance of the social model of health was demonstrated with the formation of the World Health Organization in 1948. The WHO constitution clearly outlined the need for a whole-of-government approach to health. Unfortunately, in the following 30 years governments around the world pursued a technologically driven model of health that only addressed the downstream, curative approaches of health (Solar & Irwin 2007), failing to direct health policy towards the upstream determinants of health (sometimes referred to as structural determinants). The term 'structural' is used here to make the point that the problem lies in the organisation of a society or group, not in individual behaviour. Other authors use the term 'upstream', or may make a distinction between the structural or upstream factors, such as gender or culture, and those factors that are amenable to policy change, such as free and universal health care (WHO 2022).

The 1978 Alma-Ata Declaration on primary health care and the 'health for all' movement attempted to revive action on the SDH through promoting a social model of health. While many governments in principle embrace the 'health for all' concepts and acknowledged the importance of incorporating a broader view of health that addressed aspects such as the effects of housing, education and employment on health (Solar & Irwin 2007), in the late 1970s neoliberal economic policies gained favour, making these policies difficult to implement. Neoliberal policies encourage governments to reduce public spending on health, housing, employment and other welfare services, turning away from a social model (Lal et al. 2021). This quickened during the global financial crisis so that neoliberal policies were almost universal throughout the Western world (McManus 2016).

However, work defining and refining the social model and the SDH continued. In 2003, WHO created the Commission on Social Determinants of Health (CSDH) (Kelly et al. 2006). The CSDH delivered its final report in 2008, which placed the SDH firmly on the policy and research agenda (WHO 2022). Two subsequent developments since the CSDH have been the Millennium Development Goals promoted by the United Nations and the more recent 2030 Agenda for Sustainable Development (United Nations 2022). Many of these policy proposals use the framework of Closing the Gap. Here in Australia, governments also use this term (CSDH 2008, 2018). The phrase recognises that poor health outcomes are not just about poverty but the gap between the rich and the poor.

A recent editorial reviewed what had been achieved by Australian governments in addressing the SDH, suggesting there had been little progress except in access to healthcare services. Social housing, education and services have languished over the past decade. The exception to this was policy in Indigenous affairs. The authors make the point that policy does not necessarily lead to success (Smith et al. 2018). For example, in Australia, mortality from all causes in the lowest socioeconomic suburbs was 615 per 100,000 population, while the second group was 554, the third group, 494, and the fourth 405. This last group is from suburbs with the highest incomes (Australian Institute of Health and Welfare 2020b).

Why support a social model of health? The social justice argument and the implications for government policy

HEALTH AS A HUMAN RIGHT

As health professionals and as a society it is important to qualify our notions of health and the availability of health services. One way of achieving this is through defining and understanding health as a core value or human right. The idea of health as a core value is espoused in the notion of health as a human right, as this places health as a 'right for all' (WHO 2017). If health is a right for all humans, then it falls outside the individual to solely provide for it and becomes a joint responsibility of the individual and the government to provide (WHO 2011). By viewing health as a human right, it enables governments to legislate to protect those rights and enables service providers to broaden the constructs of health to be inclusive of social conditions such as housing and education. This is the policy work of governments. It needs to be across all portfolios or intersectorial.

HEALTH AS A RIGHT ENSURES EQUITY

Where health is a human right, health services are provided regardless of people's socioeconomic position, gender, educational level, ethnicity or religion (WHO 2018b). To charge people for health services is to charge them for something that is regarded as a right. Unfortunately, in many countries where health care is not free, factors such as socioeconomic position determine the level of health that can be enjoyed by an individual (Rak & Coffin 2013).

Theoretical models for understanding the social determinants of health

If morbidity and mortality rates for a population are a result of social conditions, it is important to identify what these SDH are and to introduce policies that will reduce the impact. One approach is to examine each SDH for how it impacts on health status and to make recommendations for the kind of social policy required to eliminate the negative effects (WHO 2022). A number of social epidemiologists have taken this

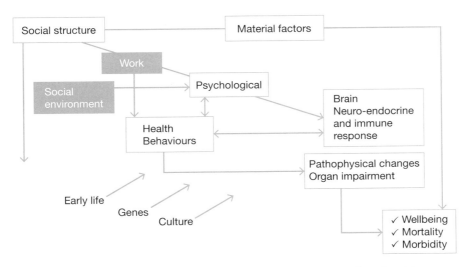

Figure 6.3 Biopsychosocial approach to understanding health

approach by identifying a range of social determinants that appear to be correlated with higher rates of morbidity and mortality for specific population groups.

Drawing on the work of these theorists, the CSDH has developed a model that integrates the social with the psychological model to form an explanatory psychosocial model. This model argues that there is a pathway or conduit between social factors in any society and the individual, their behaviour and mental states that influence health. Figure 6.3 provides a diagram of this overlap. The biopsychosocial model can be examined by looking at the social context. This is divided into two components: the socioeconomic and political context of any given society, and those factors that might be improved by governments taking a 'health in all' approach to reduce inequity. The psychological section indicates how individuals respond to healthy public policy and other social conditions in their lives. The model does not deny genetic or physical responses to illness and disease. What it does argue is that given there are clear differences in health status and outcomes between groups, the appropriate response is to introduce policies that 'close the gap' (Australian Institute of Health and Welfare 2020a).

THE SOCIAL CONTEXT

The first factor affecting the SDH is the social context of a society. From Figure 6.3 you can see that it captures some of the factors already identified as part of the upstream SDH: socioeconomic status, education and gender. What is missing from the diagram is the policy and actions required to ensure all citizens have access to education, health care, transport and employment, and do not suffer from any form of discrimination. Policies include those dealing with welfare issues such as access to housing, disability, old age and sickness benefits, and those that cover issues such as access to education, the provision of health care, anti-discrimination and affordable utilities such as power, water and communications; all these policies go some way towards achieving a reduction in inequality.

The kinds of policies a particular government puts in place will be very much influenced by its politics, values or beliefs. For example, where the political party in power believes health or education are human rights, these services will be provided free or at a cost that all can afford. When governments provide these services, this is referred to as the welfare state. Underpinning the welfare state is the idea that it is the responsibility of government to provide for its citizens' social insurance against hardship, poverty, illness or misfortune (Hall 2016). The role of the welfare state is to redistribute the resources within a society from rich to poor so that no one is destitute. This is usually done through taxation policies whereby everyone (rich and poor) subsidises those in need. The type and range of welfare provided by countries differs. A classic example is in health care. Some countries provide free, universal health care to all citizens; others have healthcare systems where patients must pay for the service, while elsewhere access to health services may be means tested or based on income (WHO 2022).

The health impact of such policies is illustrated in the differences in mortality rates between the UK (free universal health care to all), the US (private system with access to free health care means tested in its extension to the poor and elderly and the recent Affordable Care Act, which did not deliver as promised (Himmelstein et al. 2019), and Australia with a mixed public–private system (Rak & Coffin 2013). In 2019 the life expectancy for males in Australia was 81.2, in the UK it was 79.0 and in the US it was 76.3 (Australian Bureau of Statistics 2022a). These differences, while not stark, are explained partly as a result of healthcare policy where access to care is free in Australia and the UK but not so in the US (Organisation of Economic Co-operation and Development 2021).

Social context: upstream social determinants and downstream policies and actions

Factors that are upstream SDH are those that generate or reinforce social divisions, power and status differences in a society, and as a result affect people's life chances (Pickett & Wilkinson 2015). The key to understanding these factors lies in the concept of social stratification (Solar & Irwin 2007). Social stratification is the division created in a society between different groups. It can be based on income, gender, ethnicity, sexual preference, education or occupation. These factors describe one's social position in a society (Solar & Irwin 2007). Forms of social stratification differ between social and cultural groups but in all cases impact either positively or negatively on a person's access to resources, education, employment and, ultimately, health. At times they may interact to advantage or disadvantage individual life chances. This is referred to as intersectionality, not to be confused with intersectoral collaboration (Fisher et al. 2017).

In Australia these differences can be measured using a variety of tools. For example, every 5 years at the time of the national census four indexes are used to rank the population. These are collectively referred to as the Socio-Economic Indexes for Areas (SEIFA). This index measures social disadvantage by geographical area and includes income, housing, level of education, access to private health insurance, unemployment and whether or not jobs are skilled or unskilled. Once the data is collected, the population is then divided into five equal groups called quintiles according to their disadvantage. The measure is for the whole geographical area, not necessarily individuals within the area (Australian Bureau of Statistics 2022b). The other three measures used in the census are the Index of Relative Socio-Economic Advantage and Disadvantage (IRSAD), the Index of Education and Occupation (IEO) and the Index of Economic Resources (IER). Another measure epidemiologists look for is the gap between the most advantaged quintile and the least advantaged quintile. This gap is called the social gradient—it is like a sloping line going from those who are well-off to those who are socially and economically disadvantaged (Fisher et al. 2016).

Student activity

The two web addresses below provide information on various measures used in Australia and New Zealand to rank the population according to disadvantage and advantage. Look up the measures for both countries and make a list of these, then bring them to class. Be prepared to discuss what variables in both these scales might contribute to poor health outcomes.

- https://www.abs.gov.au/ausstats/abs@.nsf/Lookup/by%20Subject/2033.0. 55.001~2016~Main%20Features~SOCIO-ECONOMIC%20INDEXES%20 FOR%20AREAS%20(SEIFA)%202016~1

- www.ehinz.ac.nz/indicators/population-information/socioeconomic- deprivation-profile/

The difficulty with using a measure such as the IRSD is that while it does tell us that differences in socioeconomic status *affect* health, it does not tell us how or why. Understanding the SDH requires more than identification—the pathway between each determinant and illness must also be understood or, if not completely understood, explored. This requires evidence. This is discussed below illustrating the evidence between the social determinant and health outcomes, then pointing to possible intersectorial policy directions. The first is income.

Income

Income is the measure of the amount of money available to individuals and families to buy the material assets necessary for life. These include food, health care, shelter (housing), employment and any other assets considered essential in that society. It is a commonly used indicator of socioeconomic position. Income has a direct positive relationship with health; as income improves, health improves. Correspondingly, if income decreases, health decreases (Australian Institute of Health and Welfare 2020a). Income determines the amount of material wealth available to an individual or a family, as well as access to health care. It enables access to good food and determines the resources available to the children within the family. Adult health outcomes begin in childhood so that income and health have a cumulative effect over the lifespan. The relationship between income and health status in Australia is evident across a number of chronic diseases. Table 6.1 shows the proportion of individuals in the most disadvantaged quintile have higher rates of chronic conditions and comorbidities. Policy around pensions, welfare benefits, superannuation, taxation and free health care are all ways in which governments seek to manage (or not) income inequality.

Table 6.1

PROPORTION OF INDIVIDUALS PER QUINTILE WITH CHRONIC CONDITION

Quintile	Arthritis	Asthma	Back problems	Cancer	Chronic obstructive pulmonary disease	Diabetes	Hayfever and allergic rhinitis	Heart, stroke and vascular disease	Hypertension	Kidney
1st	19.0	13.3	18.7	2.4	3.8	7.4	18.6	6.0	13.4	1.3
2nd	17.3	12.3	17.8	2.1	3.0	5.8	18.1	5.9	12.6	1.0
3rd	14.0	9.6	16.3	1.6	2.1	4.0	19.1	3.9	9.4	0.9
4th	14.1	11.0	15.8	1.7	1.9	4.2	20.6	4.4	9.1	0.9
5th	11.4	10.0	13.6	1.3	1.9	3.4	20.1	3.9	9.0	0.9

Social class

Social class is closely related to income. One of the most intriguing findings related to social class has been the impact of the social gradient. This finding suggests that the steeper the income and social distance between people in a society, the wider the health gaps (Pickett & Wilkinson 2015). The impact of income differences is seen as one of the explanations for the poor health status of Aboriginal and Torres Strait Islander peoples in Australia. The income of Aboriginal people is higher than population groups in many underdeveloped countries, yet their mortality rates are higher. One explanation is that while Indigenous people are not as poor as some population groups in Africa or Asia, the difference in socioeconomic status between Indigenous and non-Indigenous Australians is significant and a factor in explaining their poor health (CSDH 2008, 2018). The link here may be one of comparison and it is through comparison that stress levels are affected and ill health results. In both Australia and New Zealand, governments have moved to introduce policies that attempt to close the gap between Indigenous people and Māori nations, and policies that legislate against discrimination based on race, culture, religion or sexual preferences also support 'Closing the gap'.

Education

Formal education is a reflection of both a child's and parents' circumstances. The kind of education a person achieves is determined by their parents' social position, values and income. It is also determined by the social policies of the country. Where education is provided free, people have the opportunity to gain an education independent of parental income or values; where it is costly, their education will be determined by their parents' wealth or opinion about the value of education. Education as a variable of health status is a combination of both the baseline education (received during childhood and a result of the socioeconomic position of parents) and future education (one's own socioeconomic position) as an adult (Solar & Irwin 2007). It also influences occupational and employment outcomes, further impacting on access to health care and health resources as an adult. Education also enhances a person's capacity to make healthy life choices because it exposes the adult to an array of health resources and services (Australian Institute of Health and Welfare 2020a). Free education is one policy response to this SDH. You can probably also see the relationship between education and status!

Occupation

Occupation is the type of work performed by an individual. It is an indicator of the amount of exposure to risk, social standing, income and level of education (Australian Institute of Health and Welfare 2020a). Categorising people by occupation is a powerful predictor of inequalities in morbidity and mortality, especially workplace injury. Occupation also reflects one's social standing or value in a society and may result in access to privileges such as: better education, health care and nutrition; housing and community support. Occupation may also provide the person with beneficial social networks and control over their work. There is considerable research that suggests control over one's work reduces stress and impacts directly on health (Benach et al. 2015). For example, the increase in workplace flexibility, while positive for some (university students), may not be for others. Research by Benach and colleagues (2015) explored the way workers whose contracts are casualised have higher rates of illness. This would appear to be best explained by their lack of security and power in the workplace. This lack of power appears to affect stress levels leading, for example, to higher rates of illness, possibly the result of stress on their immune system (Prathr et al. 2017). Industrial relations policies around employment are an area of intersectorial health policy.

Critical thinking

The complexity of the SDH and the way they intersect is neatly outlined in a case study by Hobbs and colleagues (2020). Their interest was in the relationship between area of deprivation, fluoridisation and the rate of children requiring hospitalisation for dental care in New Zealand where primary dental care is free. They examined children aged 0–4 and 5–12 years with increased dental disease that required hospitalisation and found that those children from the most deprived areas where there was no fluoride in the water had higher rates than children from other areas. Not all districts had fluoride across the entire period under study, making for further differences. While there was an association between dental health and fluoridisation across all districts, the impact of this public health measure was greatest for 0–4-year-olds in the most deprived areas where fluoride has been part of public health measures for at least 20 years.

There are a range of variables to consider here: socioeconomic status and deprivation; the age of the population under examination; and a particular public health measure that in this case has historically been controversial.

Student activity

You can gain insight into differential access to fluoride in the water supply in Australia and New Zealand by examining the maps on the following site:

■ https://www.adelaide.edu.au/arcpoh/dperu/fluoride/atlas.html#F1997

1. Put the cursor over a state or region and establish if the water is treated with fluoride.
2. Identify regions or districts in your state or island that do not have access to fluoride in the water.
3. Go back to the Social Health Atlas or the Atlas for New Zealand and find out other social facts about these districts or regions.

Gender

All around the world women have less access to resources such as health (female infanticide, genital mutilation, deliberate female underfeeding), income (economic dependency, lack of well-remunerated and secure employment or active discrimination in employment), education (nil or limited access to education) and housing (inability to inherit or secure housing without male support), and this has implications for the quality-of-life experience and health status (Solar & Irwin 2007). However, in Australia and New Zealand women have lower rates of mortality (they live longer) but higher rates of morbidity (they appear to be sicker), so the solutions are not clear-cut. For example, in New Zealand the life expectancy for a male is 79.5 years but increases to 83.5 years for women (Stats NZ 2022). Social stratification based on gender can be addressed by governments through policy that legislates against gendered discrimination and moves to change cultural attitudes.

Ethnicity

The active exclusion of particular groups due to their race/ethnicity has consequences for both psychological and physical health and is a result of discrimination. Discrimination also impacts on access to income and stable employment. For example, the life expectancy of First Nations Australians is currently 71.6 years for males and 75.6 for females, while for non–First Nations Australians it is 80.2 and 83.4 years respectively (Australian Institute of Health and Welfare 2020a). As discrimination is a structurally defined social and cultural concept, research and policy directives are hard to determine due to the intertwining nature with other aspects of stratification such as education, housing, health, employment and income. For example, the statistics noted about gender differences in life expectancy need to be changed to accommodate ethnicity. In New Zealand, life expectancy for Māori males is 73.4 years and 77.1 years for females; for non-Māoris, life expectancy at birth reached 80.9 years for males and 84.4 years for females in 2017–19 (Stats NZ 2018).

SOCIAL DETERMINANTS OF HEALTH AND THE EVIDENCE

Earlier we noted that the CSDH (2018) seeks evidence on the relationship between socioeconomic status and health outcomes, and while there is certainly a correlation between health status, mortality and morbidity and income, occupation, education, race and gender, it is not clear what the pathway is from the social determinant to the illness or disease. And though it might seem self-evident that the way forward is for healthy public policy, not all experts agree with the actions outlined by the CSDH that called for universal health coverage for all citizens, strong labour laws that protect workers or the implementation of sound management strategies for environmental chemicals and waste (Preda & Voigt 2015).

Understanding how it is that low income or discrimination based on gender or ethnicity leads to higher mortality or morbidity is difficult to explain, but several theories have been proposed. These include explorations of the impact of the human *fight or flight* responses on hormonal levels, metabolic rates or endocrine transmitters. The argument suggests that people in low socioeconomic groups are overloaded with psychological fight or flight demands (Lal et al. 2021).

Another theory draws on models of polygenetics and is referred to as polysocial. The authors of this approach suggest that just as scientists have not been able to separate what gene in particular predisposes an individual to a disease such as heart disease, so too, it is difficult to identify one social determent, such as poor education, as contributing to a person's chronic disease. However, in the field of polygenetics there are developments in constructing tools that would give a score to the contribution a particular gene makes to an illness condition. Figueroa and colleagues suggest the same process could be used to calculate the impact of specific social determinants on the health of an individual or a population. Their argument is that if this could be achieved it would provide more precise data on the necessary social policy, as well as the capacity to test out policy reform. They suggest that access to big data now makes this possible (Figueroa et al. 2020). This is an intriguing area to watch over the next decade.

Research focus

Source: Parry et al. 2016

A key concern of the CSDH (2008) is to ensure there is evidence in support of policies and health promotion programs to address the SDH (Lal et al. 2021). The following case study is based on these ideas.

Postnatal depression can severely affect parental–child attachment and child development, influencing the child's health, education and welfare outcomes across their lifespan (Parry et al. 2016). Evaluation research conducted by Parry and colleagues (2016) for the Communities for Children program found that for those families accessing the services the setting, income and the linkage to community influenced the uptake of the programs. Also, the program provided was based on theoretically sound evidence that directly addressed postnatal depression and assisted parents with attachment. The researchers interviewed 30 staff and parents and conducted a pre- and post-survey with 233 participants. The analysis found a positive correlation between attending the program and the post-program depression score using the Edinburgh Postnatal Depression Scale, with a strong relationship between the two variables ($r = 0.582$). Further to this, the number of times the women attended the program, their levels of depression decreased. The relationship between the two variables accounted for 33% of the variance between attendance and depression. The qualitative responses supported the statistical findings that the program was of benefit to those participating. The following quotes from parents (P) and staff (S) capture the broader aspects of therapeutic interventions.

- The cost [to the healthcare system, community and individuals] of untreated perinatal depression is just immense ... there's an overwhelming amount of research on the detrimental effects of untreated perinatal depression and anxiety on the mothers, fathers, and children ... going on to late adolescence and adulthood and then the trans-generational effects ... are enormous and costly to the community and society. This program helps, it saves money in the long term as all these problems caused by depression and anxiety can be addressed early on. (S5)

- The groups have given me the confidence to reach out and join other groups and return to study and work ... it was hard for us financially with the depression impacting on just everything ... my confidence to study ... and get a better job, and returning to work. (P18)

The quotations from staff and parents involved in this community-based program clearly recognised the outcomes for the mothers, infants and children. In many instances, the mothers believed that the Communities for Children program, had instilled the confidence and support required by them to assist not only with parenting but also in other aspects of their lives. As the SDH affects a broad range of lived experiences and health outcomes, such as income and education, this program changed aspects of the SDH as well as addressing the needs of mothers with postnatal depression. This research illustrated that there are many factors that affect treatment, access and care that are often outside the individual and acute care or biomedical setting.

Critical questions

1. Using two columns, list the social and biomedical aspects of care outlined in this case study.
2. If the rate and severity of postnatal depression decreased through the social program, does this mean depression is a purely social disease?
3. The first quote in this case study makes mention of 'trans-generational effects'. What do you think is meant by this term, and how might it operate?

SOCIAL DETERMINANTS OF HEALTH: BRINGING IN THE PSYCHOLOGICAL

Further objections to the SDH model come from a fundamental weakness in the CSDH argument; it takes little account of individual agency. Individual agency forms the third part of the biopsychosocial model of health outlined in Figure 6.3. This includes individual behaviour, decision-making, attitudes and responses to broader public policy as well as health programs. While not the subject of this chapter, it is acknowledged that there is a pathway, although it is poorly understood. While there does appear to be a cultural factor whereby poorer people are more likely to smoke, be physically inactive or have a poor diet, it would appear that there is also a stress factor associated with other aspects of their living conditions. For example, smoking may be a response to stress, and a diet high in saturated fats may lead to higher rates of heart disease. It is also possible; however, that stress linked to a social issue such as unemployment may activate the hormonal system, leading to high blood pressure (Brunner & Marmot 2006). There is now significant research in this area, but the difficulty for social policymakers is in understanding and accepting the science (Tawakol et al. 2019). Not an easy task in this era of fake news.

Chapter summary

The social model broadens the view of health beyond both the biomedical model and the biopsychological model to examine the influences on health that are determined by social circumstances. The social aspects of health have formed the basis of the SDH. The chapter argued that the social model of health suggests health is a human right, and the responsibility for providing the determinants of health sits with governments as well as individuals.

In the second section of the chapter the SDH, such as education, income, gender, ethnicity and social class, were outlined. These SDH can be directly influenced by the social and political environments and institutions within society; they can be addressed by changes to policy in the areas of health, education, housing and so on but also by health promotion programs and activities. This is where health professionals can make a difference. The CSDH response has been to: (1) identify the social determinant; (2) encourage governments to apply relevant policy across various sectors; and (3) support and fund health promotion behavioural action. Importantly, the social determinants present health professionals with a dilemma. Having diagnosed, treated and cured the illness or disease, health professionals know that in many instances they discharge the clients back into the same illness-producing social system, such as when a homeless person with mental health issues is discharged back onto the streets. Consequently, health professionals need to be social reformers! This is a difficult ask.

KEY POINTS

- The physical health of individuals is often thought to be the result of physical and psychological factors; however, mortality and morbidity rates appear to also be caused by social factors.

- These social factors are referred to as the 'social determinants of health'.

- Social epidemiologists and social theorists attempt to explain how the SDH translate to health or illness and disease for individuals and populations.

- While the evidence is clear that mortality and morbidity rates are influenced by social factors, there is considerable debate on how these social determinants affect the psychological health or behaviour of individuals or cause physical illness, although research has made significant progress in this area, partly through access to big data.

Student activity

Complete the following in small groups.

1. Using the social health atlas make a list of the SDH that affect people in your city, town or region. There is a clear relationship between poverty, gender, ethnicity and morbidity and mortality rates. Could it be argued that there are cultural practices that contribute to poorer health outcomes and cultural practices that are responses to these factors? Discuss.

2. If so, identify illness-producing behaviours and identify whether they arise from the culture or structure of a society.

3. In your view, is the position you take on these issues also linked to your political beliefs?

Cont... ▶

4. In this chapter we have suggested that the social determinants rather than individual behaviours explain many differences in mortality and morbidity rates for population groups. How does this explanation differ from a cultural explanation?
5. If you were Minister for Health, how might you go about reducing mortality and morbidity rates for people living in rural and remote regions? In your answer, consider the situation for a specific population group such as men, youth, families, Māori or Aboriginal and Torres Strait Islander peoples.

Further reading

Marmot, M., 2017. The health gap: the challenge of an unequal world. International Journal of Epidemiology 46, RN4Cast. Available: https://doi.org/10.1093/ije/dyx163.

Tawakol, A., Osborne, M. T., Wang, Y., et al. (2019). Stress-associated neurobiological pathway linking socioeconomic disparities to cardiovascular disease. Journal of the American College of Cardiology, 73(25), 3243–3255.

Weblinks

All students

World Health Organization Report into Health Inequities

https://www.who.int/teams/control-of-neglected-tropical-diseases/overview/ntds-and-covid-19

In the light of the focus on COVID-19 you might like to take a look at the neglected tropical diseases campaign and how it affects low-income nations.

World Health Organization statistics

https://www.who.int/news/item/20-05-2022-world-health-statistics-2022

This report presents the statistics from 193 states on health care within nations covering material wealth, preventable diseases, mortality rates and health trends.

Australian students

The Social Atlas

https://phidu.torrens.edu.au/social-health-atlases

This report describes the social aspects of Australia and provides information collected over several years outlining the disparities between population groups within Australia.

New Zealand students

StatsNZ

https://www.stats.govt.nz/

This webpage provides data on education, occupation, labour market, standard of living, trust and participation in government for New Zealand.

The Social Report

www.msd.govt.nz/about-msd-and-our-work/publications-resources/monitoring/social-report/index.html

This webpage features the health section of The Social Report, outlining the disparities and deprivation that occurs between people within New Zealand. It includes information such as avoidable deaths, levels of education and other factors that determine a person's wellbeing and health.

Socioeconomic Deprivation Indexes: NZDep and NZiDep, Department of Public Health

www.otago.ac.nz/wellington/departments/publichealth/research/hirp/otago020194.html

This webpage provides a number of interactive maps on socioeconomic deprivation indexes.

References

Australian Bureau of Statistics. (2022a). Life Tables, Statistics about life tables for Australia, states and territories and life expectancy at birth estimates for sub-state regions 2018-2020. Available at: https://www.abs.gov.au/statistics/people/population/life-tables/2018-2020

Australian Bureau of Statistics. (2022b). SEIFA—Using and interpreting SEIFA. Available at: https://www.abs.gov.au/websitedbs/censushome.nsf/home/seifahelpansuis?opendocument&navpos=260:

Australian Institute of Health and Welfare. (2020a). Australia's health 2020: in brief. Available at: https://www.aihw.gov.au/reports/australias-health/australias-health-2020-in-brief/contents/summary

Australian Institute of Health and Welfare. (2020b). Health across socioeconomic groups. Available at: https://www.aihw.gov.au/reports/australias-health/health-across-socioeconomic-groups

Benach, J., Vives, A., Amable, M., et al., (2015). Precarious employment: understanding an emerging social determinants of health. Annual Review of Public Health, 34, 229–253.

Brunner, E., Marmot, M., (2006). Social organization, stress and health. In M. Marmot, Wilkinson, R. (Eds), Social determinants of health. Oxford: Oxford University Press.

Commission on Social Determinants of Health (CSDH). (2008). Closing the Gap in a Generation: Health equity through action on the social determinants of health. Available at: http://www.who.int/social_determinants/thecommission/finalreport/en/

Commission on Social Determinants of Health (CSDH). (2018). Closing the Gap in a Generation. How? Available at: http://www.who.int/social_determinants/thecommission/finalreport/closethegap_how/en/index2.html

Dahlgren, G., Whitehead, M., (1991). Policies and Strategies to Promote Social Equity in Health. Stockholm, Sweden: Institute for Futures Studies.

Dahlgren, G., Whitehead, M., (2021). The Dahlgren-Whitehead model of health determinants: 30 years on and still chasing rainbows. Public Health, 199, 20–24.

Davidson, H., (2018). Medicare change to give greater access to remote Indigenous Australians. Available at: https://www.theguardian.com/australia-news/2018/apr/30/medicare-change-to-give-greater-dialysis-access-to-remote-indigenous-australians:

Diderichsen, F., Evans, T., Whitehead, M. (2001). The social basis of disparities in health. In: T. Evans, M. Whitehead, F. Diderichsen, A. et al., (Eds.), Challenging Inequities in Health: From Ethics to Action. Oxford, UK: Oxford University Press.

Figueroa, J.F., Frakt, A.B., Jha, A.K. (2020). Addressing social determinants of health: time for a polysocial risk score. JAMA, 323(16), 1553–1554.

Fisher, M., Baum, R., MacDougal, C., et al., (2016). To what extent do Australian health policy documents address social determinants of health? Journal of Social Policy, 45(3), 545–564.

Fisher, M., Baum, F.E., MacDougal, C., Newman, L., et al., (2017). Intersectorial action on SDH and equity in Australian health policy. Health Promotion International, 32, 953–963.

Government of Canada, 2013. What makes Canadians healthy or unhealthy? Available at: www.canada.ca/en/public-health/services/health-promotion/population-health/what-determines-health/what-makes-canadians-healthy-unhealthy.html#secondreport

Hall, P. (2016). The future of the welfare state. In: P. Network, Ranft R (eds) Aiming High: Progressive Politics in a High-Risk, High-Opportunity Era. London: Rowman and Littlefield International.

Himmelstein, D.U., Lawless, R.M., Thorne, D., et al., (2019). Medical bankruptcy: still common despite the Affordable Care Act. American Journal of Public Health, 109(3), 431–433.

Hobbs, M., Wade, A., Jones, P., et al., (2020). Area-level deprivation, childhood dental ambulatory sensitive hospitalizations and community water fluoridation: evidence from New Zealand. International Journal of Epidemiology, 49(3), 908–916.

Holmberg, S. (2020). Social trust – The Nordic Gold? Working Papers 2020:1. Available at: https://gupea.ub.gu.se/handle/2077/63131

Kelly, M. P., Bonnefoy, J., Morgan, A., et al., (2006). The development of the evidence base about the social determinants of health. Geneva: World Health Organization, Commission on Social Determinants of Health, Measurement and Evidence Knowledge Network.

Kowal, E., & Anderson, I. (2012). Genetic Research in Aboriginal and Torres Strait Islander Communities: Continuing the Conversation. University of Melbourne. Available at: https://www.lowitja.org.au/sites/default/files/docs/Genetics%20report%20WEB%202.pdf

Lal, A., Erondu, N., Heymann, D., et al., (2021). Fragmented health systems in COVID-19: rectifying the misalignment between global health security and universal health coverage. Lancet, 397, 61–67.

McManus, I. (2016). The Re-politization of the Welfare State After the Global Financial Crisis. Northeastern University Boston, Massachusetts.

Mirowsky, J., & Ross, C. (2017). Social Causes of Psychological Distress. New York: Routledge.

Organisation of Economic Co-operation and Development. (2021). Health at a Glance 2021: OECD Indicators. Available at: https://doi.org/10.1787/ae3016b9-en:

Parry, Y., Grant, J., & Abbott, S. (2016). Communities for Children: Final Report: The Western Perinatal Support Group (WPSG) program in Western Adelaide. Flinders University, School of Nursing & Midwifery, for Communities for Children, Wesley Uniting Care Port Adelaide.

Pickett, K.E., & Wilkinson, R.G. (2015). Income inequality and health: a causal review. Social Science & Medicine, 128, 316–326.

Prathr, A., Janicki-Deverts, D., Adler, N., et al., (2017). Sleep habits and susceptability to upper respiratory illness: the moderating role of subjective socioeconomic status. Annals of Behavioral Medicine, 51(1), 137–146.

Preda, A., & Voigt, K. (2015). The social determinants of health: why should we care? The American Journal of Bioethics, 15(3), 25–36.

Rak, S., & Coffin, J. (2013). Affordable Care Act. Practice Management, March/April. Available at: https://www.researchgate.net/profile/Janis_Coffin/publication/239943452_Affordable_Care_Act/links/589b619a92851c942ddad86a/Affordable-Care-Act.pdf.

Smith, J., Griffiths, K., Judd, J., et al., (2018). Ten years on from the World Health Organization Commission of Social Determinants of Health: progress or procrastination? Health Promotion Journal of Australia. 29(1), 3–7.

Solar, O., & Irwin, A. (2007). A conceptual framework for action on the social determinants of health. Draft discussion paper for the Commission on Social Determinants of Health. Available at: http://www.google.com.au/url?sa=t&rct=j&q=&esrc=s&source=web&cd=1&ved=0ahUKEwiw6dSog53ZAhUQ5rwKHW8uAhkQFggsMAA&url=http%3A%2F%2Fwww.who.int%2Fsocial_determinants%2Fresources%2Fhealth_equity_isa_2008_en.pdf&usg=AOvVaw31R5LIfRF9q_HAvhsp9hjJ

Stats NZ Tatauranga Aotearoa (2018). Injury Statistics – work-related claims 2016. Available at: https://www.stats.govt.nz/information-releases/injury-statistics-work-related-claims-2016

Stats NZ Tatauranga Aotearoa (2022). Life expectancy. Available at: https://www.stats.govt.nz/topics/life-expectancy

Svendsen, G., & Svendsen, G.T. (2014). The puzzle of the Scandianvian welfare state and social trust. Issues in Social Science, 3(4), http://www.macrothink.org/journal/index.php/iss/article/viewFile/8597/6971.

Tawakol, A., Osborne, M.T., Wang, Y., et al., (2019). Stress-associated neurobiological pathway linking socioeconomic disparities to cardiovascular disease. Journal of the American College of Cardiology, 73(25), 3243–3255.

United Nations. (2022). Millennium Development Goals and Beyond 2015. Available at: https://www.un.org/millenniumgoals/

World Health Organization (WHO). (2011). Rio Political Declaration on Social Determinants of Health. Available at: http://www.who.int/sdhconference/declaration/en/

World Health Organization (WHO). (2017). Human rights and health. Available at: http://www.who.int/mediacentre/factsheets/fs323/en/

World Health Organization (WHO). (2018a). The Determinants of Health. Available at: http://www.who.int/hia/evidence/doh/en/

World Health Organization (WHO). (2018b). Universal health coverage and health financing. Available at: http://www.who.int/health_financing/universal_coverage_definition/en/

World Health Organization (WHO). (2022). Social Determinants of Health. Available at: https://www.who.int/health-topics/social-determinants-of-health#tab=tab_1

Chapter 7

Behaviour change

IVANKA PRICHARD

Learning objectives

The material in this chapter will help you to:

- describe and understand the dominant psychological approaches that aim to explain health behaviours, namely
  - » behavioural/learning theory
  - » cognitive theory
  - » cognitive behaviour models
  - » the health belief model
  - » the theory of planned behaviour
  - » the transtheoretical model of behaviour change
  - » the health action process approach
  - » motivational interviewing
  - » acceptance and commitment therapy
  - » the behaviour change wheel
- use the above theories and models to explain the initiation and the continuation of health-enhancing and health 'risk' behaviours
- use the above theories and models to modify health behaviours
- identify the limitations of psychological theories and models as predictors and moderators of health behaviours.

Cont... ▶

- Social cognitive theory (196)
- Behaviour change wheel (196)
- Behaviour change therapies (196)
- Motivational interviewing (197)
- Acceptance and commitment therapy (200)

Introduction

How healthy is your lifestyle? Do you regularly follow the health practices identified in Chapter 5 for nutrition, physical activity, cigarette smoking and alcohol consumption? Have you ever made a decision about one of these health behaviours but not continued with the activity as you intended—for example, to exercise regularly? Or perhaps you did follow through with your intention and maintained the activity. Why might there be different outcomes to these scenarios when your intention was the same in both? What other factors might influence the outcomes in these two scenarios?

Such questions underpin psychological health research and contribute to theories and models that can explain and predict a person's health-related behaviours. Also, psychological theories propose models of behaviour change and identify interventions that can change unhealthy behaviours. This chapter will examine a range of psychological approaches that propose explanations as to how internal (within the person) and external (within the environment) factors influence a person's health behaviours and lifestyle.

What are health-enhancing behaviours?

Health behaviours are actions that enhance, maintain or threaten a person's health. Health-enhancing behaviours are activities that a person practises or abstains from in order to maintain health or to reduce the risk of illness or accident. Health behaviours can be either positive or negative. Health-enhancing behaviours include practices such as: following a healthy diet and eating in moderation; not driving a car while under the influence of alcohol or drugs; keeping immunisations up to date; and regular health screening such as for dental health and breast or prostate cancer. When practised regularly (such as daily teeth brushing), a health behaviour is called a health *habit*, while clusters of health behaviours are referred to as *lifestyle*.

Why focus on health-enhancing behaviours?

Up until the mid-20th century, global public health threats were mainly from infectious and communicable diseases. However, in developed countries, a shift occurred over the past 100 years whereby the major health threats are now posed by non-communicable diseases in which lifestyle plays a role in the aetiology and/or management of illness (Australian Institute of Health and Welfare [AIHW] 2021; Frieden 2010). For example, the modifiable risk factors for coronary heart disease, a leading cause of disease burden, are tobacco smoking, high blood pressure, high cholesterol level, insufficient physical activity, overweight/obesity, poor nutrition and diabetes (AIHW 2021), all of which are linked to health behaviours and lifestyle.

Disease burden is measured by disability-adjusted life years (DALYs), which comprises years of life lost (YLLs) (mortality) and years lived with disability (YLDs) (morbidity). In Australia, New Zealand and other Western nations, the health conditions with the greatest disease burden (measured by DALYs and YLDs) are cancers, cardiovascular diseases, mental illness, injuries, chronic respiratory disease and diabetes (AIHW 2021). Each of these conditions, at least in part, can be attributed to lifestyle, and the course of the conditions can be moderated by health behavioural practices. Hence, there is intuitive appeal in encouraging people to lead a healthy lifestyle to thereby reduce their disease risk and improve quality of life for people with chronic health conditions. There is also abundant research evidence about the relationship between health behaviours and physical and mental health to support the importance of lifestyle interventions in a variety of different populations (Hayes et al. 2021; Ntoumanis et al. 2021; Wickham et al. 2020).

From an individual's perspective the reasons to change health behaviours include prevention (to avoid the risk of a health problem), management (treatment of an identified health problem), recovery (living well with an ongoing health problem) and for general wellbeing. From the health professionals' and health services' perspectives, other motives include reducing the incidence and burden of the health issue in the community and the best use of resources.

Critical thinking

- What factors do you think influence a person to engage in a healthy or unhealthy lifestyle?
- Does a person choose his/her lifestyle? Explain your answer.
- Is willpower alone sufficient to ensure a person will stop a harmful behaviour or start a positive one? Explain your answer.
- Is knowledge alone enough to ensure that a person will stop a harmful behaviour or start a positive one? Explain your answer.

Health psychology: theories and models

Health psychology is interested in factors that influence the initiation, continuation, cessation and modification of behaviours that impact on health and health outcomes. To this end psychological theories propose hypotheses to explain and predict behaviour, while models (which are derived from theories) detail the processes and stages of how the behaviour under observation is enacted. In addition to observable behaviours, the health beliefs held by individuals and the impact these beliefs have on their health-related behaviours are investigated. Finally, health psychology is interested in finding effective strategies to help people overcome resistance to change their behaviour and prevent relapse, and in how to maintain positive behaviour change.

Psychological theories and models of health behaviour attempt to explain or predict a person's engagement in behaviours that influence the risk for illness or injury and the maintenance of health. Psychological theories of health behaviour fall into three broad categories: behavioural/learning theories, cognitive theories and models that use a combination of behavioural and cognitive strategies. Behavioural/ learning approaches include operant conditioning, classical conditioning and modelling or imitation (see below and Chapter 1). Cognitive approaches include the health belief model, the theory of planned behaviour, the transtheoretical model of behaviour change, and the health action process approach. **Combination models** include social cognitive theory and the behaviour change wheel. Collectively these models have informed a range of cognitive behavioural therapies including motivational interviewing and acceptance and commitment therapy. These psychological approaches to behaviour change will now be examined.

Behavioural/learning theories

Have you ever received a parking fine or speeding ticket, lost your driver's licence, been locked out of a concert until interval because you arrived late, or been refused borrowing rights at your library until you paid your fine for late returns? Do you feel motivated after your boss tells you that he is impressed with your work or smile back at someone who has just smiled at you? Most of us, without realising it, actually practise behaviour modification in our everyday lives and have it practised on us. You will be surprised by the end of this chapter to discover how much of your own behaviour is governed by the fundamental principles of learning theory, on which behavioural change programs are based, and how much of the behaviour of those around you is at least partly determined by your own behavioural change strategies.

Behavioural/learning theories propose that personality is determined by prior learning, that human behaviour is changeable throughout the lifespan and that changes in behaviour are generally caused by changes in the environment. They explain how the environment influences behaviours and forms habits and are concerned only with behaviour that is observable, and not mental or affective processes. Specifically, learning theories focus on the conditions that produce behaviour, factors that reinforce behaviour and vicarious learning through watching and imitating the behaviour of others. The three main learning approaches are:

- *classical conditioning*—learning by association
- *operant conditioning*—learning by reinforcement
- *social learning theory*—vicarious learning (modelling/observation and copying).

CLASSICAL CONDITIONING

As outlined in Chapter 1, classical conditioning was first described by the Russian physiologist Ivan Pavlov, who observed the relationship between stimulus and response through demonstrating that a dog could be conditioned to salivate (respond) to a non-food stimulus (a bell) (Pavlov 1927). For example, a patient may be receiving intravenous chemotherapy for cancer, which has the side effect of nausea. Over time the patient may experience nausea when the chemotherapy nurse enters the room, and before the injection is given. The feeling of nausea when the nurse is present has been learned through classical conditioning. Agoraphobia (the fear of leaving a safe place) can also be explained by classical conditioning. When a person with agoraphobia retreats from a public to a safe place, the behaviour is reinforced (rewarded) by a reduction in anxiety symptoms.

Critical thinking

Identify the following for agoraphobia:

- neutral stimulus
- unconditioned stimulus
- unconditioned response
- conditioned stimulus
- conditioned response (see also Chapter 1).

OPERANT CONDITIONING

BF Skinner formulated the notion of operant conditioning in which reinforcers (rewards) contribute to the probability of a response being either repeated or extinguished. Skinner's research demonstrated that the contingencies on which behaviour is based are external to the person, rather than internal. Consequently, changing contingencies could alter a person's behaviour (Skinner 1953). For example, if a child throws a tantrum when told it is bedtime, and the parent relents and allows the child to stay up later, the child learns that they can get what they want by throwing a tantrum. To reverse this behaviour the parent would need to ignore the child's tantrum and firmly insist that it is bedtime.

SOCIAL LEARNING THEORY

Social learning theory (also called modelling/observational learning) was proposed by Bandura (1969, 2016), who asserts that observational learning has a more significant influence on how humans learn than intrapsychic (psychoanalytic) or environmental (behavioural/learning) forces alone. Bandura proposed that human behaviour results from the interaction between the environment and the person's thinking and perceptions. He also asserted that humans can learn from observing—not just by doing. Observational learning differs from operant conditioning in that it is not the learner who is rewarded for the behaviour; rather, the learner observes other people being rewarded and learns vicariously through this. New behaviours are acquired by observing others being rewarded for performing a behaviour, and then imitating that behaviour—for example, a child who witnesses the success of a sports star and then starts practising the sport.

Observational learning is particularly important for children's learning because it is easier to influence a behaviour while it is being acquired rather than changing an established behaviour. Hence parents, family and schooling play a significant role in the formation of children's health habits. These habits can be both positive health behaviours, such as participating in sport and cleaning their teeth, or negative practices, such as tobacco smoking.

BEHAVIOURAL CHANGE PROGRAMS

Behavioural change programs aim to change behaviour, not attitudes, beliefs, motivation, personality or other unobserved characteristics of individuals. Behaviour may be defined as anything that a person does or says; that is, behaviour is any action or response to an environmental event that is observable and measurable. Behaviours can be overt (readily observed and counted) or covert (not readily observed but can still be counted and changed, such as thoughts and feelings using the principles described in this chapter). Regardless of the orientation of specific programs, all behavioural change programs operate on the following four tenets:

1. Behaviour can be explained by the principles of learning and conditioning.
2. The same laws of learning apply to all behaviour, both normal and abnormal.
3. Abnormal behaviour is the normal response to abnormal learning conditions.
4. Behaviour can be 'unlearned' and changed.

These four tenets underpin the four major theoretical models that have been derived from learning theory, namely, classical conditioning, operant conditioning, social/observational (imitation) learning and cognitive behaviourism (Beck 1976; Meichenbaum 1974).

Historically, behaviour therapy referred to the techniques based on classical conditioning, devised by Wolpe (1968) and Eysenck (1960) to treat anxiety; behaviour modification was used to describe programs based on the principles of operant conditioning devised by Skinner (1953) to create new behaviours in children who had an intellectual disability and patients experiencing psychotic symptoms.

In current practice, the terms behaviour therapy, behavioural change programs and behaviour modification are used interchangeably to describe therapeutic programs based on the principles of behavioural/learning theory. The term 'behavioural change program' will be used in this chapter. The following outlines the principles used when designing a behavioural change program.

Antecedent, behaviour, consequence

The principles of operant conditioning (learning by reinforcement) describe the relationship between behaviour and environmental events, both antecedents and consequences that influence behaviour. This relationship, referred to as a contingency, consists of three components:

1. antecedents (i.e. stimulus events that precede or trigger the target behaviour)
2. behaviours (i.e. responses, usually the identified problem behaviour)
3. consequences (outcomes of the behaviour; i.e. what actually happened immediately after the problem behaviour occurred).

Specifying these contingencies forms the basis of a functional analysis of behaviour. The aim of a functional analysis is to identify factors that influence the occurrence and maintenance of a particular (problem or desired) response. This process should not be confused with other explanatory models that may seek to explain behaviour in terms of a medical diagnosis or a personality trait. Behavioural change programs are more concerned with the nature of our interactions with the environment than with our nature per se.

Functional analysis of behaviour

Conducting a functional analysis of behaviour is the first step in designing a behavioural change program. It consists of the three components outlined below.

1. Selecting the target behaviour

The target behaviour must be specified in such a way that it can be readily observed and measured. The behaviour of interest may be a behavioural excess (e.g. tantrums, exceeding the speed limit, driving while intoxicated) or a behavioural deficit (e.g. an 8-year-old who cannot tie his shoelaces, an adult who does not complete recommended physiotherapy exercises, a well elderly person who does not perform self-care activities). From the examples given, it will be clear that behavioural deficits are of two types: behaviours that exist in the behavioural repertoire of the individual but that the individual does not perform, and behaviours that are not in the behavioural repertoire of the individual and must be developed. It is important to distinguish among these different groups of target behaviours because each requires the application of different behavioural change strategies.

Behaviour must never be viewed in isolation. The behavioural change agent considers the setting in which the behaviour occurs, the nature of the task and the characteristics of the client. Behaviour may be appropriately performed in one setting and not another. For example, it would be appropriate for a 3-year-old child who has just learned to take his clothes off to do so in the bathroom in his home but not in a busy shopping centre. A behavioural change program in this instance would aim to teach the child the appropriate setting for performing this newly acquired activity. Behaviour may also be considered problematic due to its rate, duration or intensity rather than the behaviour itself. For example, taking a shower is a common behaviour that may become problematic if the person spends one hour doing so or showers multiple times through the day. In this case, the behavioural change program would aim to reduce the amount of time spent in the shower or the frequency of showers.

2. Identifying current contingencies

This process involves two steps. The first is identifying the stimulus event(s) (i.e. antecedents) that precede(s) an occurrence of the problem behaviour. This includes an assessment of the physical (where the behaviour occurs) and social (who is present) environment in which the behaviour occurs. Certain behaviours will frequently occur at a high rate in one setting and be absent or occur at a low rate in others. For example, parents may complain about their child throwing tantrums and being argumentative at home to the child's teacher, who reports that the child is compliant and polite in the classroom. Alternatively, the teacher may notice that the child stays on task in some subjects and not in others or during the morning session but not during the afternoon. In a hospital, two nurses may discover that a particular patient rings the buzzer for nursing assistance twice as often for one nurse compared with another, or that a child with cerebral palsy is more likely to persist with his physiotherapy exercises when his mother is not in the treatment room. These observations provide important information about the stimulus events that may be controlling the target behaviour.

The second step requires identifying the consequences that follow the problem behaviour; that is, what happened after the behaviour was or was not performed? To follow through with our examples above, did the parents respond to the child's tantrum by giving the child what she wanted or did they ignore her tantrum behaviour? Were there any differences in each of the two nurses' responses to the buzzer ringing? For the child who does not cooperate with physiotherapy exercises when his mother is in the room, what was the mother doing in the treatment room during her child's physiotherapy sessions? Answers to these questions are essential for effective behaviour modification to occur.

3. Measuring and recording behaviour

There are five basic methods of measuring behaviour in healthcare settings:

1. narrative recording
2. counting or frequency data
3. timing or duration recording (temporal data)
4. checking or interval recording (categorical data)
5. rating (magnitude data).

Once you have specified the target behaviour and identified the setting in which this behaviour occurs, it is necessary to obtain a baseline of the frequency or length of its occurrence. The way you measure frequency or length depends on the nature of the target behaviour and what you wish to find out about the behaviour. There are many applications (apps) that can be used on smartphones, tablets and fitness trackers to record data. For example, fitness trackers can automatically record how often a person exercises, and nutrition apps can be used to record dietary intake. This information is then readily accessible to the person and also any health professionals they may consult.

Narrative recording

Narrative recording involves observing and recording behaviour in progress. It is often used in the early stages of the functional analysis of behaviour as a way of identifying possible antecedents and consequences of a given problem behaviour. Figure 7.1 provides an example of a narrative recording chart—for example, for use with a child with type 1 diabetes mellitus who refuses to take and record their blood sugar levels while at school. Recording the data can help identify what initiates and maintains the behaviour.

Name: _____
Date: _____
Setting: _____
Observer: _____
Description of problem behaviour: _____
Possible determinants of problem behaviour: _____
Behavioural consequences: _____

Figure 7.1 Narrative recording sheet for assessing problematic behaviour

Counting

Counting is the method of choice if the target behaviour is discrete (i.e. an observer can identify the beginning and end of each instance of behaviour). Behaviours such as sleep patterns, exercise and incontinence are examples of discrete, countable behaviours. Simple tally sheets or frequency counters can be used to record countable behaviours. One can also count the number of tasks completed or the percentage of items correct. Figure 7.2 provides an example of a recording chart for counting responses. In this case, the number of times the person awoke in the night is recorded. A fitness tracker can also be used to collect sleep data. It is the ideal way to record this type of data for many people because the data is collected automatically and the person only needs to wear the device, enabling easy collection of the data and increased accuracy.

Timing (duration)

When a behaviour becomes a problem because of the length of time it takes to complete the task, or when you are interested in increasing the duration of a particular behaviour, you may choose to collect temporal data. Examples of behaviours for which temporal data are appropriate are length of time it takes for a nurse to perform a given task such as a surgical dressing, the length of time it takes for a hospitalised patient to shower in the morning or the amount of time a person spends in the gym practising physiotherapy exercises. Figure 7.3 provides an example of a chart for timing the duration of a target behaviour, in this case exercising in the gym over a 4-week period.

Checking

Checking or interval recording is used when you want to know whether a person performs a specified task or not. In such cases your code requires a simple yes–no response. By checking on groups of related behaviours, you can quickly build up a picture of the person's current level of functioning. For example, you may wish to increase the self-care behaviours of a patient with advanced dementia. When he arrives at breakfast each morning, you can check whether he has combed his hair, shaved, dressed in day clothes (as opposed to pyjamas) and is wearing shoes. After you get a baseline following several days of checking, you will be ready to design a behavioural change program to address any outstanding deficits in self-care.

Name:............................. Monitored from: ../../..to ../../..Behaviour: Awakenings per night		
	Week 1	Week 2
Monday		
Tuesday		
Wednesday		
Thursday		
Friday		
Saturday		
Sunday		

Figure 7.2 Counting chart for (self) monitoring sleep disturbance over a 2-week period

Exercise record				
Name:				
Date monitoring began:				
Period commencing	Week 1	Week 2	Week 3	Week 4
Monday				
Tuesday				
Wednesday				
Thursday				
Friday				
Saturday				
Sunday				
Total				

Figure 7.3 Amount of time spent exercising over a 4-week period

Assessment of self-care behaviour

Name:				
Date:				
Hair neat/ combed				
Clean shaved				
Face clean				
Dressed appropriately				
Clothes clean				
Wearing shoes				
Hands and nails clean				

✓   Satisfactory
X   Not present or unsatisfactory
N/A Not applicable

Figure 7.4 Checklist for assessing self-care behaviour

Figure 7.4 is an example of a checklist for assessing how well a person with dementia manages their personal hygiene and grooming.

Rating

Rating is a method of assessing the quality of a response and, as such, requires a subjective judgement on the part of the observer. You may wish to assess the intelligibility of the speech of a person who is dysarthric. One quick measure of intelligibility is to ask the nursing staff and family members to rate the person on a five-point scale ranging from 1 = very difficult to understand to 5 = very easy to understand.

In summary, a functional analysis of behaviour can identify the antecedents (what triggers the behaviour) and the consequences (outcomes of the behaviour). Consider one of your own health behaviours from a behavioural/learning perspective and monitor this for 1 week using the health behaviour monitoring exercise in Figure 7.5, then complete the *Student activity.*

Health behaviour monitoring exercise

Select one of your health behaviours e.g. eating, drinking alcohol, cigarette smoking, physical activity. Monitor this behaviour for a week and record the following:					
Behaviour:					
Date	Time	Place	Antecedents ★	Consequences ☐	Reflection/comments

★ **Antecedents:** Where were you? Who else was present? What were your preceding thoughts or feelings? What events preceded/coincided with the behaviour?

☐ **Consequences:** What was the outcome? What were your subsequent thoughts or feelings?

Figure 7.5 Health behaviour monitoring chart

Student activity

Decide on a method of measuring behaviour and record one or more of your health behaviours for a week.

Discuss the following questions in small groups.

1. Do you notice a pattern regarding this behaviour? Describe.
2. What influences the maintenance (or not) of this behaviour?
3. What role do antecedents and consequences play in the initiation and continuation of this behaviour?
4. Does anything surprise you? Explain your answer.
5. What understanding has this activity provided for you about working with people who need to cease, initiate or maintain a health-enhancing or health risk behaviour?

Research focus

Source: Gass et al. 2021

The use and impact of self-monitoring on substance use outcomes: A descriptive systematic review

ABSTRACT

Background

Self-monitoring (SM), the act of observing one's own behaviour, has been used in substance use treatment because SM may bring conscious awareness to automatised substance use behaviours. Empirical findings regarding SM's effectiveness are mixed. The aim of this study was to synthesise the literature for the efficacy of SM on substance use.

Method

A literature search was conducted using MEDLINE/PubMed.

Results

Out of 2,659 citations, 41 studies with 126 analyses were included. Among analyses from studies rated moderate ($n = 24$) or strong ($n = 3$) quality, SM was shown to have a helpful effect (e.g. reducing substance use) 29% of the time; to have no effect 63.0% of the time; and to be detrimental in 8.0% of analyses. SM's helpful effects were associated with methodological characteristics including longer monitoring and phone/IVR and EMA/computer methodologies compared with paper/pencil. SM was more helpful in non–treatment seekers (35.0% of analyses showed SM to be helpful compared with 25.0% of analyses with treatment-seekers).

Conclusions

Results of this study suggest that SM, under certain circumstances, has the potential to be a low-cost, low-risk research and early intervention strategy for substance users.

◈ Critical thinking

- Why do you think recording substance use via computer methodologies or for a longer period was more helpful in reducing substance use?
- Search the internet for apps that record health behaviours. Identify and discuss the advantages and disadvantages of recording health behaviours on an app.

Cognitive theories of health behaviour

Cognitive theories of health behaviour propose that people actively interpret their environment and cognitively construct their world. Therefore, behaviour (including health-related behaviour) is a result of two factors, namely:

1. internal (within the person) events, which are the person's thoughts and perceptions about themself, the world and their behaviour in the world
2. external (within the environment) events, which are the stimuli and reinforcements that regulate behaviour.

While cognitive psychology emerged as a field of study and therapy in the 1970s, the notion that one's thinking influences one's behaviour is not new. Epictetus, the Greek Stoic philosopher, is attributed to making the statement that 'we are disturbed not by the things but by the view we take of them' and Buddha observed that 'we are what we think' (Wood 2012, p. 172). Consider the following scenario that exemplifies how different outcomes can result from different thoughts about the same situation or event.

Critical thinking

While applying sunscreen, Ben noticed a black mole on his left thigh. What feelings would Ben have and what action might he take for each of the following possible thoughts?

- 'This is just another freckle.'
- 'Oh no! I have a fatal cancer like my cousin Jarrod who died last year.'
- 'I don't remember seeing this before.'

HEALTH BELIEF MODEL

The **health belief model** (HBM) (Figure 7.6) was the first cognitive explanatory model in health psychology and continues to be used today (Skinner et al. 2015). It was developed in the 1950s by Hockbaum and Rosenstock to explain the unexpected low levels of participation in health screening and illness prevention programs (Rosenstock 1966, 1974).

Since the 1970s, the HBM has been used widely in health education and health promotion programs (Jones et al. 2014; Vincenzo et al. 2022). This cognitive model predicts the seeking of treatment or the changing of health behaviours on the basis of two main factors:

1. the person's perception of threat to his/her health, including susceptibility and severity
2. the degree to which the person believes that a particular health action or behaviour will influence the health outcome and be effective in reducing the threat; it includes an assessment of the perceived benefits of the behaviours and the perceived barriers to carrying out the new behaviour.

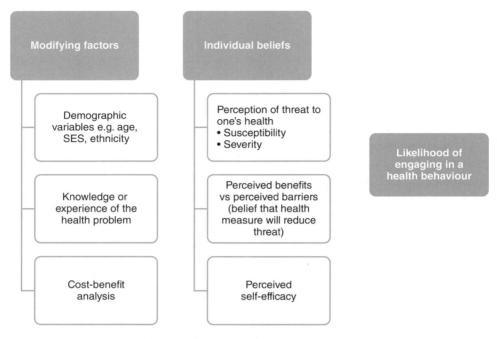

Figure 7.6 Health belief model Source: Adapted from Skinner et al. 2015

The model also incorporates cues to action (e.g. triggers such as a media campaign that raises awareness of a potential problem) and more recently self-efficacy (the belief that one can achieve a certain goal). When the model was devised, it was assumed that increased knowledge through health education programs would lead to greater participation in public health programs. However, the expected outcome of changed health behaviours following exposure to health education did not always eventuate. For example, in a study examining men's ($n = 127$) intentions to seek help for cancer symptoms, Fish and colleagues (2022) found that while symptom knowledge and the perceived benefits of help-seeking predicted intentions, the whole model only accounted for a small amount of variance in help-seeking intentions.

In addition, while health education strategies using the HBM may increase the person's motivation or intention to engage in health-enhancing behaviours, this does not necessarily translate into action. The knowledge that a particular behaviour is beneficial or harmful to one's health isn't enough, on its own, to change many people's health practices or behaviour. This is because the HBM identifies *what* to change but not necessarily *how* to make the required changes, nor does the HBM teach the skills required to make and sustain the change.

Consider the current concern being expressed about the rising consumption of energy-dense foods in Western nations. Most people know that overconsumption of these foods pose health risks and understand eating a healthy balanced diet is optimal. Yet sales and consumption of these foods continue to rise. Therefore, while the HBM is useful in predicting some health behaviours, such as regular breast screening by a woman with a family history of breast cancer, the model is not universally applicable for all people or all health issues.

·◉· Critical thinking

Consider the health behaviour of annual dental examinations recommended by dentists as a preventive strategy to identify any dental problems early. Use the HBM to explain who, in the following two scenarios, is more likely to have annual dental examinations and why.

- Adam is a recent school leaver who has started working as an apprentice electrician. Throughout his school years he attended annual dental check-ups through the school dental scheme. Two years ago he experienced severe toothache that was diagnosed as an abscess and cracked tooth. Treatment involved root canal therapy and capping of the tooth. Adam's parents' private health insurance will cover his dental expenses until he is 25 years old.

- Carrie is a recent school leaver who is currently a full-time university student. Throughout her school years she attended annual dental check-ups through the school dental scheme. Apart from the annual check-ups, Carrie never underwent any other dental treatment. Neither Carrie nor her parents have private health insurance.

THEORY OF PLANNED BEHAVIOUR

The **theory of planned behaviour** (TPB) was first proposed by Ajzen (1991; Ajzen & Maddern 1986) to help understand behaviours that other theories had failed to explain, particularly the non-uptake of healthy behaviours. The TPB is based on the premise that using cognitive and behavioural models alone isn't enough to understand health behaviours or to produce change. It proposes that social processes must also be considered. Therefore, it introduces 'social cognitions' to the previously developed cognitive models like the HBM.

The TPB (see Figure 7.7) proposes that three beliefs help predict a person's health behaviour or behavioural outcomes. These are:

1. the person's attitude to the behaviour
2. subjective norms
3. the person's perceived behavioural control.

Overall, the TPB is a better predictor of health behaviour change than previous cognitive models because it takes account of the social context in which the behaviour occurs. For example, in a high school where binge drinking is an accepted 'norm' it can be predicted that many adolescents will engage in this behaviour, despite being aware that this practice is harmful. This is because an individual may not have the confidence to be different (perceived behavioural control) and is motivated to comply with the subjective norm. Furthermore, research suggests that it is not just intention that leads to performing a certain behaviour but that social factors also play a role. Kyrrestad and colleagues' (2022) study of alcohol onset and drinking frequency among adolescents found that intentions to start drinking were predicted by subjective norms for both boys and girls. The researchers concluded that it is important for alcohol prevention programs to not only focus on attitudes and perceived behavioural control, but to also focus on environmental factors such as subjective norms.

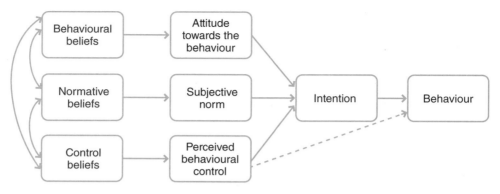

Figure 7.7 Theory of planned behaviour Adapted from: Ajzen 2015

Student activity

In small groups, use the TPB to identify and discuss the attitudes, subjective norms and perceived behavioural controls that a person might hold when they engage in the following health behaviours:

- wearing a bicycle helmet
- a teenager with asthma not using her preventer 'puffer' at school
- UV exposure
- driving a car while intoxicated.

TRANSTHEORETICAL MODEL OF BEHAVIOURAL CHANGE

The **transtheoretical model of behaviour change** (TTM) uses both behavioural and cognitive strategies. The model was developed by Prochaska and DiClemente (1984) from their research in addiction studies. It was further refined by Prochaska and colleagues. (1992), Prochaska (2006) and Prochaska and Norcross (2018).

The TTM proposes that lasting behaviour change can be achieved using cognitively based therapy to help people move towards the maintenance stage of a positive health behaviour such as stopping gambling. While the authors present the stages in a sequential manner, they stress that movement through the stages is not linear. A person will move backwards and forwards through and between the stages before maintenance is established (see Figure 7.8). It is not uncommon for a person who has reached the maintenance stage to relapse and revert to an earlier stage before achieving stable maintenance. When relapse occurs, the person is encouraged to view this as part of the cycle of change, not failure—a challenge, not a catastrophe.

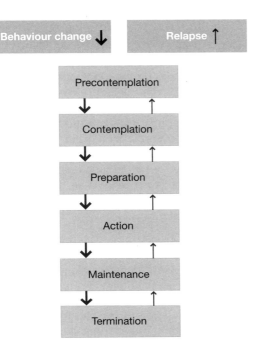

Figure 7.8 Transtheoretical model

The five stages of change of the TTM are as follows:

1. *Precontemplation*—The stage in which the person does not recognise that the behaviour poses health risks and therefore does not perceive a need to change. This may be due to lack of knowledge or information, or the person may be using denial. For example, a person with osteoarthritis may be unaware of the role of exercise in maintaining joint mobility and consequently reduce their physical activity as a strategy to manage pain. A tobacco smoker who rationalises that, 'My grandfather smoked until he was 80 years old and never suffered any ill effects' may be using denial regarding the risks associated with smoking.

2. *Contemplation*—The stage in which the person is aware that the behaviour potentially causes health problems but is ambivalent about making a commitment to change. A shift to this stage from precontemplation may be triggered by an event such as when a smoker or a close family member is diagnosed with a smoking-related health problem.

3. *Preparation*—In this stage the person acknowledges the risk inherent in the behaviour and makes a commitment to change such as purchasing nicotine patches, telling others of their intention or seeking professional assistance.

4. *Action*—This is the stage at which intervention is most effective. This is when the person takes action to change a health behaviour such as the smoker who uses nicotine replacement patches and enrols in a quit-smoking course.

5. *Maintenance or termination*—Maintenance is the stage in which the person sustains the desired health behaviour (e.g. smoking cessation), while termination applies to the health behaviours that do not need to be ongoing such as vaccination or health screening.

Transtheoretical model in clinical practice

A strength of the TTM is that it suggests strategies to work with unmotivated clients who previously were not considered amenable to intervention or treatment (Prochaska 2006; Prochaska & Norcross 2018). This enables the health professional to facilitate movement towards a stage of readiness. After identifying the stage the client is at, the health professional can then initiate interventions to facilitate the person moving to the next stage. For example, if the person is at the precontemplation stage and is unaware of the risk the behaviour poses for their health, the health professional can present the relevant health education information to the person to facilitate movement to the next stage. However, if the person is using denial in this stage, intervention is extremely difficult, whereas intervening at the action stage is more effective because the person is motivated to make changes. This is the stage at which intervention is most likely to be effective in bringing about the desired change in behaviour.

Providing intervention based on a person's stage of cessation is the principle behind the Australian National Tobacco and the New Zealand Quitline Me Mutu smoking cessation campaigns. Graphic images of the consequences of smoking on cigarette packets and in television commercials aim to shift smokers from the precontemplation to the contemplation and ultimately action stages. Quit programs also provide information about access to strategies and support services to assist smokers to move from the contemplation stage through to the action and maintenance stages.

It is important to note that once the person reaches the maintenance stage relapse is still possible, as it is at any of the preceding stages. Should relapse occur, the person's thoughts about the relapse will influence what happens next. For example, a person who views relapse as a *setback* or *challenge* can plan to return to the stage previously achieved, whereas a person who views relapse as a *failure* or *catastrophe* will not be motivated to persevere with the behaviour change.

In summary, TTM identifies the stages a person goes through when making health behaviour changes. It identifies internal and external influences, thereby identifying opportunities for intervention. It is particularly effective for changing addictive (e.g. alcohol and gambling problems) and other behaviours that pose health risks (e.g. unsafe sex).

HEALTH ACTION PROCESS APPROACH

The **health action process approach** (HAPA) is a dual-phase social cognition model that highlights the role of self-efficacy and addresses the 'intention–behaviour gap' (Schwarzer 1992, 2014) or why people do or do not complete a behaviour that they intend to complete. The model adds a social dimension to previous cognitive models (see Figure 7.9) and distinguishes between a motivational phase (where social-cognitive constructs form intentions) and a volitional phase (where intentions are enacted).

The model proposes there are three precursors to change in the motivational phase:

1. self-efficacy or the person's belief in their ability to action the change
2. outcome expectations or the belief as to whether the intended action will improve health or not
3. risk perception or whether or not changing will affect health.

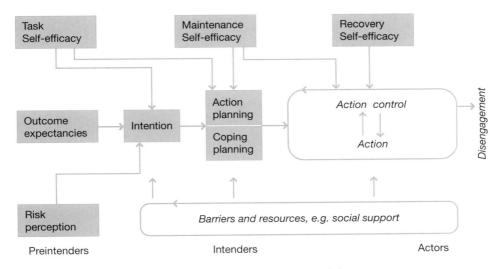

Figure 7.9 Health action process approach model Source: Schwarzer 2014

Of the three precursors, research most strongly supports the continued importance of self-efficacy in predicting behavioural outcomes (Zhang et al. 2019). Like the TPB, the HAPA proposes that the person's belief in their ability to carry out the desired behaviour predicts the person's success in doing so. For example, the model would predict that the person who believes he can comply with a recommended dietary change will be more successful in making the change than a person who believes that making the change is too difficult.

CASE STUDY: TAMARA

Tamara is a 33-year-old physical education teacher who has smoked since she was 15 years old. Both her parents smoke and, while her mother has not experienced any ill effects from smoking, her father has just been diagnosed with early-stage emphysema. Tamara started smoking because most of her friends smoked and she did not want to be the 'odd one out'. Later, when she started clubbing, she realised that smoking helped her to maintain her weight because she wasn't tempted to snack if she smoked while drinking, even though she has to go outside the venue to do so.

While studying for her degree, Tamara became aware of the potential for harm to her health if she continued to smoke. On two occasions she gave up, once for 12 months. She found social occasions to be the most difficult because people around her smoked and she longed for a cigarette in her hand when she drank alcohol. At first she allowed herself to only smoke on weekends when she was out with her friends but very soon she had resumed smoking daily. Since her father's recent diagnosis, Tamara has decided to give up smoking 'for good'.

Student activity

Complete the following in small groups.

1. Identify internal factors that influence Tamara's smoking.
2. Identify external factors that influence Tamara's smoking.
3. Explain Tamara's behaviour using:
   (a) HBM
   (b) TPB
   (c) TTM
   (d) HAPA.
4. Suggest what needs to happen for Tamara to be successful in giving up smoking.
5. Suggest the conditions required for Tamara to give up smoking.

Combination models

Combination models of behaviour change incorporate behavioural, cognitive and environmental factors and argue that it is the interaction between these factors that shape behaviour. Examples include social cognitive theory and the behaviour change wheel.

Social cognitive theory is an extension of social learning theory and considers the interaction between environmental influences, personal factors and behaviour (Bandura 1986, 1998). It is based on the premise that people learn through a combination of their own experiences and through observing what others do. Core components of the theory include: environmental/behavioural influences (e.g. modelling/observational learning), cognitive influences (e.g. self-efficacy, outcome expectancies) and supporting factors (e.g. capability, rewards and punishments, goal setting) (Kelder et al. 2015).

The **behaviour change wheel** was proposed in 2011 as a new framework for understanding behaviour change and to assist in developing behaviour change interventions (Michie et al. 2011). As you have seen throughout this chapter, there are a variety of behaviour change theories. Michie and colleagues (2011) propose that at the core of all behaviour change are three essential components: (1) capability; (2) opportunity; and (3) motivation, and the combination of these components can explain and be used to direct behaviour. They termed this the COM-B model. Since its inception, the COM-B model has been applied across a number of settings to explain health behaviours ranging from barriers to self-care for heart failure patients (Whittal et al. 2021) to explaining young adults' eating behaviours and physical activity (Willmott et al. 2021).

Behaviour change therapies

Behaviour change therapies refers to a range of interventions that use both cognitive and behavioural strategies to bring about changes in a person's behaviours and to treat some mental illnesses (e.g. depression, anxiety and phobias) and chronic illness (e.g. chronic fatigue syndrome) and to manage behavioural problems such as addictive behaviours. The underlying premise behind behaviour change therapies is that thoughts, feelings and behaviours are interrelated and changes in one or more will bring about change in one or all of these. Key elements of these approaches are a focus on:

- the present rather than the past, and identifying the problem and its extent (history is acknowledged for its contribution to the present problem but is not the focus of treatment)
- setting goals that are achievable and measurable
- collaboration between the person and the health professional to set goals and test strategies
- bringing about changes in thoughts, feelings, behaviour and psychological responses.

There are many forms of behaviour change therapies. Two examples—motivational interviewing and acceptance and commitment therapy—are discussed below.

MOTIVATIONAL INTERVIEWING

Miller and Rollnick initially developed **motivational interviewing** as a therapeutic intervention for use with people who had addictive behaviours such as drug, alcohol or gambling problems, but it is now used for a wide range of health issues (Arkowitz et al. 2015; Miller & Rollnick 2013). It evolved from the person-centred counselling approach of humanistic psychologist Carl Rogers (Hettema et al. 2005; Miller & Moyers 2018) and shares similarities with the TTM in that both approaches aim to encourage the person to recognise the need for change and then to take action to bring about change. Both models also stress the importance of the person taking responsibility for initiating and implementing the behaviour change.

In a motivational interview, a collaborative conversation about change encourages the person to explore all the beliefs and values they hold for and against a behaviour that requires change—to thereby create a state of cognitive dissonance (conflict) for the person. The person is asked to make a list of the positive and negative consequences of the behaviour. For example, eliciting statements like 'gambling gives me a buzz when I win' and 'my relationship with my partner is suffering because of my gambling' are conflicting outcomes of continuing to gamble. The person is then encouraged to make a decision about whether or not they wish to stop gambling. If they decide to make the behavioural change (i.e. stop gambling), the health professional then assists the person to develop and implement a plan to facilitate the behaviour change. The key points of the motivational interviewing counselling approach are as follows:

- Motivation to change is elicited from the client and not imposed externally.
- It is the client's task, not the counsellor's, to articulate their ambivalence.
- Direct persuasion is not an effective method for resolving ambivalence.
- The counselling style is generally a quiet and eliciting one.
- The counsellor is directive in helping the client to examine and resolve ambivalence.

- Readiness to change is not a client trait but a fluctuating product of interpersonal interaction.

- The therapeutic relationship is more like a partnership or companionship than expert/recipient roles (Arkowitz et al. 2015; Miller & Rollnick 2013).

Four principles underpin a motivational interviewing counselling approach:

1. empathy expression, whereby the counsellor conveys understanding of the person's situation and perspective

2. non-confrontation, to allow the person to identify the discrepancies for themselves

3. accept resistance as a part of the process of change

4. encourage self-efficacy and optimism about the person's ability to change (Arkowitz et al. 2015; Miller & Rollnick 2013).

A significant component of the motivational interviewing approach is for the health professional to resist telling the person what they should or should not do and to not lead the person to a decision by coercion as this can lead to resistance (Palmer 2016). Rather, the role of the therapist is to assist the person to come to their own decision and to assist them in developing and implementing an action plan. This is done through a set of core skills that include open-ended questions, affirming and recognising a commitment to change, reflective listening and being able to summarise what has been said (Miller & Rollnick 2013). See the *Research focus* for an example of using motivational interviewing to promote lifestyle skills needed to manage type 2 diabetes.

⊙ Critical thinking

Using the motivational interviewing approach, make a list of the positive and negative consequences of tobacco smoking, regular physical exercise and cocaine use.

Research focus

Source: Steffen et al. 2021

ABSTRACT

Introduction
Motivational interviewing is an effective style of collaborative communication for promoting lifestyle changes in managing type 2 diabetes and arterial hypertension. This study evaluates the effectiveness of motivational interviewing in managing these conditions in primary health care.

Study design
This study is a double-blind parallel-group randomised controlled trial performed between June 2018 and July 2019.

Cont... ▶

Setting/participants

The trial was conducted in Brazil and included people with type 2 diabetes and arterial hypertension.

Intervention

The participants were randomised to the test/motivational interviewing and usual care groups. The test/motivational interviewing group received the nursing consultation intervention on the basis of motivational interviewing conducted by professionals with 20 hours of training, and the usual-care group received conventional nursing consultation.

Main outcome measures

The main outcome measure was the mean difference in HbA_{1c}. The secondary outcome measures were the mean differences in blood pressure and adherence levels.

Results

After a mean follow-up of 6 months, 174 participants completed the study (usual-care group = 80; test/motivational interviewing group = 94). There were statistically significant differences between the groups, with improvement in the test/motivational interviewing group for systolic blood pressure ($p < 0.01$), diastolic blood pressure ($p < 0.01$) and total adherence score as measured by the Martín–Bayarre–Grau questionnaire ($p = 0.01$) and its operational dimensions of treatment adherence and personal involvement ($p = 0.03$, $p = 0.03$). The test/motivational interviewing group showed significantly reduced HbA_{1c} levels (0.4%) at the end of the study ($p < 0.01$).

Conclusions

In the context of primary health care, the nursing consultation based on motivational interviewing was shown to be a more effective care strategy than usual care for improving blood pressure levels and adherence levels in people with type 2 diabetes and arterial hypertension. Moreover, motivational interviewing was shown to be useful in reducing HbA_{1c} levels in diabetes management.

Critical thinking

Steffen and colleagues' 2021 research showed that a psychological strategy (motivational interviewing) helped people to better manage their type 2 diabetes.

- List other physical health problems for which motivational interviewing could be used to bring about health behavioural change.
- Identify the desired behavioural change for each of these health problems.

ACCEPTANCE AND COMMITMENT THERAPY

Acceptance and commitment therapy (ACT) was developed by Steven Hayes and colleagues in the 1980s (Hayes 2004; Hayes et al. 1999). The model uses acceptance and mindfulness meditation strategies, alongside evidence-based psychological and behaviour strategies, to change the way people perceive things rather than changing the things themselves. ACT is underpinned by the belief that human suffering is a normal experience. Rather than trying to eradicate unpleasant thoughts and feelings, the person needs to stop struggling with the troublesome experiences and they will then become less bothersome. The acronym ACT refers to:

- accepting one's current reactions
- choosing a valued direction
- taking action.

The intervention is underpinned by six core principles:

1. *Contact with the present moment*—Using mindfulness strategies to experience the 'here and now'.
2. *Cognitive diffusion*—Learning to perceive thoughts as cognitive perceptions and not threatening realities.
3. *Acceptance and willingness*—Opening up to unpleasant feelings and experiencing these for what they are rather than trying to push them away from conscious thought.
4. *The observing self*—Developing an awareness that thoughts, feelings, physical body are aspects of self, but do not define the self.
5. *Values*—Clarifying what is truly important in order to lead a meaningful life.
6. *Commitment action*—Goal setting in keeping with values.

Research has shown that ACT interventions are effective in a range of situations including treatment of depression, anxiety, pain disorder, substance use disorders and psychosis (Australian Psychological Society 2018). ACT interventions also show promise for promoting health behaviours such as physical activity (Pears & Sutton 2021).

Critical thinking

'Change is easier to initiate than sustain.'

- Consider this statement in relation to a health-enhancing behaviour of your own that you have tried to modify—in other words, taking up a new behaviour or discontinuing an existing one.
- Which model best explains your success or otherwise for this health behaviour?

Student activity

Carol is a problem gambler who says sincerely that she wants to stop gambling because of the impact on her life, relationships and health. Nevertheless, she regularly attends the local hotel where she plays the 'pokies'. Away from the hotel Carol states she will no longer gamble. Her goal is to be a non-gambler; she is aware of the risks to her associated with gambling and she believes she can stop.

Complete the following in small groups.

1. Discuss why willpower has not been enough to enable Carol to curb or stop gambling.
2. Identify which theories explain her behaviour.
3. Suggest strategies that could help Carol to succeed in curbing her gambling.
4. Which theories/models underpin these suggested strategies?

Limitations of psychological models

While behavioural and cognitive approaches to initiating and maintaining health behaviours can be effective, they do not provide a universal explanation for all people in all situations. Commentators suggest this is because relying on a person's behavioural response and cognitive process is a narrow, reductionist approach to understanding human behaviour (Crossley 2000; Murray 2010). Cognitive and behavioural models of health behaviour often do not take into consideration other psychological and social factors that influence the initiation, continuation or cessation of health behaviours.

The models also assume rational decision making and do not take into account unconscious processes as identified in psychoanalytic theory such as the defence mechanism of denial. Nor do they acknowledge the contribution of affective states such as fear or the physiological component of some practices such as nicotine addiction in tobacco smoking or genetics. Significantly, the models in their original formations do not consider where the person is located in the lifespan or the social contexts of people's lives. Social factors (which are examined in more detail in Chapter 6) that are not specifically considered in psychological behavioural change theories include the following.

- *Socioeconomic status*—Does the person have access to the resources needed to make the change?
- *Social connectedness*—Does the person have enough social support to carry out the activity?
- *Gender*—Do men and women respond in the same way to similar health challenges?
- *Ethnicity*—What role does ethnicity play in health behaviours?
- *Culture*—How applicable are psychological theories developed in Western cultures to people from non-Western cultures?

Finally, while many of these models are good predictors of behavioural *intention,* intentions in and of themselves do not always translate into actual behavioural *outcomes* (Sheeran & Webb 2016). They are, therefore, more effective in predicting who is at risk of health problems but not particularly useful in predicting who will be successful in engaging in health-enhancing behaviours, or who will be successful in changing unhealthy behaviours.

Chapter summary

This chapter presented a range of psychological theories and models that propose explanations as to how internal and external factors influence a person's health behaviours and lifestyle. These theories and models provide useful insights into the motivators and reinforcers for why a person does or does not engage in health-enhancing behaviours or why a person engages in behaviours that pose health risks. These understandings also identify possibilities to change health behaviours, but this knowledge needs to be applied within a framework that also considers the social contexts of the person's life.

KEY POINTS

- Health behaviours are influenced by a range of physical, psychological and social factors.
- Psychological theories and models can predict a person's health behaviours.
- Psychological theories and models identify strategies whereby people can change health behaviours.
- While psychological theories and models provide useful insights for understanding, predicting and changing health behaviours, they nevertheless have limitations and are not necessarily universally applicable.

Further reading

Arkowitz, H., Miller, W., Rollnick, S., 2015. Motivational Interviewing in the Treatment of Psychological Problems, 2nd edn. Guilford Press, New York.

Cooper, D. (Ed.), 2011. Interventions in Mental Health-Substance Use. Radcliffe, London.

Harris, R., 2017. ACT Questions & Answers: A Practitioner's Guide to 150 Common Sticking Points in Acceptance & Commitment Therapy. Harbinger Publication, California.

Weblinks

Australian National Tobacco Campaign

www.quitnow.gov.au

The Australian National Tobacco Campaign is part of the Australian Government's continuing efforts to reduce the level of tobacco use among Australians and is aimed directly at smokers, both youth and adults.

Information on Self-Efficacy

http://p20motivationlab.org

This website provides resources and publications about self-efficacy including the writings and video interviews of Albert Bandura.

The Health Action Process Approach

http://userpage.fu-berlin.de/~health/hapa.htm

This website provides an overview of research and publications relating to Schwarzer's 2014 health action process model.

The Quit Group

www.quit.org.nz

Quitline/Me Mutu is a New Zealand website that provides support and information for people who want to stop smoking.

References

Ajzen, I., 1991. The theory of planned behavior. Organizational Behavior and Human Decision Processes, 50(2), 179–211.

Ajzen, I., 2005: Attitudes, Personality and Behaviour, 2nd edn. Milton-Keynes: Open University Press/McGraw-Hill.

Ajzen, I. 2015. Consumer attitudes and behavior: the theory of planned behavior applied to food consumption decisions. Rivista di Economia Agraria/Italian Review of Agricultural Economics, 70(2), 121–138.

Ajzen, I., Maddern, M., 1986. Predictions of goal-directed behaviour: attitudes, intentions and perceived behavioural control. Journal of Experimental Social Psychology 22, 453–474.

Arkowitz, H., Miller, W., Rollnick, S., (Eds.). 2015. Motivational Interviewing in the Treatment of Psychological Problems, (2nd edn) Guilford Press, New York.

Australian Institute of Health and Welfare (AIHW), 2021. Australian Burden of Disease Study: Impact and causes of illness and death in Australia 2018. AIHW, Canberra.

Australian Psychological Society, 2018. Evidence-based Psychological Interventions in the Treatment of Mental Disorders: A Review of the Literature. 4th edn. Australian Psychological Society, Melbourne.

Bandura, A., 1969. Principles of Behaviour Modification. Holt, Rhinehart & Winston, New York.

Bandura, A., 1986. Social Foundations of Thought and Action: A Social Cognitive Theory. Englewood Cliffs, NJ: Prentice-Hall

Bandura, A., 1998. Health promotion from the perspective of social cognitive theory. Psychology and Health, 13 (4), 623–649.

Bandura, A., 2016. The power of observational learning through social modelling. In: Stenberg, R., Fiske, S., Foss, D. (Eds.), Scientists Making a Difference: One Hundred Eminent Behavioral and Brain Scientists Talk About Their Most Important Contributions. Cambridge University Press, Cambridge, (Chapter 50).

Beck, A.T., 1976. Cognitive Therapy and Emotional Disorders. International Universities Press, New York.

Crossley, M., 2000. Rethinking Health Psychology. Open University Press, Buckingham.

Eysenck, H.J., 1960. Behaviour Therapy and the Neuroses. Pergamon, London.

Fish, J.A., Prichard, I., Ettridge, K., et al., 2022. Predicting men's intentions to seek help for cancer symptoms: a comparison of the Theory of Planned Behaviour and the Health Belief Model. Australian Journal of Psychology, 74 (1), 1–10.

Frieden, T., 2010. A framework for public health: the health impact pyramid. American Journal of Public Health 100 (4), 590–595.

Hayes L, McParlin C, Azevedo LB, et al. 2021. The effectiveness of smoking cessation, alcohol reduction, diet and physical activity interventions in improving maternal and infant health outcomes: a systematic review of meta-analyses. Nutrients 13 (3), 1036.

Hayes, S., 2004. Acceptance and commitment therapy, relational frame theory, and the third wave of behavioral and cognitive therapies. Behavior Therapy 35, 639–665.

Hayes, S., Strosahl, K., Wilson, K., 1999. Acceptance and Commitment Therapy: An Experimental Approach to Behaviour Change. Guilford Press, New York.

Hettema, J., Steele, J., Miller, W., 2005. Motivational interviewing. Annual Review of Clinical Psychology 1, 91–111.

Jones, C. J., Smith, H., & Llewellyn, C. 2014. Evaluating the effectiveness of health belief model interventions in improving adherence: a systematic review. Health Psychology Review, 8(3), 253–269.

Kelder, H., Hoelscher, D., Perry, C.L. 2015. How individuals, environments, and heath behaviours interact: Social Cognitive Theory. In: Glanz, K., Rimer, B.K., Viswanath, K. (Eds.), Health Behavior and Health Education: Theory Research and Practice. 5th edn. Jossey-Bass, San Francisco, pp. 159–182.

Kyrrestad, H., Mabille, G., Adolfsen, F., et al., 2020. Gender differences in alcohol onset and drinking frequency in adolescents: an application of the theory of planned behavior. Drugs: Education, Prevention and Policy. 29, 1–11.

Meichenbaum, D.H., 1974. Cognitive Behaviour Modification: An Integrative Approach. Plenum, New York.

Michie, S., van Stralen, M.M., West, R. 2011. The behaviour change wheel: A new method for characterising and designing behaviour change interventions. Implementation Science 6, 42.

Miller, W.R., & Rollnick, S., (2013). Motivational interviewing: Helping people change (3rd edn). Guilford Press.

Miller, W., Moyers, T., 2018. Motivational interviewing and the clinical science of Carl Rogers. Journal of Consulting and Clinical Psychology 85 (8), 757–766.

Murray, M., 2010. Health psychology in context. The European Health Psychologist 12, 39–41.

Ntoumanis, N., Ng, J.Y.Y., Prestwich, A., et al. 2021. A meta-analysis of self-determination theory-informed intervention studies in the health domain: effects on motivation, health behavior, physical, and psychological health. Health Psychology Review, 15 (2), 214–244.

Palmer, C., 2016. Therapeutic interventions. In: Evans, R., Nizette, D., O'Brien, A. (eds.), Psychiatric and Mental Health Nursing, fourth ed. Elsevier, Sydney, (Chapter 25).

Pavlov, I.P., 1927. Conditioned Reflexes: An Investigation of the Physiological Activity of the Cerebral Cortex. Oxford University Press, London.

Pears, S. & Sutton, S. 2021. Effectiveness of Acceptance and Commitment Therapy (ACT) interventions for promoting physical activity: a systematic review and meta-analysis. Health Psychology Review, 15 (1), 159–184.

Prochaska, J., 2006. Moving beyond the transtheoretical model. Addiction (Abingdon, England) 101 (6), 768–778.

Prochaska, J., DiClemente, C., 1984. The Transtheoretical Approach: Crossing Traditional Boundaries of Therapy. Dow Jones/Irwin, Chicago.

Prochaska, J., DiClemente, C.C., Norcross, J.C., 1992. In search of how people change: applications to addictive behaviors. The American Psychologist 47, 1102–1114.

Prochaska, J., Norcross, J., 2018. Systems of Psychotherapy: A Transtheoretical Analysis, 9th edn. Oxford University Press, London.

Rosenstock, I., 1966. Why people use health services. The Milbank Memorial Fund Quarterly 44, 94–124.

Rosenstock, I., 1974. Historical origins of the health belief model. Health Education Monographs 2, 1–8.

Schwarzer, R., 1992. Self-Efficacy: Thought Control of Action. Hemisphere, Washington.

Schwarzer, R., 2014. Health action process approach. Available: http://userpage.fu-berlin. de/~health/hapa.htm (Accessed 31 March 2022).

Sheeran, P., Webb, T.L. 2016. The Intention-Behavior Gap. Social and Personality Psychology Compass, 10, 503–518.

Skinner, B.F., 1953. Science and Human Behaviour. Macmillan, New York.

Skinner, C. S., Tiro, J. & Champion, V. L. 2015. The Health Belief Model. In: Glanz, K., Rimer, B.K. Viswanath, K. (Eds.), Health Behavior and Health Education: Theory Research and Practice. 5th edn. Jossey-Bass, San Francisco, pp. 75–94.

Steffen, P.L.S., Mendonça, C.S., Meyer, E. et al. 2021. Motivational interviewing in the management of type 2 diabetes mellitus and arterial hypertension in primary health care: an RCT. American Journal of Preventive Medicine 60, e203–e212.

Vincenzo, J.L., Patton, S.K., Lefler, L.L., et al., 2022. A qualitative study of older adults' facilitators, barriers, and cues to action to engage in falls prevention using health belief model constructs, Archives of Gerontology and Geriatrics, 99, 104610.

Whittal, A., Störk, S., Riegel, B., et al., 2021. Applying the COM-B behaviour model to overcome barriers to heart failure self-care: A practical application of a conceptual framework for the development of complex interventions (ACHIEVE study). European Journal of Cardiovascular Nursing. 20, 261–267.

Wickham, S.-R., Amarasekara, N.A., Bartonicek, A., et al., 2020. The big three health behaviors and mental health and well-being among young adults: a cross-sectional investigation of sleep, exercise, and diet. Frontiers in Psychology, 11, 579205.

Willmott, T.J., Pang, B. & Rundle-Thiele, S. 2021. Capability, opportunity, and motivation: an across contexts empirical examination of the COM-B model. BMC Public Health 21, 1014.

Wolpe, J. 1968, Psychotherapy by reciprocal inhibition. Conditional Reflex 3, 234–240.

Wood, J., 2012. Interpersonal Communication: Everyday Encounters, 7th edn. Cengage Learning, Wadsworth.

Zhang, C., Zhang, R., Schwarzer, R., et al., 2019. A meta-analysis of the health action process approach. Health Psychology, 38 (7), 623–637.

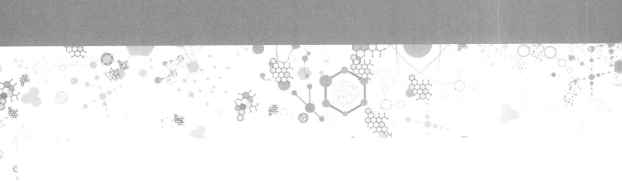

Section 2
Aspects of psychology in healthcare practice

Chapter 8

Learning objectives

The material in this chapter will help you to:

- describe basic interpersonal communication principles
- understand the importance of person-centred communication
- identify the key skills of active listening to facilitate effective communication
- identify important ethical communication issues
- understand the process of cultural safety and intercultural communication
- understand the role of communication within a multidisciplinary team
- identify communication issues between health professionals such as horizontal bullying
- understand the role of health professionals in health education to promote evidence-based health literacy.

Key terms

- Person-centred communication (210)
- Active listening (211)
- Intercultural communication (215)
- Power imbalance (218)
- Professional boundaries (218)
- Self-disclosure (218)
- Health literacy (223)
- Advocacy (226)
- Multidisciplinary team (227)
- Interdisciplinary team (227)

Introduction

It could be claimed that effective communication is the core of health care and is a key requirement for safe and effective practice. It occurs when a client describes their joint pain to a physiotherapist, when a paramedic hands over a patient to an emergency nurse or when a pharmacist listens to the symptoms being described by a customer. It is part of a health professional's everyday working practice and is a complex and multifactorial process that is vital in all parts of healthcare interactions. Furthermore, effective communication can increase a client's perceptions of healthcare quality, satisfaction and treatment outcomes by building partnerships to support mutual cooperation (Australian Commission on Safety and Quality in Health Care [ACSQHC] 2017). The National Safety and Quality Health Service Standards highlight the need for effective communication between professionals, organisations, services and clients (ACSQHC 2017).

Being able to communicate effectively will assist you in working with clients, families and carers, supporting them in shared responsibility and decision making about their health and lifestyle. Effective communication is not just about being able to talk clearly; it is also about listening and understanding what has been communicated. Listening is critical when working with other people, and a health professional who can listen well will find people more willing to talk openly and honestly about their health issues.

Health psychologists are interested in knowing how health professionals communicate in practice and what can be done to improve this to enhance the relationship between all parties involved. This chapter will examine the fundamental aspects of communication in healthcare practice, focusing on the challenges and variables health professionals need to consider when working with other people in care delivery. The partnerships that can be developed from effective communication are examined in Chapter 12.

Person-centred communication

Person-centred communication is one of the most important dimensions of health professional–client communication. In the past, clients have often been seen as a 'diagnosis' ('the broken leg in bed 1'), with a focus on assessment and symptom management. Lack of attention to other factors such as the social, psychological and behavioural aspects of the person's life has left the client without a context for their health issue and often feeling 'unheard'. Research in clinical settings has shown that people who are provided client-centred care experience better health outcomes (Edvardsson 2017; Hack et al. 2017) and greater client satisfaction (McMillan 2017). Research in the United States and Europe also demonstrates a strong correlation between client satisfaction and the interpersonal skills of health professionals (Bauchat et al. 2016; Boissy et al. 2016), making it even more vital for health professionals to develop effective communication skills and behaviours in their daily practice. So with this in mind, what is person-centred communication?

Person-centred communication is a collection of skills used by health professionals that are respectful and responsive to the client's needs, values and preferences (Delaney 2018). It is not always easy to define the exact level or type of communication required for each client because the variation in people's needs and experiences are unique for each individual. What is important to remember is that person-centred communication is not limited to verbal communication but embraces all forms of communication that can affect client care such as written and non-verbal elements. Success depends on both parties (the client and the health professional) being able to speak, question and listen. It is a two-way process in which the language and meaning in the message is correctly understood by both, enabling an accurate exchange of information, thus enabling the client to take part in their own care (Delaney 2018).

SKILLS OF COMMUNICATION

In providing appropriate health care, it is important for all health professionals to consider their own communication style by examining the skills they already possess and those they need to develop to be able to communicate successfully with clients, families and other health/service providers. It also helps to have a personal awareness of the likely barriers of communication in practice. Inadequate communication can cause distress for clients and their families. Confusion, uncertainty and being unsure of what's being said can leave clients feeling unclear of their illness, diagnosis, treatment or management plan.

Most communication textbooks focus on the process of communication or identify groups of different behaviours and qualities that are collectively known as communication skills. The essence of good communication lies within the skills required to deliver and receive the message effectively and include such skills as **active listening**, reflection, empathy, body language and vocal style. Whether referred to as attending behaviours or micro skills, the key element of good communication is to extract the unique experiences and preferences of the client and respond appropriately and effectively (O'Kane & Smith 2017).

FACILITATING THE INTERACTION

When meeting a client and their family, it's good practice to always begin by introducing yourself, saying who you are (status/discipline) and what role you will play in their care. Similarly, check how the client would like to be addressed and if they have any questions or concerns.

Ways of encouraging the person to speak about their experience may vary. Ivey and colleagues (2022) write about the importance of 'open invitations to talk' or open-ended questions in encouraging communication in comparison with closed questions. Open-ended questions provide emotional space and often encourage longer responses: 'Tell me what it's been like to have rheumatoid arthritis'; 'Could you tell me ...?'; 'I'm wondering ...'; 'Some people have experienced ... how does it feel for you?' Closed questions are often effective when requiring factual content and shorter responses: 'How many years have you had rheumatoid arthritis?'; 'What is your date of birth?'; 'Do you have a regular doctor?' Both types of questions are useful in health care, but sometimes closed questions get in the way of two-way interaction, and open-ended questions don't always yield clear information, so it's helpful to know what information you are seeking to guide the conversation (Balzer Riley 2021). Of course, the response will also depend on the individual. It is not a satisfactory experience for the client to be asked repeated closed questions, with no other comments. There is also the danger that continued open-ended questions generate little concrete information and can annoy the client. A variety of different types of questions and comments will often not only produce more in-depth responses, it will also help build rapport and encourage the client to be more cooperative (Balzer Riley 2021). Practice will help in developing these skills. Reflecting on your everyday communication, it may be surprising to find how often each of these kinds of questions are already used. The following micro skills also facilitate effective communication:

- minimal encouragers
- empathy
- reflection
- summarising.

Minimal encouragers

Minimal encouragers can indicate to the person that the helper understands what they are saying. These can be non-verbal, such as the occasional eye contact, leaning forward or nodding the head, or verbal, such as: 'Oh?', 'So?', 'Then?', 'And?', 'Uh-huh' or a restatement of the same words spoken by the other person: 'So you feel that the treatment was a waste of time ...'. Sometimes silence is very effective, showing the client you are listening and allowing them to gather their thoughts and say more about a particular topic (Kemerer 2016). It is useful to observe how other people show their interest in what someone is saying to them and how different behaviours encourage or discourage a conversation continuing. The important skill is to be aware of how the interaction is flowing and how the client is responding to what the health professional is saying. If the client appears anxious or annoyed, or displaying clues to other feelings, then it is better to explore these in the first instance: 'You seem a little anxious. Are you happy to continue?' This demonstrates concern and also helps build rapport. There are a variety of ways of showing clients you understand what is being said and that also help you organise your own thoughts.

Empathy

An important aspect of communication is the use of empathy whereby the health professional lets the person know he or she is sensing the person's thoughts and emotions. Gerace (2017, 2018) believes our daily interactions hinge on the skill of being able to take others' perspectives and to feel with the other person; this in turn adds to one's understanding of their experience and the ability to help them. The question is whether empathy is a quality inherent in the individual or if it is a skill that can be taught. Rogers (1987, p. 38) states that 'sensitive empathy, with all its intensity and personal involvement, cannot be taught' whereby Gerace (2017, 2018) asserts that health professionals can in fact improve their empathy by engaging in deliberate perspective-taking skills such as imagining oneself in another's situation. While some health professionals may be naturally empathic, there is always good reason for all health professionals to strengthen their skills in this important aspect of building rapport and a relationship with clients.

Reflection

As a beginning health professional, it is often helpful to practise reflection of feelings—that is, reflecting back the person's feelings, listening and responding to the emotions being expressed, not just the content of what they have said (Ivey et al. 2022). The actual words used will vary, but it may simply mean repeating back what the other person has said such as, 'So you were anxious about taking the medication?' Similarly, it might be more supportive to the client to say, 'I get the feeling it was quite a frightening time for you.' Of course, while this can be supportive to clients, some may find it threatening because they might not wish to divulge their feelings. Another useful technique is paraphrasing. At intervals during the interaction it can help to check you are correct in understanding the meaning of what's being said by simply repeating back what the other person has said in your own words. This not only conveys understanding, it adds clarity to the conversation and reduces the possibility of misunderstanding: 'So you are finding it difficult to express yourself since the stroke and on occasions struggle to understand what others are saying' (O'Kane & Smith 2017).

Summarising

At the end of a discussion, summarising the conversation can prove useful. This is similar to paraphrasing but sums up the whole conversation. 'So, if I've got it right, what you have been telling me is ...' This can help clients review what they have told you and once again benefit the health professional by checking they have understood what has been said (Balzer Riley 2021). In a busy clinical environment summarising may take extra time, but it can frequently help improve your understanding of a situation and a client may appreciate and feel their health issues have been understood accurately. It has been the writer's experience that international healthcare students, with English as a second language, often find summarising helpful because it provides a clarification tool to use when they aren't clear what the client has said.

Common identified skills for effective communication in a healthcare setting between client and provider are noted in Table 8.1.

Table 8.1	
EFFECTIVE COMMUNICATION IN A HEALTHCARE SETTING	
Engage	Establish eye contact to show interest.
	Ask both open and closed questions to encourage clients to be exact about their health concerns/behaviour.
	Ask the goals and preferences of the client in recognition of their role and involvement in their own care and to ensure decisions are appropriate, realistic and facilitate self-management.
Listen	Use 'active listening' such as clarifying, paraphrasing and responding to verbal and non-verbal cues to help ascertain what the client is concerned about.

Cont... ▶

Table 8.1	
EFFECTIVE COMMUNICATION IN A HEALTHCARE SETTING—cont'd	
Clarify/ reflect	Summarise information to show clients they have been heard. Constantly check if the client has understood the information, and provide opportunities to question what's being said to avoid misunderstandings and avoid the loss of critical information.
Enquire	Enquire about all areas of the person's life, not just the problem area. This ensures you get an accurate description of not only the physical problem but the social and psychological impact it may be having on the client and family.
Convey empathy	Be empathic by reflecting and verbalising your sense of the client's feelings and meanings of the problem behaviour. It acknowledges the client as a person and will show you are trying to see things from their point of view and offering support.

Adapted from Maguire & Pitceathly 2002

The importance of language

Words alone do not convey meaning or understanding. It is important to remember that a layperson may have less knowledge about basic anatomy and physiology than you might assume. Medical terminology that has become part of a health professional's everyday language is useless jargon if not understood by the listener. Therefore, health professionals cannot assume that everyone with whom they engage will understand their meaning (Silverman et al. 2016).

LANGUAGE AND CULTURE

Throughout the decades, linguists and anthropologists have proposed that words and language are strongly influenced by culture, with language playing a key part in enabling a person to identify who they are as an individual and in society (Otto 2017). Vygotsky (1962) proposed that children are born with the skills for language development that are then shaped by the child's cultural and social experience. Given the culture in which a person develops has its own values, beliefs and tools, these in turn influence cognitive functions, including language development. Often a person's culture will influence the way they see and engage with the world, so it is useful for health professionals to reflect on their own culture and try to understand it in the context of their practice. Culture, however, is multifaceted and should not be reduced to a particular behaviour or attribute in one particular population group but considered in light of all available information including thoughts, beliefs, attitudes, behaviour, background, heritage and spirituality.

In a multicultural society, language proficiency between clients, families and the members of the health team may differ considerably. Language barriers such as working with foreign language–speaking clients or people with cultural differences can present challenges to providing effective communication. Similarly, linguistic differences such as the use of colloquial language, slang words and euphemisms, particularly by people too embarrassed to speak about personal matters, can cause confusion and misunderstanding. Unless familiar with the terminology, it may appear to the health professional that a client is speaking a whole new language. For example, an elderly lady may ask to 'spend a penny' to describe her need to urinate or a child may say they have a 'tummy bug' to describe a recent virus they are recovering from. In some cultures there may be several words within the language that can be used to describe one concept, whereas in other languages even one word may not be present for that concept. Ultimately, what means one thing to one person may mean something entirely different to somebody else, so it is up to the health professional to avoid language that can be misleading or ambiguous by clarifying all medical terminology. Asking the client to repeat their understanding of the issue ensures all parties have a shared understanding.

INTERCULTURAL COMMUNICATION AND CULTURAL SAFETY

While most health services offer the use of interpreters, translation officers, Aboriginal liaison officers or health liaison officers to support linguistic communication, it may not always encompass all aspects of cultural safety. Originally proposed to redress Māori health inequities, Māori nurses in New Zealand developed a model of cultural safe practice (see Table 8.2) (Nursing Council of New Zealand 2011). Though the elements of cultural awareness, cultural sensitivity and cultural safety are interrelated, they should also be understood in their own right to guarantee culturally safe communication with others. The foundation of all culturally safe practice is communication. Implementing critical self-examination and reflecting on the power structures that influence health inequity, the impact of colonisation on minority groups and safeguarding cultural safety as being defined by those who receive it will certainly support health professionals in their practice.

Strongly linked with cultural safety is the process of **intercultural communication**. Effective intercultural communication demonstrates a meaningful and respectful understanding no matter what a person's identity and culture. It acknowledges

Table 8.2		
KEY ELEMENTS TO ACHIEVING CULTURAL SAFETY IN HEALTHCARE PRACTICE		
Cultural awareness	Cultural sensitivity	Cultural safety
A beginning step towards understanding there is difference. Many people undergo courses designed to sensitise them to formal ritual and practice rather than the emotional, social, economic and political context in which people exist.	Alerts health professionals to the legitimacy of difference and begins a process of self-reflection on the powerful influences from their own life experiences that may impact on their interaction with others.	An outcome of health education that enables safe service to be defined by those who receive the service. It is achieved when the client perceives their health care was delivered in a way that respected and preserved their cultural integrity.

Source: Adapted from Nursing Council of New Zealand 2011

communication processes may be different even within a similar culture. For example, within Australia the First Nations population reflects a heterogeneous society with several different and unique language groups and clans. Similarly, though English is the official language of Australia and New Zealand, it is not a first language for a significant number of citizens. Australia and New Zealand have a growing multicultural population with a huge diversity of first, second and subsequent generations who each may have distinctive cultural and linguistic needs (Kerrigan et al. 2020). Intercultural communication is a valuable aspect of maintaining cultural safety and if not addressed can contribute to a breakdown in communication and ultimately have a significant impact on the effectiveness of health care. For instance, ineffective communication has been identified in Australian research as one of the main factors leading to poor health outcomes in Indigenous Australians (Curtis et al. 2019; Jennings et al. 2018). A health professional who can identify factors that impede or enable communication in health service delivery, recognise the unique differences in people, maintain cultural awareness, be sensitive to clients' needs and engage in culturally safe dialogue will play an important role in maintaining effective communication and the delivery of safe clinical services.

There are several mnemonic tools that enhance the communication experience by building a mutual understanding of care. These include the LEARN model (Berlin & Fowkes 1983), the ETHNIC(s) model (Levin et al. 2000) and the ADHERE model (Soto-Greene et al. 2004), but some of the key areas to consider when engaging with people from culturally diverse backgrounds are as follows:

- Speak clearly and simply without being simplistic or patronising.
- Place yourself in the client's situation and think how you would like to be treated.
- Clarify meaning: both yours and that of others.
- Be aware of your own non-verbal behaviour and the way you interpret that of others.
- Monitor your own style and the way you respond to difference.
- Relate to others as individuals, recognising similarities rather than only differences.
- Ensure you understand your clients' living arrangements, relationships and accessibility to health services.
- Ask questions if you do not understand (if in doubt, ask).

☀ Critical thinking

- Have you had experience learning a second language? What were the challenges and benefits from doing this?
- Think of a time when you tried to convey a particular verbal message but the recipient did not understand you.
  - » What reasons may have caused this misunderstanding?
  - » How did you resolve the issue? Did this help or hinder the situation?
  - » How will you address the issue if it occurs in a health setting?
- How is language different in personal and professional relationships?

The health professional–client relationship

In identifying the skills needed for effective communication, it is easy to see them as mere lists made up of concrete, discrete behavioural actions without considering the importance of relationship development and the connection needed between clients and health professionals. The importance of caring and humanity is emphasised by the seminal speech from Dr Francis Peabody:

One of the essential qualities of the clinician is interest in humanity, for the secret of the care of the patient is in caring for the patient.

(Peabody 1927)

Similarly, pioneers such as Jean Watson and Kristen Swanson have developed theories based around the concept of caring, with identified elements that support factors such as commitment, trust and continuity and are central to caring practice, communication and the healthcare relationship (Wolf & France 2017). Through the helping relationship, health professionals and clients may share a sense of two people working together, having a sense of shared humanity that is essential to the spiritual, psychological and humanistic dimensions of the relationship (Stein-Parbury 2021). Although clinical skills and knowledge are very important in being a safe and competent health professional, it must never be forgotten that the tasks and procedures are being implemented on real people with real feelings of pain, fear and a wide range of other emotions and sensations. To be able to enter into their experience is not simply a right for health professionals but a privilege that clients have given via their consent and trust.

INTERPERSONAL RELATIONSHIPS, ETHICS AND COMMUNICATION

Interpersonal relationships can be both personal and professional, with interpersonal interactions being central to both (Balzer Riley 2021). Personal relationships may include friendships and intimate or romantic relationships, whereas a health professional–client relationship, though therapeutic, is a professional relationship established to meet the needs of the client. What, then, is the best way to relate to clients? How does a client wish for health professionals to relate to them? By being sensitive to how a client behaves in interactions and modifying responses in line with this is a good starting point. Sitting in the waiting room of a health clinic, you may observe the approaches of various receptionists to clients. Some vary their style depending on the client. They may address them using their first name or title; they know the client and how to communicate with them. Others don't vary in their approach, always using the first name or a colloquial term such as 'darl'; it is interesting to see how some clients are quite relaxed about this, while others visibly bristle. Being an effective communicator means trying to 'read' clients and how they respond to what you say and do (Balzer Riley 2021). Of course, the task will often dictate the interaction; you might be assessing the person's health status, taking a blood specimen or consulting them about their dietary needs, while at the same time engaging in a conversation about the weather or their interests outside the healthcare situation. Conversation may act as a means of lessening the client's (and sometimes the health professional's) anxiety or generally defusing the tension of a situation. Again, the focus should always be on the client and what their needs are.

Ethical behaviour is essential for delivering high-quality health care. As a health professional there are explicit ethical obligations related to communication that are fundamental to developing and maintaining a professional relationship (Houghton 2016). These can include informed consent, confidentiality and conflict to name a few. Each brings with it fresh challenges the health professional may face on a daily basis. Let's look at three common ethical issues of communication in more detail. These are **power imbalance**, **professional boundaries** and **self-disclosure**.

Power imbalance

When health professionals are consulted, it is more often than not because they are seen as an expert in a particular area and the client is seeking help from someone who they deem has the skill and knowledge to help them. Though not necessarily perceived by the health professional, having the skills, knowledge, influence and authority that the client requires inadvertently leads to an inherent power disequilibrium between the two parties. The practitioner is in a position of power, while the client may feel vulnerable.

It is important for the client to feel comfortable in confiding their concerns or health issues with the health professional without feeling they are relinquishing their own responsibility and control over any decisions concerning them. A health professional who provides information encourages the client to be an active partner in the therapeutic alliance. Using micro skills during communication will go some way to alleviating this power imbalance, whereas a misuse of this power is considered abuse.

Professional boundaries

As Sharma (2015) asserts, 'the concept of relationship boundaries helps to identify and avoid situations in which harm or exploitation of the patient might occur'. Thus, knowing the bounds of one's behaviour when working with clients is useful to avoid violating the parameters of the relationship. In today's healthcare environment, however, roles are much less differentiated than in previous years, and health workers might now be more open and reveal more of their own personalities than before. For example, in many health services, health professionals wear casual-looking clothes rather than a formal uniform or the traditional white coat, so it can be confusing for a person to know the role of the person assisting them. At a time when roles are more blurred and many express the need to be treated as equals, developing a relationship with the appropriate professional boundaries can be an uncertain road to navigate.

Ultimately, the relationship one forms with a client differs from those we form with friends and family. On occasion it may be appropriate to be informal and engage in some aspects of social conversation with a client, though initially the key issue is to be first sensitive to the individual and work at establishing a helping relationship. For example, it might be preferable to address someone by their title and family name until it is later established the person is comfortable to be called by their first name.

While some boundaries are very clear and inviolable (e.g. physical, verbal or sexual abuse) others can be blurred (e.g. when the client asks about your marital status or invites you on a date), and require the health professional to be aware of when the professional relationship may cross a boundary or move into a 'grey' area. This requires self-reflection on the part of a health professional and the willingness to discuss the relationship dilemma with a manager or supervisor who will be able to consider the context of the relationship and offer advice. Being aware of one's responsibility at all times helps establish and maintain a professional relationship by setting clear boundaries regardless of how the client has behaved.

Another 'grey' area to consider is the possibility of a dual relationship. This can become particularly apparent in small communities, such as in rural and remote areas (Sharma 2015). Due to a small population size, the health professional may have both a personal and a professional relationship with the client—that is, they are a close friend as well as the practitioner caring for them. It is therefore of paramount importance that all aspects of the relationship such as role and boundary shifts are clarified by articulating what your role and responsibilities will include while working with the person as a health professional. Communicating in such a transparent manner helps protect client confidentiality and ensures the client's needs are a priority.

Self-disclosure

There are invisible boundaries that all people erect around themselves, depending on the situation. This impacts on who one chooses to disclose personal information to. Self-disclosure (revealing personal information about our lives to others) is generally accepted as a valuable tool in personal relationships and can be just as valuable in a professional relationship if used appropriately and in moderation. Although self-disclosure by the health professional to the client is unacceptable in most contexts, it may be appropriate in special circumstances. For example, a mother who has recently experienced a 28-week gestation pregnancy loss and is struggling to grieve for the child may find it useful to hear about what proved helpful in the grieving process from a health professional who has gone through a similar experience. This kind of select and limited disclosure may be helpful in meeting the therapeutic needs of the client.

It is never acceptable for a health professional to disclose information that is self-serving or intimate. To avoid blurring boundaries, the required skill is to know what is considered suitable personal information to discuss and to ask the question 'Is it appropriate to do so?' while remaining within the scope of the professional relationship. It is the responsibility of health professionals to direct their attention to the needs of the client as being first and foremost, rather than their own. In reflecting on this, one can ask: 'Whose needs are being served by my self-disclosure?'

☉ Critical thinking

Consider the behaviours, language and beliefs that define a professional relationship.

- How does this differ from a personal one?
- How is this decided?

Student activity

In small groups, address the questions posed by the given scenarios.

Discuss the key issues identified and the implications each may have on health professionals and their communication practice with clients.

Scenario 1
You are a doctor providing primary health care for a small Aboriginal community. While you are at the post office collecting your mail on your day off, the wife of a client who is under your care asks for your opinion on her husband's latest blood results. What ethical issues arise in this situation? How would you respond and why?

Scenario 2
You are the nurse on a surgical ward preparing a 50-year-old woman for a hysterectomy. She is very anxious and tearful, saying she is afraid that she will no longer feel 'whole' or like a woman. You are of a similar age and have gone through the same surgical procedure. Do you think it would be helpful to share your experience with her? Explain why.

COMMUNICATING BAD NEWS

Arguably one of the most difficult tasks for health professionals is breaking bad news to a client or their family. It's a conversation that can often cause discomfort and be stressful for those involved in care. For decades social psychologists have been examining the communication process of delivering bad news, with the term, 'MUM effect' coined in 1970 to reflect the reluctance of conveying news that may provoke a negative emotion in the receiver (Rosen & Tesser 1970). The MUM effect is based on the assumption that people would prefer to keep silent, that is, 'mum's the word' when faced with the difficult situation of choosing what to say. Historically, withholding bad news was common practice (Oken 1961). However, as health care advances, beliefs of what information is shared has also changed. With the progression of person-centred care, keeping a person involved and updated in all aspects of their care is strongly advocated, so health professionals are often faced with the sensitive issue of communicating bad news as well as good news. More recent research informs us that most people prefer to be told the truth about their health and accept that families often play a key role in this process (Igier et al. 2015; Zolkefli 2018).

The delivery and reception of information can be on many different levels and is unique to each person. What is considered bad news for one person may not be so distressing for someone else, therefore bad news is a subjective experience. As proposed by Buckman (1984), it is not the role of a health professional to judge what defines bad news but instead take into account 'any news that adversely and seriously affects an individual's view of his or her future'. Other researchers suggest the term 'bad news' be replaced with 'significant news' (Mishelmovich et al. 2016), but there appears to be little uptake of this.

Health professionals are not necessarily taught how to deliver bad news, yet the delivery of the information can have a dramatic impact on the person's understanding of the situation and their response. While most bad news may be delivered by the leading physician, there are many instances when other health professionals are required to be involved or take the lead due to their established relationship with the client.

One of the most commonly used strategies developed to assist health professionals when faced with the task of breaking bad news is known as SPIKES approach (Baile et al. 2000; see Box 8.1). This is an excellent tool to support and

Box 8.1 The SPIKES approach

S	Setting up	Plan ahead for details such as being sure you are in a private, comfortable setting. Check to see if the client wishes for others to be present. Prepare what you will say. Avoid being interrupted.
P	Perception of condition / seriousness	Ask what the client knows. Ask open-ended questions to find out how they perceive the medical situation. In this way you can correct any misunderstanding the patient has and tailor the news to the patient's understanding and expectations.
I	Invite the client to provide information	Find out how much detailed information the client wants to know about their diagnosis and prognosis. Allow the client to nominate another person to communicate on their behalf.
K	Knowledge—giving the facts	This is 'telling' the information. Be clear, specific and concise. Provide small amounts of information at a time and give the client time to listen and process what's being said. Check for understanding. Provide time by pausing between each piece of information. Avoid medical jargon. Communicate in ways that help the client assimilate the information. 'Unfortunately it's not good news. I'm sorry to tell you ...' is one example of how you can initiate the step of delivering the information.
E	Explore emotions and empathise	Be prepared for a reaction by anticipating the response. Address the client's emotions using active listening skills such as identifying the primary emotion and conveying that you recognise what the client is feeling such as distress, fear or any other emotion. Resist trying to 'soften' the news by making it sound more hopeful or better than it is. Express empathy and support and clarify any uncertainties the client may have.
S	Strategy and summary	Check out for further questions or concerns and clarify any outstanding issues. Present treatment or care options available and plan for the next step.

Source: Adapted from Baile et al. 2000

facilitate empathic communication by prompting health professionals to consider different aspects of conveying information. Yet, as with any such strategy, there is risk of it becoming a 'tick box' exercise and therefore is not without flaw. Remaining empathic, allowing time to digest the information and actually listening to what's being said in both verbal and non-verbal messages contributes significantly to quality clinical practice.

Other influences on communication in healthcare settings

Individual health professional–client interactions may not always be successful. Some health professionals, as well as clients, are not easy to work with and may behave in unreasonable ways, be uncooperative or be physically or verbally aggressive at times. Particularly, but not just in large healthcare organisations, status can be an issue. Some health professionals within the service may be considered, or consider themselves, to have higher status than others. Furthermore, administrators you may not know or ever communicate with make decisions affecting the work situation. This may give the feeling of a narrow span of control, which may in turn lead to a high level of informal communication or gossip between staff such as, 'Did you hear about ...?'

The diverse educational backgrounds of professionals and staff in a healthcare service may contribute to communication problems. Various disciplines may have jargon or specialised language that other health professionals (or clients) may not understand. Different staff will have varying qualifications, which can make for rivalry between different disciplines. A person may be an excellent health professional but have little or no administrative skill but, because of their seniority, may have been given management responsibilities. Decisions they make and how they communicate these decisions to others in the team may not always be appropriate and effective for team working.

An ongoing concern in health care is the issue of horizontal violence or bullying, sometimes called lateral violence. Though horizontal violence takes many forms, one of its common characteristics includes 'overt and covert non-physical hostility'. Such communication from one or more people towards an individual can be disrespectful, offensive or undermining, leading to feelings of helplessness, humiliation and being harassed or bullied. One group highlighted as frequently, but not exclusively, exposed to horizontal violence are new nursing graduates, though the problem can manifest between any team members irrespective of gender, age, experience or discipline (Taylor & Taylor 2017).

In light of this issue and the others mentioned, it is important to consider ways of dealing with challenging situations or trying to avoid them happening, and to promote better communication between all levels of staff. Various ways of sharing decision making and promoting consultation are to be encouraged within organisations and teams. This should include ensuring there is provision for down–up as well as up–down communication between all areas of the hierarchy through regular meetings and social contact. Another way of enhancing staff-to-staff communication and providing for professional growth and development is to encourage and provide clinical supervision, support and mentoring. And finally, all organisations should have a good mix of staff from a variety of cultural and ethnic backgrounds.

Health literacy and client education

Although much of a health professional's time centres on treatment, an important role in working with clients is that of providing information to individuals and groups. Apart from professionals who work full-time in health promotion, many health professionals may think their role in client education is limited to handing out a booklet or showing a DVD to a client before they are discharged. However, with increasingly short lengths of stay in hospital and people being more knowledgeable about health matters, it is an area of increasing importance in clinical practice and research, particularly in relation to health literacy.

Health literacy describes a range of outcomes related to a person's ability to access, process and understand health information that allows them to make the most appropriate decisions concerning their personal health and wellbeing. Incorporating far more than the narrow concept of health education, health literacy encompasses and addresses political, social and environmental factors that also influence health such as those discussed in Chapter 6.

Common components of health literacy include:

- *functional literacy*—skills such as reading, writing and numeracy

- *conceptual literacy*—skills such as seeking, appraising, evaluating and comprehending information

- *health literacy as empowerment*—increasing individual and collective participation via motivation, commitment, advocacy and political actions.

With debate still in its infancy as to what constitutes 'health literacy', Sorensen and colleagues (2012) proposed an integrated conceptual model reflecting the key points taken from existing models developed over the past decade. This framework (Fig. 8.1) identifies the dimensions of health literacy where skills such as listening, reading, writing, numeracy, interpreting and appraising information are essential if the client is to function and navigate healthcare services effectively (Liu et al. 2020; Sorensen et al. 2012).

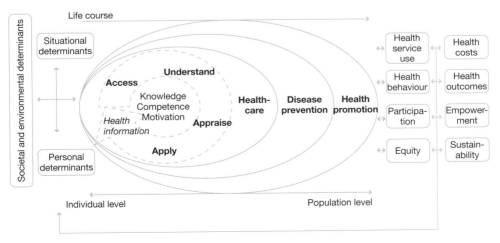

Figure 8.1 Integrated model of health literacy Source: Sorensen et al. 2012

Recent research indicates that low health literacy can result in poor health outcomes, increased healthcare costs and higher hospitalisations. For example, a person with limited health literacy is more at risk of missing appointments, less likely to follow health advice or more likely to mismanage their medications (Australian Institute of Health and Welfare 2020; Rudd 2015; World Health Organization 2022a). With about 60% of the population in both Australia and New Zealand struggling to meet their healthcare needs due to a lack of sufficient health literacy, it is now part of national policy highlighting key strategies of how it can be improved within health and the public sector (ACSQHC 2014; Ministry of Health 2015). Being health literate empowers people to use the information they have received and to act on it effectively, hence communication between the client and health professional involves information dissemination, participation and critical analysis to ensure a shared understanding of the health issue and the options available. The overarching aim is to foster individual and collective actions for long-term health, safety and quality.

Various professional bodies emphasise the importance of educating clients about their health status. For example, the Australian Physiotherapy Association (2011) includes in its standards the importance of providing education to clients as part of health promotion and prevention strategies. For most health professionals, client education is a core part of their role since it helps clients gain knowledge and, therefore, supports them in managing their needs. The approach one takes will depend on whether a health professional is working in the community or in a hospital. A healthcare worker in the community may work with individuals, groups, families or carers implementing planned and programmed education sessions, whereas in a hospital you are more likely to work with the individual client and their particular health issue.

So, what are the communication skills needed for successful client education? The foundations of delivering education must be based on sound approaches with a proper understanding of clients' requirements and their ability and motivation to learn, including aspects of culture and literacy. You can first find out what the client already knows by asking questions such as, 'What do you think is going on?' and then move towards questions that address the gaps. It is useful to predict questions the client may ask or information they might wish to know. Questions such as 'What will happen to me?', 'Will it be painful?' and 'When will I know the results?' are common to many areas in healthcare practice. Effective education takes time and patience on the part of health professionals.

SOCIAL MEDIA AND HEALTH LITERACY

With universal use of online search engines and social media, information is easily accessible. A person may already have ideas of what they believe should or should not happen in relation to their health. While online healthcare information has the potential to be an asset to the industry by educating people, promoting healthy behaviours and supporting informed decision making, it is also fraught with difficulties (Laranjo 2015). The recent plague of anti-vaccination messages is a perfect example of scaremongering that can lead to negative health outcomes (Davidson

2017), particularly in relation to the coronavirus pandemic. Although some of the sourced online information is reliable and trustworthy information, the World Health Organization (2022b) warns of an 'infodemic' of information that inaccurately links the COVID-19 outbreak to the 5G mobile network, conspiracy theories, global engineered bioweapons and anti-vaccination messaging.

Consequently, information a client presents may not always reflect best practice, particularly if they have been exposed to false, inaccurate or misleading information. Whether it be a cure for cancer, the use of supplements to enhance energy levels or the latest fad diet, online marketing in the health, nutrition and exercise industry frequently lacks credible evidence, yet is a growing multibillion-dollar business with little or no regulation in Australia and New Zealand.

Celebrity endorsements, personal anecdotes, pseudoscience and scaremongering are often employed to perpetuate a myth, market an alternative or suggest a 'miracle cure'. When a person wants answers or a 'quick fix', it can be difficult to recognise fact from fiction, with many people not knowing how to evaluate good from bad information. Encouraging people to look at multiple sources and review health information sceptically is a way forward to debunk pseudoscience and create an opportunity to discuss evidence-based information and improve health literacy.

A health practitioner's skills of active listening are once again extremely important. The client may be anxious or fearful and unable to process any information being said; therefore, the health professional will need to identify the cues to respond appropriately, whether it is a matter of reassuring the person's uncertainties or expanding their knowledge about the health issue. In such circumstances it can be helpful to also provide written information for the client. In other words, once the cognitive, behavioural and emotional needs of the client have been addressed and understanding is clear to all involved parties, then you can feel confident the client has learned something. In this context not only has education occurred but also person-centred communication.

CASE STUDY: JEMMA

Jemma saw a photo online of a celebrity stating how easy it was to lose her 'baby weight' after giving birth. It depicts the celebrity with a slim, toned figure holding her newborn baby and smiling. The photo distresses Jemma. She has been struggling with her body image since having twins 12 months before and though she would not be considered overweight according to medical criteria, she feels 'fat' and embarrassed that she does not look like the celebrity in the photo. Alongside the photo is an advertisement for a weight-loss pill with before and after photos from people who have tried the pill and a slogan stating, 'Proved to be clinically effective'. Jemma decides to buy the pill despite its high cost.

Advocacy

The healthcare literature defines **advocacy** as protecting and promoting the rights of people who may be vulnerable and incapable of protecting their own interests, and though this is true it can also be argued that it has several dimensions from legal and ethical obligations to philosophical debates about the foundations of healthcare practice. For instance, it may be as straightforward as a professional representing a client by speaking to a senior health professional on behalf of a client who is too anxious to ask questions, is unable to speak for themselves or who wishes for a second opinion, through to a 'whistleblower' publicly exposing unsafe or illegal practices.

For the purpose of this chapter, we are interested in the more specific qualities and skills of being an advocate that enable health professionals to assure people they are getting quality care, whether for the purpose of changing policy and legislation, accessing relevant health and social care information or supporting a person's decision making.

Deemed a professional obligation, various codes of conduct and professional standards underline the importance of advocacy when working with clients. This will involve developing a therapeutic relationship to help promote and protect the client's involvement in making decisions and to act as a mediator between clients and others involved in their care. Communication is central to each of these. Otherwise, how else can one ensure the client is in a position to make informed decisions about their care? The most common features of communication in the role of client advocate include the ability to involve people in all aspects of their own health care by listening, respecting, responding, sharing and supporting people's contributions, including their right to decline treatments (Water et al. 2016). In recognising the need for advocacy, you should also recognise that conflict may occur on some occasions. For example, possible disagreement within the team about a client's management plan, or the decisions made by the client and their family that conflict with those of the healthcare team may lead to differences of opinions emerging. It is essential at times like these for each party to define the area of disagreement in a safe way and to address any concerns. It may be that a resolution cannot be found, but discussing the issue openly can go some way to at least helping understand each other's perspective. Remember, in such situations it is the health professional's responsibility to always keep the client's and family's best interests in mind rather than their own while considering the consequences of how far you as a health professional might wish to take the issue.

Team communication

As a health professional, you may find yourself in a variety of healthcare settings, ranging from large institutions where communication passes down a hierarchy from an administration that has little to do with the everyday life of health professionals, to small teams where there may be a team leader who encourages shared or individual decision making. Up until now the chapter has focused mainly on the one-to-one relationship between a health professional and client. Yet health care frequently involves teamwork, requiring professionals to work effectively with each other using good communication and interpersonal skills.

Multidisciplinary team working usually involves a group of people from different disciplines working independently but simultaneously with the same client, whereas **interdisciplinary team** working facilitates people from different disciplines working collaboratively towards the same goal or outcome. Health professionals for the most part work within either a multidisciplinary team, an interdisciplinary team or a combination of both (Department of Health 2021). Having clear team communication processes enhances not only the team functioning but also an individual member's commitment to the team and its goals. But this is not always an easy process. The training and education of health professionals is often discipline-specific, leading to differences in values, priorities and different communication styles. Teams do not suddenly start to work well together. They need to develop, grow and mature. The team dynamics will constantly change as new staff arrive and established members leave. As in any group of humans spending time together, the dynamics are often complicated, with potential for problems to arise, particularly in relation to communication between members. The more members there are in a team, the more opportunity for misunderstandings and errors being made in communication. In health care this can quite literally be a matter of life and death; therefore, the need for effective communication is critical.

Many of the problems in communication within health care occur due to a breakdown in the listening process. Hearing and listening are distinctly different. Though a team member may hear what is being said, to truly listen requires that person to actively attend, interpret, evaluate and respond to both the verbal and the non-verbal message being relayed. As previously discussed in this chapter, the use of active listening skills is important to let the sender know you are listening and understand everything being said. Repetition, clarification, paraphrasing and reflection are important skills to master whether you are working with one individual or a team.

TeamSTEPPS is one of many team training programs offering structured communication tools to improve interpersonal communication between health professionals. It recommends various mnemonics to aid the communication process between team members. One such mnemonic is SBAR (TeamSTEPPS 2014), which can deliver clear communication about a client's condition in a concise way to other health professionals. SBAR stands for:

- *Situation*—what is happening to the client?
- *Background*—what is the clinical background?
- *Assessment*—what do I think the problem is?
- *Recommendation*—what would I recommend?

Some health services have also added 'Identity', making the mnemonic ISBAR to reflect the process of identifying yourself, the health professional and the client before communicating the relevant information.

Other factors may also influence the ability to work and communicate as part of a health team. With the challenge of increased workloads, staff shortages and the urgency of completing tasks or making decisions within a certain timeframe impacting on health professionals on a frequent if not daily basis, your ability to communicate effectively may become compromised. You may also be distracted by the tasks that need to be completed, begin to experience stress-related behaviour, begin to question personal issues in terms of your own life and its meaning or develop a sense of depersonalisation for both clients and staff.

All these factors contribute to poor communication and to treatment regimens that become focused on completing treatment in the time allowed, rather than on the client's needs.

Research focus

Source: Rowan et al. 2022

ABSTRACT

Background
The use of 'huddles' as part of a daily team communication tool is credited with improving outcomes and adding to patient and employee satisfaction. The aim of the study was to systematically review the literature to explore the impact of huddles within multidisciplinary teams on job satisfaction, engagement and teamwork.

Methods
A systematic review of peer-reviewed literature between the years 2000 and 2020 was undertaken by searching five academic databases, screening for studies that used daily huddles as part of an multidisciplinary team communication tool and included variables such as teamwork and job satisfaction.

Results
From the identified 445 articles, 12 met the criteria for review.

Conclusion
Each study reported favourable evidence of the positive impact of huddles on teamwork and engagement with others. The effectiveness of daily huddles in a healthcare setting demonstrated a significant improvement in the job satisfaction and teamwork for those staff involved within the multidisciplinary team.

Critical thinking

- In your profession, what other disciplines may you work with in health?
- How will you maintain effective communication between each member of the team and the discipline?
- Are you part of any decision making in clinical practice? With whom? How do you find it? What is helpful and what hinders this process?
- Think about a time when an important decision had to be made about a client in your work environment.
  » Were all health professionals in the team involved in the decision? When planning beforehand and defining roles etc., who ultimately had the last word?
  » Was there open communication between all members of the team in making decisions?

Chapter summary

Communication is a fundamental aspect of the health professional–client relationship. As a health professional, whether introducing yourself, assessing clients or working with them to achieve treatment or educational goals, combining effective communication skills with clinical skills and knowledge can help facilitate positive working relationships between you and your clients. Furthermore, an efficient multidisciplinary healthcare team requires effective communication between its members. In summary, good communication skills are an essential part of being a competent health professional.

KEY POINTS

- Communication is a fundamental part of the relationship between health professionals and clients.
- Maintaining ethical obligations related to communication is necessary when developing and maintaining a professional relationship.
- Situation variables influence the quality and type of communication.
- Language and culture play an important role in the communication process.
- Multidisciplinary teamwork is an important aspect of healthcare delivery.
- Client education facilitates self-management of health problems.
- Client advocacy promotes the rights of vulnerable people.

Further reading

Ali, M. 2017. Communication skills 1: benefits of effective communication for patients. Nursing Times 113 (12), 18–19.

Australian Commission on Safety and Quality in Health Care (ACSQHC), 2014. Health Literacy: Taking Action to Improve Safety and Quality. ACSQHC, Sydney.

Elsevier Inc. 2019. Effective Communication for Health Professionals. 2nd edn. Elsevier.

McLeod, S., 2018. Communication rights: fundamental human rights for all. International Journal of Speech-Language Pathology 20 (1), 3–11.

Spieldenner, A., Toyosaki, S. 2020. Intercultural Health Communication. Peter Lang Publishing, Bern.

Villagran, M., Goldsmith, J., Wittenberg-Lyles, E., et al., 2010. Communicating COMFORT: a communication-based model for breaking bad news in health care interactions. Communication Education 59, 220–234.

Walker, C., 2021. Cultural safety and health equity in medical practice. In: Morris K. (ed.), Cole's Medical Practice in New Zealand, 14th edn. Medical Council of New Zealand, Wellington.

World Health Organization, 2016. Framework on People-Centred Integrated Health Services. WHO, Geneva.

Weblinks

Communication skills for health professionals

www.oscehome.com/Communication-Skills.html

This site provides information to improve communication skills particularly related to client interviews.

Cultural connections for learning

www.intstudentsup.org/diversity/cultural_safety/

This site provides international students and clinical staff valuable resources to promote resilience and effective working in the healthcare workforce.

Diversity RX

www.diversityrx.org

This site lists important issues in cross-cultural communication to promote cultural competence.

Clinical and communication skills

www.cetl.org.uk/learning/downloads.html

This site has a variety of resources freely available to enhance practical skills and communication in several settings.

Therapeutic communication skills

www.youtube.com/watch?v=xpFkrD02t1A&feature=related.&gl=AU&hl=en-GB

This video discusses the elements of basic communication and demonstrates various therapeutic communication skills.

References

Australian Commission on Safety and Quality in Health Care (ACSQHC), 2014. National Statement on Health Literacy: Taking Action to Improve Safety and Quality. ACSQHC, Sydney.

Australian Commission on Safety and Quality in Health Care (ACSQHC), 2017. National Safety and Quality Health Service Standards, 2nd edn. ACSQHC, Sydney.

Australian Institute of Health and Welfare, 2020. Health Literacy. Available: https://www.aihw.gov.au/reports/australias-health/health-literacy (accessed 10 February 2022).

Australian Physiotherapy Association, 2011. Standards for Physiotherapy Practices, 8th edn. Available: www.physiotherapy.asn.au/DocumentsFolder/Resources_Private_Practice_Standards_for_physiotherapy_practices_2011.pdf. (Accessed 9 February 2022).

Baile, W.F., Buckman, R., Lenzi, R., et al., 2000. SPIKES—a six-step protocol for delivering bad news: application to the patient with cancer. The Oncologist 5 (4), 302–311. 1 Aug.

Balzer Riley, J., 2021. Communication in Nursing, 9th edn. Elsevier, Missouri.

Bauchat, J.R., Seropian, M., Jeffries, P.R., 2016. Communication and empathy in the patient-centered care model—why simulation-based training is not optional. Clinical Simulation in Nursing 12 (8), 356–359.

Berlin, E.A., & Fowkes, W.C.1983. A teaching framework for cross- cultural health care. The Western Journal of Medicine, 139(6), 934–938.

Boissy, A., Windover, A.K., Bokar, D., et al., 2016. Communication skills training for physicians improves patient satisfaction. Journal of General Internal Medicine 31 (7), 755–761.

Buckman, R., 1984. Breaking bad news: why is it still so difficult? British Medical Journal (Clinical Research Ed.) 288 (6430), 1597–1599.

Curtis, E., Jones, R., Tipene-Leach, D., et al. 2019. Why cultural safety rather than cultural competency is required to achieve health equity: a literature review and recommended definition. International Journal for Equity in Health. 18 (1), 174.

Davidson, M., 2017. Vaccination as a cause of autism—myths and controversies. Dialogues in Clinical Neuroscience 19 (4), 403–407.

Delaney, L.J., 2018. Patient-centred care as an approach to improving health care in Australia. Collegian (Royal College of Nursing, Australia) 25 (1), 119–123.

Department of Health. 2021. An interdisciplinary approach to caring. State Government of Victoria, Melbourne.

Edvardsson, D., Watt, E., Pearce, F., 2017. Patient experiences of caring and person-centredness are associated with perceived nursing care quality. Journal of Advanced Nursing 73 (1), 217–227.

Gerace, A. 2018. The power of empathy. Available http://psytalk.psyssa.com/wp-content/uploads/2018/12/The-power-of-empathy-The-Australian-Psychological-Society.pdf (Accessed 12 February 2022)

Gerace, A., 2017. Knowing me, knowing you: better living through empathy. Available: www.psychologytoday.com/blog/knowing-me-knowing-you/201708/better-living-through-empathy. (Accessed 12 February 2022)

Hack, S.M., Muralidharan, A., Brown, C., et al., 2017. Provider behaviours or consumer participation: how should we measure person-centered care? The International Journal of Person Centered Medicine 17 (1), 14–20.

Houghton, D. 2016. Using ethical decision making and communication skills to minimize conflict. In: Robichaux, C. (ed) Chapter 3. Ethical Competence in Nursing Practice Competencies, Skills, Decision Making. Springer Publishing Company, New York.

Igier, V., Sastre, M.M., Sorum, P.C., et al., 2015. A mapping of people's positions regarding the breaking of bad news to patients. Health Communication 30 (7), 694–701.

Ivey, A.E., Ivey, M.B., Zalaquett, C.P., 2022. Intentional Interviewing and Counseling: Facilitating Client Development in a Multicultural Society, 10th edn. Cengage Learning, Belmont.

Jennings, W., Bond, C., Hill, P.S. 2018. The power of talk and power in talk: a systematic review of Indigenous narratives of culturally safe healthcare communication. Australian Journal of Primary Health. 24 (2), 109–115.

Kemerer, D., 2016. How to use intentional silence. Nursing Standard 31 (2), 42–44.

Kerrigan, V., Lewis, N., Cass, A., et al., 2020. 'How can I do more?' Cultural awareness training for hospital-based healthcare providers working with high Aboriginal caseload. BMC Medical Education 20 (1), 173.

Laranjo, L., Arguel, A., Neves, A.L., et al., 2015. The influence of social networking sites on health behavior change: a systematic review and meta-analysis. Journal of the American Medical Informatics Association 22 (1), 243–256.

Levin S.J., Like R.C., Gottlieb J.E. 2000. ETHNIC: A framework for culturally competent clinical practice. Patient Care, 9 (special issue), 188.

Liu C, Wang D, Liu C, et al. 2020. What is the meaning of health literacy? A systematic review and qualitative synthesis. Family Medicine and Community Health. 8:e000351. Available: https://fmch.bmj.com/content/8/2/e000351 (Accessed 9 February 2022)

Maguire, P., Pitceathly, C., 2002. Key communication skills and how to acquire them. BMJ 325 (7366), 697–700.

McMillan, S., Kelly, F., Hattingh, H.L., et al., 2017. The impact of a person-centred community pharmacy mental health medication support service on consumer outcomes. Journal of Mental Health 27 (2), 164–173.

Ministry of Health, 2015. A Framework for Health Literacy. Ministry of Health, Wellington.

Mishelmovich, N., Arber, A., Odelius, A., 2016. Breaking significant news: the experience of clinical nurse specialists in cancer and palliative care. European Journal of Oncology Nursing 21, 153–159.

Nursing Council of New Zealand, 2011. Guidelines for cultural safety, the Treaty of Waitangi and Māori Health in nursing education and practice. New Zealand, Wellington.

O'Kane, D., Smith, A., 2017. Therapeutic communication. In: Contemporary Psychiatric-Mental Health Nursing: Partnerships in Care. Pearson, Melbourne, pp. 172–193 (Chapter 9).

Oken, D., 1961. What to tell cancer patients: a study of medical attitudes. JAMA: The Journal of the American Medical Association 175, 1120–1128.

Otto, B., 2017. Language Development in Early Childhood, 5th edn. Pearson, Upper Saddle River.

Peabody, F. W. 1927. The Care of the Patient. JAMA: The Journal of the American Medical Association. 88, 877–882.

Rogers, C., 1987. Comments on the issue of equality in psychotherapy. Journal of Humanistic Psychology 27 (1), 38–39.

Rosen, S., Tesser, A., 1970. On reluctance to communicate undesirable information: the MUM effect. Sociometry 33 (3), 253–263.

Rowan, B.L., Anjara, S., De Brún, A., et al. 2022. The impact of huddles on a multidisciplinary healthcare teams' work engagement, teamwork and job satisfaction: a systematic review. Journal of Evaluation in Clinical Practice 28 (3), 382–393.

Rudd, R.E. 2015. The evolving concept of health literacy: new directions for health literacy studies. Journal of Communication in Healthcare 8 (1), 7–9.

Sharma, P., 2015. A case of a patient/physician boundary issue in rural practice and measures to avoid or maintain dual relationships. The Primary Care Companion for CNS Disorders 17 (2).

Silverman, J., Kurtz, S.M., Draper, J., 2016. Skills for Communicating with Patients, 3rd edn. CRC Press London.

Sorensen, K., Van den Broucke, S., Fullam, J., et al., 2012. European Health Literacy Project: health literacy and public health: a systematic review and integration of definitions and models. BMC Public Health 12, 80.

Soto-Greene, M., Salas-Lopez, D., Sanchez, J., et al. 2004. Antecedents to effective treatment of hypertension in Hispanic populations. Clinical Cornerstone 6 (3), 30–36.

Stein-Parbury, J.M., 2021. Patient and Person: Interpersonal Skills in Nursing, 7th edn. Elsevier, Sydney.

Taylor, R.A., Taylor, S.S., 2017. Enactors of horizontal violence: the pathological bully, the self-justified bully and the unprofessional co-worker. Journal of Advanced Nursing 73 (12), 3111–3118.

TeamSTEPPS, 2014. Fundamentals Course: Module 3. Communication. Agency for Healthcare Research and Quality, Rockville. Available: www.ahrq.gov/teamstepps/instructor/fundamentals/module3/slcommunication.html#sl10. (Accessed 10 February 2022).

Vygotsky, L.S., 1962. Thought and Language. MIT Press, Cambridge.

Water, T., Ford, K., Spence, D., et al., 2016. Patient advocacy by nurses – past, present and future. Contemporary Nurse 52 (6), 696–709.

Wolf, Z.R., France, N., 2017. Caring in nursing theory. International Journal for Human Caring 21 (2), 95–108.

World Health Organization, 2022a. About Health Literacy. WHO, Geneva. Available: https://www.euro.who.int/en/health-topics/health-determinants/behavioural-and-cultural-insights-for-health/health-literacy/about-health-literacy. (Accessed 9 February 2022).

World Health Organization, 2022b. Let's flatten the infodemic curve. WHO, Geneva. Available: https://www.who.int/news-room/spotlight/let-s-flatten-the-infodemic-curve (Accessed 9 February 2022).

Zolkefli, Y. 2018. The ethics of truth-telling in health-care settings. The Malaysian Journal of Medical Sciences, 25 (3), 135–139.

Chapter 9
Stress and coping

GABRIELLE RIGNEY

Learning objectives

The material in this chapter will help you to:

- distinguish between stress as a stimulus, a process and a response
- describe the stress reaction
- understand the effects of stress on health and illness
- identify external moderators of stress
- understand how cognitive appraisals and personality styles influence a person's coping response.

Key terms

Introduction

Stress is a term that is used in everyday conversation and frequently featured in the popular press and social media. It has also been the focus of psychological research for decades. The concentration of stress research has principally been in three areas, namely, to examine stress as: (1) a response—the person's reaction; (2) a stimulus—the event or stressor that prompted the reaction; or (3) a process—the transaction between the person and the environment.

Although stress is generally considered a state to be avoided, the experience and outcomes of stress are, nevertheless, not always negative. At times a stressful occurrence may even be welcome. Desired events like a promotion at work and getting married produce similar physical and psychological reactions, as do unwelcome events like redundancy and divorce. Furthermore, events that are ambiguous, uncontrollable, unpredictable or unrelenting are stressful, as are multiple demands that tax the person's ability to cope (Taylor 2021).

Consider the statement 'I am feeling *stressed*'. How often have you heard or said this? What does this statement mean? What causes stress and how is it experienced? Does everyone experience stress in the same way? Is stress always harmful and how can it be managed when it is excessive? The answers to such questions will be explored in this chapter. The concept of stress will be considered and factors that make an event stressful will be identified. The health consequences of stress will also be examined and, finally, moderators of stress will be examined.

What is stress?

Stress is a physical, cognitive, emotional and behavioural reaction of a person (or organism) to a stressful event—*stressor*—that threatens, challenges or exceeds the person's internal and external coping resources. The threat may be actual (e.g. being robbed at knife point) or perceived (e.g. a student who believes he will fail an upcoming exam). The threat or stressor can be physically or emotionally challenging, or both. The person may perceive it as either a positive or a negative event. See Table 9.1 for examples of physical and emotional stressors.

Stress prompts the person into action. The precipitating stressor may be a major life event like a disaster such as a tsunami, or a minor life event such as daily hassles like being late for an appointment because you were caught up in traffic. Also, the precipitating event can be viewed as negative, harmful and threatening, or challenging and exciting by the person. Moreover, the same event may be perceived differently by different people, as evidenced by the scenario in the following *Student activity*.

Table 9.1

EXAMPLES OF STRESSORS

Physical stressors	Emotional stressors
Undergoing surgery	Diagnosis of a chronic disease
Insomnia	Marriage
Loss of eyesight	Overseas travel
Heat stress	Redundancy
Physical trauma	Relationship breakup
Pain	Moving to a new house
Illness	Winning the lottery

Student activity

Imagine you are given a gift voucher for a tandem parachute jump from an aeroplane as a birthday present.

1. Would you be excited by the prospect of this adventurous opportunity or terrified at the very thought of doing this?
2. Pair up with a student whose perception is opposite to yours (negative or positive) and discuss the reason for your view.
3. Listen to the other person's explanation to gain an understanding of their view.
4. List reasons why one event might produce different reactions in different people.

Stress as a response, stimulus or process

Stress is a topic of interest not only to health professionals but also to the general public, as evidenced by the number of publications on the topic in the popular psychology literature such as in self-help books, the internet and health and lifestyle magazines. Also, stress is one of the most investigated phenomena in health psychology research regarding examining the relationship between psychology and disease. Despite this, not all researchers use the concept in the same way. Research that investigates the relationship between stress and health falls into three main categories that view stress as one of the following:

1. *response*—the person's physical and psychological reaction to the stressor
2. *stimulus*—a stressor in the environment that precipitates a stress reaction
3. *process*—a transaction between the person and the environment.

STRESS AS A RESPONSE

Stress as a response refers to a person's physiological and psychological reactions to a perceived threat or stressor, such as a student who discovers that the hard disk on their computer is corrupted and they do not have another copy of an assignment that is due that day. Physical symptoms include dry mouth, palpitations, appetite changes and insomnia, while psychological responses can include anxiety and forgetfulness and, in extreme circumstances, burnout or post-traumatic stress disorder (PTSD). Physiologists in the first half of the 20th century such as Cannon and Selye were the first researchers to describe the stress response and pioneered research in this field.

Fight or flight

Walter Cannon (1932) was a physiologist and early stress researcher who first described the *fight or flight* response—a primitive, inborn protective mechanism to defend the organism against harm. The response is a physical reaction by an organism (including humans) to a perception of threat. Cannon observed that when an organism was threatened the sympathetic nervous system and the endocrine system were aroused, preparing the organism to respond to the anticipated danger by either reacting aggressively (fight) or by fleeing (flight).

The physiological mechanism of this involves arousal of the sympathetic nervous system that stimulates the adrenal glands to secrete catecholamines (adrenaline and noradrenaline), which then elevate blood pressure, increase the heart rate, divert blood supply from internal organs to muscles and limbs and dilate pupils to enable the organism to take action in the face of a threat (see Fig. 9.1). Activation of the endocrine system prompts the adrenal glands to secrete cortisol, which provides a quick burst of energy, heightens alertness and memory, and increases the organism's pain threshold. Together they enable the organism to confront or withdraw from the threat.

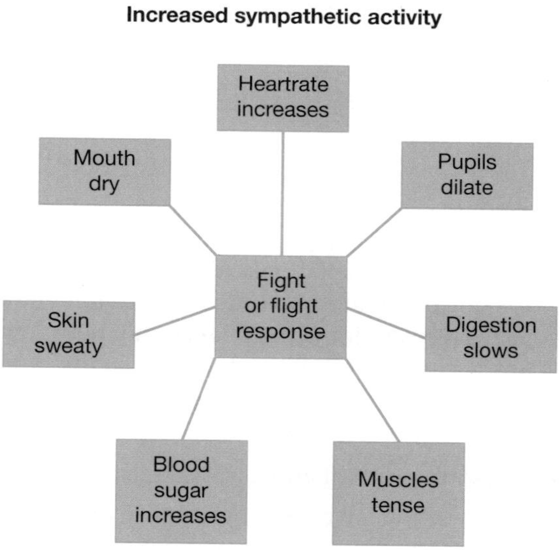

Increased sympathetic activity

Figure 9.1 Fight or flight response

The fight or flight response is adaptive when arousal enables the person to take action: to either address or escape the threat. However, prolonged arousal, which is unrelenting or for which adaptation does not occur, is potentially harmful and can lead to long-term health consequences. For example, when caught speeding by a radar and pulled over by a police officer, neither fight nor flight is an adaptive response.

In the landmark Whitehall I and II studies, British civil servants in lower level jobs experienced greater stress due to having less control of their workload than higher level employees (Marmot et al. 1997). Also, the final report of the World Health Organization's (WHO) Commission on Social Determinants of Health states that 'stress at work is associated with a 50% excess risk of coronary heart disease and there is consistent evidence that high job demand, low control and effort–reward imbalance are risk factors for mental and physical health problems' (WHO 2008, p. 8; see also Li et al. 2016) and that chronic exposure to social and environmental stressors leads to biological wear and tear (Braveman & Gottleib 2014; McEwen 2017).

General adaptation syndrome

Hans Selye (1956) was another pioneer stress researcher who identified the relationship between stress and illness in a model he called the general adaptation syndrome (GAS). GAS provides a biomedical explanation of the stress response and how it influences health outcomes. The theory identifies a pattern of reaction to a threat or challenge and proposes that stress is the person's non-specific response to the specific environmental stressor. Selye defined this as a demand on the body that induces the stress response—the person is required to adapt (Selye 1956). GAS is non-specific in that the response is the same regardless of stimuli—that is, whether the stressor is physical or emotional or whether it is viewed as positive or negative.

GAS includes three phases:

1. *alarm reaction*—in which the organism is alerted to a perceived threat
2. *resistance stage*—in which the body attempts to regain equilibrium and adapt to the stressor
3. *exhaustion stage*—occurs when the body's attempts to resist the stressor are unsuccessful.

When a threat is perceived, the body's reaction is one of *alarm* and the person is mobilised to take action. In this phase, nervous system arousal and alterations to hormone levels prepare the person for action. Initially this includes the activation of the autonomic nervous system, leading to adrenaline and noradrenaline being secreted by the adrenal medulla. Subsequently, the pituitary gland produces adrenocorticotrophic hormone, which stimulates the release of corticosteroids by the adrenal cortex.

With continued exposure to the threat, *resistance* occurs. In this phase hormones remain raised and the immune system aroused as the person takes further action to cope with the stressor. The *exhaustion* phase follows if the person is unsuccessful in adapting to or overcoming the threat. Exhaustion weakens the body's defences, making the person vulnerable to disease due to depleted physiological resources.

Despite the influence of Selye's stress response model on stress research, it does not escape criticism. First, that it describes a physiological process and overlooks the role of cognitive appraisal as identified by Lazarus and Folkman (1984); second, not all people respond in the same physiological way to stress; and third, Selye's model refers to responses to *actual* stress, whereas a person can experience the stress response to an *anticipated* stressor (Taylor 2021). For example, in agoraphobia the person fears the anxiety they might experience if they leave their 'safe place', usually their home.

In summary, the stress response is an automatic reaction that enables a person to take action in order to adapt to, or make changes in response to, a perceived or actual threat or stressor. The stress response is most effective for stressors that are of short-term duration and where adaptation is possible. However, should adaptation not be achievable or the stress prolonged, the person is at risk of developing health problems as a consequence.

Research focus

Source: Tanaka et al. 2018

WHITEHALL I AND II

The first Whitehall study (1967–1976) examined the health of 18,000 male British civil servants aged between 20 and 64 years over a period of 10 years. The findings of Whitehall I identified an inverse gradient between the position participants held in the hierarchy of the civil service and mortality. In other words, people in senior positions lived longer than those in the lower employment grades. Low-grade workers experienced higher rates of coronary heart disease and three times the mortality rates of workers in the highest grades, and this finding was statistically significant. The researchers also identified social determinants that were associated with these adverse health outcomes (Marmot et al. 1987).

Whitehall II followed up on the findings of Whitehall I with a prospective cohort study of more than 10,000 men and women, aged 35–55 years employed in the British civil service between 1985 and 1998 with the purpose of identifying the relationship between occupational and psychosocial factors in the workplace and risk for coronary heart disease for both men and women. The researchers concluded that 'low control in the work environment is associated with an increased risk of future coronary heart disease among men and women employed in government offices' (Bosma et al. 1997, p. 558). A further prospective study examined the role of socioeconomic inequality in recovery from poor physical and mental health (Tanaka et al. 2018).

ABSTRACT

Background
Few studies have examined the influence of socioeconomic status on recovery from poor physical and mental health.

Methods
Prospective study with four consecutive periods of follow-up (1991–2011) of 7,564 civil servants (2,228 women) recruited while working in London. Health

Cont... ▶

was measured by the Short-Form 36 questionnaire physical and mental component scores assessed at beginning and end of each of four rounds. Poor health was defined by a score in the lowest 20% of the age–sex-specific distribution. Recovery was defined as changing from a low score at the beginning to a normal score at the end of the round. The analysis took account of retirement status, health behaviours, body mass index and prevalent chronic disease.

Results
Of 24,001 person-observations in the age range 39–83, a total of 8,105 identified poor physical or mental health. Lower grade of employment was strongly associated with slower recovery from poor physical health (OR 0.73 (95% CI 0.59 to 0.91); trend *p* = 0.002) in age, sex and ethnicity-adjusted analyses. The association was halved after further adjustment for health behaviours, adiposity, systolic blood pressure and serum cholesterol (OR 0.85 (0.68 to 1.07)). In contrast, slower recovery from poor mental health was associated robustly with low employment grade even after multiple adjustment (OR 0.74 (0.59 to 0.93); trend *p* = 0.02).

Conclusions
Socioeconomic inequalities in recovery from poor physical health were explained to a considerable extent by health behaviours, adiposity, blood pressure and serum cholesterol. These risk factors explained only part of the gradient in recovery for poor mental health.

Critical thinking

- Identify and discuss the key finding of the Whitehall studies.
- Suggest ways that stress could be reduced for workers in lower grade positions.
- Why do you think people in lower level jobs experienced more stress than people in higher level jobs?

Student activity

Complete the following in small groups.

1. Consider the health profession that your present education is preparing you for, such as physiotherapy, paramedic practice, nursing or social work.
2. Identify potential work-related stressors for this professional group and classify them as 'able to be controlled by the health professional' or 'over which health professionals have low control'.
3. Discuss how events classified as being low control can be made less stressful.

Cont... ▶

If possible, do the following before the tutorial:

- Interview a health professional working in the field and ask them to identify controllable and uncontrollable stressors in their work life.
- Compare and discuss the stressors identified by the health professional with those on lists compiled by other students in the group.

Critical thinking

Imagine you are driving from your home in the hills to your university to sit a health psychology exam when a cat suddenly darts in front of your car. You brake quickly, swerve and, fortunately, avoid hitting the cat. You are not injured but your car came to a halt against a fence post and sustained significant damage to the front end. Water is now leaking from the damaged radiator. When you try to call for assistance, you discover your mobile phone is out of range. The road is quiet and traffic infrequent. You know that the nearest house is about 5 kilometres further on. Consider the following.

- What might your physical response be?
- How might you feel at this point?
- What are your thoughts?
- What might you do?

Discuss your responses with your fellow students.

STRESS AS A STIMULUS

Another approach to stress research is to view **stress as a stimulus** that produces a reaction. According to Yerkes and Dodson (1908), stress is the stimulus that prompts action, and the amount of stress experienced predicts how well the person performs. The stimulus can be a major life event such as those identified by Holmes and Rahe in 1967. Alternatively, the stimulus may be an accumulation of minor life events or hassles as described by Kanner and colleagues in a study that compared the stress from daily hassles and uplifts with the stress produced by major life events (Kanner et al. 1981).

The Yerkes–Dodson law

Yerkes and Dodson (1908) hypothesised that a relationship exists between arousal and performance and that stress is a stimulus that prompts a person to take action. According to the Yerkes–Dodson law, when stressed (aroused) a person's performance increases to a maximum point after which performance reduces. The relationship is represented graphically as an inverted 'U' (see Fig. 9.2).

The model proposes there is an optimal level of arousal (stress) at which a person is challenged and thereby performs at their best. With too little arousal, the person is not motivated enough to take action in response to the stimulus and hence performance is minimal. Increasing arousal energises the person to take the action required to achieve a goal such as study to pass an exam. However, excessive arousal

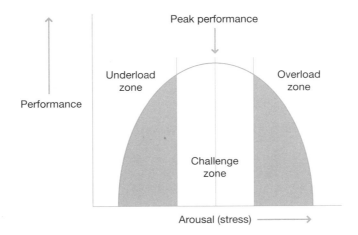

Figure 9.2 Yerkes–Dodson law

can result in the person being overloaded and, consequently, performance deteriorates, such as in the case of a student who is highly anxious about a forthcoming exam and loses concentration or becomes ill.

MAJOR LIFE EVENTS

The theory that major life events are a stimulus for stress emerged from the research of Holmes and Rahe, who proposed that major or frequent changes in one's life predisposes the person to illness due to the cumulative effect of the life stressors. The researchers proposed this hypothesis after they observed that tuberculosis infection commonly followed a major crisis or multiple life crises. They subsequently developed a tool to measure the impact of life changes on health and to predict individual vulnerability to illness: the social readjustment rating scale (SRRS) (Holmes & Rahe 1967).

This tool consists of 43 items: 17 are rated as desirable such as going on vacation; 18 are rated as undesirable such as the death of a close friend; and 8 are classified as neutral such as 'major change in responsibilities at work' (Holmes & Rahe 1967, p. 214). Such a change may be the consequence of a promotion that is desirable, but it could be the result of a restructure and reduction of staff at the workplace, which would be undesirable because there would be fewer people to undertake the workload.

Items in the SRRS are given a weighting that reflects the magnitude of the stressful stimulus (see Table 9.2). For example, the death of a spouse was found to be the most stressful life event and was given a score of 100. A score of 150–299 for the preceding year places the person at moderate risk for illness, whereas a score of 300 in the preceding 6 months or more than 500 in the preceding year places the person at high risk of developing a stress-related illness.

Since its development in the 1960s, the Holmes–Rahe SRRS is one of the most widely cited tools in stress research. Thirty years later Scully and colleagues (2000) replicated the research to examine the usefulness of the tool as an indicator of health risk and to consider the validity of criticisms raised in the literature in relation to the tool. Scully and colleagues' research found that the relative weightings and rank order of the selected life

Table 9.2

SCULLY ET AL.'S UPDATED SOCIAL READJUSTMENT RATING SCALE

Holmes & Rahe 1967		Selected life events	Scully et al. 2000	
Rank order	Weight		Rank order	Weight
1	100	Death of a spouse	1	100
2	73	Divorce	2	58
3	65	Marital separation	4	51
4	63	Jail term	5	50
5	63	Death of a close family member	8	45
6	53	Personal injury or illness	3	57
7	50	Marriage	6	50
8	47	Fired at work	13	34
9	45	Marital reconciliation	15	28
10	45	Retirement	29	18
11	44	Change in health of family member	7	46
12	40	Pregnancy	16	27
13	39	Sex difficulties	10	36
14	39	Gain of new family member	23	21
15	39	Business readjustment	40	12
16	38	Change in financial state	9	43
17	37	Death of a close friend	12	35
18	36	Change to different line of work	14	30
19	35	Change in number of arguments with spouse	17	26
20	31	Mortgage more than $51,000	18	30

Source: Scully et al. 2000

events remained valid and concluded that SRRS continues to be 'a robust instrument for identifying the potential for the occurrences of stress-related outcomes' (Scully et al. 2000, p. 875). Table 9.2 compares weight and rank order for selected life events in Holmes and Rahe's seminal study and the replication by Scully and colleagues.

Recently, researchers have developed updated taxonomies that consider in more detail some of modern life's important changes and events. For example, Haimson and colleagues (2021) created the Major Life Events Taxonomy, which highlights the frequency of more modern life events such as mental health struggles and gender transition. Interestingly, this study also examined how likely major life events were to be shared through social media, providing evidence for using social media as 'social transition machinery' (p. 934). The COVID-19 pandemic can also be considered a major life event, given the vast changes in people's everyday lives that occurred driven by associated restrictions.

Not everyone experiences or responds to major life events in the same way, though. In a study of coping following multiple negative life events, Armstrong and colleagues (2011) found that participants were more resilient following a stressful event if they had a high score on scales for emotional self-awareness, emotional expression, emotional self-control and emotional self-management.

⚆ Critical thinking

Despite Scully and colleagues' conclusion that life-change events are 'useful predictors of stress-related symptom scores' (2000, p. 875), three life events did lower their rank order by more than nine places. These were:

■ retirement
■ gain of new family member
■ business readjustment.

Consider why these three life events may be perceived as less stressful in the 21st century than they were in the 1960s.

MINOR LIFE EVENTS

Kanner and his colleagues were interested to see if minor as well as major life events had health consequences for a person. The researchers defined minor stressful events that were irritating or frustrating as *hassles*. Minor life events would cause inconvenience for the person rather than require a major adjustment as is required with major life events (Kanner et al. 1981). Examples of such stressful events include: discovering that your mobile phone battery is flat when you want to make a phone call; arriving late to watch a soccer grand final and being told that you cannot enter the stadium until half-time; or finding that an ATM machine is out of order when you need to withdraw cash. Findings from Kanner and colleagues' research demonstrated that hassles can have an impact on health. This occurred when multiple hassles occurred at once or when minor life events occurred concurrently with a major life event and when minor stressful events were prolonged or repeated, such as a person who was late for work three times in one week due to traffic congestion.

In summary, it is evident that both major and minor events may stimulate a stress reaction in humans that, in turn, can affect health. Nevertheless, the presence of a stressful stimulus is not predictive of how someone will respond to the stressor. Different people will respond differently to the same stressor, and the same event can lead to positive or negative outcomes in different people. For example, a person who has a dog phobia will react differently from a dog lover when a dog is present. This observation prompted psychologists studying stress to examine the relationship between the person, their perceptions and their environment—that is, stress as a process.

STRESS AS A PROCESS

The notion of **stress as a process or transaction** was first introduced by Richard Lazarus and later refined in collaboration with his colleague Susan Folkman (Lazarus 1966; Lazarus & Folkman 1984). Lazarus's theory proposed that stress was a transaction between the person and their environment. The transaction involves the person making a cognitive assessment (appraisal) of the demands of the stressor and the **coping resources** available to them. Lazarus distinguished between stressors that are negative (*distress*) and positive (*eustress*).

In appraising an event or situation, a person will ask one of three questions. Is the event:

1. relevant or irrelevant (to the person)?
2. benign or positive (eustress)?
3. threatening or harmful (distress)?

Lazarus's theory proposes that distress is experienced when a person perceives that a stressor is potentially negative and also believes that their available resources are insufficient to meet the demands of this particular stressor. **Cognitive appraisal** is the term used to describe the process of perceiving the stressor and of judging one's ability to manage or respond to the stressor.

Cognitive appraisal occurs at two levels: primary and secondary. Primary appraisal refers to a person's judgement as to whether this event or situation is negative (poses a threat), positive (provides opportunity/challenge) or benign (neutral/irrelevant). Secondary appraisal refers to a person's assessment of their personal (internal) and environmental (external) resources to respond to the stressful event or situation (Lazarus & Folkman 1984). These two processes are carried out simultaneously as the person assesses the threat and their ability to manage (see Table 9.3).

Table 9.3	
COGNITIVE APPRAISAL	
Primary	Is the event challenging, irrelevant or threatening? Is the significance of the event positive, neutral or negative?
Secondary	What are my coping resources? • Internal (within the person) • External (within the environment) How adequate are my coping resources?

CASE STUDY: SAMARA

Samara is a third-year social work student who was awarded the grade of high distinction (95%) for her health psychology essay. The lecturer recommended that Samara submit an abstract of the paper for presentation at a forthcoming international psychology conference.

Critical thinking

Identify Samara's thoughts. Should she appraise this event as:

- positive
- neutral
- negative?

Identify possible secondary appraisal for each of the above scenarios.

EFFECTS OF STRESS ON HEALTH

Stress can affect a person's health physically or psychologically (or both) and can have short- or long-term consequences. Physical outcomes include impaired immunity, vulnerability to infection and increased risk for cancer and cardiovascular and autoimmune diseases. Numerous studies have shown that students' immunity is compromised in the period surrounding exams (Taylor 2021). Psychological consequences of excessive and prolonged stress include cognitive, emotional and behavioural problems, and in extreme circumstances stress can lead to disorders such as anxiety, depression or risky health behaviours like drug and alcohol abuse. Let us examine these effects in more detail.

PHYSICAL EFFECTS OF STRESS

The physical functions of the body are regulated by the nervous, endocrine and immune systems. In humans the nervous system comprises the central and peripheral nervous systems. The central nervous system consists of the brain and spinal cord, the peripheral nervous system and all the other neural structures and pathways in the body. The immune system defends us against infection, including bacteria and viruses, and can protect against some cancers. The endocrine system consists of glands and organs that secrete hormones to regulate metabolism, growth and development. Malfunction in one of these systems will affect the other systems and cause illness. However, Dhabhar (2014; 2018) found that physical consequences of stress only occurred following chronic, not short-term, stress. According to Dhabhar, short-term or **acute stress** enhances immunological response, whereas **chronic stress** suppresses protective immune responses and/or exacerbated pathological immune responses.

Research focus

Source: Dhabhar 2018

ABSTRACT

The researchers proposed that in contrast to chronic stress that can have harmful effects, the short-term (fight or flight) stress response (lasting for minutes to hours) is nature's fundamental survival mechanism that enhances protection and performance under conditions involving threat/challenge/opportunity. Short-term stress enhances innate/primary, adaptive/secondary, vaccine-induced and anti-tumour immune responses, and post-surgical recovery. Mechanisms and mediators include stress hormones, dendritic cell, neutrophil, macrophage and lymphocyte trafficking/function and local/systemic chemokine and cytokine production. Short-term stress may also enhance mental/cognitive and physical performance through effects on brain, musculoskeletal and cardiovascular function, reappraisal of threat/anxiety and training-induced stress-optimisation. Therefore, short-term stress psychology/physiology could be harnessed to enhance immuno-protection, as well as mental and physical performance. The review aimed to provide a conceptual framework and targets for further investigation of mechanisms and conditions under which the protective/adaptive aspects of short-term stress/exercise can be optimised/harnessed, and for developing pharmacological/biobehavioural interventions to enhance health/healing and mental/cognitive/physical performance.

Critical thinking

- Make a list of 'good' and 'bad' stress.
- Identify and discuss ways that these stressors can enhance or hinder health.

PSYCHONEUROIMMUNOLOGY

Psychoneuroimmunology is the multidisciplinary scientific study of the relationship between the nervous system and the immune system. George Solomon coined the term psychoneuroimmunology in 1964, but it would be another decade before research in the field became widespread. This occurred in the 1970s following a finding by Robert Ader, an American psychiatrist, that the immune system of rats could be suppressed through classical conditioning (which was discussed in Chapter 1). Ader published these findings with his colleague, Cohen (Ader & Cohen 1975).

Ader and Cohen's evidence that immune functioning could be affected by manipulating psychological processes was a significant milestone in psychoneuroimmunology research. Subsequently, research that investigates the relationship between stress and the immune system has intensified. There is now a substantial body of knowledge to support the hypothesis that immune system alteration precipitated by psychological processes, including stress, can cause physical illness. This applies not only to illnesses that are caused by infection and delayed wound healing but also to autoimmune and metabolic diseases like multiple sclerosis, asthma and rheumatoid arthritis, and to some cancers (Straub & Cutolo 2018).

IMMUNE SYSTEM

The immune system is the body's protection against infection and illness. Its primary function is to detect foreign cells in the body and eradicate them. It consists of organs (e.g. the spleen) and cells (e.g. lymphocytes) that detect pathogens like bacteria, viruses and cancer-producing cells and destroys them. Cells within the immune system have receptors for neuropeptides and hormones enabling them to respond to nervous and neuroendocrine system signals. Nerve fibres connect immune system organs and cells to the autonomic nervous system. Consequently, the central nervous system moderates stress through changes in immune cell activity. Because the brain and nervous system are connected to the immune system by neuroanatomical and neuroendocrine pathways, immune functioning can be affected. Figure 9.3 shows the pathway for central nervous system effects on the immune system.

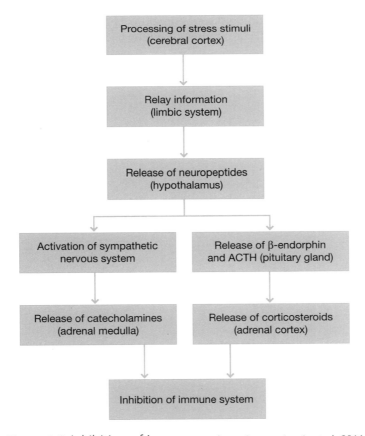

Figure 9.3 Inhibition of immune system Source: Lewis et al. 2011

Immunosuppression

Immunosuppression is a consequence of stress that can result from being exposed to both short- and long-term stress. There is an extensive body of research that links stress to immune dysregulation. Effects include: reduced number and function of natural killer cells (whose role is to respond to and reject viral and tumour cells); increased production of proinflammatory cytokines (which are implicated in depression and sleep disorders); and decreased monocytes (which protect the body from foreign substances, e.g. infection) (Seiler et al. 2020). The clinical consequences of immunosuppression include chronic low-grade inflammation, delayed wound-healing, poor response to vaccines and increased susceptibility to bacterial and viral infections (Seiler et al. 2020).

Pathways between the central nervous, endocrine and immune systems travel in two directions. What this means is that not only can the central nervous system affect the endocrine and immune systems but these both have the potential to also affect the central nervous system (see Fig. 9.4).

As a consequence of the interrelationship between the three systems, not only can cognitions and emotions influence immunity and endocrine function but the immune and endocrine systems can send messages to the brain and influence behaviour. For example, both adrenal corticosteroids and catecholamines can cause immunosuppression that, in turn, can lead to illness behaviour such as tiredness and appetite reduction. Also, in addition to adrenocortical hormones, other hormones, including thyroid and growth, can suppress immune function.

In summary, there is now clear evidence that stress-induced immunosuppression can lead to illness. Research that identifies these links provides opportunities for

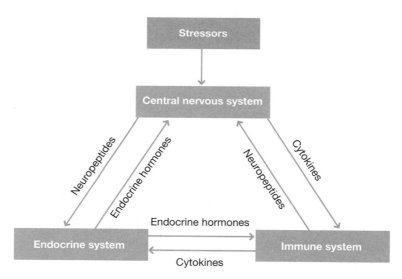

Figure 9.4 Neurochemical links between the nervous, endocrine and immune systems Source: Lewis et al. 2011

intervention and prevention (Moraes et al. 2018). Nevertheless, despite the body of research demonstrating the links between stress and illness, many questions remain unanswered, namely, how much stress is required to bring about changes to the immune system and how can stress-induced immunosuppression be prevented or mediated? And why are some people affected and others not?

Psychological effects of stress

The psychological and behavioural health effects of stress also have both acute (short-term) and chronic (long-term) consequences. Acute stress consequences can include cognitive changes (forgetfulness and obsessional thoughts), affective changes (anxiety and mood alteration) and changes to health behaviours (dietary changes, altered sleep patterns and increased tobacco smoking and alcohol/drug use). In the longer term, unrelieved chronic stress can have serious lifestyle consequences such as burnout and be a contributing factor in mental illnesses like clinical depression, anxiety disorders and PTSD.

BURNOUT

Burnout is a psychological syndrome characterised by emotional exhaustion, depersonalisation, cynicism and a diminished sense of self-efficacy and personal accomplishment that occurs as a consequence of prolonged chronic workplace stress (Maslach 2003; Schaufeli et al. 2018). According to Maslach (2003) anyone who works with needy people, and particularly healthcare workers, is at risk of burnout. Maslach and Jackson (1981) developed the first tool to identify burnout in human services workers. Their tool measures: (1) emotional exhaustion; (2) depersonalisation; and (3) reduced personal accomplishment—and has an optional fourth subscale of reduced involvement.

Burnout produces a range of negative outcomes for workers' health and wellbeing including anxiety and depression, psychosomatic problems such as headaches and physical health problems such as immunosuppression leading to increased vulnerability to infection (Søvold et al. 2021; Kielcolt-Glaser et al. 2014). Other serious consequences of chronic workplace stress include hypertension, coronary heart disease, excessive alcohol use and mental illness (Søvold et al. 2021; Williams et al. 2020).

In 2022 the American Psychological Association identified burnout and stress as one of 14 emerging trends of the COVID-19 pandemic era. Pandemic-related stressors have become persistent and indefinite, which increases the risk of burnout. People who work closely with others, such as health professionals and teachers, are particularly vulnerable to burnout (American Psychological Association 2022a; Elbarazi et al. 2017). A review of 91 studies examining burnout in nursing found that a range of adverse job characteristics such as high job and psychological demands, low control or schedule flexibility, tensions in workplace relationships, low autonomy and job insecurity were all associated with burnout (Dall'Ora et al. 2020). These findings have implications for how individual nurses and the organisations they work for address workplace stressors.

Student activity

1. In the week preceding the tutorial, search the literature for an article about burnout in your intended profession and note:
   - the factors identified as contributing to burnout
   - recommendations and solutions proposed.
2. During the tutorial:
   - form small groups and present key issues from the article you found to your fellow students
   - discuss the implications of the key issues to their intended profession and yourself.

POST-TRAUMATIC STRESS DISORDER

PTSD is a serious, debilitating mental illness that affects some people who experience or witness an extremely traumatic stressful event—one which is outside the realm of usual human experience and involves the threat of death or serious injury. Examples of such events include being the victim of an assault, witnessing a person being run over by a train or the soldier in a war zone who is exposed to gunfire that results in the death and injury of colleagues and bystanders.

Features of PTSD include insomnia, intrusive thoughts and dreams about the traumatic event, irritability and outbursts of anger, poor concentration, hypervigilance and an exaggerated startle reflex. People with PTSD may also experience survivor guilt, relationship difficulties, detachment from loved ones, anxiety symptoms and clinical depression (Elders 2017). Furthermore, a study of Vietnam War veterans found that veterans with PTSD also had a 'pattern of physical health outcomes that is consistent with altered inflammatory responsiveness' (O'Toole & Catts 2008, p. 33). In other words, the stress experienced by these soldiers had not only produced psychological symptoms but also immunosuppression and consequent physical disorders.

While it is clear that experiencing a traumatic stressful event causes PTSD, there are still many unanswered questions about this condition. In particular: Why do some people develop PTSD after an extremely traumatic event while others do not? And is stress debriefing beneficial to all victims following a traumatic stress or can this increase psychological distress?

Assessing distress in generalist healthcare settings

There are many assessment tools that health professionals can use to assess psychosocial distress in their clients. The Kessler-10 (K10) and K10+ are frequently used in clinical practice because they are informative and easily administered and scored. The K10 consists of 10 questions rated on a Likert scale about how the person has felt over the past four weeks; for example: In the past 4 weeks how often did you feel hopeless? A score of > 20/50 indicates mental distress (Australian Mental Health Outcomes and Classification Network 2022). The K10+ has four extra questions that assess variables relevant to distress. Another variant of this tool is the K10L3D, which asks the same questions as the K10 but asks the client to reflect only over the past 3 days (Australian Mental Health Outcomes and Classification Network 2022; Black Dog Institute 2022).

Coping

We will now examine psychological explanations for how people cope with excessive stress and stressors. Coping refers to the process of managing demands that challenge or exceed a person's resources. Its purpose is to enable the person to tolerate or adjust to stressful events or realities, retain a positive sense of self and achieve harmonious relationships with others. It includes an evaluation of one's coping resources and the options available to determine if they are sufficient to overcome the threat. Lazarus and Folkman (1984) describe it as the cognitive and behavioural strategies that the person uses to manage the demands perceived to challenge or exceed their resources.

COPING RESOURCES

The coping resources one calls on may be internal (within the person), external (within the environment) or both. Internal resources refer to qualities and attributes that the person possesses and can use in response to the stressor. They include the person's cognitive and behavioural responses to stress, personality attributes and disposition. External coping resources are factors external to the person, such as other people and tangible resources they can access that enable them to deal with the stressor. See Table 9.4 for examples of internal and external coping resources.

Internal coping resources: personality attributes and disposition

Personality refers to the qualities that comprise a person's cognitive, affective and behavioural makeup, and which distinguishes people from each other. Personality attributes and disposition are internal resources that can facilitate or hinder coping. Attitudes and disposition identified as influencing coping include: locus of control (Rotter 1966); self-efficacy (Bandura 1977); optimism, pessimism and wellbeing (Diener et al. 2018; Seligman 1994, 2011); and resilience (Garmezy 1987). Let us examine the role of personality attributes and disposition in coping.

Table 9.4	
EXAMPLES OF COPING RESOURCES	
Internal	External

Health status
Spirituality
Personality attributes
  • Optimistic outlook
  • Self-efficacy
  • Resilience
Communication skills
Problem-solving skills
	Supportive
	  • Family
	  • Social network
	  • Workplace
	Resources
	  • Time
	  • Financial

Locus of control

Locus of control (LOC) is a construct described by the social learning theorist Julian Rotter (1966). It refers to a person's belief regarding responsibility for reinforcement of a particular behaviour and whether the person believes that reinforcements (outcomes) are controlled by the self, others or by chance (see also Chapters 6 and 7).

People are described as possessing an internal LOC when they believe their behaviour influences outcomes, whereas a person who has an external LOC believes that forces outside the self influences outcomes, that is, chance, fate or other more powerful people. Rotter's model was further refined by Wallston and colleagues (1978) and Wallston (2018) to propose a 'health LOC' (HLOC) that comprises three attributional constructs, namely, internal, external and powerful others. For example, a person with diabetes who has one of these three attributional constructs would say:

- *internal*—how I manage my diabetes will limit complications

- *external*—no matter what I do my blood sugar levels are always unstable

- *powerful others*—my doctors know more about this than me so I will leave management of my condition to them.

Rotter proposed that a person with an internal attributional style would take more responsibility for their health; however, this only occurs when the reinforcements or outcomes are valued by the person. For example, Rotter's theory would predict that a person with an internal LOC who valued fitness is more likely to engage in exercise than a person with an internal LOC who did not value fitness.

Furthermore, the model does not predict coping when the desired outcome is not exclusively under the control of the person—for example, a person who has cancer and believes that by adhering to the prescribed treatment they will overcome the disease. While this will initially facilitate coping, should the cancer not be cured, it can have a detrimental impact on the person, who may consequently become depressed. For example, a study that examined HLOC in cancer patients found that while a high internal HLOC assisted functioning in cancer patients early in the disease, there was a decrease in internal HLOC scores the longer the patients were sick (Gibek & Sacha 2019).

Self-efficacy

Bandura, too, was a social learning theorist who believed that human behaviour results from the interaction between the person's perception and thinking and the environment. He proposed the construct of *self-efficacy*, which he described as a personal belief that one is capable of taking action to achieve desired or required outcomes (Bandura 1977, 2001, 2016).

According to Bandura's model, the thoughts a person has about a particular event or circumstance (their *self-talk*) predict the outcome because the person is cognitively rehearsing the eventual outcome. Self-talk can be either positive or negative. Positive talk increases the likelihood of a positive outcome because the person engages in behaviours that will bring about the desired outcome. For example, a person learning a new skill who tells themselves that 'once I master this, I will be right' will engage in behaviours to achieve this, such as practising the skill. Alternatively, the person whose self-talk is negative (e.g. 'I will never be able to manage this') is unlikely to practise and therefore less likely to acquire the skill.

Optimism and pessimism

Martin Seligman is a cognitive psychologist who developed the theory of learned helplessness as a cognitive behavioural explanation of depression (Seligman 1974). He later focused his attention on learned optimism, arguing that psychological research has focused excessively on illness without enough attention being given to wellness (Diener et al. 2018; Seligman 2011). Seligman is attributed as being the founder of the specialist field of *positive psychology.*

A person with an optimistic attribution style believes they can influence the outcomes in certain circumstances. For example, a person with diabetes who has an optimistic attribution style may make the statement, 'Fluctuations in my blood sugar levels are a challenge to be managed'. Whereas a person with a pessimistic style who believes that the outcome has nothing to do with their actions may make the statement, 'Even if I watch my diet my blood sugar levels are high, so I don't bother'.

Rasmussen and colleagues (2009), in a meta-analytic review of optimism and physical health, found that optimism was a significant indicator of physical health, although the exact mechanism of how optimism affects health and disease was not evident. Furthermore, an optimistic outlook is not necessarily the ideal approach in all circumstances and at times may be unrealistic. Segerstrom (2006), for example, found that when an optimist persists in trying to cope with a significant stressor and is unsuccessful, they may experience further stress and impaired immune functioning.

Resilience

As discussed in Chapter 5, resilience refers to the ability to cope with and bounce back from adversity. Research in this area was initiated by Garmezy (1987), who observed that some children coped well despite their adverse family situation. Garmezy identified *protective* factors for these children and explored what facilitated their coping—that is, what enabled some children to be resilient despite living in a challenging family situation.

This and subsequent research has shown that being resilient involves:

- having caring and supportive relationships within the family and with others
- being able to make realistic plans and take steps to carry them out
- having a positive view of oneself and belief in one's abilities
- good communication and problem-solving skills
- being able to manage strong feelings and impulses.

Being resilient, though, doesn't mean that you will never feel stressed, anxious or depressed; it means that you have the requisite internal and external resources to call on in challenging times (American Psychological Association 2022b).

Garmezy (1991) concluded that resilience did not influence vulnerability to stress but, rather, enabled people to cope with challenges and adversity. That is to say that a resilient person is not less vulnerable to stress but that in a stressful situation they are

> ## Box 9.1 Strategies to build resilience
>
> 1. **Connect.** Seek, ask for and accept support from others.
>
> 2. **Don't let problems become overwhelming.** Attempt to look further than the current crisis and consider how the situation is temporary and how the future will improve.
>
> 3. **Acknowledge that change occurs and is part of day-to-day life.** Focus on those situations that can be changed and accept those that cannot.
>
> 4. **Make small and realistic steps towards your goals.** Taking small, regular steps helps you progress towards goals that may have first appeared daunting.
>
> 5. **Take action.** Actively working on problems rather than ignoring them in the hope they will disappear helps progress towards resolution.
>
> 6. **Use challenges in life as a learning curve.** The opportunity to reflect and learn about yourself in challenging situations can build resilience for the future.
>
> 7. **Trust you are 'good enough'.** Fostering confidence in your strength, ability and skills to face and resolve problems supports a positive sense of self.
>
> 8. **Maintain context.** Take time to consider stressful events from a wider perspective so it is proportional to the situation and doesn't become overwhelming.
>
> 9. **Stay positive.** Keep an optimistic and hopeful attitude towards your goals.
>
> 10. **Look after your own needs.** Take time to consider what you need and actively pursue the things you enjoy.

Adapted from American Psychological Association 2020

likely to use more adaptive coping strategies than those employed by a person who is less resilient. Furthermore, resilience is not a static trait—it can be enhanced. See Box 9.1 from the American Psychological Association (2020), which outlines strategies that focus on four core components to help build resilience.

Other ways of strengthening resilience may be helpful. For example, some people write about their deepest thoughts and feelings related to trauma or other stressful events in their life. Meditation and spiritual practices help some people build connections and restore hope.

The key is to identify ways that are likely to work well for you as part of your own personal strategy for fostering resilience.

COPING STRATEGIES

Coping strategies are the actions people take in response to stress. Lazarus and Folkman (1984) separate coping strategies into two categories: emotion-focused and problem-focused. In using either or both of these coping strategies, the person is active, not passive, and enters a process of engagement with the stressor, which they call a transaction.

Emotion-focused coping uses self-regulation to control one's emotional response to a stressor. Stress is moderated when the person engages in strategies that help manage their affective response to the stressor. For example, a person who seeks support from family and friends when given the diagnosis of a terminal illness is using an emotion-focused approach. Problem-focused coping addresses the stressor itself to resolve stress. If the person in the example above had researched the internet for information about the treatments available for their particular illness, they would have been using a problem-focused strategy. See Table 9.5 for examples of problem- and emotion-focused coping strategies.

Furthermore, at times both emotion- and problem-focused strategies can be used to respond to the same stressor. A systematic review examining psychological resilience and coping behaviours among healthcare workers during the COVID-19 pandemic found that both emotion- and problem-focused coping strategies were effectively used to manage stress (Labrague 2021). And while people use both problem- and emotion-focused coping strategies, individuals do have a preferred style. Also, a person may use different styles in different situations such as being emotion-focused at home and problem-focused at work (Taylor 2021). Regardless, neither style is preferable—it depends on the context and the demands of the situation.

In summary, while the general intent of coping strategies is to facilitate coping, this is not always the outcome. What if, for example, the person who is given the diagnosis of a terminal illness uses the defence mechanism *denial* (as discussed in

Table 9.5

EMOTION- AND PROBLEM-FOCUSED COPING STRATEGIES

Stressor	Emotion-focused	Problem-focused
Being diagnosed with diabetes	Joins a diabetes support group	Enrols in a diabetes education class
Made redundant at work	Takes a holiday	Registers with an employment agency
Having recurrent arguments with partner	Goes out with friends	Seeks relationship counselling
Waking up feeling ill on the day of an exam	Rolls over and goes back to sleep	Makes a GP appointment to obtain a medical certificate
A child who is bullied at school	Spends lunchtime in the library to avoid the bullies	Reports the bullying to a teacher

Chapter 1)? This is an emotion-focused coping strategy that, in the short term, achieves the outcome of minimising the person's anxiety. However, denial is not an effective long-term coping strategy because it does not assist the person and their family to adjust to the reality and consequences of the illness. Furthermore, Hulbert-Williams and colleagues' (2011) study of psychosocial predictors of cancer adjustment found that cognitions and appraisals were more predictive of the outcome than emotions. They concluded that 'the comparative importance of cognitions in outcome prediction suggests that supportive interventions might usefully include therapeutic techniques aimed at cognitive re-structuring and/or psychological acceptance of distressing thoughts and feelings' (Hulbert-Williams et al. 2011, p. 11).

EXTERNAL COPING RESOURCES

In addition to a person's unique response to stressors, coping is also dependent on the external resources available to the person. These include, but are not limited to, social support (family and friends), education, employment and time. Socioeconomic status is a significant resource for health, with poverty and disadvantage being predictors of shorter lifespan, poorer health and reduced quality of life (Baum 2008). Conversely, people of higher socioeconomic status generally have more tangible external resources at their disposal to deal with stressors. See Chapter 6 for a more detailed account of the influence of social factors on health.

Social support

Social support refers to the perceived comfort, understanding and help a person receives from others. It was first described as a moderator of stress by Cobb (1976), who defined social support as the perception of being loved and cared for, of feeling esteemed and valued, and of having a social network such as family and friends who could provide resources in times of need. Support may mediate stress either by reducing the impact of stress (buffering effect) or by reducing the likelihood of adverse events (direct effect). Five types of social support that can influence health outcomes are:

- *emotional support*—involves providing empathy and concern for the person, which provides comfort, reassurance and a sense of being loved during difficult times

- *esteem support*—occurs when others express positive regard or encouragement for the person or validate the person's views and feelings that build feelings of self-worth and competence in the person

- *instrumental support*—refers to providing direct assistance like lending the person money or babysitting their children during stressful times, which reduces demand on the person's own resources

- *information support*—involves giving advice and making suggestions to assist decision making or providing feedback on action taken to affirm decisions made, which facilitates self-efficacy

- *network support*—involves being a member of a group of people who share similar values, interests or experiences that provides the person with a sense of belonging, or helps the person to realise they are not the only person who has experienced the particular stressor.

Evidence that social support also influences health outcomes is abundant (Taylor 2021). A perception that one has adequate social support during illness can moderate the harmful effects of stress and, conversely, having inadequate social support while ill is associated with adverse outcomes. For example, Zhang and colleagues (2007), in a longitudinal study of 1,431 elderly people with diabetes, demonstrated a relationship between perceived social support and mortality. Findings were that people who reported a low level of social support had the highest risk of death over the 6 years of the study. People with moderate social support had 41% less risk of death than people with the lowest reported level of social support. Furthermore, those who reported the highest levels of support were 55% less likely to have died.

Nevertheless, despite the reported beneficial effects of social support, there are some circumstances when it is unhelpful. This can occur when: the help provided is not what the recipient perceives they require; the help is excessive, leading to depletion of the person's coping skills and overdependence on the helper; or harmful coping strategies are encouraged such as excessive alcohol use.

COPING WITH ILLNESS

Being diagnosed with an illness is a stressor that requires a response from the person. How the person copes is influenced by a number of factors including: whether the illness is acute, chronic or terminal; whether the person experiences pain, disability or loss; whether stigma is associated with the illness such as mental illness; whether treatment is available; the person's attribution style, such as internal or external LOC; and whether the person has sufficient social support and financial resources to assist coping. Importantly, coping with illness will be influenced by whether the person's quality of life is affected. Quality of life refers to the person's perception of their wellbeing in their physical, functional, psychological/emotional and social/occupational domains (Fallowfield 2009).

Common emotional reactions to illness include denial, anxiety and depression (Taylor 2021). These responses produce additional stressors for the person, particularly when the illness is chronic. The 'self-regulation model' for coping with chronic illness was proposed by Leventhal and colleagues (1998) to explain how people cope with the stress of living with a chronic illness. Self-regulation refers to the person proactively taking action to manage their health condition and to limit the negative effects of the illness. The stimulus to take action can be either internal—such as a person with diabetes who feels light-headed so checks their blood sugar level—or external—such as a person with diabetes who keeps a record of their daily blood sugar levels because they know their doctor will want to review them at the next appointment. The self-regulation model is a cognitive one that considers a person's view of their physical and social environments, as well as thoughts about themselves. See Chapter 4 for further discussion of chronic illness.

Chapter summary

This chapter presented an overview of stress and coping. Stress was defined as the physical and psychological phenomenon experienced when a person perceives an event to threaten, challenge or exceed their available coping resources. While popular opinion views stress as a negative experience and one to be avoided, psychological research demonstrates that stress is a common experience that is a necessary part of everyday life, and that stress stimulates a person to take action in response to life's challenges and threats. Nevertheless, when stress is extreme, prolonged or the person is unable to adapt, negative health consequences can result. This also occurs when the person is overloaded with multiple stresses.

Coping was defined as the processes and strategies that a person adopts as they attempt to accommodate the actual or perceived discrepancies between stressful demands and their coping resources. When coping processes are adaptive, they enable the person to respond to and manage the challenge. However, when coping resources are not enough to manage the threat, physical and psychological illness can result. In summary, this chapter has demonstrated that the process whereby a person perceives and responds to stress is complex and influenced by a range of factors that are both internal and external to that person.

KEY POINTS

- Stress and stressors are present in everyday life.
- Essentially people experience stress in the same way, although people may respond in different ways to the same stressor.
- Some stress and stressors are beneficial because they stimulate the person to take action.
- Prolonged and cumulative minor stressors can affect health.
- Traumatic stress can lead to both short- and long-term health consequences.
- How a person copes with stress is influenced by factors that are both internal (within the person) and external (within the environment).

Further reading

Cooper, C., Quick, J., 2017. The Handbook of Stress and Health: A Guide to Research and Practice. Wiley, UK.

Dhabhar, F.S., 2018. The short-term stress response–Mother nature's mechanism for enhancing protection and performance under conditions of threat, challenge, and opportunity. Frontiers in Neuroendocrinology, 49, 175–192.

Haimson, O.L., Carter, A.J., Corvite, S., et al., 2021. The major life events taxonomy: social readjustment, social media information sharing, and online network separation during times of life transition. Journal of the Association for Information Science and Technology, 72 (7), 933–947.

Hill Rice, V., 2012. Handbook of Stress, Coping and Health: Implications for Nursing Research, Theory and Practice, 2nd edn. Sage, Thousand Oaks.

Labrague, L.J., 2021. Psychological resilience, coping behaviours and social support among health care workers during the COVID-19 pandemic: a systematic review of quantitative studies. Journal of Nursing Management, 29 (7), 1893–1905.

Manfredi, R., Wong, M., Ramsey-Lucas, C., et al., 2018. Evolving from individual wellness to departmental wellbeing: how to achieve resilience and longevity in palliative medicine. Journal of Pain and Symptom Management 55 (2), 609–610.

Scully, J., Tosi, H., Banning, K., 2000. Life events checklist: revisiting the social readjustment rating scale after 30 years. Educational and Psychological Measurement 60 (6), 864–876.

Weblinks

American Psychological Association

www.apa.org/topics/stress/index.aspx

The APA's 'stress' webpage includes tips on stress management and links to publications and research.

Phoenix Australia – Centre for Posttraumatic Mental Health

https://www.phoenixaustralia.org/resources/

The Centre for Posttraumatic Mental Health undertakes trauma-related research, policy advice, service development and education. This website is a resource for health professionals who work with people who have experienced traumatic events.

Black Dog Institute: The Psychological Toolkit

www.blackdoginstitute.org.au/education-training/health-professionals/psychological-toolkit

The Psychological Toolkit contains practical resources for health professionals to use in assessing and managing distress and mental health problems in their clients.

Positive Psychology Centre

www.ppc.sas.upenn.edu

The Positive Psychology Centre promotes training, education and the dissemination of positive psychology. This website contains resources research and publications about positive psychology including the writings of Martin Seligman.

References

Ader, R., Cohen, N., 1975. Behaviourally conditioned immunosuppression. Psychosomatic Medicine 37, 333–340.

American Psychological Association, 2020. Building your resilience. Available: https://www.apa.org/topics/resilience/building-your-resilience. (Accessed 8 June 2023).

American Psychological Association, 2022a. Burnout and stress are everywhere. Available: https://www.apa.org/monitor/2022/01/special-burnout-stress

American Psychological Association, 2022b. Building your resilience. Available: https://www.apa.org/topics/resilience. (Accessed 10 March 2022).

Armstrong, A., Galligan, R., Critchley, C., 2011. Emotional intelligence and psychological resilience to negative life events. Personality and Individual Differences 51, 331–336.

Australian Mental Health Outcomes and Classification Network, 2022. Kessler–10+. Available: www.amhocn.org/publications/kessler-10. (Accessed 10 March 2022).

Bandura, A., 1977. Self-efficacy: towards a unifying theory of behaviour change. Psychological Review 84, 191–215.

Bandura, A., 2001. Social cognitive theory. Annual Review of Psychology 52, 1–26.

Bandura, A., 2016. The power of observational learning through social modelling. In: Stenberg, R., Fiske, S., Foss, D. (eds.), Scientists Making a Difference: One Hundred Eminent Behavioral and Brain Scientists Talk About Their Most Important Contributions. Cambridge University Press, Cambridge, (Chapter 50).

Baum, F., 2008. The New Public Health, 3rd edn. Oxford University Press, Melbourne.

Black Dog Institute, 2022. K10. Available: www.blackdoginstitute.org.au/docs/default-source/psychological-toolkit/k10.pdf?sfvrsn=4. (Accessed 10 March 2022).

Bosma, H., Marmot, M., Hemingway, H., et al., 1997. Low job control and risk of coronary heart disease in Whitehall II (prospective cohort) study. BMJ 314, 558–565.

Braveman, P., Gottlieb, L., 2014. The social determinants of health: it's time to consider the causes of the causes. Public Health Reports 129 (Suppl. 2), 19–31.

Cannon, W., 1932. The Wisdom of the Body. Norton, New York.

Cobb, S., 1976. Social support as a moderator of life stress. Psychosomatic Medicine 38, 300–314.

Dall'Ora, C., Ball, J., Reinius, M. et al., 2020. Burnout in nursing: a theoretical review. Human Resources for Health 18 (1), 1–17.

Dhabhar, F.S., 2018. The short-term stress response–Mother nature's mechanism for enhancing protection and performance under conditions of threat, challenge, and opportunity. Frontiers in Neuroendocrinology, 49, 175–192.

Dhabhar, F., 2014. Effects of stress on immune function: the good, the bad and the beautiful. Immuniologic Research 58 (2–3), 198–210. Available: https://link.springer.com/article/10.1007/s12026-014-8517-0.

Diener, E., Seligman, M., Choi, H., et al., 2018. Happiest people revisited. Perspectives on Psychological Sciences 13 (2), 176–178.

Elbarazi, I., Loney, T., Yousef, F., et al., 2017. Prevalence of and factors associated with burnout among health care professionals in Arab countries: a systematic review. BMC Health Services Research 17, 491. Available: www.ncbi.nlm.nih.gov/pmc/articles/PMC5513024/. (Accessed 10 March 2022).

Elders, A., 2017. Anxiety, trauma and stress-related disorders. In: Evans, K., Nizette, D., O'Brien, A. (eds.), Psychiatric and Mental Health Nursing, 4th edn. Elsevier, Sydney, (Chapter 19).

Fallowfield, L., 2009. What is quality of life? Health Economics. Available: www.medicine.ox.ac.uk/bandolier/painres/download/whatis/WhatisQOL.pdf. (Accessed 26 September 2009).

Garmezy, N., 1987. Stress, competence and development: continuities in the study of schizophrenic adults and the search for stress resistant children. American Journal of Orthopsychiatry 57 (2), 159–174.

Garmezy, N., 1991. Resiliency and vulnerability to adverse developmental outcomes associated with poverty. American Journal of Behavioral Science 34, 416–430.

Gibek, K., & Sacha, T., 2019. Comparison of health locus of control in oncological and non-oncological patients. Contemporary Oncology, 23 (2), 115.

Haimson, O.L., Carter, A.J., Corvite, S., et al., 2021. The major life events taxonomy: social readjustment, social media information sharing, and online network separation during times of life transition. Journal of the Association for Information Science and Technology, 72 (7), 933–947.

Holmes, T., Rahe, R., 1967. The social readjustment rating scale. Journal of Psychosomatic Research 11, 213–218.

Hulbert-Williams, N., Neal, R., Morrison, V., et al., 2011. Anxiety, depression and quality of life after cancer diagnosis: what psychosocial variables best predict how patients adjust? Psycho-Oncology 21 (8), 857–867.

Kanner, A., Coyne, J., Schaefer, C., et al., 1981. Comparison of two models of stress management: daily hassles and uplifts versus major life events. Journal of Behavioral Medicine 4, 1–39.

Kielcolt-Glaser, J., Glaser, R., Christian, L., 2014. Omega-3 fatty acids and stress-induced immune dysregulation: implications for wound healing. Military Medicine 179 (11), 129–133.

Labrague, L. J., 2021. Psychological resilience, coping behaviours and social support among health care workers during the COVID-19 pandemic: a systematic review of quantitative studies. Journal of Nursing Management, 29 (7), 1893–1905.

Lazarus, R., 1966. Psychological Stress and the Coping Process. McGraw-Hill, New York.

Lazarus, R., Folkman, S., 1984. Stress, Appraisal and Coping. Springer, New York.

Leventhal, H., Leventhal, E., Contrada, R., 1998. Self-regulation, health and behaviour: a perceptual-cognitive approach. Psychology and Health 13, 717–733.

Lewis, S.L., Bucher, L., Heitkemper, M., et al. (eds), 2011. Lewis's Medical-Surgical Nursing: Assessment and Management of Clinical Problems, 8th edn. Elsevier, St Louis.

Li, J., Loerbroks, A., Bosma, H., Angerer, P. 2016, Work stress and cardiovascular disease: a life course perspective. Journal of Occupational Health 58 (2), 216–219.

Marmot, M., Bosma, H., Hemingway, H., et al., 1997. Contribution of job control and other risk factors to social variations in coronary heart disease incidence. The Lancet 350, 235–239.

Marmot, M., Kogevinas, M., Elston, M., 1987. Social economic status and disease. Annual Review of Public Health 8, 111–135.

Maslach, C., 2003. Job burnout: new directions in research and intervention. Current Directions 12, 189–192.

Maslach, C., Jackson, S., 1981. The measurement of experienced burnout. Journal of Occupational Behaviour 2, 99–113.

McEwen, B.S. (2017). Allostasis and the epigenetics of brain and body health over the life course: the brain on stress. JAMA Psychiatry, 74(6), 551–552.

Moraes, L.J., Miranda, M.B., Loures, L.F., et al., 2018. A systematic review of psychoneuro-immunology-based interventions. Psychology, Health & Medicine, 23(6), 635–652.

O'Toole, B., Catts, S., 2008. Trauma, PTSD and physical health: an epidemiological study of Australian Vietnam veterans. Journal of Psychosomatic Research 64, 33–40.

Rasmussen, H., Scheier, M., Greenhouse, J., 2009. Optimism and physical health: a meta-analytic review. Annals of Behavioural Medicine 37, 239–256.

Rotter, J., 1966. Generalized expectancies for internal and external control of reinforcement. Psychological Monographs: General and Applied 80, 1–28.

Schaufeli, W.B., Maslach, C., Marek, T. (eds.), 2018. Professional Burnout: Recent Developments in Theory and Research. Taylor and Francis, London.

Scully, J., Tosi, H., Banning, K., 2000. Life events checklist: revisiting the social readjustment rating scale after 30 years. Educational and Psychological Measurement 60 (6), 864–876.

Segerstrom, S., 2006. How does optimism suppress immunity: evaluation of three affective pathways. Health Psychology 25, 653–657.

Seiler, A., Fagundes, C.P., Christian, L.M., 2020. The impact of everyday stressors on the immune system and health. In: Choukèr, A (ed). Stress Challenges and Immunity in Space (pp. 71–92). Springer, Cham, Switzerland.

Seligman, M., 1974. Depression and learned helplessness. In: Friedman, J., Katz, M. (eds.), The Psychology of Depression: Theory and Research. Winston-Wiley, Washington.

Seligman, M., 1994. Learned Optimism. Random House, Sydney.

Seligman, M., 2011. Flourish: A New Understanding of Happiness and Well-Being. Free Press, New York.

Selye, H., 1956. The Stress of Life. McGraw-Hill, New York.

Søvold, L.E., Naslund, J.A., Kousoulis, A.A., et al., 2021. Prioritizing the mental health and well-being of healthcare workers: an urgent global public health priority. Frontiers in Public Health, 9, 679397.

Straub, R.H., Cutolo, M., 2018. Psychoneuroimmunology – developments in stress research. Wiener Medizinische Wochenschrift, 168 (3), 76–84.

Tanaka, A., Shipley, M., Welch, C., et al., 2018. Socioeconomic inequality in recovery from poor physical and mental health in mid-life and early old age: prospective Whitehall II cohort study. Journal of Epidemiology and Community Studies 72, 309–313.

Taylor, S., 2021. Health Psychology, 10th edn. McGraw-Hill, New York.

Wallston, K., 2018. Multidimensional health locus of control (MHLC) scales. Available: https://nursing.vanderbilt.edu/projects/wallstonk/index.php. (Accessed 10 March 2022).

Wallston, K., Wallston, B., DeVellis, R., 1978. Development of the multidimensional health locus of control (MHLC) scales. Health Education and Behavior 6 (1), 160–170.

Williams, E.S., Rathert, C. and Buttigieg, S.C., 2020. The personal and professional consequences of physician burnout: a systematic review of the literature. Medical Care Research and Review, 77(5), 371–386.

World Health Organization (WHO), 2008. Closing the Gap in a Generation: Health Equity Through Action on the Social Determinants of Health. WHO Commission on the Social Determinants of Health, Geneva.

Yerkes, R., Dodson, J., 1908. The relation of strength of stimulus to rapidity of habit formation. Journal of Comparative Neurology and Psychology 18, 459–482. Available: http://psychclassics.yorku.ca/Yerkes/Law. (Accessed 20 August 2018).

Zhang, X., Norris, S., Gregg, E., et al., 2007. Social support and mortality among older persons with diabetes. Diabetes Educator 33 (2), 273–281.

Chapter 10

Loss

DEB RAWLINGS

Introduction

Mourning is regularly the reaction to the loss of a loved person, or to the loss of some abstraction which has taken the place of one, such as fatherland, liberty, an ideal and so on ... It is well worth noticing that, although grief involves grave departures from the normal attitude to life, it never occurs to us to regard it as a morbid condition and hand the mourner over to medical treatment. We rest assured that after a lapse of time it will be overcome and we look upon any interference with it as inadvisable or even harmful.

(Freud 1917, pp. 243–244)

With these words over a century ago, Freud laid the foundation for understanding the psychological elements of loss, grief and mourning. Indeed, he began to explore the link between grief and healthcare responses. Since then, descriptions of how people grieve and what helps those who experience loss have evolved and expanded. This chapter will explore a range of key theories, models and constructions related to loss, grief, mourning and responses to grief (see Table 10.1), with specific reference to ideas considered relevant to those working in health care. Suggestions for helping responses will be discussed.

The use of seminal literature has been used throughout the chapter, citing authors who are pioneers in this field, and who have established and conceptualised work that continues to influence theories and philosophies today. Note that the term 'health professional' refers to those from a wide range of disciplines who work in healthcare settings such as a doctor, nurse, social worker or psychologist. The term 'patient' or client is used for those who receive services from and are cared for by health professionals.

Table 10.1	
MODELS OF LOSS, GRIEF AND MOURNING	
Model	Key concepts
Levels of loss (Weenolsen 1988)	Loss is experienced at five levels: • primary • secondary • holistic • self-conceptual • metaphorical.
Ambiguous loss (Boss 2000, 2016)	Some losses are particularly difficult because they are uncertain, unclear or indeterminate; the lost loved one can be: • physically absent but psychologically present • physically present but psychologically absent.

Cont... ▶

Table 10.1	
MODELS OF LOSS, GRIEF AND MOURNING—cont'd	
Model	Key concepts
Disenfranchised loss (Doka 2016)	Some losses are not openly acknowledged or socially supported—specific types of relationships, losses, grievers, circumstances and ways of grieving are not socially recognised.
Nonfinite loss (Bruce & Schultz 2001)	Experiences such as disability, dementia and infertility involve loss that unfolds throughout the lifespan and awareness of the discrepancy between life's events and 'what should have been'.
Chronic sorrow (Burke et al. 1992; Olshansky 1962)	Some losses, particularly those related to disability, involve intense, pervasive and recurring sadness over a long period of time.
Tasks of mourning (Worden 2010)	There are four tasks involved in the process of grieving: • to accept the reality of the loss • to work through the pain of grief • to adjust to an environment without the lost person/thing • to emotionally relocate the lost person/thing and move on with life.
Continuing bonds (Klass et al. 1996, 2014)	It is normal and important for grievers to maintain a continuing connection with the person/thing that is lost, rather than having to 'let go'.
Dual process model (Stroebe & Schut 1999)	The grief process involves loss-oriented work and restoration-oriented work and the oscillation and interaction between these two aspects of grieving.
Complicated grief (Worden 2010)	Between 10% and 20% of grievers experience ongoing, problematic grief, often associated with factors such as the nature of the relationship with the lost person/thing, lack of preparation for the loss and lack of perceived support.
Prolonged grief disorder (Prigerson et al. 2008)	This classification of grief is included in the 2013 *Diagnostic and Statistical Manual of Mental Disorders* (DSM-5) and emphasises the griever's intrusive thoughts and persistent, disruptive yearning for the lost person

Defining loss

Loss, in one form or another, will affect all of us—whether we are patients or practitioners. Because loss is a universal experience, defining it may seem unnecessary. Loss, write Harvey and Weber (1999, p. 320), involves 'a reduction in a person's resources, whether personal, material, or symbolic, to which the person was emotionally attached! When a loss occurs it is natural to grieve or mourn the loss. This process of grief has been described as a 'natural emotional consequence of attachment and loss, whether it is the loss of limb, country, employment, marriage, or other crucial relationships, and mourning is the public face of that grief' (Sallnow et al. 2022).

Types of loss

The range of possible losses is almost limitless. How can we attempt to understand the diverse types of losses? Weenolsen (1988), a seminal researcher in the field, proposes the following classification:

- *Major versus minor loss*—We frequently focus on major losses such as the death of a family member or the devastation of a bushfire. But seemingly minor losses can have major significance. Weenolsen describes minor losses as 'the many small deaths of life' (1988, p. 21) that can affect us profoundly because they represent larger losses. For example, older people can experience the termination of their driver's licence as the loss of capabilities, mobility and independence, leading to a strong sense of grief.

- *Primary versus secondary loss*—While primary losses usually are identified easily, secondary or derivative losses may not be recognised and can be just as painful. A major illness, such as chronic fatigue or heart disease, can lead to secondary losses of unemployment, significant financial loss, family stress and reduced life choices. Health professionals are challenged to recognise the range of secondary losses experienced by their patients in order to respond holistically to loss-related needs.

- *Actual versus threatened loss*—A loss need not actually occur for a grief response to be generated. Weenolsen notes that a threat to safety, self-identity or health can result in a sense of loss—'a biopsy may be negative but the self is not the same afterward' (1988, p. 22). Couples undergoing in-vitro fertilisation treatment can experience a powerful sense of loss each time a treatment is unsuccessful, complicated by the prospect of childlessness.

- *Internal versus external loss*—Weenolsen (1988) argues that all losses have an external and internal element. External losses frequently will involve the associated loss of an internalised self-ideal or societal ideal. This type of loss is common after such health-related experiences as mastectomy, amputation, acquired brain injury, burns or alopecia. These external losses can challenge the internalised social constructions about appearance, body image, beauty or gender, leading to potentially profound grief reactions.

- *Chosen versus imposed loss*—Losses can result from both chosen and imposed life events. For example, migration as a refugee is imposed by persecution or dislocation, leading to the loss of family connections, freedom and financial security. However, choosing to migrate, while often involving positives such as new opportunities, can also involve associated grief such as a sense of loss of homeland, national identity, connections to their past, shared experiences with family 'back home' and continuity of cultural practices. Other life choices, such as to not marry or not to have children, can result in a strong sense of regret and grief about what 'might have been' (e.g. during menopause) even though in some instances the loss was chosen.

- *Direct versus indirect loss*—Weenolsen (1988) describes how loss can occur through the experiences of another person. She notes, for example, the grief that parents (and often grandparents) can experience through the losses affecting their children, such as serious illness, school difficulties, failed relationships or family problems.

LEVELS OF LOSS

Weenolsen also describes five levels of loss, a framework that is particularly useful for understanding the full impact of loss situations:

1. *The primary level of loss*—This level of loss is most evident and generally dominates people's perception of a loss situation.

2. *The secondary level of loss*—This level is about the derivative, concrete losses that follow directly from, usually with some immediacy after, a primary loss. For example, the primary loss of a diagnosis of childhood cancer can lead to such secondary losses as financial pressure due to medical expenses and work time lost due to demands of doctors' appointments for parents, and for the child (and potentially any siblings) disruption of school attendance and performance due to treatment and side effects.

3. *The holistic level of loss*—This level relates to the more abstract losses associated with primary and secondary losses such as loss of future, dreams, status and security. Childhood cancer can result in the loss of hopes for the person's child, loss of safety as the child's life is threatened and loss of family security as the future of a family member becomes uncertain.

4. *The self-conceptual level of loss*—A primary loss can lead to changes in how a person sees themselves because part of the self is perceived to be lost. A child with cancer may now see themself as 'sick', 'different', 'less competent' in school and a 'burden' on the family's emotional and financial resources.

5. *The metaphorical level of loss*—This level recognises the idiosyncratic meaning that a loss has because the person's beliefs are challenged. A significant loss can lead to questioning of values, beliefs and a person's philosophical views. Childhood cancer, for example, may challenge assumptions that children will outlive their parents, that parents are able to protect their children from harm or that God will not allow children to suffer.

There are some important implications from Weenolsen's five-level framework. As Weenolsen (1991, p. 56) writes, acknowledging the levels 'helps us understand better why loss affects us so deeply'. When we see patients who are grieving, we often witness intense and pervasive reactions. Awareness that they are grieving at several levels can help us make sense of these responses. Second, Weenolsen's model demonstrates how **grief** 'unfolds' through the levels and is not static or one-dimensional. Third, this framework provides a guide for more comprehensive support and intervention when working with grieving people. The responses of a health professional should consider and address all levels of loss, rather than focus only on the primary loss.

AMBIGUOUS LOSS

Ambiguous loss has been described as the most devastating of all losses in personal relationships due to the uncertain, unclear and indeterminate nature of the loss (Boss 2000, 2016). Boss, an influential researcher in the field, describes two types of ambiguous loss. The first type occurs when a loved one is perceived as physically absent but psychologically present. The second type of ambiguous loss is experienced when a loved one is perceived as physically present but psychologically absent. Health-related conditions such as addictions, mental illnesses and brain injury involve this type of ambiguous loss. The physically present–psychologically absent dilemma also occurs in palliative care with people living with dementia, for example, where others may treat the dying person as if they are already dead (social death) or where the patient lacks consciousness of existence (a psychological death) (Blandin & Pepin 2015; Borgstrom 2017). As medical advances can maintain life longer, more families will experience the stress associated with ambiguous loss—for example, those families who have a loved one with a prolonged disorder of consciousness (Zaksh et al. 2019).

Lack of control makes coping with ambiguous loss so difficult. Five factors can interfere with coping (Boss 2000, 2016):

1. people are confused by the indefinite nature of the loss and become immobilised
2. the uncertainty prevents adjustment and results in 'frozen' relationships with the ambiguously lost person
3. the ambiguous loss is not recognised by the community, with little validation and no rituals
4. ambiguous losses are more confronting, reminding people that life is not always rational or just (this reality can cause potential supports to withdraw)
5. because ambiguous loss can be prolonged, those who experience it become physically and emotionally exhausted.

To help people deal with ambiguous loss, Boss states that 'clinicians need to realize that by sharing knowledge they are empowering families to take control of their situation even when ambiguity exists' (Boss 2000, p. 23).

Ambiguous loss also can be traumatising, with symptoms similar to post-traumatic stress disorder (Boss 2000, 2016). Ambiguous loss usually involves a series of psychological ups and downs, with hopes repeatedly dashed so that continuing to try to cope seems futile and learned helplessness can develop. Boss highlights the importance of allowing those experiencing ambiguous loss to tell their story, to receive validation and to have someone help them make sense of what they are experiencing.

A note about non-death loss

At this point, it is also worth making the point that while loss has traditionally been associated with death, the impact of loss and grief unrelated to death is now being recognised as important and is increasingly being considered in the literature. For example, non-death loss could include:

- children in foster care (loss of family, community, identity, normalcy) (Mitchell 2018)

- incarceration (grief, stigma separation—experienced by families and the person in prison) (King & Delgado 2021).

ANTICIPATORY GRIEF AND LOSS

Anticipatory grief was first noted by Erich Lindemann in 1944, since described as a 'forewarning of loss' (Fulton et al. 1996). Nielsen and colleagues (2016) in their work with caregivers of terminally ill patients talk of 'pre-loss grief', indicating that grief symptoms are already present before the death. Anticipatory grief is also recognised in situations without a death, such as with missing persons, parents with children who have lifelong disabilities, or in people living with dementia. Rogalla, in her study with 120 people who faced an impending loss via terminal illness, found that proactively seeking social support and practising coping techniques during this time may be beneficial (Rogalla 2020).

LOSS AND GRIEF FOLLOWING A MAJOR EVENT

Since 2019 the spotlight has been on death, grief and loss on a global scale as a result of the COVID-19 pandemic, mirroring that of other large-scale contagions of the past (Kunzler et al. 2021). The COVID-19 death toll has been in the millions, with an example of the broader impact estimating that more than 5 million children have had a parent or caregiver die (Hillis et al. 2021). Historically, such outbreaks are not new, with the Spanish flu (1918) seeing between 17 and 50 million deaths and the intermittent outbreaks of Ebola since 1976 causing many deaths across the globe. Each such event is profound and changes the landscape of dying, with often lifelong health and social consequences. For example: 'COVID-19 has not only changed how we live but also how we die; complicating the dying process for those with the disease, as well as those dying from other causes and complicating the grieving process for those left behind' (Bauld et al. 2021, p. 269).

COVID-19 illustrates an event where multifaceted losses have occurred, not only of loss of life but of freedom and of personal and social connections (e.g. inability to travel and lockdown) (Bauld et al. 2021). As a result of worldwide restrictions many people died alone (possibly in hospital on a ventilator), with relatives able to neither visit nor say goodbye. Such an impersonal and traumatic death can potentially lead to poor bereavement outcomes (Neimeyer & Lee 2021). Health professionals have also seen unimaginable numbers of deaths, often trying to connect the dying to loved ones via technology to facilitate goodbyes (Bauld et al. 2021). In tandem with this, the loss or interruption to rituals that traditionally help in grieving and mourning has had implications for how people have coped with their grief (Rawlings et al. 2022). This has included an absence or postponement of funerals, restrictions to numbers attending and the inability to offer comfort and support with touch. Changes to the service itself has seen new rituals being enacted such as funerals being conducted online, a distinct difference from the traditional, accustomed ways of saying goodbye (Rawlings et al. 2022). In turn, it is now predicted that there will be a wave of complicated grief in the face of such multiple losses, with COVID-19 also affecting usual sources of support (Carr et al. 2020; Johns et al. 2020; Jordan et al. 2021). This will require health professionals to offer a coordinated approach to bereavement care, albeit with limited time and available resources (Borghi & Menichetti 2021; Mayland et al. 2020; Pearce et al. 2021). Improved communication between health professionals and families before, during and after death, adapting mourning rituals, training in bereavement care and improved bereavement resources are all ways in which bereavement care can be improved (Borghi & Menichetti 2021; Mayland et al. 2020; Pearce et al. 2021).

It has been said that most people in their lifetime will experience one severe event (Bonanno et al. 2011). Such an event could include conflict (war), mass shootings, bombings or natural disasters such as drought, fires, hurricanes or floods. Australia, along with many other countries, regularly sees bushfires sweep across vast areas with losses to life, land, fauna and ecosystems (Harms et al. 2021). Major flooding is one of the costliest natural disasters that occur in a country. It is often associated with major impact both immediate and long term. As a result of flooding, human life can be lost, homes and businesses destroyed and livestock and crops demolished. Major losses have resulted, seeing sudden traumatic bereavement, delayed shock, loss of employment and loss of community cohesions, as well as trauma for not only the survivors but also the rescuers (Gearing 2018). There is evidence to suggest that many people who experience a natural disaster continue to suffer their losses emotionally, economically and physically 5 years following the disaster. This appears more apparent in areas of existing socioeconomic vulnerability, including those with poorer overall health and pre-existing mental health conditions (McMahon & Kiem 2018; Rolfe et al. 2020).

These major events can cause displacement, economic and/or social disruption, with the resulting impact on the health system relative to the losses experienced (Edwards et al. 2019; Marson & Legerton 2021). These large-scale events require long-term support (Gearing 2018), with many countries recognising the need for psychological responses tailored to the disaster including psychological first aid, the promotion of positive psychological growth and resilience and social support (Palinkas et al. 2020). Special attention to at-risk populations such as those with a pre-existing mental health issue, financial hardship or other vulnerability should be a priority (Harms et al. 2015, Dyregrov et al. 2015; Eliot & Meglin 2019; Palinkas et al. 2020; Riefels et al. 2013).

DISENFRANCHISED LOSS AND GRIEF

A concept that has significantly expanded awareness about the nature and impact of loss is **disenfranchised grief**. Kenneth Doka (2016), a seminal researcher in the field, defined disenfranchised grief as the grief that people experience following losses that are not or cannot be openly acknowledged, socially sanctioned or publicly shared. Losses are disenfranchised by the dominant societal norms or *rules* that define acceptable feeling, thinking and spiritual expression when loss occurs (Doka 2002, 2016). Loss experiences that fall outside these rules are not recognised. Doka's work has effectively integrated the psychological and the social elements of loss and grieving by acknowledging that a person's experience of grief is often affected by factors external to the griever.

Doka has proposed the following typology of losses that are disenfranchised:

- *the relationship is not recognised* (e.g. friends, ex-partners, professional helpers, internet relationships, gay partners, companion animals/pets)
- *the loss is not acknowledged* (e.g. abortion, miscarriage, infertility, secondary losses, non-death losses, loss of connection to land)

- *the griever is excluded* (e.g. children, the aged, people with intellectual disabilities)

- *circumstances of the death* (e.g. AIDS-related deaths, suicides, murders, COVID-19)

- *ways people grieve* (e.g. different styles of grieving, cultural differences in grieving).

Health professionals have all been exposed to social norms about 'acceptable' loss and grieving, and therefore it is helpful to be aware of how these norms may influence our professional thinking and practices, possibly resulting in disenfranchising attitudes and behaviours. As noted in Doka's typology above, many health-related losses are not acknowledged—for example, losses associated with elective abortion (Corr 2002).

Health professionals may also contribute to disenfranchising processes. With a focus on treatment, cure, rehabilitation and recovery, the losses can potentially be perceived as healthcare 'failures'. Similarly, the focus of health professionals is often on symptomatology. Corr argues that referring to grief *symptoms* disenfranchises grief by failing to recognise the essentially natural and healthy responses to loss found in many grieving behaviours. Speaking about the *signs*, *manifestations* or *expressions* of grief avoids disenfranchising and even pathologising the wide range of appropriate responses to loss (Corr 2002).

Finally, the grief of health professionals may be disenfranchised (Spidell et al. 2011). Such professionals may not be considered as 'legitimate' grievers when, for example, a patient dies. The health professional–patient relationship may not be recognised as one in which the health professionals' grief is appropriate. Indeed, the concept of 'being a professional' often promotes emotional distance from the patient, resulting in potentially disenfranchising their own grief. For example, after a patient has died, nurses are often expected to manage the dead body, preparing for the next admission, with little recognition given to the nurse as a griever. Resilience plays a key role in how a person deals with loss, particularly in relation to how health professionals may respond to a patient's death (Bonanno et al. 2011; Lyng et al. 2021). While some health professionals working in areas where death is a frequent occurrence (e.g. palliative care) have fostered their ability to manage and face the ongoing losses associated with a person dying, others working in areas such as aged care and intensive care sometimes do not have the time to grieve, severely testing their ability to 'bounce back'. Consider this in light of Chapter 9 when looking at stress and coping.

Following a death in any culture, funerals or rituals are held to mark the end of that person's life and as a starting point for recovery (Mitima-verloop et al. 2019). Funerals and other rituals are useful in providing structure and procedures for gradually facing the reality of a loss. Within health care it is not feasible nor healthy to attend funerals for every patient who has died. Traditionally oncology and palliative care memorial services have been hosted to acknowledge those who have died, and more recently aged care facilities have initiated their own rituals as a sign of respect and acknowledgment after a death (Rawlings & Devery 2020). A ritual called 'the pause' has emerged in recent years whereby a resuscitation team pause for a few seconds of silence following an unsuccessful resuscitation. This has been established to honour the life that has ended and to also recognise the effort of the team involved (Cunningham & Ducar 2019). It has proven to reduce stress, recharge and focus staff before going onto the next patient (Cunningham & Ducar 2019).

Student activity

1. Identify as many services and resources as you can in your local community that are available for grieving people and/or their families. Once you have completed your list, share your findings and ideas with at least one other student in your class. Compiling relevant local or community resources can be a useful exercise to support you when needing to refer clients or families, or for access yourself.

2. Review Doka's typology of disenfranchised losses on page 272. Under each of the five categories, write down three ways that the healthcare system can disenfranchise the loss and grief of patients and/or families. Then propose strategies by which disenfranchising practices can be avoided or redressed. This enables you to consider how to be inclusive in your practice and work towards patient-centred care.

NONFINITE LOSS AND CHRONIC SORROW

Another concept of particular relevance to the field of health care is **nonfinite loss**. Bruce and Schultz (2001) developed this term through their work with families of children with developmental disabilities. They recognised that parents can experience ongoing loss and grief as the impact of their child's disability unfolds throughout the lifespan. Nonfinite loss is contingent on three elements: life stage development, passage of time and a lack of synchrony between lived experience, hopes and expectations. This type of loss often goes unidentified or recognised until the person reflects back and realises what did not happen in life, in comparison with 'what should have been' (Bruce & Schultz 2001, p. 8).

Nonfinite loss has been associated with situations such as: congenital or acquired disabilities; traumatic injury; ongoing, degenerative or terminal illnesses such as dementia, multiple sclerosis or cancer; adoption; infertility; separation and divorce; and sexual abuse. These experiences can challenge, even shatter, preconceived ideas of what the world should be like, leading to ongoing, nonfinite loss and grief (Bruce & Schultz 2001). Parents of a child with a disability can be repeatedly reminded of what their child has not been able to achieve in comparison with the hopes and dreams they had for that child (Ray & Street 2007).

Five cycles of nonfinite grief can be experienced, involving themes of shock, protest/demand, defiance, resignation/despair and integration (Bruce & Schultz 2001). The nonfinite nature of the grieving means these cycles recur: 'The cycles are not linear, have no end-point and are prone to recycling again and again' (Bruce & Schultz 2001, p. 163).

Similar to nonfinite loss and grief is chronic sorrow. Olshansky (1962) first described chronic sorrow as the intense, pervasive and recurring sadness observed in parents of children with an intellectual disability. Other studies have examined chronic sorrow among parents of children with chronic illness or disability (Coughlin & Sethares 2017) and the carers of people with a lived experience of schizophrenia (Chang et al. 2017). Chronic sorrow, while often continuing through a person's life, is considered 'a normal reaction to the significant loss of normality in the affected individual or the caregiver' (Burke et al. 1992, p. 232). Many people and their families with long-term illnesses will experience nonfinite loss and chronic sorrow. By missing or mislabelling a person's grief, a health professional runs the risk of disenfranchising the loss and/or responding inappropriately. Chronic sorrow is best treated through recognising the family's recurrent experiences of grief and providing supportive responses to their sadness.

Research focus

Source: Tseng et al. 2017

ABSTRACT

Aims and objectives
To explore couples' perceptions of the effects of perinatal loss on their marital relationship, social support and grief 1 year post-loss and to analyse what factors changed the severity of their grief.

Background
Perinatal losses are traumatic events in the lives of families and can have serious long-term consequences for the psychological health of parents and any subsequent children.

Design
A prospective follow-up study.

Methods
At a teaching hospital in southern Taiwan, the researchers recruited a convenience sample of 30 couples whose babies either miscarried or were stillborn. At 1 month, 3 months, 6 months and 1 year after the pregnancy loss, all participants completed four questionnaires. To analyse the changing status of their grief and its related factors, the researchers used a generalised estimating equation to account for correlations between repeated observations.

Results
Post-bereavement grief levels fell over the four time-points. Mothers reported feeling more grief than did the fathers. Couples with a history of infertility, no religious beliefs or no living children before the loss felt more grief from a perinatal miscarriage or stillbirth. Furthermore, couples reported more grief if their marital satisfaction level was low, if their socioemotional support from the husband's parents was low or if they had never participated in a ritual for their deceased baby.

Conclusions
Six months post-loss is the crucial period for bereaved parents after a perinatal loss. Being a mother, having no previous living children and

Cont... ▶

low-level socioemotional support from the husband's parents are significant high-risk factors for a high level of grief 1 year after perinatal death.

Relevance to clinical practice
The researchers recommended that health professionals increase their ability to identify the factors that psychologically affect post-loss grief. Active post-loss follow-up programs should focus on these factors to offer specific support and counselling.

Critical thinking

- In relation to the Tseng and colleagues' (2017) study above, having no living children was one of the risk factors for experiencing a high level of grief. Why do you think this is so? Consider Worden's first task of mourning and the concepts of disenfranchised grief and ambiguous loss in your thinking.

- Using Table 10.2 on page 282 as a guide, describe grief support activities you would suggest for women identified by Tseng and colleagues (2017) as being at risk of experiencing high-level grief following a miscarriage or pregnancy loss.

Responses to loss

Since Freud's early writing about grief, health professionals have been trying to understand how people respond to loss. Freud's notion that mourning occurred over time has been accepted and this time element of mourning has been described as the grief process.

THE GRIEF PROCESS

The grief process has been recognised in various ways. One approach has been to identify phases or stages in grieving. Erich Lindemann (1944) outlined three phases in the grief process: emancipation from bondage to the deceased, readjustment to the environment without the deceased and the formation of new relationships. Parkes (1972, 1988) and later Bowlby (1980) referred to four phases associated with grieving—numbness, yearning to recover the lost person, disorganisation and despair, and reorganisation. Sanders' (1999) model proposed five phases in the mourning process: shock, awareness of loss, conservation-withdrawal, healing and renewal. In her work with terminally ill patients, Kübler-Ross (1969) identified five psychological stages in the dying process. Her staged model (intended to be neither linear nor sequential) of denial, anger, bargaining, depression and acceptance has been used to describe the grieving process for not only individuals but their families too (Corr 2021). It is, however, not to be used to 'define a rigid model of how people react to mortality' (Ross Rothweiler & Ross 2019, p. 3). The phase/stage view of grief has been criticised for inferring that the grieving process is essentially 'passive'. Attig (2015) cautions against any medical conceptualisations of grief because these too imply that grief is a kind of illness that happens to people and over which people have no choice once a major bereavement occurs. Instead, Attig (2015) sees grieving as an active process through which the griever *relearns* their world.

TASKS OF MOURNING

Psychologist William Worden also argued for a more active view of grieving and developed a widely accepted model for the tasks of mourning. Worden (2010) states that a task model fits better with the concept of 'grief work' as described by Freud and Lindemann; that is, grievers need to *act* to move through the grief process. The task model is also seen as consistent with the psychological concept of developmental tasks associated with all human growth. Finally, Worden sees the task model as more useful for practitioners because 'the approach implies that mourning can be influenced by intervention from the outside' (2010, p. 26).

Worden's four tasks of mourning set out specific focal points for grievers' actions:

1. *To accept the reality of the loss*—'The first task of grieving is to come full face with the reality that the person is dead, that the person is gone and will not return' (Worden 2010, p. 27). This task addresses the numbness, shock and denial noted in phase models. Denial most often involves the facts of the loss, the meaning of the loss or the irreversibility of the loss. Full denial of a loss may be rare, but degrees of denial are not uncommon. As a recognised defence mechanism (Hooley et al. 2016), denial serves to protect us from the anxiety that may overwhelm us. So we face experiences in smaller parts to deal with what we feel ready to face. Sometimes grievers are described by others as 'being in denial'; health professionals should be aware of not doing this in a way that is dismissive or disenfranchising of patients' or families' grief.

    Worden states that both intellectual and emotional acceptance of a loss is necessary; less experienced practitioners can overlook emotional acceptance. This task is more difficult for grievers who have experienced a sudden, unexpected death, especially if the body is not seen. If Weenolsen's levels of loss are also considered, the complexity of this task is further evident. As the levels of loss unfold, the reality of the loss keeps changing, requiring this task to be revisited.

2. *To work through the pain of grief*—Sadness, guilt, anger, loneliness and depressive feelings are often involved in grieving. The intensity of grievers' emotional pain can go beyond what they have previously experienced, and they may wonder if they are 'going crazy'. Because experiencing intense grief pain is so difficult, some people will try to avoid working on this task through stopping painful thoughts, numbing feelings through alcohol or drugs, distracting themselves through work or other activities, or evading painful thoughts and feelings by the 'geographic cure' of moving from place to place (Worden 2010, p. 31). Some people are afraid of 'breaking down', stating 'If I allow myself to start feeling (e.g. crying), I'm afraid I will never stop!'. McKissock and McKissock (2012) also describe the 'pharmacological' effects of major loss, as the griever's biochemistry works to numb the immediate emotional reactions. Further emotional distress can be experienced as the numbing wears off in the weeks following the loss. Family and friends do not like to see their loved ones hurting and may feel helpless about how to

respond. As a result, they (and health professionals) can do or say things that give the message 'We don't really want to see your pain'. This is one way that grief responses can be disenfranchised, as discussed above.

3. *To adjust to an environment in which the lost person/thing is missing*— Worden (2010) identifies three types of adjustment: external adjustments, internal adjustments and spiritual adjustments. External adjustments refer to the many functional changes that occur after the death of a loved one. New skills, roles and knowledge—such as cooking meals, driving the family car, parenting without a partner or managing finances—have to be developed. This process can be a challenge both practically and emotionally because many grievers find their energy levels low, their cognitive abilities taxed and their willingness to face more change limited. Internal adjustments relate to changes in the griever's sense of self. These adjustments often will depend on the nature of the relationship and the attachment with the lost person/thing. For example, a relationship that is highly dependent (i.e. one person depends on another to meet their own needs) can lead to significant internal adjustment difficulties. Spiritual adjustments involve making sense of or finding meaning in the loss, similar to Weenolsen's idiosyncratic loss discussed above. Basic assumptions such as 'The world is a good place', 'The world makes sense' and 'I am a worthy person' can be replaced by ideas that 'The world sucks!', 'Life is not fair!' and 'I must have done something bad for this to happen!' (Worden 2010).

4. *To emotionally relocate the lost person/thing and move on with life*—This task focuses on the importance of grievers 'finding a place' for the loss in their life while still moving ahead. Worden originally expressed this task as 'withdrawing emotional energy from the deceased and reinvesting it in another relationship' (2010, p. 35). However, bereaved people subsequently told Worden that withdrawing was not what they did in their grieving; they tried to stay connected to their loved one. Worden therefore revised this task. Grievers, sometimes with the help of a caring professional, seek to 'find an appropriate place for the dead in their emotional lives—a place that will enable them to go on living effectively in the world' (Worden 2010, p. 36). The importance of *staying connected* is evident in the not uncommon stories grievers tell about how upsetting it is when others do not talk about the deceased person, acting as if the dead person never existed.

CONTINUING BONDS

The importance of 'staying connected' has been reinforced in the work on continuing bonds. Klass and colleagues (1996, 2014) present the findings of various theorists and researchers that support the value for grievers in sustaining their relationship with the lost person. They too question the usefulness of grievers having to 'let go':

We cannot look at bereavement as a psychological state that ends and from which one recovers. The intensity of feelings may lessen and the mourner become more future- rather than past-oriented; however, a concept of closure, requiring a determination of when the bereavement process ends, does not seem compatible with the model suggested by these findings. We propose that rather than emphasizing letting go, the emphasis should be on negotiating and renegotiating the meaning of the loss over time.

(Silverman & Klass 1996, pp. 18–19)

The ways in which grievers achieve continuing bonds are creative and fascinating. They reflect the individualised meanings that connecting practices have for the grievers and their families. One family whose daughter died from cancer established a memorial fund at her primary school to cover the costs of their daughter's class cohort for an annual excursion until her class had graduated from their final year of primary school. This memorial provided a continuing bond for both the family and their daughter's school friends.

THE DUAL PROCESS MODEL

Another perspective on how people respond to loss is presented in the **dual process model**. Stroebe & Schut (1999, 2010) argue that the concept of 'grief work' does not capture the complexity of activity involved in the process of grieving. They maintain that grief work focuses too much on the need to confront the personal, intrapsychic loss of the loved one without recognising the interpersonal processes that support mourning, the diversity of stressors grievers need to deal with (in addition to the lost relationship) and the fluctuating nature of grief that can involve swings between the confrontation and avoidance of changes and stressors.

Consequently, the dual process model is constructed around two realms: loss-oriented and restoration-oriented coping (see Fig. 10.1). *Loss-orientation* 'refers to the concentration on and dealing with, processing of some aspect of the loss experienced itself, most particularly, with respect to the deceased person' (Stroebe & Schut 1999, p. 212). This orientation includes the traditional view of grief work, with its focus on relationship or bonds to the deceased person and the ruminations about the deceased, life together, circumstances surrounding the death and yearning for the deceased. Loss-orientation is usually more evident in early bereavement, although it can dominate the griever's attention periodically over time.

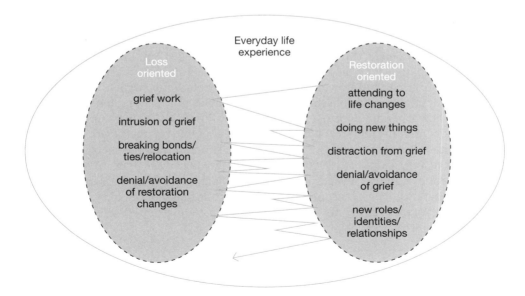

Figure 10.1 The dual process model Source: Stroebe & Schut 2010

Restoration-orientation addresses the added stressors associated with a major loss such as those found in Weenolsen's levels of loss. These stressors include undertaking new tasks, organising one's life without the deceased person, developing a new identity and constructing some meaning in one's new world. A central element of the dual process model is oscillation: the alternation between loss- and restoration-oriented coping. Stroebe and Schut view oscillation as a dynamic, back-and-forth process that allows the griever to alternately confront or avoid the loss, depending on various ongoing psychological, social and practical demands. This alternation is seen as having major mental and physical health benefits. The griever may choose to take 'time off' from grieving, to avoid feelings experienced as too painful at a given point and indeed to use denial in a beneficial way. Stroebe and Schut, citing findings about the severe detrimental psychological and physical effects of unremitting avoidance of grief, argue that the dual process model acknowledges the coping value of the oscillation between confrontation and avoidance. The model's flexibility is seen as accommodating such variables as gender, social and cultural differences in grieving styles and methods (Stroebe & Schut 1999). Overall, the dual process model effectively expresses the unpredictable, vacillating and ongoing complexities of the grief experience. Fiore's (2021) systematic review found that the dual process model accurately represents the bereavement experience and may be more effective than traditional grief therapy.

FOUR ELEMENTS OF GRIEF RESPONSES

Worden (2010) has identified four categories of grief responses—feelings, physical sensations, cognitions and behaviours—that usefully capture the wide range of reactions seen in those experiencing uncomplicated grief.

Feelings

Feelings most commonly include shock, sadness, anger, guilt, anxiety, loneliness, helplessness, yearning, despair, depression, emancipation and relief—sometimes even a lack of feeling (anhedonia) (Stroebe et al. 2001; Worden 2010). Particularly difficult to accept and manage can be feelings of anger and guilt. Anger 'is at the root of many problems in the grieving process' (Worden 2010, p. 12). Anger can be directed at the person who died, family members, a seemingly insensitive friend or God / the world. Health professionals can find themselves the target of such anger. It is important to recognise that this anger almost invariably is not intended as a personal attack. It generally comes from the frustration that nothing could prevent the death/loss and the anxiety that results from 'being left' on one's own. Grievers also frequently identify something that should, or should not, have been done in relation to the loss, resulting in feelings of guilt. Anxiety can range from insecurity to anxiety or panic attacks, even phobias in complicated grief reactions. Bereaved people can feel positively about being freed from controlling or abusive relationships or relieved that physical and emotional pain is ended with the death of a suffering loved one.

Physical reactions

Lindemann (1944) is credited with first describing the physical reactions of grief. Such physical sensations as fatigue, hollowness in the stomach, shortness of breath, muscle weakness, oversensitivity to noise and a sense of depersonalisation can exist (Worden 2010). Grievers will sometimes report having the physical symptoms of the person who died (Stroebe et al. 2001). Many grievers may not recognise the link between their physical reactions and their grief. It is important therefore for health professionals to identify the physiological elements of grieving and assist grievers in receiving both medical care and grief support.

Cognitive reactions

Cognitive reactions to loss can include disbelief, confusion, problems with memory and concentration, lowered self-esteem, hopelessness, sense of unreality, preoccupation with thoughts of the deceased, sense of presence and hallucinations (Stroebe et al. 2001; Worden 2010). It is not unusual for grievers to find their thinking dominated by images and ruminations about the person who died and experiences associated with the death. Some thoughts can be reassuring, such as positive memories about times spent with the deceased loved one, while other thoughts can be distressing. For example, an adult bereaved son reported how the image of his dying father kept appearing over and over again, like a video replaying repeatedly. Thought disturbances are the adjustment required to 're-think' the world in which the lost person or thing is gone.

The cognitive gap or incongruence that results from the absence of a loved one can take some time to be resolved. Preoccupation, sense of presence and hallucinations represent some of the powerful thoughts that occur in grievers' efforts to stay connected to the lost person while cognitively adjusting to life without that person. Worden (2010) is clear that cognitive processes such as visual and auditory hallucinations belong in a list of normal responses to major loss. Kauffman (2002, p. 72) supports this view, stating that 'the hallucinatory power of the image of the deceased functions to mitigate and integrate death loss'. Hallucinations reflect the strong desire to keep alive what is lost because the person is adjusting to the reality of life with that loss. While some grievers may be disconcerted, fearful or ashamed of hallucinatory thoughts, many find them reassuring, with some even seeking them out through those who claim they can make contact with the dead. Kauffman (2002) argues that if such processes as sense of presence or hallucinations are ignored, suppressed or discouraged by self or others, important grief work is disenfranchised and possibly blocked.

Behavioural reactions

Grievers may engage in a range of behavioural reactions. Common behaviours include agitation, crying, social withdrawal, sleep disturbances, appetite changes, absent-minded behaviour, avoiding reminders of the deceased, searching and calling out, sighing, restless overactivity and visiting places or carrying objects that remind them of the deceased (Stroebe et al. 2001; Worden 2010). Behavioural changes will usually correct themselves over time (Worden 2010) as the griever gradually integrates the impact and meaning of the loss. Because behaviours are often the visible expressions of feelings and thoughts, it is important that health professionals know how to interpret such behaviours. Pomeroy and Garcia (2009, p. 52) distinguish between life-depleting and life-enhancing behaviours (see Table 10.2). These authors note that behaviours can be life-enhancing at one point and life-depleting at another.

Table 10.2

COMMON BEHAVIOURS ASSOCIATED WITH EXPECTED GRIEF

Expected experiences	Life-enhancing behaviours	Life-depleting behaviours
Thoughts and preoccupation with the deceased Feelings of yearning, longing and searching for the deceased Emotional pain Fluctuating pangs of grief Social withdrawal Loss of interest A mix of negative emotions: sadness, anger, anxiety, guilt, shame Sometimes positive emotions: relief, warmth when re-living happy memories	Crying Talking about the loss Reaching out for support Accepting assistance Taking care of yourself Exercising Getting rest/sleep Seeking out symbolic connection with the deceased	Substance abuse High risk-taking behaviours Compulsive/excessive behaviours (e.g. eating, shopping, working, gambling) Withdrawal and isolation Agitated, aggressive and demanding behaviours Anxiety-driven behaviours Suicidal gestures or attempts

Sources: Bui 2018; Pomeroy & Garcia 2009

CASE STUDY: ELLY

You are doing a practicum as a student health professional at a local teaching hospital. You have been asked to see Elly, a 49-year-old woman who has come for an appointment at the renal outpatient clinic. Your task is to take Elly's medical and social history before she sees the clinician.

After you greet Elly, introduce yourself and explain why you have come to see her, Elly relates the following information.

She was born with cerebral palsy. She currently requires a walker/Zimmer frame to walk, or a wheelchair for longer distances.

Since her childhood, Elly has been hospitalised frequently for numerous surgeries throughout her life, including operations on her legs as a child. Elly states that she wore full leg braces as a child due to her cerebral palsy.

Cont... ▶

Three years ago Elly was diagnosed with a cancerous lump in her lower back. She had surgery, chemotherapy and radiotherapy for this cancer.

Elly lives in a public housing unit that is specially equipped to assist her with activities of daily living. She lives alone. Her husband of almost 20 years died suddenly 8 years ago of a heart attack. Elly's husband was 15 years older than her. Elly has no children. She reports one pregnancy but seems reluctant to discuss this further. She says she had a hysterectomy at age 21.

Elly's family history reveals that both her parents are dead. Her mother died of cancer and her father from a heart attack. She reports that a sister died of suicide, a brother died of drowning and another brother died of cancer.

Elly indicates that over the past 6 years her sleep has been disrupted. She sleeps for between 4 and 5 hours per night, sometimes less. When you ask Elly about particular reasons for this sleep pattern, she says that sometimes she has disturbing dreams from which she wakes suddenly and in a sweat. Elly does not want to talk further about her dreams.

Elly tells you that she believes her cerebral palsy is worsening. She also notes that she currently sees medical specialists for liver, heart, neurological and cancer problems.

⚘ Critical thinking

- While taking Elly's history, you are struck by the number of losses in her life. Using Weenolsen's framework of five levels of loss, identify the losses that you think Elly has, or may have, experienced throughout her life.

- Are there any areas of Elly's experience that you believe could be explored further in terms of her losses and her experience of grief?

- Considering that you have just met Elly and that this may be your only contact with her, can you think of any appropriate, brief comments or responses that you could make to Elly that would acknowledge her losses and show you understand her losses to some degree? Write out three possible comments/responses.

CULTURAL CONSIDERATIONS

It is worth noting that many of the concepts about loss and grief in this chapter have come from, and are arguably dominated by, what might broadly be called Western culture (Merritt 2011; Stillion & Attig 2015). Yet, the context of health care is multicultural, and cross-cultural studies show significant differences in grieving between cultures (Rosenblatt 2017).

In considering the cultural variations to 'normal' reactions to a loss, it is important for health professionals to put their own assumptions aside. As noted by Rosenblatt (2015): 'Each culture has its own approaches to dealing with death which almost always involve a core of understandings, spiritual beliefs, rituals, expectations and etiquette' (p. 25), highlighting that there is no universal behaviour in response to a death.

Efforts to understand how a person or family from any given culture might grieve runs the risk of being simplistic and therefore unhelpful (Rosenblatt 2017). The following five questions have been highlighted as particularly important to ask those coping with the death of a loved one:

1. What are the culturally prescribed rituals for managing the dying process, the body of the deceased, the disposal of the body and commemoration of the death?

2. What are the family's beliefs about what happens after death?

3. What does the family consider an appropriate emotional expression and integration of the loss?

4. What does the family consider to be the gender rules for handling the death?

5. Do certain deaths carry a stigma (e.g. suicide), or are certain types of death especially traumatic for that cultural group (e.g. death of a child)?

Although detailed examination of grief-related cultural beliefs and practices is not possible here, examples of cultural beliefs and practices include the following:

- In some cultures, bereaved people 'somaticize grief, so that a grieving person often feels physically ill' (Rosenblatt 2008, p. 212).

- The Japanese practice of ancestor worship (Valentine 2009) involves an elaborate set of rituals and enables the living to maintain personal, emotional bonds with relatives who have died over a period of 35–50 years. A focal point for ancestor worship is an altar in the home—memorial/connecting rituals not seen in Western societies.

- Australian Aboriginal and Torres Strait Islander people view the loss of land and identity as continuing pervasive losses that influence and interact with their current losses, resulting in what has been described as 'malignant grief' (Merritt 2011). A wide range of death and dying customs are also practised called 'sorry business', with diverse beliefs and ceremonies (Carlson & Frazer 2015). Consult the web resources listed at the end of this chapter for more information.

- In New Zealand, the potential loss of these traditional practices following a death in the Māori culture arguably sees the need to reconnect to whanau (family) and traditions such as how to grieve and lament (Eldridge 2014).

- In some cultures, wailing, tearing clothes and anger in response to a death are expected behaviours, while for others, such overt displays are unwelcome (Rosenblatt 2015).

Health professionals clearly cannot and need not be 'experts' in the various cultures of their patients. But by striving to provide care that is culturally sensitive and safe, you can learn from and work with people to provide culturally appropriate grief support and care (Muir-Cochrane et al. 2018). The need for ongoing staff training and standards for cultural safety is a key area to ensure culturally secure service delivery and should be a template for all providers in meeting the needs of those from culturally diverse populations (Gubhaju et al. 2020).

Children and loss and grief

Children can respond to loss in very different ways from adults. It often depends on their age and developmental stage, manifesting in different feelings and behaviours (Alvis et al. 2022). For example, small children may not understand the irreversibility of a death and may react only to the grief of those around them. Children slightly older may fear their own death or that of a loved one and be curious or angry about the death. Also to note is the moderating factors that may impact on children's grief reactions such as the circumstances of the death and their relationship to the deceased (Alvis et al. 2022).

It is important that health professionals recognise the support specific to children such as honesty, making them feel safe, ongoing conversations about the death and involving them in what is happening (Australian Centre for Grief and Bereavement 2014).

Delivering bad news

Delivering bad news to clients is at times a necessary component of care delivery and communication for health professionals. Invariably, this will result in actual or perceived loss for the person. Girgis (2017) suggests that while this communication is never easy, the best way to start is to be aware that the news is going to change the person's life. When delivering the bad news, it is important to: communicate in person—not over the telephone unless unavoidable; find out what the person knows and what support they have; convey empathy; keep the message simple; let the person ask questions; and listen to the person's concerns. Things to avoid when delivering bad news include using jargon, rushing the person (they need time to absorb the information) and to fail to recognise the person's situation through using platitudes, euphemisms or comparisons to others' situations (Muir-Cochrane et al. 2018). A useful tool is SPIKES—a six step protocol for delivering bad news that has been used effectively in oncology and palliative care (Baile et al. 2000):

- Setting up
- Perception of condition / seriousness
- Invite the client to provide information
- Knowledge—giving the facts
- Explore emotions and empathise
- Strategy and summary.

For more, see 'Communicating bad news' in Chapter 8.

Responding to those who are grieving

All health professionals will encounter patients or clients who have experienced significant losses. Most deaths occur in healthcare facilities, particularly hospitals, nursing homes and hospice/palliative care settings. Therefore, it is essential that such professionals can recognise their patients' grief and respond in appropriate and helpful ways.

Efforts to determine what kinds of assistance are effective with grievers have identified three levels of intervention. The first level, described as primary preventive intervention (Neimeyer & Currier 2009), would offer assistance to all grievers experiencing uncomplicated grief. Apart from the costs of such a universal approach, there is evidence that primary prevention is not needed by everyone (Worden 2010) and that it generally is not effective (Neimeyer 2015). Secondary preventive interventions focus on people who are at risk of complications in their grieving and may result in beneficial outcomes, at least in the short term (Schut et al. 2001). A third level of intervention involves those who experience complicated grief, and research indicates that such intervention reliably achieves positive outcomes for the griever (Neimeyer 2015).

What works and doesn't work in assisting those who are bereaved remains an area of ongoing debate and research. The appreciation that grievers express for the concern, care and support shown by others during times of significant loss clearly indicates there is benefit from such helping actions. For this reason, health professionals need to be willing to offer support to grieving patients and families while being respectful of those who do not want assistance. Consider, too, the fact that people are increasingly going to the internet for information and support. Traditional face-to-face support such as that provided by mental health professionals, grief/bereavement counsellors or spiritual advisors may not be accessed and/or may be replaced or supplemented with online support communities (Hartig & Viola 2016).

The scope of this chapter does not allow a comprehensive discussion of intervention methods. However, Worden (2010, p. 52) sets out four useful goals for grief support and counselling, based on his tasks of mourning:

1. Increase the reality of the loss.
2. Help grievers deal with their feelings.
3. Help the griever overcome obstacles to readjustment after the loss.
4. Help the griever find a way to remember the deceased/lost object while being prepared to reinvest in life.

Box 10.1 summarises guidelines that health professionals can consider in supporting those who are grieving.

Box 10.1 How health professionals can support someone who is grieving

Help the griever actualise the loss
Help grievers express their loss—health professionals can provide a 'fresh' listening ear for the story of loss.
Actively involve grievers in discussions around end-of-life care—this helps make the approaching death more real.

Help the griever identify and experience feelings
Be willing to empathise with the griever's painful feelings.
Responses such as 'It seems like you are really missing _____', or 'I imagine you must be very lonely since _____ died' help name and express feelings associated with loss.

Assist living without the deceased
Connect grievers to support groups and services that assist grievers with the adjustments involved after a significant loss.

Help find meaning in the loss
Meaning making in grief is highly individual, but health professionals can facilitate the process.
Ask grievers what their loss has meant to them, and share stories of how others have found meaning.
Share your own perceptions of meaning—for example, 'It sounds like your life would never have been as happy without your relationship with _____'.
Introduce grievers to meaning-making exercises—for example, creating treasure boxes for children following the death of a parent, taking photographs or copying footprints following a stillbirth (see also Neimeyer 2015).

Facilitate emotional relocation of the deceased/lost object
Support grievers in remembering and reminiscing about who/what has been lost.
Support grievers regarding concrete efforts to remain connected to the lost person or thing such as via a Facebook 'In memoriam' page.
Be cautious about grievers' efforts to quickly find a 'replacement'.

Provide time to grieve
Recognise that active grieving can take time—for example, 2 years or longer.
Avoid giving messages that people should 'be over' their grief.
Remember and support continuing grief at special times—for example, on the anniversary of a death, birthdays or holidays.
Educate the griever's support system (family, friends) that grieving takes time.

Interpret normal behaviour
Help grievers understand and 'make sense' of their often intense grief responses.
Assure grievers that their reactions are not uncommon while still acknowledging how the griever might be upset or worried about their reactions.
Connect grievers with those who have had similar experiences—for example, support groups.

Cont... ▶

Box 10.1 How health professionals can support someone who is grieving—cont'd

Allow for individual differences

Recognise the great diversity of grieving responses that can be demonstrated. Avoid imposing a 'prescription' about how grievers should react. Educate those around the griever that differences in grieving styles and methods are to be expected.

Consider defences and coping styles

Watch for potentially unhelpful grief responses such as excessive use of alcohol or drugs, withdrawal, refusal to be reminded of the loss, 'burying' themselves in work or some other activity. Within a trusting relationship, help the griever explore more useful ways of coping.

Identify grief complications and refer

Monitor for grief complications (see 'Complicated grief' in this chapter). In keeping with professional ethics, recognise your own practice limitations. Refer grievers with complications for more advanced assistance such as a doctor, spiritual/religious advisor, counsellor, social worker or bereavement counsellor.

Adapted from Worden 2010

Research focus

Source: Holm et al. 2019

ABSTRACT

Bereavement and spousal loss lead to emotional and practical problems, especially for those in failing health. The aim of this study was to explore the meaning of bereavement in older adults after the death of their spouse. The participants took part in in-depth interviews. The themes and sub-themes were identified using a hermeneutic approach. One overall theme, 'Struggling to maintain pride and dignity', three themes and six sub-themes emerged. The first theme, 'Understanding health decline', included one sub-theme: 'Difficulty asking for help'. The second theme, 'A lonely painful struggle', had three sub-themes: 'Striving to avoid feeling sorry for oneself', 'Searching for meaning when life becomes meaningless' and 'Sensing that one's spouse is present'. In the third theme, 'Feeling misunderstood in the dialogue with others', two sub-themes emerged: 'Longing for support to achieve inclusion' and 'Togetherness is the best medicine'. It is vital to prevent older adults from carrying a permanent state of grief with them for the rest of their life.

⊙. Critical thinking

- In view of the findings from Holm and colleagues (2019) how do you think health professionals who work with people in aged care settings (e.g. a residential aged care facility or at home) could support their patients in their long-term grieving for a deceased spouse? For example, how could such settings assist their patients in 'Striving to avoid feeling sorry for oneself' or 'Searching for meaning when life becomes meaningless'?

- Are there specific things that could be done in terms of the physical environment, staff training or specific inclusive practices?

Complicated grief

Within the loss and grief field, perhaps one of the most enduring and challenging questions has been: 'When is a person's grieving not normal?' Most people grieve normally and can manage their grief by using internal and external resources, thus slowly adjusting and adapting to a new life following the loss. But if these processes are not followed and/or the grief remains unresolved, it can progress to become clinically relevant (Thiemann et al. 2021).

The difficulty in understanding 'not-normal' grief is illustrated by the variety of terms that have been used to describe such a phenomenon including abnormal, pathological, prolonged, unresolved and dysfunctional grief (Shear 2015). The preferred term in the past has been 'complicated grief' but is now changing to **prolonged grief disorder**, a recognised mental health disorder. It is estimated that 10% of people experience a prolonged, painful grieving process in which the loss is not integrated into the person's life and interferes with their everyday activities (Thiemann et al. 2021).

In the first few months after a loss, distinguishing uncomplicated grief from prolonged grief is generally difficult due to the intensity of grief in its early acute period. However, after 6 months, more complicated grief is evident through such indicators as suicidal thoughts and gestures, depressive disorders, post-traumatic reactions and persistent grief reactions (Ray & Prigerson 2006).

The *Diagnostic and Statistical Manual of Mental Disorders* (DSM5 TR), an American reference book (American Psychiatric Association 2022) and the World Health Organization International Classification of Diseases 11th Revision (ICD-11) are both authoritative guides used for diagnosing and classifying psychiatric disorders. Each present criteria for a person to be diagnosed with prolonged grief disorder including the following:

- The death occurred at least 12 months ago.
- The grief response has included yearning/longing and preoccupation with the deceased.
- Three out of eight symptoms have been experienced.
- Clinically significant distress or impairment has been experienced.

- Duration and severity of the reaction is significant.

- Major depressive disorder is excluded (Prigerson et al. 2021).

One of the difficulties in identifying complex grief has been the lack of valid and reliable measurements of grief. Several grief inventories and questionnaires have been developed such as the PG-13-R tool, which is arguably one of the most reliable tools for assessing grief symptoms; however, the usefulness of many other tools has been questioned (Prigerson et al. 2021).

Theorists and researchers have for some time explored factors that contribute to prolonged grief (Burke & Neimeyer 2014). Is it due to the griever's personality, previous life experiences, lack of social support or the nature of the loss? Interestingly, some commentators propose that complicated grief be viewed as an attachment disorder (Prigerson et al. 2008; Ray & Prigerson 2006; Rider 2017). Previously, Bowlby (1982) recognised grief as a response to separation and argued any difficulties experienced while grieving as an adult were related to disruptions in a person's childhood attachment with parents or significant others. Three pathological attachment patterns were identified:

1. An anxious attachment to parents would result in insecure attachments to significant others in adulthood, overdependence and *chronic grief* following a major loss.

2. A child who was reluctant to accept care and was highly self-sufficient was described as compulsively self-reliant and therefore likely to deny loss and experience *delayed grief.*

3. Chronic grief also was likely to be experienced by a compulsive caregiver, someone whose role as a child was one of giver rather than receiver of care.

Prigerson's research group (Ray & Prigerson 2006) suggests that attachment-related risk factors for complicated/prolonged grief include:

- the closeness of the relationship with the deceased

- dependent, confiding, close relationships—these lead to poorest bereavement adjustment, whereas conflicted relationships result in lower rates of bereavement disorders

- weak parental bonding

- damaged sense of security due to childhood abuse or severe neglect

- childhood separation anxiety

- people who are generally averse to change of any kind.

Two other risk factors are the griever's perception of being unsupported and lack of preparation for the death. This latter factor, among others, makes suicide deaths particularly difficult to deal with. (Loss through suicide has been identified as a specific risk factor for complicated grief.) For more about helping those bereaved through suicide, see Linde and colleagues (2017).

Significant negative health outcomes have been associated with complicated/prolonged grief, including cancer risk, hypertension, suicidal ideation, hospitalisations, alcohol/cigarette consumption and depressive symptoms (Buckley et al. 2009; Ray & Prigerson 2006; Shear 2015). For example, people experiencing complicated/prolonged grief at 6 months post-loss are 16 times more likely to have changes in smoking at 13 months post-loss, seven times more likely to experience changes in eating and almost three times more likely to experience depression (Zhang et al. 2006, p. 1195).

The formalisation of prolonged grief disorder as a mental health condition means a more accurate assessment/diagnosis; increased consistency of practice within the loss and grief field; and greater access to appropriate services by those experiencing prolonged grief disorder. It should enable grievers to more readily access mental health services under Medicare funding.

Chapter summary

This chapter highlights the importance that experiences of loss and grief reactions can play in the lives of those with whom we work as health professionals. Losses and grief reactions need to be incorporated into health assessments and appropriate supportive responses included in healthcare plans. If this does not happen, we run the risk of further disenfranchising the grief of our clients and missing opportunities to assist them in their grief work. Health professionals from all disciplines are positioned to play a key role in identifying, assessing and supporting grief reactions. It is hoped that readers of this chapter will consider how they can take up this challenge in their practice.

KEY POINTS

- Most people with whom health professionals work have experienced significant loss or losses that can affect physical, social, emotional and psychological wellbeing.
- While a major factor in grief is loss of a loved one through death, there also are many non-death losses experienced by clients and their families.
- The loss and grief of patients is often unrecognised, leading to the disenfranchisement of their loss experiences.
- Grief is expressed through a diverse range of feelings, thoughts, behaviours and physical reactions that health professionals can learn to identify.
- Health professionals can play a vital role in identifying and supporting the grief of clients and their families.
- Some grief can become more complicated and can be assessed by health professionals so appropriate assistance can be provided.

Further reading

McKissock, M., McKissock, D., 2012. Coping with Grief, 4th edn. ABC Books, Sydney.

Neimeyer, R., 2015. Techniques of Grief Therapy. Routledge, New York.

Stillion, J., Attig, T., 2015. Death, Dying and Bereavement: Contemporary Perspectives, Institutions and Practices. Springer, New York.

Thompson, N., Doka, K., 2017. Disenfranchised grief. In: Thompson, N., Cox, G. (eds.), Sociology of Death, Grief and Bereavement: A Guide to Theory and Practice. Routledge, London, (Chapter 21).

Worden, W., 2010. Grief Counselling and Grief Therapy: A Handbook for the Mental Health Practitioner, 4th edn. Springer, New York.

Weblinks

Australian Centre for Grief and Bereavement

www.grief.org.au

This website for the Australian Centre for Grief and Bereavement (Melbourne) has an extensive list of related websites, provides information on the peer-reviewed journal *Grief Matters: The Journal of Grief and Bereavement* and describes continuing education events.

Australian Child & Adolescent Trauma, Loss & Grief Network

www.earlytraumagrief.anu.edu.au

Affiliated with the Australian National University, this network brings together evidence-based resources and research to make them more accessible to those working with, or interested in, children and young people who have been affected by trauma and grief.

National Centre for Childhood Grief

https://childhoodgrief.org.au/bereavement-c-a-r-e-centre/

On this website you will find details of the children and family bereavement counselling programs and education courses, previously facilitated through the Bereavement Care Centre.

GriefLink

www.grieflink.asn.au

This South Australian website provides information on many aspects of death-related grief for the general community and professionals in contact with people who are grieving.

Skylight (New Zealand)

https://skylight.org.nz

Skylight is a not-for-profit trust in New Zealand that provides resources for families, children and friends who are experiencing trauma, loss and grief.

CareSearch

www.caresearch.com.au

An evidence-based palliative care website with information, resources, literature searches and a systematic review collection on bereavement and grief.

Australian Indigenous Health*Info*Net

https://healthinfonet.ecu.edu.au/learn/health-system/palliative-care/grief-and-bereavement/

A website helping to close the gap by providing the evidence base to inform practice and policy in Aboriginal and Torres Strait Islander health.

References

Alvis, L., Zhang, N., Sandler, I.N., et al., 2022. Developmental manifestations of grief in children and adolescents: caregivers as key grief facilitators. Journal of Child and Adolescent Trauma, 1–11. 10.1007/s40653-021-00435-0.

American Psychiatric Association, 2022. Diagnostic and Statistical Manual of Mental Disorders (DSM5 TR). American Psychiatric Association, Washington.

Attig, T., 2015. Seeking wisdom about mortality, dying and bereavement. In: Stillion, J., Attig, T., 2015. Death, Dying and Bereavement: Contemporary Perspectives, Institutions and Practices. Springer, New York.

Australian Centre for Grief and Bereavement. 2014. Children and Loss and Grief. Online. Available: https://www.grief.org.au/ACGB/Publications/Resources_Bereaved/Grief_Information_Sheets/ACGB/ACGB_Publications/Resources_for_the_Bereaved/Grief_Information_Sheets.aspx?hkey=19bfe37f-d79f-4e70-85e7-82b94bca248b

Baile, W.F., Buckman, R., Lenzi, R., et al., 2000. SPIKES-A six-step protocol for delivering bad news: application to the patient with cancer. The Oncologist, 5, 302–311.

Bauld, C.M., Letcher, P., Olsson, C.A., 2021. Supporting the dying and bereaved during COVID-19. Australian Psychologist 56(4), 269–273.

Blandin, K., Pepin, R., 2015. Dementia grief: a theoretical model of a unique grief experience. Dementia (Basel, Switzerland) 16 (1), 67–78.

Bonanno, G.A., Westphal, M., Mancini, A.D., 2011. Resilience to loss and potential trauma. Annual Reviews in Clinical Psychology 7, 511–535.

Borghi, L., Menichetti, J., 2021. Strategies to cope with the COVID-related deaths among family members. Frontiers in Psychiatry 12, Article 622850.

Borgstrom, E., 2017. Social Death. QJM: An International Journal of Medicine 110 (1), 5–7.

Boss, P., 2000. Ambiguous Loss: Learning to Live with Unresolved Grief. Harvard University Press, Cambridge.

Boss, P., 2016. The context and process of theory development: the story of ambiguous loss. Journal of Family Theory & Review. 8 (3), 269–286.

Bowlby, J., 1980. Loss: Sadness and Depression, vol. 3. Attachment and Loss. Penguin Press, London.

Bowlby, J., 1982. Attachment and loss: retrospect and prospect. The American Journal of Orthopsychiatry 52, 664–678.

Bruce, E., Schultz, C., 2001. Nonfinite Loss and Grief: A Psychoeducational Approach. Paul H Brookes, Baltimore.

Buckley, T., Bartrop, R., McKinley, S., et al., 2009. Prospective study of early bereavement on psychological and behavioural cardiac risk. Internal Medicine Journal 39, 370–378.

Bui, E., 2018. Grief: From normal to pathological reactions. In Bui, E. (ed.), Clinical Handbook of Bereavement and Grief Reactions, Current Clinical Psychiatry, Humana Press New Jersey (Chapter 5).

Burke, L., Neimeyer, R., 2014. Complicated spiritual grief 1: a reaction to complicated grief symptomology following violent death bereavement. Death Studies 38 (1–5), 259–267.

Burke, M., Hainsworth, M., Eakes, G., et al., 1992. Current knowledge and research on chronic sorrow: a foundation for inquiry. Death Studies 16, 231–245.

Carlson, B., Frazer, R., 2015. 'It's like going to a cemetery and lighting a candle': Aboriginal Australians, Sorry business and social media. AlterNative: an International Journal of Indigenous Peoples 11 (3), 211–224.

Carr, D., Boerner, K, Moorman, S., 2020. Bereavement in the time of coronavirus: unprecedented challenges demand novel interventions. Journal of Aging & Social Policy 32 (4–5), 425–431.

Chang, K., Huang, X., Cheng, J., et al., 2017. The chronic sorrow of caregivers of clients with schizophrenia in Taiwan: a phenomenological study. Perspectives in Psychiatric Care 52 (2).

Corr, C., 2002. Revisiting the concept of disenfranchised grief. In: Doka, K. (ed.), Disenfranchised Grief: New Directions, Challenges and Strategies for Practice. Research Press, Champaign.

Corr, C., 2021. Should we incorporate the work of Elisabeth Kübler-Ross in our current teaching and practice and, if so, how? OMEGA – Journal of Death and Dying 83(4) 706–728.

Coughlin, M., Sethares, K., 2017. Chronic sorrow in parents of children with a chronic illness or disability: an integrative literature review. Journal of Pediatric Nursing 37, 108–116.

Cunningham, T., Ducar, D.M., 2019. Benefits of using the pause after death in emergency departments: a Delphi study. Southern Medical Journal 112 (9), 469–474.

Doka, K. (Ed.), 2002. Disenfranchised Grief: New Directions, Challenges and Strategies for Practice. Research Press, Champaign.

Doka, K., 2016. Grief is a Journey, Aria Books, New York.

Dyregrov, A., Salloum, A., Kristensen, P., et al., 2015. Grief and traumatic grief in children in the context of mass trauma. Current Psychiatry Reports 17, 48.

Edwards, B., Gray, M., Hunter, B., 2019. The social and economic impacts of drought. Australian Journal of Social Issues, 54, 22–31.

Eldridge, V., 2014. Whanau respond to tangihanga and grief. Kai Tiaki Nursing New Zealand 20 (4), 15–17.

Eliot, K., Meglin, J.A., 2019. Dances of loss, grief, and endurance in the face of trauma. Dance Chronicle 42 (3), 265–269.

Fiore, J., 2021. A systematic review of the dual process model of coping with bereavement (1999–2016). OMEGA – Journal of Death and Dying 84 (2), 414–458.

Freud, S., 1917. Mourning and melancholia. The standard edition of the complete psychological works of Sigmund Freud, volume XIV (1914–1916): on the history of the psycho-analytic movement. Papers on Metapsychology and Other Works, 237–258.

Fulton, G., Madden, C., Minichiello, V., 1996. The social construction of anticipatory grief. Social Science Medicine 43 (9), 1349–1358.

Gearing, A., 2018. Post-disaster recovery is a marathon, not a sprint. Pacific Journalism Review 24 (1), 52–68.

Girgis, L., 2017. Physicians practice: how to give bad news to your patients. Available: https://www.physicianspractice.com/view/communicating-bad-news-to-your-patients

Gubhaju, L., Williams. J., Jones, J., et al., 2020. 'Cultural security is an on-going journey…' Exploring views form staff members on the quality and cultural security of services for Aboriginal families in Western Australia. Environmental Research and Public Health, 17, 8480.

Harms, L., Block, K., Gallagher, H.C., et al., 2015. Conceptualising post-disaster recovery: Incorporating grief experiences. British Journal of Social Work 45, Suppl 1, i170–i187.

Harms, L., Gibbs, L., Ireton, G., et al., 2021. Stressors and supports in postdisaster recovery: experiences after the Black Saturday bushfires. Australian Social Work 74 (3), 332–347.

Hartig, J., Viola, J., 2016. Online grief support communities: therapeutic benefits of membership. OMEGA – Journal of Death and Dying 73 (1), 29–41.

Harvey, J., Weber, A., 1999. Why there must be a psychology of loss. In: Harvey, J. (ed.), Perspectives on Loss: A Sourcebook. Bruner/Mazel, Philadelphia.

Hillis, S.D., Unwin, H.J.T., Chen, Y., et al., 2021. Global minimum estimates of children affected by COVID-19-associated orphanhood and deaths of caregivers: a modelling study. Lancet 398, 391–402.

Holm, A.L., Severinsson, E., Berland, A.K., 2019. The meaning of bereavement following spousal loss: a qualitative study of the experiences of older adults. SAGE Open, 9(4) https://doi.org/10.1177/2158244019894273

Hooley, K., Butcher, J., Nock, M., et al., 2016. Abnormal Psychology, 17th edn. Pearson, Boston.

Johns, L., Blackburn, P., McAuliffe, D., 2020. COVID-19, Prolonged grief disorder and the role of social work. International Social Work 63(5), 660–664.

Jordan, T.R., Wotring, A.J., McAfee, C.A., et al., 2021. The COVID-19 pandemic has changed dying and grief: Will there be a surge of complicated grief? Death Studies 46 (1), 84–90.

Kauffman, J., 2002. The psychology of disenfranchised grief: liberation, shame and self-disenfranchisement. In: Doka, K. (Ed.), Disenfranchised Grief: New Directions, Challenges and Strategies for Practice. Research Press, Champaign.

King, K.M., Delgado, H., 2021. Losing a family member to incarceration: grief and resilience. Journal of Loss and Trauma 26 (5), 436–450.

Klass, D., Silverman, P., Nickman, S. (eds.), 1996. Continuing Bonds: New Understandings of Grief. Taylor and Francis, Philadelphia.

Klass, D., Silverman, P., Nickman, S. (eds.), 2014. Continuing Bonds: New Understandings of Grief. Taylor and Francis, Philadelphia.

Kübler-Ross, E., 1969. On Death and Dying. Macmillan, New York.

Kunzler, A.M., Stoffers-Winterling, J., Stoll, M., et al. 2021. Mental health and psychosocial support strategies in highly contagious emerging disease outbreaks of substantial public concern: A systematic scoping review. PLoS One 16(2), e0244748.

Linde, K., Tremi, J., Steinig, J., et al., 2017. Grief interventions for people bereaved by suicide: a systematic review. PloS One Explore: Sport and Exercise Science Collection. Available: https://journals.plos.org/plosone/article?id=10.1371/journal.pone.0179496

Lindemann, E., 1944. Symptomatology and management of acute grief. The American Journal of Psychiatry 101, 141–148.

Lyng, H.B., Ree, E., Wibe, T., et al., 2021. Healthcare leaders' use of innovative solutions to ensure resilience in healthcare during the COVID-19 pandemic: a qualitative study in Norwegian nursing homes and home care services. BMC Health Services Research 21, 878.

Marson, S.M., Legerton. M., 2021. Disaster diaspora and the consequences of economic displacement and climate disruption, including hurricanes Matthew (October 8, 2016) and Florence (September 14, 2018) in Robeson County, North Carolina. Natural Hazards 107, 2247–2262.

Mayland, C.R., Harding, A.J.E., Preston, N., et al., 2020. Supporting adults bereaved through COVID-19: a rapid review of the impact of previous pandemics on grief and bereavement. Journal of Pain and Symptom Management 60 (2), e33–e39.

McKissock, M., McKissock, D., 2012. Coping with Grief, 4th edn. ABC Books, Sydney.

McMahon, G.M., Kiem, A.S., 2018. Large floods in South East Queensland, Australia: Is it valid to assume they occur randomly? Australasian Journal of Water Resources 22 (1), 4–14.

Merritt, S., 2011. First Nations Australians – surviving through adversities and malignant grief. Grief Matters 14 (3), 74–77.

Mitchell, M.B., 2018. 'No one acknowledged my loss and hurt': Non-death loss, grief and trauma in foster care. Child Adolescent Social Work 35, 1–9.

Mitima-verloop, H.B., Mooren, T.T.M., Boelen, P.A., 2019. Facilitating grief: an exploration of the function of funerals and rituals in relation to grief reactions. Death Studies 45 (9), 735–745.

Muir-Cochrane, M., Barkway, P., Nizette, D., 2018. Pocketbook of Mental Health, 3rd edn. Elsevier, Sydney.

Neimeyer, R., 2015. Techniques of Grief Therapy. Routledge, New York.

Neimeyer, R., Currier, J., 2009. Grief therapy: evidence of efficacy and emerging directions. Current Directions in Psychological Science 18 (6), 352–356.

Neimeyer, R.A., Lee, S.A., 2021. Circumstances of the death and associated risk factors for severity and impairment of COVID-19 grief. Death Studies 46 (1), 34–42.

Nielsen, M.K., Neergaard, M.A., Jensen, A.B., et al., 2016. Do we need to change our understanding of anticipatory grief in caregivers? A systematic review of caregiver studies during end-of-life caregiving and bereavement. Clinical Psychology Review 44, 75–93.

Olshansky, S., 1962. Chronic sorrow: a response to having a mentally defective child. Social Casework 43, 191–193.

Palinkas, L.A., O'Donnell, M.L., Lau, W., et al., 2020. Strategies for delivering mental health services in response to global climate change: A narrative review. International Journal of Environmental Research and Public Health 17, 8562.

Parkes, C.M., 1972. Bereavement: Studies of Grief in Adult Life. Tavistock, London.

Parkes, C.M., 1988. Bereavement as a psychosocial transition: process of adaptation to change. Journal of Social Issues 44, 53–65.

Pearce, C., Honey, J.R., Lovick, R., et al., 2021 'A silent epidemic of grief': a survey of bereavement care provision in the UK and Ireland during the COVID-19 pandemic. BMJ Open 11:e046872.

Pomeroy, E., Garcia, R., 2009. The Grief Assessment and Intervention Workbook: A Strengths Perspective. Brooks/Cole, Belmont.

Prigerson, H., Vanderwerker, L., Maciejewski, P., 2008. A case for inclusion of prolonged grief disorder in DSM-V. In: Stroebe, M., Hansson, R., Schut, H., et al. (eds.), Handbook of Bereavement Research and Practice: Advances in Theory and Intervention. American Psychological Association, Washington DC.

Prigerson, H.G., Boelen, P.A., Xu, J., et al., 2021. Validation of the new DSM-5-TR criteria for prolonged grief disorder and the PG-13-Revised (PG-13-R) scale. World Psychiatry 20, 96–106.

Rawlings, D., Devery, K., 2020 Bereavement care in older people. Australian Nursing and Midwifery Journal 27 (1), 14–17.

Rawlings, D., Miller-Lewis, L., Tieman, J., 2022. Impact of the COVID-19 pandemic on funerals: experiences of participants in the 2020 Dying2Learn MOOC. OMEGA – Journal of Death and Dying. https://doi.org/10.1177/00302228221075283

Ray, A., Prigerson, H., 2006. Complicated grief: an attachment disorder worthy of inclusion in DSM-V. Grief Matters 9 (2), 33–38.

Ray, R., Street, A., 2007. Non-finite loss and emotional labour: family caregivers' experiences of living with motor neurone disease. Journal of Clinical Nursing 16 (3a), 35–43.

Rider, M., 2017. Two case reports: using simulated reattachment to treat persistent complex bereavement disorder and PTSD. Explore: The Journal of Science and Healing 13 (6), 414–417.

Riefels, L., Pietrantoni, L., Prati, G., et al., 2013. Lessons learned about psychosocial responses to disaster and mass trauma: an international perspective. European Journal of Psychotraumatology 4, 22897.

Rogalla, K.B., 2020. Anticipatory grief, proactive coping, social support, and growth: exploring positive experiences of preparing for loss. OMEGA – Journal of Death and Dying 81 (1), 107–129.

Rolfe, M., Pit, S.W., McKenzie, J.W., et al., 2020. Social vulnerability in a high-risk flood-affected rural region of NSW, Australia. Natural Hazards 101, 631–650.

Rosenblatt, P., 2017. Researching grief: cultural, relational and individual possibilities. Journal of Loss and Trauma: International Perspectives on Stress & Coping 22 (8), 617–630.

Rosenblatt, P., 2008. Grief across cultures: a review and research agenda. In: Stroebe, M., Hansson, R., Schut, H. (eds.), Handbook of Bereavement Research and Practice: Advances in Theory and Intervention. American Psychological Association, Washington DC.

Rosenblatt, P.C., 2015. Grief in small scale societies. In: Parkes, C.M., Laungani, P., Young, W. (eds.). Death and bereavement across cultures. 2nd edn. Taylor & Francis Group, Abingdon.

Ross Rothweiler, B., Ross, K., 2019. Fifty years later: reflections on the work of Elisabeth Kübler-Ross M.D. The American Journal of Bioethics 19 (12), 3–4.

Sallnow, L., Smith, R., Ahmedzai, S.H., et al. on behalf of the Lancet Commission on the Value of Death, 2022. Report of the Lancet Commission on the Value of Death: bringing death back into life. www.thelancet.com Published online 31 January 2022. Available: https://doi.org/10.1016/S0140-6736(21)02314-X (accessed 15/02/2022)

Sanders, C.M., 1999. Grief the Mourning After: Dealing with Death and Bereavement, 2nd edn. Wiley, New York.

Schut, H., Stroebe, M., van den Bout, J., et al., 2001. The efficacy of bereavement interventions: determining who benefits. In: Stroebe, M., Hansson, R., Stroebe, W. (eds.), Handbook of Bereavement Research: Consequences, Coping and Care. American Psychological Association, Washington DC.

Shear, K., 2015. Complicated grief. The New England Journal of Medicine 372 (2), 153–160.

Silverman, P., Klass, D., 1996. Introduction: What's the problem? In: Klass, D., Silverman, P., Nickman, S. (eds.), Continuing Bonds: New Understandings of Grief. Taylor and Francis, Philadelphia.

Spidell, S., Wallace, A., Carmack, C., et al., 2011. Grief in healthcare: an investigation of the presence of disenfranchised grief. Journal of Health Care Chaplaincy 17, 750–786.

Stillion, J., Attig, T., 2015. Death, Dying and Bereavement: Contemporary Perspectives, Institutions and Practices. Springer, New York.

Stroebe, M., Hansson, R., Stroebe, W., et al., 2001. Introduction: concepts and issues in contemporary research on bereavement. In: Stroebe, M., Hannson, R., Stroebe, W. (eds.), Handbook of Bereavement Research: Consequences, Coping and Care. American Psychological Association, Washington DC.

Stroebe, M., Schut, H., 1999. The dual process model of coping with bereavement: rationale and description. Death Studies 23, 197–224.

Stroebe, M., Schut, H., 2010. The dual process model of coping with bereavement: a decade on. OMEGA – Journal of Death and Dying 61 (4), 273–289.

Thiemann, P., Street, A.N., Heath, S.E., et al., 2021. Prolonged grief disorder prevalence in adults 65 years and over: a systematic review. BMJ Supportive & Palliative Care: bmjspcare-2020-002845.

Tseng, Y.F., Cheng, H.R., Chen, Y.P., et al., 2017. Grief reactions of couples to perinatal loss: a one-year prospective follow-up. Journal of Clinical Nursing 26, 5133–5142.

Valentine, C., 2009. Continuing bonds after bereavement: a cross-cultural perspective. Bereavement Care 28 (2), 6–11.

Weenolsen, P., 1988. Transcendence of Loss Over the Life Span. Hemisphere, New York.

Weenolsen, P., 1991. Transcending the many deaths of life: clinical implications for cure versus healing. Death Studies 15, 59–80.

Worden, W., 2010. Grief Counselling and Grief Therapy: A Handbook for the Mental Health Practitioner, 4th edn. Brunner-Routledge, New York, pp. 89–104.

Zaksh, Y., Yehene, E., Elyashiv, M., et al., 2019. Partially dead, partially separated: establishing the mechanism between ambiguous loss and grief reaction among caregivers of patients with prolonged disorders of consciousness. Clinical Rehabilitation 33 (2), 345–356.

Zhang, B., El-Jawahri, A., Prigerson, H., 2006. Update on bereavement research: evidence-based guidelines for the diagnosis and treatment of complicated bereavement. Journal of Palliative Medicine 9 (5), 1188–1203.

Chapter 11

Pain

MATT SUTTON & MAT PRIOR

Learning objectives

The material in this chapter will help you to:

- explain what pain is
- understand the basic neurophysiology of pain
- describe a biopsychosocial model of pain
- explain the difference between nociceptive and neuropathic pain and the role of central sensitisation
- explain the roles of beliefs, fear avoidance, distress, coping strategies, and environment in a chronic pain presentation
- explain the difference between acute and chronic pain and describe some of the factors that can contribute to the transition from acute to chronic
- describe the main evidence-based interventions for pain
- describe the components of a cognitive behavioural approach to managing pain
- understand that in the case of chronic pain the treatment goal shifts from trying to reduce or eliminate the pain to learning to live with the pain and return to normal activities and function despite the pain.

Key terms

- Pain (300)
- Nociception (302)
- Allodynia (302)
- Peripheral sensitisation (302)
- Central sensitisation (304)
- Catastrophising (307)
- Fear avoidance (307)

Introduction

Pain is a significant issue within society. It is a leading reason for which people seek health care and can have profound effects, impacting physical function and limiting a person's ability to take part in normal activities.

Although pain is a common issue, it is a highly complex one. Our understanding of pain has evolved considerably over the past 20–30 years, largely due to the advent of advanced imaging that allows us to understand how pain affects different regions of the brain. In fact, up until this time, pain was mostly considered to be a passive and simple process of the result of a noxious stimuli sending pain messages to the brain. We now know it is a much more complex process, with the sensation of pain involving multiple regions of the brain and being influenced by a range of biological, psychological and social factors. Therefore, the pain experienced by different people even with the same stimuli will commonly be different. The same stimuli may actually result in a pain experience for one person but not for another. This clearly does not align with the historical conceptualisation of pain as being a purely biological process. Thus, the experience of pain is highly individualised. But there is still a lot we do not understand, particularly about chronic, or persistent, pain. Many mechanisms are proposed to help explain pain that are largely theoretical, lacking strong empirical evidence. However, what is undebatable is the critical role psychosocial influences such as anxiety and depression have in the pain experience. Although the shift towards a greater focus on the psychosocial influences on the pain experience has greatly expanded our understanding of this complex process, it remains critical to have a foundational knowledge of the biological aspects of pain science to best manage this condition. This multifactorial nature of pain contributes to its complexity and is therefore best considered within a biopsychosocial framework, recognising that biological, psychological and social factors all play a significant role in the development and experience of pain.

A further challenge is the concept of chronic, or persistent, pain—particularly where pain may continue in the absence of tissue pathology. The extent of chronic pain is significant; for example, within Australia, about 1 in 5 adults aged over 45 experience chronic pain, with the associated economic impact, in terms of both healthcare costs and impact on workforce participation and productivity, exceeding A$73 billion (Australian Institute of Health and Welfare 2020). Despite the significant resources and huge volume of research into pain, there is still limited evidence-based management strategies to effectively manage it, and no cure is likely in the near future.

What is pain?

Although we have all experienced pain and have awareness of it, adequately defining pain is challenging. Pain is a subjective phenomenon that is highly individualised, varying greatly in terms of quality and severity (Raja et al. 2020). However, a clear definition is essential to have a framework by which we can gain a greater understanding of it.

The International Association for the Study of Pain defines pain as 'an unpleasant sensory and emotional experience associated with, or resembling that associated with, actual or potential tissue damage' (Raja et al. 2020, p. 1976).

There are two important components to this definition to emphasise. First, that pain is not only characterised by sensory qualities but also associated emotional aspects. As such, the experience of pain can be affected by emotion, past experience, thoughts and beliefs. The second component to emphasise is that tissue damage is not essential for pain to occur, nor is the severity of pain a reliable indicator of tissue damage. This is because pain is not a sensory input from our tissues to our brain, but rather an *output* of our brain, based on a complex interplay of sensory inputs and neural processing. This is contrary to longstanding beliefs about pain and can be a challenging concept for both patients and clinicians to comprehend.

Our understanding of pain has evolved significantly over time. Early models of understanding equated pain with injury or damage—with the belief that body tissues encountered a noxious stimulus (e.g. a cut to the skin or the strain of a muscle), which followed a single nerve path up to the brain, where we gained conscious appreciation of this as 'pain'. This has been the historical basis of biomedical approaches to pain in the health professions, whereby the amount of pain is believed to be proportional to tissue damage, and treatment is directed to where the pain is felt. *(Essentially, 'I feel pain in my foot, therefore there must be something wrong with my foot.')*

Although intuitive, assuming that pain must be linked with injury, and that pain is proportional to injury severity, is incorrect. Numerous examples highlight how tissue damage may not result in a pain response, and vice versa. These include congenital analgesia (people who are born without the ability to feel pain and therefore have no automatic warning system of injury), episodic analgesia (the inability to feel pain in certain situations such as when trying to survive on the battlefield), phantom limb pain (the experience of pain in a limb that does not exist) and, most commonly for many people in our society, the persistence of pain long after physiological tissue healing is complete (Frediani & Bussone 2009).

THE BIOPSYCHOSOCIAL MODEL OF PAIN

These examples, along with greater recognition of the emotional experience of pain, have led to more modern conceptual models of pain being proposed; these consider and explain pain in a biopsychosocial framework. This recognises that pain can be generated and influenced by not only tissue-based or biological factors but psychological and social factors as well (Raja et al. 2020).

To say that pain may be generated and influenced by psychosocial factors in no way makes it any 'less real' or diminished in comparison with pain occurring with tissue damage. It is important to recognise that thought, emotion and memory involve the firing of neural impulses and subsequent processing within the brain, just as sensory inputs from peripheral tissues do.

In considering these different influences, one of the most pre-eminent researchers to expand our understanding of pain, Ronald Melzack, proposed a neuromatrix theory of pain (Melzack 1990), which we can use to conceptualise this complex interplay of different neural pathways within the brain. This interplay can, under certain circumstances, function together to create a certain pattern of activity that gives rise to what we experience and perceive as 'pain'. As such, no singular brain region is responsible for 'pain'; rather it involves activity in a distributed network of widespread brain regions, with this being demonstrated by numerous functional imaging studies (Martucci & Mackey 2016; Mouraux & Iannetti 2018; Peyron & Fauchon 2019).

From this, we can appreciate how pain is both a complex and multifaceted phenomenon. Although unpleasant, pain can be seen as an adaptive evolutionary response to help us recognise and respond to potential threats of harm; if, after weighing up and processing all the relevant inputs, and in the context of knowledge, beliefs and experience, the brain perceives enough threat, a pain experience may be the result.

PAIN MECHANISMS

Within the biopsychosocial model of pain, there are several different pain states, or 'pain mechanisms'. To effectively treat people in pain, it is critical to have an understanding of these pain mechanisms and how they present.

Nociceptive pain

The nociceptive pain mechanism is considered an 'input-dominant' mechanism of pain, whereby sensory input from the body tissues, such as skin or muscle, influences the generation of pain. Input-dominant mechanisms of pain can be understood by learning the neural pathways and basic neurophysiology involved. **Nociception** is the nervous system's signalling of dangerous or potentially dangerous stimuli through the activation and firing of specialised sensory nerve cells called nociceptors (Moseley & Butler 2017; Raja et al. 2020). Nociceptors are activated in response to noxious stimuli, typically either chemical, mechanical or thermal, and this process would be expected to occur in response to injury or tissue damage such as a cut to the skin, a burn or the strain of a muscle. A simplified version of the nociceptive pathway is depicted in Figure 11.1.

In this simplified example of the nociceptive pathway, nociceptors are activated by such a stimulus, generating a nerve impulse along the neuron. This reaches the cerebral cortex not directly but via a series of neurons and synaptic connections. Although some vague sensory appreciation occurs at the thalamus, greater appreciation of the stimulus and its origin occurs when the nerve impulse reaches the cerebral cortex—specifically, the primary somatosensory cortex, which is the brain region responsible for receiving and processing sensory information from the body (Woller et al. 2017).

Note that this is a simplified example, with the potential for influences along this pathway to either increase or inhibit impulse transmission. For instance, following physical trauma, nociceptors can become sensitised by the release of chemicals from the damaged tissue and sensory nerve endings by an inflammatory response. This consequently lowers their threshold for subsequent nerve impulse generation, resulting in a sensitised state in which normally non-painful stimuli, such as light touch, is perceived as painful (**allodynia**) (Woller et al. 2017). This process is called **peripheral sensitisation**, and one common example to illustrate this would be following a sprained ankle, whereby the area becomes painful in response to even light touch.

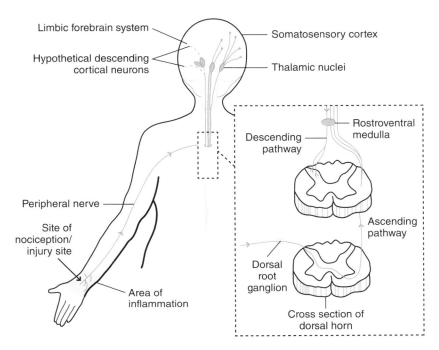

Figure 11.1 Nociceptive pathways Source: Center for Substance Abuse Treatment 2012

Conversely, the body is also able to increase the threshold for nociceptive nerve impulse generation via inhibitory influences. If our brain deems that a pain response is not the most appropriate for the situation, it can trigger the release of chemical neurotransmitters in response to nociception. An example of this is the release of endorphins, which can have an exceptionally strong analgesic, or pain inhibiting, effect. This process is known as descending inhibition, with chemical neurotransmitters blocking or moderating nociceptive transmission at the spinal cord level (Millan 2002; Moseley & Butler 2017). An example of this in action would be the situation of battlefield survival mentioned previously, whereby the brain prioritises survival strategies over generating a pain response.

Although differing types of nociception exist depending on the type of inciting stimuli, there are generally common clinical characteristics. With respect to nociceptive pain of the musculoskeletal system, these include the relationship of pain to movement or activity, localised pain to touch, potential associated inflammatory signs (swelling, redness, heat) and positive response to simple analgesia and anti-inflammatory medication (Shraim et al. 2020).

Neuropathic pain

Neuropathic pain refers to pain arising from a lesion or disease of the nervous, or somatosensory, system (Finnerup et al. 2021; Nijs et al. 2021b). Like nociceptive pain, it is also considered an input-dominant mechanism. Nerve tissue can become a source of pain from a variety of mechanisms, with consideration of the detailed physiological processes of these being beyond the scope of this chapter (for more, see Colloca et al. 2017). Neuropathic pain may occur in a range of conditions such as with traumatic nerve injury, diabetic polyneuropathy, multiple sclerosis and radiculopathy (Finnerup et al. 2021).

Neuropathic pain can be of high intensity and may often be described by patients as 'burning', 'shooting' or 'shock-like' (Colloca et al. 2017; Finnerup et al. 2021; Shraim et al. 2020). Aggravations of neuropathic pain can occur spontaneously or as an exaggerated response to minor stimulation. Patients with neuropathic pain may also describe altered sensation (e.g. numbness, 'pins and needles') and/or autonomic and motor changes, depending on the location and severity of the lesion (Finnerup et al. 2021).

Nociplastic pain

Conceptually, both nociceptive and neuropathic pain are relatively simple constructs when considered as being driven by damage to body tissue—for example, muscle (nociceptive) or nerve (neuropathic). However, the concept of nociplastic pain is significantly more complex. Although the brain is crucial in the generation and processing of pain with all pain states, this takes on extra significance with respect to nociplastic pain. Nociplastic pain is the terminology given to pain that is believed to arise from abnormal sensory processing and pain modulation within the central nervous system (the brain and spinal cord). It may occur even in the absence of harm or noxious stimuli to the local tissues or somatosensory system (Fitzcharles et al. 2021; Nijs et al. 2021b). This has also been referred to as central or centrally driven pain, highlighting the role of the sensitised central nervous system in generating a pain response.

From an evolutionary perspective, we generally see pain as being adaptive; that is, it serves a useful purpose by alerting us to potential danger or harm. In contrast, nociplastic pain may occur in the absence of harm, and therefore we consider pain in this context to be maladaptive, or unhelpful.

A key component, or mechanism, within nociplastic pain is **central sensitisation**. This refers to a state of the central nervous system that amplifies neural signalling, typically leading to a lowering of the activation threshold of the sensory system, with subsequent pain hypersensitivity (Nijs et al. 2021a). Although central sensitisation is commonly associated with chronic pain, it is not exclusive to it and can occur to some degree with all injuries. But this sensitised state usually resolves; only when it fails to resolve, or persists beyond usefulness, does it become maladaptive (Raja et al. 2020).

Consider again the simplified nociceptive pathway presented earlier. Under normal circumstances, the impulse reaching the brain is equal in magnitude to the impulse travelling along each step in the neural pathway from the periphery; therefore, our brain receives an 'accurate' representation of the nature of the stimulus. However, in a sensitised state, many changes can act to amplify the signal along this pathway. Increased chemical neurotransmitter activity may occur at the synapses between these neurons, increasing their excitability and thus the likelihood and magnitude of their subsequent firing. As a result, the brain receives greater sensory input than is proportionate to the original stimulus. Also, neuroplastic changes reorganise neural pathways, and synaptic connections can occur in the long term. This may provide a means for non-nociceptive information (e.g. touch) to synapse with and gain access to nociceptive pathways, leading to erroneous interpretation of the stimulus at the brain.

Collectively, these changes are conducive to increasing the likelihood and magnitude of nociceptive impulses being generated and transmitted to the brain (hyperalgesia), along with non-nociceptive input being erroneously interpreted (allodynia). The net effect of this results in the brain interpreting information it receives (whether that stimulus be movement, touch or other function) as being a greater threat than it actually is, which increases the chances and magnitude of a pain response.

Similarly, changes can also occur at the cerebral cortex, including increased chemical neurotransmitter activity and further reorganisation of nerve cells and conduction pathways. This heightened situation creates an environment where it is easier to trigger patterns of neural activity that may result in pain. Consequently, other stimuli and nerve impulses—including thought, emotion and associative stimuli such as taste and smell, which would ordinarily not trigger a pain response—now have the potential to activate the pain processing pathways (Harte et al. 2018; Moseley & Butler 2017).

Although pain states are highly individualised, there are several clinical characteristics that suggest central sensitisation and/or nociplastic pain (Box 11.1). Recognising these characteristics and the predominant pain state is important because it allows for appropriate management strategies to be determined. For example, mild to moderate nociceptive pain is likely to be effectively managed by simple analgesics such as paracetamol and non-steroidal anti-inflammatories (NSAIDs), but nociplastic pain is less likely to be amenable to simple analgesics and requires a multifaceted approach to management (outlined later in this chapter).

Pain mechanisms can co-exist

It is important to recognise that pain states rarely exist in isolation, and elements of each can co-exist within a person's presentation. For example, a client with a lumbar

---

Box 11.1 Clinical characteristics of central sensitisation

- Pain persists beyond known healing times
- Widespread, non-anatomical distribution of pain
- History of failed interventions
- Pain may be linked to thoughts and feelings
- Pain associated with high levels of functional disability
- Disturbed sleep
- Pain disproportionate to injury/pathology
- Unpredictable, non-mechanical behaviour of pain
- Constant, unremitting pain
- Association with maladaptive psychosocial factors
- Pain may be severe/irritable
- May have associated dysthesias
- Unresponsive to simple analgesia/anti-inflammatory medication

Sources: Nijs et al. 2021b; Shraim et al. 2020

disc herniation and associated nerve root compression may have both nociceptive and neuropathic pain, although a person with chronic nociplastic pain may have periods in which they experience additional nociceptive episodes, contributing to the overall pain experience. Similarly, elements of central sensitisation may be present with any pain state, influencing the perception and experience of pain.

Factors that influence the pain experience

As we can see, the nature of pain is complex and is influenced by a range of physiological, psychological and social factors (the biopsychosocial model of pain). In the previous section, we explored the physiological, or neurophysiology, of pain. In this section, we will take a closer look at some of the psychological and social, or environmental, factors that influence the pain experience.

ATTITUDES AND BELIEFS

What the pain means to a particular person at a particular time will have a clear influence on how that person subsequently responds. For example, if a person wakes in the night with stomach pain, they may think 'I should not have eaten so much', groan, roll over and eventually fall back to sleep. However, if they think that the pain may be an indicator of stomach cancer (perhaps because they saw a program on television about stomach cancer the previous night or because they have a close relative with that disease), they are then likely to begin monitoring the pain, become worried and distressed, be unable to fall back to sleep and so on. Pain can sometimes be accepted as a necessary accompaniment to another valued goal such as in childbirth or in the pursuit of sporting success. It can even be pursued for pleasure as in certain sexual practices. A number of cognitive factors can influence the pain experience:

- Pain has evolved as a warning system, interrupting other thoughts and behaviours and signifying the need for immediate *attention*. In fact, chronic pain has been shown to result in a negative effect on the allocation of both voluntary and involuntary-directed attention given to cognitive tasks (Gubler et al. 2021), with obvious negative consequences for ability to carry out day-to-day tasks. Attention to the pain will also be influenced by whether the person tends to 'catastrophise' about pain and their level of hypervigilance or tendency to monitor physical symptoms. However, the relationship between attention and pain is complex, with a number of other factors playing a role such as the context in which the pain is experienced and demands of a concurrent task (Gubler et al. 2021).

- *Expectations* or expectancies about pain can shape pain experiences (Zaman et al. 2021). Studies have shown that when expectations about pain are manipulated, the level of pain changes. Expectations in this context can refer to 'response expectancies' or the response a person predicts they will have to a certain stimulus—for example, a pain medication or an activity. As shown in placebo studies, response expectancies can have a significant impact on the actual pain experience (Vase & Wartolowska 2019). For example, several large studies have shown that sham acupuncture achieves similar outcomes to actual acupuncture, with the most robust indicator of improvement in both sham and actual acupuncture groups being expectation of pain relief (Xiang et al. 2018).

Expectations can also refer to 'efficacy expectancies' (in this case pain self-efficacy) or a person's confidence that they will be able to perform a range of tasks or engage in activities despite pain. A meta-analysis of studies on self-efficacy has shown that it has strong associations with levels of disability, distress and pain intensity (Martinez-Calderon et al. 2018).

CATASTROPHISING

Catastrophising is a robust psychological predictor of pain-related outcomes. It refers to the tendency to exaggerate the negative consequences of actual or anticipated pain to an extreme. It extends to beliefs and feelings the pain is uncontrollable and will inevitably lead to the worst possible outcome. It comprises elements of rumination about the pain, magnification of its effects and helplessness or pessimism (Petrini & Arendt-Nielsen 2020). The Pain Catastrophising Scale (Sullivan et al. 1995) is a commonly used outcome measure to evaluate pain catastrophising in clinical practice, attempting to quantify each of the constructs of catastrophising: rumination ('I can't stop thinking about how much it hurts'), magnification ('It's awful and I feel that it overwhelms me') and helplessness ('There's nothing I can do to reduce the intensity of the pain'). A large number of studies have attested to the link between catastrophising about pain and increases in disability, distress and pain intensity. Indeed, it has been suggested that pain catastrophising is more disabling and emotionally distressing than the actual nociceptive sensory experience of pain itself (Spada et al. 2016). Cognitive behavioural therapy (CBT) has been identified as one of the most effective interventions to reduce high levels of pain catastrophising, but the overall effect size has been questioned as being potentially only minimally clinically significant (Schütze et al. 2018).

FEAR AVOIDANCE

People in pain can evidence a high level of '**fear avoidance**' such that they become fearful of engaging in physical activity due to the risk of increased pain and/or (re) injury and therefore avoid the activity. Over time this can result in significantly reduced activity levels, increased disability, deconditioning and depression or distress (Baez et al. 2018). High work-related fear avoidance beliefs are linked with higher levels of sick leave and potentially negatively influence the prognosis for people with chronic low back pain, with poorer recovery for both pain and disability measures (Trinderup et al. 2018). Fear avoidance provides an excellent example of the interaction of three separate levels of the biopsychosocial model. Beliefs or appraisals of pain at one level result in anxiety or fear at the next level that, in turn, results in disability or pain behaviours at the next. The latter then further entrench the negative aspects of the pain experience and therefore fear avoidance becomes established. As pain becomes chronic, disability and distress will become further entrenched, with a diminishing chance of reversal.

PSYCHOLOGICAL DISTRESS (SUFFERING)

For many people pain, by definition, entails suffering. Nevertheless, the degree of suffering is clearly variable and likely to be influenced by a range of factors such as the duration and severity of pain and the degree to which the person believes they can continue to function despite pain and maintain some control over their lives

(Martinez-Calderon et al. 2018). The contributors to distress and suffering for a person with pain can be widespread and significant. They may experience a wide range of losses both material and intangible, covering everything from employment and finances to changes in relationships, being able to maintain independence, issues of self-worth and so on. They also often experience symptoms such as fatigue, difficulty concentrating, muscle tension, disturbed sleep, side effects of medication and deconditioning. They are much more likely to suffer from depression and anxiety (Gómez Penedo et al. 2020). They may have numerous fears or worries, including fear about the cause of the pain or that the doctors have missed something, fear of reinjury, worries about the future, financial concerns and so on. In addition, they may have to deal with a range of health professionals and undergo a variety of tests and interventions. A lack of understanding and validation from clinicians and significant others is also a common theme for people with chronic pain, with potential negative consequences to mental wellbeing (Nicola et al. 2021).

This lack of understanding and possible disbelief can be particularly difficult for people suffering from pain. It is not possible to see pain, and very often, especially in conditions such as fibromyalgia and chronic fatigue syndrome, there are no specific markers on tests or scans. In the past this was often interpreted as indicating that the person did not have a physical problem, rather they were suffering from a psychiatric disorder. We now know that the phenomenon of pain is extremely complex, that a wide range of variables can contribute to the experience, and most importantly of all that pain per se will not show up on a test. Many medically unexplained pains are now understood to be the result of central neurophysiological (nociplastic) mechanisms as discussed earlier in this chapter.

Given all the issues faced by people with persistent pain it is not surprising that a large proportion may be diagnosed as having depression or an anxiety disorder (Gómez Penedo et al. 2020). Although issues of measurement and definition make establishing prevalence difficult, few would dispute that it is a major issue for a large number of such people, with studies suggesting people with chronic pain are twice as likely to suffer from depression and 50% more likely to suffer anxiety (Gómez Penedo et al. 2020).

In addition to anxiety and depression, a sense of injustice or anger is a very common feature of a persistent pain presentation (Sommer et al. 2019). There are many possible sources of this including: perceived negligence or error by another person or institution; perceived poor medical treatment; a lack of understanding from employers, family or friends; conflict with an insurer over having treatments approved or funding forwarded; frustration at not being able to do things; and so on (Scott et al. 2016).

PARTNER OR SIGNIFICANT OTHER

One potentially critical influence to help understand the variability of the functional impact of pain is the partner, or significant other, of the person experiencing chronic pain. It is widely recognised that high levels of self-efficacy, or confidence in one's capability to perform the behaviors needed to achieve a desired outcome, correlates strongly with improved functional outcomes. But for people with similar levels of both self-efficacy and disease status, partners can have a significant effect on functional outcomes. People with partners that provide empathetic communication in response to their pain are significantly more likely to have improved physical functioning, whereas solicitous responses, those that seek to reduce pain symptoms, such as taking over tasks, can have a negative effect on physical activity levels (Hemphill et al. 2016).

Note that the dynamics can be complex, with a number of other factors influencing outcome such as the person's level of depression and their satisfaction with the marriage or relationship. Contrary to what might be expected within an operant learning framework, punishing responses to pain behaviour from a partner can also serve to increase that behaviour, possibly by contributing to levels of depression (Clark et al. 2018). Importantly it is the *perception* on the part of the pain patient of the partner's response that matters.

GENDER AND CULTURAL FACTORS

Gender appears to have an influence on pain, studies showing that women have higher pain sensitivity, report more pain and have greater variability in their responses to pain (both acute and chronic) than men (Pieretti et al. 2016). The reasons for this are not clear, but studies have suggested that gender differences in nociceptive processing and hormonal influences may play a role. Stereotypic gender roles appear to have a small to moderate influence, especially in the reporting of pain in experimental pain responses (Fillingim 2017), with both men and women reporting that women are more comfortable than men to report pain. However, for some conditions such as cancer and acute low back pain, men report similar and even greater pain intensity (Sluka 2016).

In the case of cultural factors, the research is again not conclusive, partly because culture is itself not a clear construct and can be influenced by factors such as ethnicity, gender, education and religion. The information available suggests that cultural factors, particularly those influenced by ethnic background, can be important in the expression and conceptualisation of pain. For example, studies have shown that certain ethnic groups may report higher levels of pain and display a higher level of pain but have lower levels of disability associated with this (Sluka 2016). It should be noted that determining definitive outcomes for the effect of culture on pain is extremely challenging due in part to the crossover of definitions around ethnicity, race and culture, along with a large number of variables associated with any experimental approach. Applying broad generalisations across cultural groups is inappropriate and unhelpful. It is critical that health professionals recognise that cultural factors may influence a person's pain responses due to a multitude of environmental influences and work with them to establish the best way to manage their condition. Also, health professionals should be mindful of any internal or systemic biases when managing people with pain across different cultures. For example, data collected on opioid prescribing in the United States from 2016 to 2017 showed that white patients were significantly more likely to be prescribed a higher dosage of opioids than black patients (Morden et al. 2021). The reasons for this may be complex, but such findings also suggest the possibility of stereotyping.

THE HEALTHCARE SYSTEM AND HEALTH PROFESSIONALS

The attitudes and beliefs a health professional has about pain can influence their approach or behaviour to managing the people they treat for pain-related conditions.

For example, physiotherapists with increased levels of fear avoidance who manage people with low back pain are more likely to provide unsuitable advice such as delayed return to work and physical activity as well as increased risk of over-treatment (Gardner et al. 2017). Also, overuse and inappropriate use of investigations by health professionals results in a significant risk of mismanagement for people with pain-related disorders. For example, it has been shown that early magnetic resonance imaging (MRI) for people with low back pain has an iatrogenic effect of worse disability and medical costs (Sajid et al. 2021). A possible explanation for this may be that ongoing recommendations for biomedical investigations, interventions and passive treatments can imply there is indeed something wrong and that it needs to be fixed before normal life activities can be resumed.

Research focus

Source: Rahyussalim et al. 2020

Low back pain is an extremely common complaint, with patients and health professionals alike often attributing pain—particularly persistent pain—to degenerative changes in the lumbar spine. However, this review of the literature identified significant proportions of asymptomatic adults, with no previous history of back pain, as demonstrating degenerative changes including vertebral endplate changes, reduction in vertebral disc height and disc bulging as shown on MRI. Also, the presence of low back pain was only weakly associated statistically with any degenerative changes found on imaging.

It would not be correct to conclude from this review that degenerative changes cannot contribute to pain, but that it highlights the inconsistent relationship between tissue structure, pathology and pain.

Critical thinking

Mull over the study described in the *Research focus* on the significance of the lack of correlation of imaging findings and pain. With this in mind:

- Consider a patient with chronic low back pain who has received a scan that showed moderate degenerative disc disease. As a health professional, how important do you think these findings are in order to assist in management planning? Justify your response.

- This time, consider the above scenario as if you are the patient. How do you think you would feel after being given the diagnosis of degenerative disc disease? What would you like your treating health professional to do or say as a response?

- Considering your understanding of some of the potential psychological contributors to the pain experience, what are some potentially negative consequences of a patient being given the above diagnosis? What are the potential positive consequences? Justify your answers.

The work environment

There appear to be several work-related factors that influence a person's pain experience. Unsatisfactory work–family balance, exposure to a hostile work environment and poor job security is associated with an increased risk of experiencing low back pain at work (Yang et al. 2016). Several factors relating to the workplace have also been identified as impacting on outcome in terms of return to work. Symptomatic factors, such as widespread and high-intensity pain, high levels of disability and presence of previous pain episodes are associated with a poorer return to work prognosis (Artus et al. 2017). Also, addressing fear avoidance beliefs is associated with a more positive work-related outcome (Becker & Childress 2019).

Return to work outcomes also appear to be associated with compensable status, or whether the person is seeking financial compensation, commonly through third-party insurance or work-related insurance such as WorkCover in Australia. A study of all patients discharged from hospital following major trauma over a 5-year period in a large Australian state were followed up, with the proportion of compensable patients returning to work significantly lower than those not seeking compensation at both 12 and 24 months (Gabbe et al. 2016). This finding is consistent with many systematic reviews, which also conclude compensation following trauma is associated with not only poorer return to work outcomes but also greater functional impairment and more severe symptoms (Giummarra et al. 2016).

The reasons for these poorer outcomes are unclear, but proposed contributing factors include the possibility of increased stress associated with the processes of making compensation claims and the ongoing feelings of injustice or lack of fairness associated with the process. Of notable importance is that people in the compensation system are required, by the system itself, to constantly report and demonstrate their symptoms in order to be compensated, which, in turn, encourages focusing on disability rather than rehabilitation. As we can see, there are many social determinants influencing the pain experience, which again reinforces the individualised nature of this condition (see Chapter 6 for more on the social determinants of health).

How long does pain last?

ACUTE VERSUS CHRONIC PAIN

Acute pain is short-lived; it can last from a few seconds to a few hours but generally less than 3 months and is associated with injury, disease or inflammation of somatic, visceral or nervous system structures. Mechanistically, acute pain can be either nociceptive or neuropathic. Acute pain is generally thought to have a protective biological function; for example, when a person touches a hot stove, pain alerts them to immediately withdraw their hand. Likewise, following a fracture, pain imposes significant limitation of function that is useful in preventing further damage and assist healing.

While the distinction between acute and chronic pain may be made on the basis of duration of symptoms, with greater than 3 months generally considered chronic, the underlying cause of the pain should also influence how we perceive the distinction between the two states. Chronic pain has been defined as pain that endures beyond the expected time for which the affected tissue should have healed (Mills et al. 2019). For example, the healing process for a small muscle tear should be complete within

3 to 6 weeks, thus pain that endures longer than this may be considered chronic. Consequently, the definition of chronic pain needs to consider not only the duration of pain but also the underlying cause, or pathology, of the pain. In fact, in order to develop a deeper understanding of the concept of chronic pain, we should also consider the *type* of pain, or pain mechanism, driving the symptoms.

The nervous system changes that occur in response to injury or disease were discussed earlier in this chapter. Acute pain may be associated with anxiety and fear, particularly if it is unexpected and severe and may develop into a long-term or chronic state if not managed appropriately (Mills et al. 2019). Therefore, the purpose of acute pain management is to identify the cause and provide suitable management until healing occurs. Analgesia may be necessary, particularly in the case of severe trauma and postoperative pain, to reduce the risk of acute pain persisting (Mills et al. 2019). Under normal conditions the pain and associated nervous system responses usually disappear within days or weeks of recovery.

Chronic pain, on the other hand, results in numerous pathophysiological peripheral and central nervous system changes and is only rarely amenable to effective biomedical treatments that may be effective for acute pain. It may be partially driven by a low level of underlying pathology (e.g. as in osteoarthritis), but often such pathology fails to explain the presence and/or extent of the pain experienced. For example, the pain experienced by two people with very similar levels of osteoarthritis are rarely the same. Clearly, there are other factors that influence the pain experience other than the actual pathology. Although pain may have been initiated by an injury or disease, the factors that maintain it are more than likely both physically and pathogenetically removed from the originating cause (Treede et al. 2019).

In some cases, it may be possible to address the initial pathology resulting in significant reduction or resolution of pain and its associated consequences. For example, pain and secondary changes such as central sensitisation, mood disturbance and disability will generally disappear following a procedure (e.g. hip replacement surgery) that successfully resolves the initial pathology, regardless of chronicity (e.g. Greimel et al. 2018). However, in other cases, it may be impossible to identify or adequately treat the initial pathology, as is overwhelmingly the case for low back pain. In such instances, the focus should be on dealing with the initial pathology if possible, but of equal importance is to identify and address the consequences of pain such as depression, sleep disturbance, loss of meaning in relationships/work, avoidance of activities due to fear and physical changes like loss of strength or conditioning. Persisting with the search for a cause of or a cure for their chronic pain can prevent a person from accepting and dealing with their pain and can prolong or exacerbate their suffering and disability (Clewley et al. 2018).

TRANSITION FROM ACUTE TO CHRONIC PAIN AND DISABILITY

Approximately 20% of Australians over the age of 45 live with chronic pain, resulting in a significant financial and social cost. The intensity, duration and location of pain all appear to have a direct correlation with the level of physical activity limitation and disability (Dueñas 2016). However, many people with chronic pain continue to lead active lives despite ongoing pain. It should be appreciated that many people who live with chronic pain do not have an associated reduction in physical activity levels, with a wide variation in disability levels reported in the literature (Dueñas 2016).

Table 11.1

RISK FACTORS FOR TRANSITION OF PAIN FROM ACUTE TO CHRONIC, ACCORDING TO THE COLOURED FLAG SYSTEM

Flag	Type	Examples
Red	Signs of serious pathology	Tumour; infection; cauda equina syndrome; fracture; neurological signs
Orange	Psychiatric issues	Major depression; schizophrenia
Yellow	Psychological factors	High levels of distress or anxiety; beliefs about pain (e.g. increased pain means further damage); expectation of need for resolution of pain; over-reliance on passive treatments; avoidance of activity due to fear of pain and/or damage
Blue	Perceptions about workplace and health	Job dissatisfaction; belief that there is a lack of support at work; belief that the job is too demanding physically and/or mentally; attribution of pain condition to work
Black	System factors—occupational and legal	Availability of modified duties; lack of support from the workplace; limitations imposed by legislation or the return to work system; conflict with the insurer or workplace

Source: Nicholas et al. 2011

Consequently, it would be very useful to be able to predict who might be at risk of developing chronic pain and a high level of disability as early as possible and provide appropriate interventions. There has been extensive research into which factors might be relevant in developing chronic pain, and a range of psychological, social and environmental risk factors have been identified. Table 11.1 outlines some of these factors, differentiating psychological factors from work and biomedical risk factors. These different domains are often referred to according to a system of coloured flags. For example, psychological factors are generally referred to as 'yellow flags' (Glattacker et al. 2018). A number of screening tools have been developed to help health professionals identify people at risk for persisting pain and disability.

Once pain does become chronic, it can have a strong impact on the psychological, physical and social wellbeing of a person. People can develop unhelpful beliefs and thoughts contributing to low mood, sleep disturbance and feelings of frustration, helplessness and anxiety. They may lose confidence in their ability to perform tasks, significantly reduce their activity levels and become fear avoidant, with consequent deconditioning and often associated weight gain (Hulla 2019). Repeated unsuccessful attempts to seek a cure along with increasing reliance on medication can lead to further frustration and helplessness, and often aversive side effects. They may also experience loss of status, relationship breakdown and loss of employment. So, in order to positively manage chronic pain, it becomes necessary to assess the relative

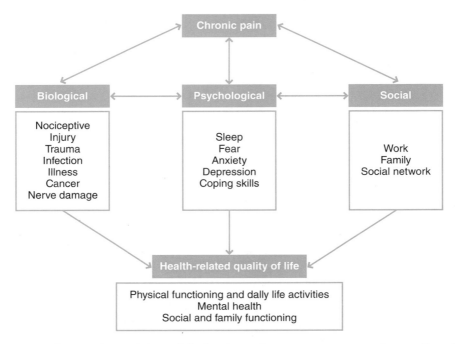

Figure 11.2 Biopsychosocial model of pain and consequences on the quality of life Source: Dueñas et al. Journal of Pain Research 2016 9, 457–467. Originally published by and used with permission from Dove Medical Press Ltd.

contributions of physical, psychological and environmental factors, and their consequences. This is referred to as a biopsychosocial approach to pain management.

Figure 11.2 illustrates the potential impact of chronic pain for people within a biopsychosocial framework. It shows how every factor has the potential to impact on every other factor. For example, a person may withdraw from participating in social physical activities because of pain and in turn gain weight, deconditioning and loss of social contact, followed by a drop in mood. Then, due to low mood, they may struggle in being motivated to become active again and therefore the low mood and deconditioning become further entrenched.

Interventions and management for pain

When considering best practice pain management, we need to first understand the causes or drivers that are resulting in a person's pain. If pain is a result of an acute injury, such as a sprained ankle, we understand that the nociceptive signalling is a result of the mechanical disruption to somatic tissue, such as ligaments, resulting in a mechanical nociceptive response. Also, an inflammatory environment is produced in this setting, leading to chemical mediators such as substance P being released into the local area, resulting in chemical sensitivity and an additional inflammatory nociceptive response. Therefore, the best way to manage pain in this situation is to treat the mechanical injury (e.g. short-term immobilisation followed by graduated loading) and the inflammatory response (e.g. rest, ice, compression, elevation). Although it is appreciated that no two people's pain experiences are identical, even in the presence of similar, or even identical pathologies due to the multifaceted nature of pain, it is expected that the pain will resolve once the tissue has completed healing and there is no longer an inflammatory environment present. It becomes much more complex, however, when we do not expect pathology to resolve—for example, for conditions such as cancer and osteoarthritis, or if pain endures despite the lack of any identifiable pathology, such as for many cases of chronic low back pain. Although it is more complex, the principle of identifying the cause or drivers resulting in persistent pain remains key to the approach to management. The challenge very much lies in firstly identifying the drivers, which may be biological, psychological and/or social, and then determining an effective, evidence-based approach to intervention.

PHARMACOLOGY

When considering interventions for pain, many people consider medications as a first line of treatment. But the evidential support for the effectiveness of medication is surprisingly low in many instances and needs to be considered in the context of potentially harmful side effects, as is the case for any intervention type.

Acute musculoskeletal (nociceptive) pain can respond well to a short course of a variety of medications from simple analgesics such as paracetamol and non-steroidal anti-inflammatory drugs (NSAIDs), usually used for mild to moderate pain, to opioids such as tramadol, tapentadol, oxycodone and morphine, which may be used for short-term treatment of severe pain following an injury or after acute surgery.

Neuropathic pain, on the other hand, generally does not respond well to NSAIDs and opioids (Alles & Smith 2018). However, tricyclic antidepressants, in lower doses than would normally be used for treating depression, can be effective in treating neuropathic pain and may also help with sleeplessness and comorbid depression. But side effects need to be considered, including weight gain, constipation, blurred vision, drowsiness, poor concentration and clouded thinking. Anticonvulsants generally reduce the abnormal firing of sensory nerves that occurs with neuropathic pain. The newer anticonvulsants, such as gabapentin and pregabalin, have fewer side effects but are nevertheless still associated with adverse reactions such as impaired memory and concentration. Also, the newer serotonin-noradrenaline reuptake inhibitor antidepressants (e.g. duloxetine) have established efficacy in treating neuropathic pain and are recommended as first-line treatments, along with tricyclic antidepressants, gabapentin and pregabalin (Fitzmaurice & Rayen 2018).

Over the past two decades, opioids that were traditionally used for cancer pain have become mainstream in managing chronic non-cancer (musculoskeletal) pain, with an exponential increase in the prescription of these drugs. This is despite the fact there is no high-quality data on the benefits of opioid therapy for managing this type of pain over the long term and that long-term use may be associated with iatrogenic effects such as overdose and opioid-induced hyperalgesia (Von Korff & Franklin 2016). Although trials usually last less than 12 weeks, a recent randomised clinical trial over 12 months (the first of its kind) found no superior benefit in pain-related function for opioid versus nonopioid medication therapy for patients with moderate to severe chronic musculoskeletal pain (Krebs et al. 2018).

Australia's *Annual Overdose Report 2021* (Penington Institute 2021) shows that more Australians have died from drug overdoses than from car accidents since 2014, with prescription drugs detected in most overdose deaths and half of these involving pharmaceutical opioids. The profile of drug-induced deaths in Australia has changed from that of younger people overdosing on heroin to middle-aged people dying from misuse of prescription drugs in a polypharmacy setting, with unintentional drug-induced deaths involving legal opioid nearly trebling over the past 14 years to 2021 (Penington Institute 2021).

Over the past decade, cannabinoids have been increasingly introduced as an analgesic pharmacological intervention. However, there is no current consensus on the role of this medication, nor currently strong evidential support for managing chronic, acute or cancer-related pain (Fisher et al. 2021).

Research focus

Source: Krebs et al. 2018

Despite the widespread use of opioids to treat chronic musculoskeletal pain, there is little quality data on their effectiveness, especially over the long term. The current study was designed to compare the effectiveness of opioid medication with nonopioid medication over 12 months for patients with moderate to severe chronic back pain or hip or knee osteoarthritis pain. Outcomes were pain-related function and pain intensity. The results showed that treatment with opioids was not superior to treatment with nonopioid medications for improving function. In fact, pain intensity was significantly lower with nonopioid treatment. In addition, adverse medication-related symptoms were significantly more common in the opioid group. The authors concluded that opioid therapy for moderate to severe musculoskeletal pain is not supported.

Critical thinking

Consider the study described in the *Research focus* on the use of opioids for treating chronic pain.

- Given the lack of evidence as to the effectiveness of opioids in treating chronic pain, why do you think the medical profession has continued to prescribe them, and in increasing doses?
- From your understanding of the potential causes for the persistence of pain beyond expected healing times (i.e. chronic pain), can you guess why long-term opioid use is unlikely to be an effective treatment?
- What other factors might influence a doctor's decision to prescribe opioids for someone with chronic pain? Consider aspects from the consumer/patient, prescriber and systemic perspectives.
- What kinds of patients do you think are most likely to be prescribed opioids and why?

Cont... ▶

- Can a medication, any medication, be expected to successfully control the impact of pain over a lifetime, or could there be other more effective and less harmful ways of dealing with it?

SURGERY

Surgery has a major role to play in managing some pain conditions, such as where a lesion or abnormality can be identified and resected, repaired, reconstructed, reinforced or replaced, but long-term outcomes are not as good if the main reason for surgery is pain relief (Cohen & Raja 2019). For example, outcome studies have concluded that although surgery can be indicated for patients with specific spinal conditions, such as cauda equina syndrome, there is little advantage of surgery over conservative treatment at 12–24 months for patients with low back pain and sciatica (Jensen et al. 2019). There is also the possibility that surgery may make the pain worse.

INJECTIONS

Different types of injections can be used to treat pain; these include local anaesthetic blocks and steroid injections. Local anaesthetic blocks may be useful as a diagnostic procedure and can assist in temporarily reducing chronic pain. However, they also have a well-established placebo effect, and so any reduction in symptoms must be treated with caution for a definitive diagnosis. Steroid injections can be helpful in reducing inflammation in some acute conditions, but they cannot be repeated very often and there is no available evidence to suggest they provide anything other than short-term pain relief.

STIMULATION TECHNIQUES

A variety of stimulation techniques have also been used for treating pain with varying levels of success. These include acupuncture, transcutaneous electrical nerve stimulation (TENS), spinal cord stimulation and deep brain stimulation. Acupuncture has been shown to be useful for some types of acute and chronic pain, but the effects are short-lived, and in the case of chronic pain, treatment needs to be repeated at regular intervals (Gattie et al. 2017). The other stimulation techniques mentioned above are thought to act on inhibitory mechanisms at the level of the spinal cord and brain and can be useful for treating certain types of neuropathic and chronic pain (Moisset et al. 2020).

PHYSICAL THERAPIES

A number of physical and manual therapies are used to treat both acute and chronic musculoskeletal pain, although there is continuing debate about the effectiveness of such treatments in the long term. Historically, physiotherapy has been largely associated with passive modalities such as massage, manipulation, ultrasound, hot packs and cold packs. These can be helpful in relieving acute musculoskeletal pain. But, as the effects are short-lived, they are less useful in managing chronic pain and in returning people to normal activities because they largely focus on managing biological impairments, and as we have seen, pain experience is multifaceted and is strongly influenced by both psychological and social factors. Consequently, it is widely recognised and increasingly adopted within the physiotherapy profession that best practice must incorporate the beliefs, attitudes and emotional responses to both pain and the circumstances contributing to a person's pain experience. This approach has been called 'psychologically informed practice', whereby treatment of people anywhere along the pain continuum incorporates systematic attention to the psychosocial factors that are associated with poorer treatment outcomes (Archer et al. 2018). Indeed, the physiotherapy profession is significantly involved in ongoing research into pain science and management, with the profession increasingly adopting psychosocial assessment and treatment strategies with a stronger focus on the role of exercise and education in managing pain.

Research focus

Source: Holopainen et al. 2020

There is strong evidence that, in addition to biomechanical factors, chronic musculoskeletal pain is also associated with a complex interplay of cognitive, psychological and social factors that when targeted effectively can improve patient outcomes.

The profession of physiotherapy has been established in Australia and New Zealand for years, with the majority of this time having a focus on treating physical impairments. Over the past 20 years, there has been a much greater focus on identifying and managing other factors influencing pain presentations considered within the psychosocial domain. However, this paradigm shift in understanding of pain mechanisms has not necessarily led to a widespread change in behaviour of health professionals such as physiotherapists. Furthermore, studies have shown that physiotherapists lacked confidence in their ability to identify, communicate about and manage cognitive, psychological and social factors when treating patients with chronic pain.

The aim of this systematic review was to investigate physiotherapists' perspectives on learning and implementing a biopsychosocial management approach to musculoskeletal pain conditions.

Four key themes were identified in this review:

- recognising that both an understanding and management practices for these conditions has undergone a significant change
- the benefits to the profession through potentially improved health outcomes and establishing best practice strategies
- the clinical challenges resulting from changing practices such as perceived lack of time to provide necessary education as well as the malalignment of patient expectations with 'traditional' physiotherapy practice
- the issue of ensuring the profession is adequately educated to facilitate management in the psychosocial realm, an area traditionally outside the scope of the profession.

EXERCISE AND PHYSICAL ACTIVITY

Exercise and increased physical activity levels have shown benefits across a wide range of pain presentations, both acute and chronic (Booth et al. 2017). Interestingly, despite the nature of the pain presentation, chronicity or pathology, there are no specific types of exercises that are shown to be of greater benefit than another. However, any exercise program should adhere to a number of key principles. Most critically, it must not be harmful—for example, overloading a recently healed muscle risks causing further damage to that muscle tissue—so a sound understanding of tissue healing and exercise principles is critical. Any exercise or physical activity should not be too intensive as to result in a flare-up of symptoms; it should ideally involve a mix of aerobic, resistance and flexibility components, and be comfortably achievable and goal-oriented.

Exercise can be beneficial in reversing some of the secondary changes that occur such as decreased mobility and strength and reduced fitness. A recent systematic review of exercise programs for workers with physically demanding jobs by Sundstrup and colleagues (2020) concluded that strength, or resistance, training programs reduces the prevalence of musculoskeletal disorders and pain. Interestingly, this review could not find enough evidence to support the benefits for aerobic- or stretching-based exercise programs, which obviously does not necessarily mean they are not effective interventions but that there is a lack evidence to support them in this setting. Further insight into the intensity and duration of an exercise program is provided by a recent review which has shown that pain presentations with a predominant central sensitisation mechanism respond to low-intensity exercise over long periods, whereas nociceptive driven presentations respond to higher intensity exercises over a shorter period (Ferro Moura Franco et al. 2021). It is important to note that for those experiencing chronic pain, exercise is not an end in itself but a means of exposure to feared or avoided activities and forms a series of stepping stones towards achieving functional goals, as well as increasing general physical conditioning, which enables improved function and participation. The mechanisms that result in pain relief from exercise are not clearly understood, but the release of endogenous opioids is theorised as the primary mechanism for short-term pain relief. Interestingly, the effect size of exercise-induced analgesia is likely influenced by the person's expectations of the outcome, with those expecting a hyperalgesic, or painful, response more likely to actually experience an increase in pain and, conversely, those expecting a hypoalgesic response more likely to experience pain relief after exercise (Vaegter et al. 2020). This may in part explain the variable response people with chronic pain experience after exercise.

EDUCATION

Education is a critical component for managing both acute and chronic pain, with an established evidence base. While often used in conjunction with other treatment modalities, education should be considered as a distinct intervention strategy in its own right. When considered as a treatment modality it is often referred to as pain neuroscience education. This provides a framework to establish an educational approach for patients based on the neurobiology and neurophysiology of pain and pain processing by the nervous system. A key focus of pain neuroscience education, or any educational approach for patients experiencing chronic pain, is to change a patient's perception, or cognition, that pain is directly correlated with tissue damage to a perception that pain is due to a sensitised, or upregulated, nervous system. Studies have shown that this educational approach alone can be effective in improving people's ability to cope with their pain, reduce fear avoidance behaviours and improve both willingness and ability for physical activity (Louw et al. 2016; Watson et al. 2019). Given both the complex nature of pain and the influence of cognition of a person's pain experience, this is not surprising. Current evidence suggests that while an educational approach is effective at improving the above outcomes, to see significant improvements in pain and disability, education alone is not a viable intervention, and should be used as an adjunct with other evidence-based approaches to chronic pain management (Wood & Hendrick 2019).

GRADED EXPOSURE AND PACING

As we have established, for a person experiencing chronic pain, a stimulus that would normally not produce a nociceptive response, such as walking for a short distance, now does so (allodynia). It is suggested that the nervous system interprets such stimuli as threatening, and thus the threshold for a nociceptive response is reduced. Graded exposure provides a mechanism to slowly expose the person to increasing stimuli, with the purpose of enabling the nervous system to 'reinterpret' such stimuli as non-threatening. For example, if it takes 10 minutes of walking to flare up pain symptoms, a walking program may be developed whereby the person walks for 5 minutes initially, and gradually increases walking times over several weeks to establish confidence that this is achievable, reducing the threat value of the activity, and consequently increasing the threshold of the nervous system to interpret this as noxious or nociceptive. Also, increasing physical activity will result in improved physical conditioning, which is also strongly associated with improved functional outcomes. Although there is some evidence of the benefits of graded exposure for people with chronic back pain, it appears the benefits are similar to that of a general exercise program (López-de-Uralde-Villanueva et al. 2016), with minimal evidential support for this treatment approach currently available for other chronic pain presentations.

Critical thinking

Consider the study described in the *Research focus* investigating physiotherapists' experiences and perspectives of a biopsychosocial approach to the assessment and intervention process.

- Given the known limitations of purely biomedical approaches when managing chronic pain, why is there reluctance among physiotherapists to practise in a biopsychosocially informed way? Is this also a problem for other health professionals? Do not forget to consider financial and societal factors.

- What is your opinion of physiotherapists' perception that clients expect hands-on treatment when they consult a physiotherapist? What would you expect from a physiotherapy treatment?

Cont... ▶

- Why is it important for all health professionals to be aware of the biopsychosocial model of care when managing patients with chronic pain?

- How would a health professional change their clinical practice to incorporate attention to the psychosocial factors that are associated with poorer treatment outcomes? Think about this question from your own perspective.

PSYCHOLOGICAL APPROACHES

A range of psychological strategies can be used to help people manage both acute and chronic pain. In the case of acute pain, information and education about what is going to happen in a proposed treatment and what to expect in terms of pain can be helpful in allaying fears and reducing distress—for example, before a surgical procedure. Training a person in ways to calm themselves—such as by relaxation, forms of meditation and self-hypnosis—can also be beneficial. Attentional techniques like distraction can be useful. However, studies on the effectiveness of all these techniques suggest they have variable rates of success (McClintock et al. 2019). Repeated practice by a person appears to be important, as does structure, specific (written) instructions and an understanding that the primary goal is to reduce distress rather than pain. In the case of education and information it is important to check what the beliefs and concerns of the person actually are. This can effectively be achieved in many instances through using outcome measures. Examples of suitable outcome measures are the Pain Catastrophizing Scale, the Tampa Scale of Kinesiophobia and the Orebro Musculoskeletal Pain Questionnaire. Simply providing education and information will not necessarily remove fear if the educational messages do not address the person's specific concerns.

In the case of chronic pain, the above techniques can also be beneficial, but the emphasis shifts to long-term management of the pain, rather than simply dealing with the current episode of pain. In practice this means learning to live with the pain and returning to normal activities and function despite pain. People can sometimes interpret this as 'a last resort' or as an indication that they are being told their pain is 'all in their head'. Therefore, it is essential to clarify the rationale and benefits of psychological management strategies when introducing them. Education in the physiological mechanisms causing persisting pain can play an important role in reassuring people that persisting pain is not necessarily a sign of further damage and that it is safe to upgrade activity levels. Psychological strategies can be introduced at the same time as biomedical interventions, or in a planned sequence. In the case of chronic pain, it can sometimes be useful to introduce psychological strategies when biomedical interventions have been completed because of the shift in emphasis from pain reduction to pain management. Note that this is no longer viewed as an either/or outcome. There is now extensive research showing that active self-management and the pursuit of valued goals and activities despite pain leads to a reduction in pain (Geraghty et al. 2021).

CASE STUDY: PENELOPE

Penelope is a married 30-year-old mother of two children aged four and two. Apart from several months off work for the birth of each child, she had worked part-time as a legal secretary for 7 years. A year ago she slipped and fell while getting heavy files down from a shelf in her workplace. She experienced an immediate onset of pain in her lower back and left leg and was advised by her GP to take 2 weeks off work and rest. Her pain did not resolve, and a subsequent MRI scan identified a posterolateral disc bulge at L4/5, mildly abutting the thecal sac, without disc protrusion or nerve root compromise. She was prescribed analgesic medication and referred for physiotherapy.

After 3 months, the pain had not resolved. Penelope was then referred to an orthopaedic surgeon for review, but surgery was not recommended. Instead she was advised to try to increase her activity levels but to stop if the pain increased. She was also prescribed stronger analgesics. Now, a year later, Penelope has not returned to work, she is doing little housework and her two children are being cared for during the day by relatives. She reports feeling depressed and hopeless and her GP has started her on antidepressants. She describes herself as previously having been a very active, cheerful person and is frustrated by her current inability to do things. She reports difficulty with remembering things and poor concentration, which she thinks may be a side effect of the pain medication she is on. She is anxious that her pain has not resolved and is concerned that increases in pain are a sign of further damage. She believes that overall her pain is getting worse. She worries that the doctors may have missed something and both she and her husband believe that her pain would have to resolve before she could become more active.

As well as physiotherapy, Penelope has tried acupuncture and has weekly massages. She has tried to do the exercises given to her by her physiotherapist but then usually takes extra medication to cope with the increased pain and spends the following day resting to recover. Recently she has stopped doing the exercises altogether. Her sleep is disrupted, and she frequently naps during the day. Penelope's husband is working extra shifts to meet their financial commitments and has taken over her chores at home. He has apparently tried to be supportive, but they are now arguing more and sleep in separate rooms. Penelope notes that when she is very distressed or upset her pain is worse. The family no longer has any social activities and Penelope rarely attends her children's activities. Penelope's job still remains open for her, but she says she could not sit for long enough to do her previous work and is concerned about her poor concentration and memory.

Student activity

1. Do you think Penelope's pain is nociceptive, neuropathic, nociplastic or a mixed pain state? Why do you think this?
2. What potential psychosocial factors may be contributing to Penelope's pain state?

Cont... ▶

3. Who are the key people and health professionals who need to be involved in Penelope's management plan?
4. What management approaches do you think would be appropriate to assist Penelope? Consider a multifaceted approach, with different interventions having effect on different domains.

COGNITIVE BEHAVIOURAL APPROACHES

There is good evidence that CBT to help people manage pain, particularly chronic pain, is effective for the targeted outcomes (e.g. increased function, improved mood, improved quality of life) (Hadley & Novitch 2021). It can be delivered in individual sessions with different health professionals (e.g. a physiotherapist and a psychologist), but the evidence suggests it is more effective when delivered as part of a structured program, possibly in a group. Programs can vary in intensity—for example, from 1 day a week for a couple of hours to intensive programs over several weeks that require full-time attendance. The intensity of the program required will depend on the level of disability and distress of the person. Whatever the method of delivery, it is important that all health professionals working with a person adhere to a consistent message and work within the same biopsychosocial framework.

CBT for chronic pain comprises several components. Ideally it would be delivered by a physiotherapist and psychologist, specially trained in the area of chronic pain management, who work together as an integrated team. However, independent practitioners from a range of disciplines can use the principles of CBT to help a person establish active pain management strategies and begin progress towards valued goals. In a more intensive setting, other health professionals may be involved including, but not limited to, a doctor or pain specialist (to rationalise and/or reduce medication), a nurse, an occupational therapist and a work rehabilitation adviser.

The typical components of a cognitive behavioural pain management approach include:

- education about pain, including the difference between acute and chronic pain, and reconceptualising the pain as hurt/harm and a brief simple explanation of oversensitivity of the nervous system
- setting goals across a range of areas including home tasks, work, family activities/relationships, recreation, sport/hobbies and identifying what physical (e.g. walking and standing) and psychological (e.g. crowds, bright noisy environments) tolerances will need to be worked on to achieve those goals (see Table 11.2)
- establishing structure and routine with daily and weekly goals/planners
- improving sleep patterns, with regular getting-up times, daily activity and no naps
- upgrading activity levels and tolerances in a paced manner so as to progress towards goals, avoid overdoing and underdoing, and promote quota-dependent behaviour rather than pain-dependent behaviour (see Fig. 11.3)
- programmed exercises and stretches to increase aerobic capacity and strength, functional tolerances and flexibility

Table 11.2 SETTING GOALS		
Long-term goal	**Short-term goals**	**Areas to work on**
Return to work	• Sit longer • Walk further • Increase time at computer • Lift up to 10 kg occasionally • Cope with public transport • Increase confidence in dealing with public	• Identify and improve sitting and walking tolerances • Identify and improve keyboard tolerance • Train technique and improve lifting tolerance • Improve abdominal and back extensor strength • Catch local bus, gradually upgrade time/number of stops • Gradually increase time in public situations such as at shopping centres, social events
Surfing	• Lying on stomach • Paddling • Balance	• Identify and improve prone lying tolerance • Improve back and shoulder mobility • Improve scapular muscle and upper limb strength • Identify and improve paddling tolerance • Improve abdominal and back extensor strength • Improve hip and lower limb strength • Improve balance

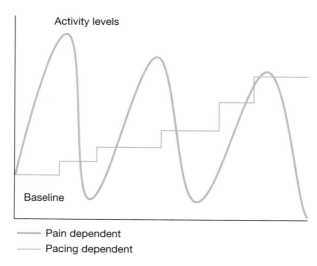

Activity levels

Baseline

——— Pain dependent
——— Pacing dependent

Figure 11.3 Using pacing to structure activity levels

- applied relaxation training to reduce anxiety, distress and tension, especially during flare-ups in pain or when stressed

- desensitisation to the pain, to change the relationship with it, reduce distress and learn to accept it and remain calm

- identifying unhelpful beliefs and associated behaviours, feelings and bodily responses (see Figs 11.4 and 11.5)

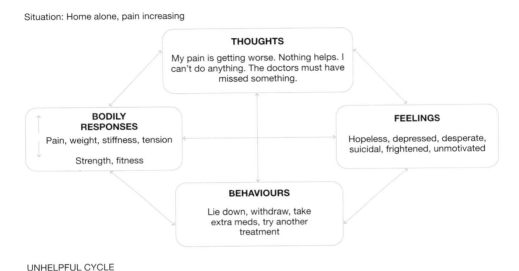

Figure 11.4 The unhelpful cycle of thoughts, feelings, behaviours and bodily responses

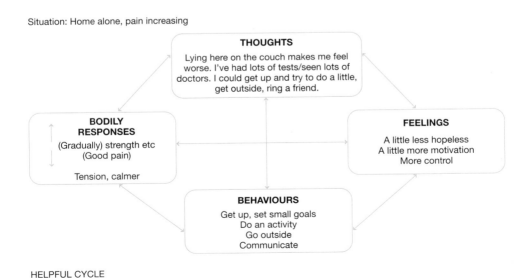

Figure 11.5 The helpful cycle of thoughts, feelings, behaviours and bodily responses

- learning effective problem-solving techniques for common issues faced by people living with chronic pain such as flare-ups, dealing with stress and communication difficulties (see Box 11.2)

- reducing medication use and other passive strategies such as resting or avoiding activities

- formulating a flare-up plan because this is when people are most vulnerable to returning to old ways (see Table 11.3)

- addressing communication issues with family and friends and involving them in management plans

- where relevant, formulating a plan to return to work.

Box 11.2 Problem solving

Step 1: What is the problem?
Think about and discuss the problem or goal carefully, then write down exactly what you believe to be the main problem or goal.

Step 2: List all possible solutions
Try to think of all possible solutions, even bad ones. List all possible solutions without any evaluation of them at this stage.

Step 3: Consider and weigh-up each possible solution
Quickly go down the list of possible solutions and assess the main advantages and disadvantages of each one.

Step 4: Choose the best or most practical solution
Choose the solution that can be carried out most easily with your present resources (time, money, skills, etc.)

Step 5: Plan how to carry out the best solution (keep it simple)

Step 6: Do it!

Step 7: Review how well the solution was carried out and praise yourself for your efforts.

Table 11.3		
FLARE-UP PLAN		
Helpful actions	Helpful thoughts	Unhelpful actions
<ul><li>Replan, reprioritise</li><li>Pace</li><li>Delegate, communicate</li><li>Calm down, relax, desensitise</li><li>Do gentle stretches</li><li>Go for a walk</li><li>Plan enjoyable undemanding activities (e.g. sitting in garden, doing a puzzle, talking to a friend, watching a comedy, listening to music, baking)</li></ul>	<ul><li>'I can still move my body; I just need to pace myself'</li><li>'This is a flare-up; I have not done more damage'</li><li>'I can choose how I respond to this and how I think about it; I am not at the mercy of my pain'</li><li>'I know it will settle down again'</li><li>'I don't have to get everything done today; I can change my plans'</li><li>'Getting upset and distressed will definitely not help'</li><li>'This is just an episode I have to get through'</li></ul>	<ul><li>Catastrophise</li><li>Get distressed</li><li>Go to bed</li><li>Self-medicate</li><li>Cancel everything</li></ul>When it's over:<ul><li>Review how I managed</li><li>Reset goals and baselines</li><li>Get back into my routine</li></ul>

A NOTE ON MANAGING CHRONIC PAIN AND OTHER CHRONIC CONDITIONS

In the case of any chronic condition, it is important for all those involved, from GPs to allied health professionals, to specialists to patients, to friends and family, to recognise the importance of having a structured long-term plan that is shared and understood by all. This plan should cover the role of medical practitioners, medications, allied health practitioners and all relevant others, actions for flare-ups (especially for presentations to hospital) and have agreed goals. It is usual to have one central person, such as the GP, who receives and disseminates all relevant information and then coordinates care. It is essential that the person experiencing the chronic condition be involved in formulating the plan and deciding on its elements when looking at person-centred care.

If such a plan is not put into place, there is a risk that a person with a chronic condition will continue to be managed in the acute paradigm, with unnecessary and unhelpful ongoing tests, rounds of specialists, drug trials and passive treatments, and little progress towards valued goals. This can be a concern, particularly when the person presents to a medical facility with a flare-up of their condition and there is no coordinated plan for management.

Chapter summary

This chapter gives an overview of the current understanding of the experience of pain. It explains the neurobiological basis of pain, which is critical to develop a foundational knowledge of pain science. This includes the difference between nociceptive and neuropathic pain, the role of central sensitisation and the distinction between acute and chronic pain. It further explains that despite this neurobiological basis, the presentation of pain can only be usefully explained and understood when all relevant psychological and environmental factors are considered. This is particularly important in the case of chronic pain, where biomedical interventions have only limited effectiveness and the emphasis shifts from pain relief to pain management and specifically to more adaptive management of relevant psychosocial factors.

KEY POINTS

- Pain is a complex phenomenon and best considered in a biopsychosocial context, recognising that biological, psychological and social domains can all influence it.
- Pain is an output of the brain; not a sensory input to it.
- The experience and perception of pain is both variable and highly individualised.
- There is an inconsistent relationship between tissue pathology and pain.
- Pain is best understood within a biopsychosocial model, with factors at all levels impacting on the experience.

Further reading

Ballantyne, J.C., Fishman, S.M., Rathmell, J.P., 2018. Bonica's Management of Pain. Lippincott Williams & Wilkins.

Castelnuovo, G. & Schreurs, K.M., 2019. Pain management in clinical and health psychology. Frontiers in Psychology, 10, 1295. doi: 10.3389/fpsyg.2019.01295.

Flor, H., Turk, D.C., 2015. Chronic Pain: An Integrated Biobehavioral Approach. Lippincott Williams & Wilkins.

International Association for the Study of Pain (IASP) Task Force on Taxonomy, updated 14 December 2017, from 'Part III: Pain Terms, A Current List with Definitions and Notes on Usage' (pp 209–214). Classification of chronic pain, second ed. IASP Press, Seattle, 1994. http://www.iasp-pain.org/resources/terminology

Melzack, R., Wall, P.D., 1982. The Challenge of Pain. Basic Books, New York.

Moseley, G.L., Butler, D.S., 2017. Explain Pain Supercharged. Noigroup Publications: Adelaide.

Weblinks

International Association for the Study of Pain (IASP)

www.iasp-pain.org

The IASP was founded in 1973 and is the world's largest multidisciplinary organisation focused specifically on pain research and treatment. It brings together scientists, health professionals, healthcare providers and policymakers to stimulate and support the study of pain. The website gives details of all its activities, publications, events and meetings and also provides links to many other useful websites.

PAIN—The Official Journal of the IASP

https://journals.lww.com/pain/Pages/default.aspx

PAIN is the official journal of the ISAP, which publishes 18 issues per year of original research on the nature, mechanisms and treatment of pain. This peer-reviewed journal provides a forum for disseminating research in the basic and clinical sciences of multidisciplinary care.

The Australian Pain Society

www.apsoc.org.au

The Australian Pain Society was formed in 1979 as the Australian chapter of the International Association for the Study of Pain.

The New Zealand Pain Society

www.nzps.org.nz

The New Zealand Pain Society was formed in 1984 as the New Zealand chapter of the International Association for the Study of Pain.

References

Alles, S.R., Smith, P.A., 2018. Etiology and pharmacology of neuropathic pain. Pharmacological Reviews, 70 (2), 315–347.

Archer, K.R., Coronado, R.A., Wegener, S.T., 2018. The role of psychologically informed physical therapy for musculoskeletal Pain. Current Physical Medicine and Rehabilitation Reports 6, 15–25.

Artus, M., Campbell, P., Mallen, C.D., et al., 2017. Generic prognostic factors for musculoskeletal pain in primary care: a systematic review. BMJ Open, 7 (1), e012901.

Australian Institute of Health and Welfare, 2020. Chronic pain in Australia. AIHW, Canberra. Available: https://www.aihw.gov.au/getmedia/10434b6f-2147-46ab-b654-a90f05592d35/aihw-phe-267.pdf.aspx?inline=true

Baez, S., Hoch, M.C., Hoch, J.M., 2018. Evaluation of cognitive behavioral interventions and psychoeducation implemented by rehabilitation specialists to treat fear-avoidance beliefs in patients with low back pain: a systematic review. Archives of Physical Medicine and Rehabilitation, 99 (11), 2287–2298.

Becker, B.A., Childress, M.A., 2019. Nonspecific low back pain and return to work. American Family Physician, 100 (11), 697–703.

Booth, J., Moseley, G.L., Schiltenwolf, M., et al., 2017. Exercise for chronic musculoskeletal pain: a biopsychosocial approach. Musculoskeletal Care, 15 (4), 413–421.

Center for Substance Abuse Treatment 2012. Managing Chronic Pain in Adults with or in Recovery From Substance Use Disorders. Rockville (MD): Substance Abuse and Mental Health Services Administration (US). Report No.: (SMA) 12-4671. PMID: 22514862.

Clark, S.M., Leonard, M.T., Cano, A., et al., 2018. Beyond operant theory of observer reinforcement of pain behavior. In: Vervoort T, Karos K, Trost Z, et al. Social and Interpersonal Dynamics in Pain (pp. 273–293). Springer, Cham.

Clewley, D., Rhon, D., Flynn, T., et al., 2018. Health seeking behavior as a predictor of healthcare utilization in a population of patients with spinal pain. PloS One, 13 (8), e0201348.

Cohen, S.N., Raja, S.P., 2019. Ch 27 Pain. In: Goldman L, Schafer A. Goldman-Cecil Medicine, 26th edn; 2 Volume Set. Elsevier, Cambridge.

Colloca, L., Ludman, T., Bouhassira, D., et al., 2017. Neuropathic pain. Nature Reviews Disease Primers, 3, 17002.

Dueñas, M., Ojeda, B., Salazar, A., et al., 2016. A review of chronic pain impact on patients, their social environment and the health care system. Journal of Pain Research, 9, 457–467.

Ferro Moura Franco, K., Lenoir, D., dos Santos Franco, Y.R., et al., 2021. Prescription of exercises for the treatment of chronic pain along the continuum of nociplastic pain: a systematic review with meta-analysis. European Journal of Pain, 25 (1), 51–70.

Fillingim, R.B., 2017. Sex, gender, and pain. In: Legato MJ. Principles of Gender-Specific Medicine (pp. 481–496). Academic Press.

Finnerup, N.B., Kuner, R., Jensen, T.S., 2021. Neuropathic pain: from mechanisms to treatment. Physiological Reviews, 101 (1), 259–301.

Fisher, E., Moore, R.A., Fogarty, A.E., et al., 2021. Cannabinoids, cannabis, and cannabis-based medicine for pain management: a systematic review of randomised controlled trials. Pain, 162, S45–S66.

Fitzcharles, M., Cohen, S.P., Clauw, D.J., et al., 2021. Nociplastic pain: towards an understanding of prevalence pain conditions. Lancet, 397 (10289), 2098–2110.

Fitzmaurice, B.C., Rayen, A.T.A., 2018. Treatments for neuropathic pain: up-to-date evidence and recommendations. BJA Education, 18 (9), 277.

Frediani, F., Bussone, G., 2019. When does the brain choose pain? Neurological Sciences, 40 (S1), 27–29.

Gabbe, B.J., Simpson, P.M., Harrison, J.E., et al., 2016. Return to work and functional outcomes after major trauma. Annals of Surgery, 263 (4), 623–632.

Gardner, T., Refshauge, K., Smith, L., et al., 2017. Physiotherapists' beliefs and attitudes influence clinical practice in chronic low back pain: a systematic review of quantitative and qualitative studies. Journal of Physiotherapy, 63 (3), 132–143.

Gattie, E., Cleland, J.A., Snodgrass, S., 2017. The effectiveness of trigger point dry needling for musculoskeletal conditions by physical therapists: a systematic review and meta-analysis. Journal of Orthopaedic & Sports Physical Therapy, 47 (3), 133–149.

Geraghty, A.W., Maund, E., Newell, D., et al., 2021. Self-management for chronic widespread pain including fibromyalgia: A systematic review and meta-analysis. PLoS One, 16 (7), e0254642.

Giummarra, M.J., Ioannou, L., Ponsford, J., et al., 2016. Chronic pain following motor vehicle collision. The Clinical Journal of Pain, 32 (9), 817–827.

Glattacker, M., Heyduck, K., Jakob, T., 2018. Yellow flags as predictors of rehabilitation outcome in chronic low back pain. Rehabilitation Psychology, 63 (3), 408.

Gómez Penedo, J.M., Rubel, J.A., Blättler, L., et al., 2020. The complex interplay of pain, depression, and anxiety symptoms in patients with chronic pain: a network approach. The Clinical Journal of Pain, 36 (4), 249–259.

Greimel, F., Dittrich, G., Schwarz, T., et al., 2018. Course of pain after total hip arthroplasty within a standardized pain management concept: a prospective study examining influence, correlation, and outcome of postoperative pain on 103 consecutive patients. Archives of Orthopaedic and Trauma Surgery, 138 (12), 1639–1645.

Gubler, D.A., Zeiss, S., Egloff, N., et al., 2021. 'The effect of chronic pain on voluntary and involuntary capture of attention: an event-related potential study.' Behavioral Neuroscience, 136 (2), 195–205.

Hadley, G., Novitch, M.B., 2021. CBT and CFT for Chronic Pain. Current Pain and Headache Reports, 25 (5), 1–4.

Harte, S.E., Harris, R.E., Clauw, D.J., 2018. The neurobiology of central sensitization. Journal of Applied Behavioral Research, 23 (2), e12137.

Hemphill, R.C., Martire, L.M., Polenick, C.A. et al., 2016. Spouse confidence and physical function among adults with osteoarthritis: The mediating role of spouse responses to pain. Health Psychology, 35 (10), 1059.

Holopainen, R., Simpson, P., Piirainen, A., et al., 2020. Physiotherapists' perceptions of learning and implementing a biopsychosocial intervention to treat musculoskeletal pain conditions: a systematic review and metasynthesis of qualitative studies. Pain, 161 (6), 1150–1168.

Hulla, R., Brecht, D., Stephens, J., et al., 2019. The biopsychosocial approach and considerations involved in chronic pain. Healthy Aging Research, 8 (01), 6–12.

Jensen, R.K., Kongsted, A., Kjaer, P. et al., 2019. Diagnosis and treatment of sciatica. BMJ, 367, l6273.

Krebs, E.E., Gravely, A., Nugent, S., et al., 2018. Effect of opioid vs nonopioid medications on pain-related function in patients with chronic back pain or hip or knee osteoarthritis pain. The SPACE randomized clinical trial. JAMA: The Journal of the American Medical Association 319 (9), 872–882.

López-de-Uralde-Villanueva, I., Munoz-Garcia, D., Gil-Martinez, A., et al., 2016. A systematic review and meta-analysis on the effectiveness of graded activity and graded exposure for chronic nonspecific low back pain. Pain Medicine, 17 (1), 172–188.

Louw, A., Zimney, K., Puentedura, E.J., et al., 2016. The efficacy of pain neuroscience education on musculoskeletal pain: a systematic review of the literature. Physiotherapy Theory and Practice, 32 (5), 332–355.

Martinez-Calderon, J., Zamora-Campos, C., Navarro-Ledesma, S., et al., 2018. The role of self-efficacy on the prognosis of chronic musculoskeletal pain: a systematic review. The Journal of Pain, 19 (1), 10–34.

Martucci, K.T., Mackey, S.C., 2016. Imaging pain. Anesthesiology Clinics, 34 (2), 255–269.

McClintock, A.S., McCarrick, S.M., Garland, E.L., et al., 2019. Brief mindfulness-based interventions for acute and chronic pain: a systematic review. The Journal of Alternative and Complementary Medicine, 25 (3), 265–278.

Melzack, R., 1990. Phantom limbs and the concept of a neuromatrix. Trends in Neurosciences, 13 (3), 88–92.

Millan, M.J., 2002. Descending control of pain. Progress in Neurobiology, 66 (6), 355–474.

Mills, S., Nicolson, K.P., Smith, B.H., 2019. Chronic pain: a review of its epidemiology and associated factors in population-based studies. British Journal of Anaesthesia, 123 (2), e273–e283.

Moisset, X., Lanteri-Minet, M., Fontaine, D., 2020. Neurostimulation methods in the treatment of chronic pain. Journal of Neural Transmission, 127 (4), 673–686.

Morden, N.E., Chyn, D., Wood, A., et al., 2021. Racial inequality in prescription opioid receipt – role of individual health systems. New England Journal of Medicine, 385 (4), 342–351.

Moseley, G.L., Butler, D.S., 2017. Explain Pain Supercharged. Noigroup Publications: Adelaide.

Mouraux, A., Iannetti, G.D., 2018. The search for pain biomarkers in the human brain. Brain, 141 (12), 3290–3307.

Nicholas, M.K., Linton, S.J., Watson P.J., et al., 2011. The 'Decade of the Flags' Working Group. Early identification and management of psychological risk factors ('yellow flags') in patients with low back pain: a reappraisal. Physical Therapy 91, 737–753.

Nicola, M., Correia, H., Ditchburn, G., et al. 2021. Invalidation of chronic pain: a thematic analysis of pain narratives. Disability and Rehabilitation, 43 (6), 861–869.

Nijs, J., George, S.Z., Clauw, D.J., et al., 2021a. Central sensitisation in chronic pain conditions: latest discoveries and their potential for precision medicine. Lancet Rheumatology, 3 (5), 383–392.

Nijs, J., Lahousse, A., Kapreli, E., et al., 2021b. Nociplastic pain criteria or recognition of central sensitization? Pain phenotyping in the past, present and future. Journal of Clinical Medicine, 10 (15), 3203.

Penington Institute, 2021. Australia's Annual Overdose Report. Available: https://www. penington.org.au/overdose/overdose-projects-campaigns/australias-annual-overdose-report/

Petrini, L. and Arendt-Nielsen, L., 2020. Understanding pain catastrophizing: putting pieces together. Frontiers in Psychology, 11, 3450

Peyron, R., Fauchon, C., 2019. Functional imaging of pain. Revue Neurologique, 175 (1–2), 38–45.

Pieretti, S., Di Giannuario, A., Di Giovannandrea, R., et al., 2016. Gender differences in pain and its relief. Annali dell'Istituto superiore di sanita, 52 (2), 184–189.

Rahyussalim, A.J., Zufar, M.L.L., Kurniawati, T., 2020. Significance of the association between disc degeneration changes on imaging and low back pain: a review article. Asian Spine Journal, 14 (2), 245–257.

Raja, S.N., Carr, D.B., Cohen, M., et al., 2020. The revised International Association for the Study of Pain definition of pain: concepts, challenges, and compromises. Pain, 161 (9), 1976–1982.

Sajid, I.M., Parkunan, A., Frost, K., 2021. Unintended consequences: quantifying the benefits, iatrogenic harms and downstream cascade costs of musculoskeletal MRI in UK primary care. BMJ Open Quality, 10 (3), e001287.

Schütze, R., Rees, C., Smith, A., et al., 2018. How can we best reduce pain catastrophizing in adults with chronic noncancer pain? A systematic review and meta-analysis. The Journal of Pain, 19 (3), 233–256.

Scott, W., McEvoy, A., Garland, R., et al., 2016. Sources of injustice among individuals with persistent pain following musculoskeletal injury. Psychological Injury and Law 9, 6–15.

Shraim, M.A., Masse-Alarie, H., Hall, L.M., et al., 2020. Systematic review and synthesis of mechanism-based classification systems for pain experienced in the musculoskeletal system. The Clinical Journal of Pain, 36 (10), 793–812.

Sluka, K.A., 2016. Mechanisms and management of pain for the physical therapist. Lippincott Williams & Wilkins.

Sommer, I., Lukic, N., Rössler, W. et al., 2019. Measuring anger in patients experiencing chronic pain–A systematic review. Journal of Psychosomatic Research, 125, 109778.

Spada, M.M., Gay, H., NikČevic, A.V., et al., 2016. Meta-cognitive beliefs about worry and pain catastrophising as mediators between neuroticism and pain behaviour. Clinical Psychologist, 20 (3), 138–146.

Sullivan, M.J., Bishop, S.R., Pivik, J., 1995. The pain catastrophizing scale: development and validation. Psychological Assessment, 7 (4), 524.

Sundstrup, E., Seeberg, K.G.V., Bengtsen, E., et al., 2020. A systematic review of workplace interventions to rehabilitate musculoskeletal disorders among employees with physical demanding work. Journal of Occupational Rehabilitation, 30 (4), 588–612.

Treede, R. D., Rief, W., Barke, A., et al., 2019. Chronic pain as a symptom or a disease: the IASP Classification of Chronic Pain for the International Classification of Diseases (ICD-11). Pain, 160 (1), 19–27.

Trinderup, J.S., Fisker, A., Juhl, C.B., et al., 2018. Fear avoidance beliefs as a predictor for long-term sick leave, disability and pain in patients with chronic low back pain. BMC Musculoskeletal Disorders, 19 (1), 1–8.

Vaegter, H.B., Fehrmann, E., Gajsar, H., et al., 2020. Endogenous modulation of pain. The Clinical Journal of Pain, 36 (3), 150–161.

Vase, L., Wartolowska, K., 2019. Pain, placebo, and test of treatment efficacy: a narrative review. British Journal of Anaesthesia, 123 (2), e254–e262.

Von Korff, M.R., Franklin, G. 2016. Responding to America's iatrogenic epidemic of prescription opioid addiction and overdose. Medical Care, 54 (5), 426–429.

Watson, J.A., Ryan, C.G., Cooper, L., et al., 2019. Pain neuroscience education for adults with chronic musculoskeletal pain: a mixed-methods systematic review and meta-analysis. The Journal of Pain, 20 (10), 1140.e1–1140.e22.

Woller, S.A., Eddinger, K.A., Corr, M., et al., 2017. An overview of pathways encoding nociception. Clinical and Experimental Rheumatology, Suppl. 107 (5), 40–46.

Wood, L., Hendrick, P.A., 2019. A systematic review and meta-analysis of pain neuroscience education for chronic low back pain: short-and long-term outcomes of pain and disability. European Journal of Pain, 23 (2), 234–249.

Xiang, Y., He, J., Li, R., 2018. Appropriateness of sham or placebo acupuncture for randomized controlled trials of acupuncture for nonspecific low back pain: a systematic review and meta-analysis. Journal of Pain Research, 11, 83.

Yang, H., Haldeman, S., Lu, M.L. et al., 2016. Low back pain prevalence and related workplace psychosocial risk factors: a study using data from the 2010 National Health Interview Survey. Journal of Manipulative and Physiological Therapeutics, 39 (7), 459–472.

Zaman, J., Van Oudenhove, L., Vlaeyen, J.W., 2021. Uncertainty in a context of pain: disliked but also more painful? Pain, 162 (4), 995–998.

Chapter 12
Partnerships in health

DEB O'KANE

Learning objectives

The material in this chapter will help you to:

- understand the dynamics of health professional–client partnerships
- understand the issues in client engagement with treatment
- appreciate the importance of involving clients in their own care
- gain insight into differences in treatment expectations between health professionals from different cultural backgrounds
- understand how effective partnerships impact on working with people who have chronic illness, disability or complex health issues
- appreciate the interplay between clients' and health professionals' attitudes and backgrounds in the clinical setting and the influence of these and environmental factors on successful treatment outcomes.

Key terms

- Partnership (336)
- Compliance (338)
- Adherence (338)
- Concordance (338)
- Chronic conditions (339)
- Biomedical (341)
- Person-centred practice (341)
- Recovery-oriented care (344)
- Health locus of control (351)
- Collaborative practice (355)

Introduction

The title of this chapter takes for granted the fact that the health professional–client relationship requires the involvement of at least two people. Those two people may encounter each other in a variety of settings: in a busy acute surgical ward; in an outpatient or emergency department; in the client's own home; in practice rooms; in a community health centre; or in an ambulance to give only some examples. Whatever the setting, something is happening—an encounter between two human beings, both with varying agendas, needs, attitudes and feelings.

As already discussed in Chapter 8, communication is essential to establish and maintain personal and professional relationships, from our own family and friends to the colleagues we work with or the clients and families in our care. In clinical practice, it remains the responsibility of health professionals to initiate and maintain a working relationship with their clients and team members. This may prove to be easy or challenging. Not all clients are good communicators, and some may exhibit behaviour that requires the health professional to seek support from other team members in managing a situation. However, whatever the client's personal qualities are, it is important to think about how you approach interactions with recipients of care and your own motivations and goals for the relationship. These are factors health professionals have control of and are responsible for.

Person-centred communication goes some way to thinking about how an alliance can be established with people we work with and care for. However, as well as being a relationship between two people, it also helps to see the relationship as a **partnership**. In health care, the term 'partnership' is often used to reinforce the concept of a relationship where health professionals and clients both share some degree of responsibility for treatment decisions, implementation and outcomes. This is particularly important when working with people experiencing chronic and enduring health issues such as arthritis, diabetes or heart disease. Also, partnerships can occur across multiple sectors and include a variety of people, disciplines and organisations, all with a clear purpose or goal in mind. A partnership such as this brings together a diverse range of skills and resources, offering more opportunities to impact on health issues such as chronic illness, health prevention, health promotion and education. This chapter discusses the significance of partnerships and considers practice implications that can build or limit these partnerships.

Fostering partnerships

It is first beneficial to examine the language used for the people being cared for within a healthcare setting because this shows how language and the power of language can influence partnerships. Historically when someone is a recipient of a health service, whether in the public or private sector, inpatient or community, they are generally known as a 'patient'. But more recently, a wider variety of terms have been used in various fields of health care such as 'client', service user or 'customer', with the aim of trying to identify and describe the relationship between the parties involved. The term or label we use to describe a person can invoke different perceptions, attitudes and behaviours towards that person. Using person-centred language, as described in Chapter 8, advocates for seeing the person as human rather than a diagnosis, which in turn can alter how people are viewed and ultimately reduce stigma in areas that historically have been negatively perceived (Albury et al. 2020; Granello & Gibbs 2016). Other literature suggests it is an innate human quality to place labels on people not only in health care but to a population at large if there are easily recognisable traits, behaviours or characteristics to distinguish particular groups of people. This might include skin colour or clothes, for example. So while labels can serve a purpose by providing us with generic information about a person or population, they can also be problematic, especially when they are used to stereotype people. Common labels heard in practice that have negative connotations include 'frequent flyer', 'drug addict' or 'attention seeker'.

A label is very powerful. The use of one word can not only identify the recipient of care but also the relationship and possible power dynamics (Costa et al. 2019). Language influences the very nature of how health professionals establish and maintain a professional relationship due to the assumptions we make from the terms we use. For example, the term 'patient' originates from Latin verb 'pati' meaning to suffer or bear. It implies a person is the passive recipient of care with health professionals (*the experts*), actively making decisions concerning their health. With such a term suggesting little equality in the relationship, areas such as mental health practice have applied different terms both nationally and internationally. Australians tend to use the term 'consumer', while Britons use the term 'service user'. Each term, though different, has the same underlying value—that is, for the person to feel empowered rather than stigmatised and to ultimately have a voice and impact on care delivery. More recently, however, it has been suggested that such alternative labels do little to change the relationship dynamic and in fact cause more issues by people receiving care feeling they are defined within the context of an economic or commercial relationship. Arguably, changing language does not equate to a person suddenly becoming empowered. It is a matter of semantics, and far more important than nomenclature is acknowledging the preference of the person receiving care whether to be called patient, client or consumer. Protecting the rights of individuals and self-determination are central tenets to good practice, and so asking a person how they would like to be addressed goes a long way to fostering effective partnerships with those people with whom we work.

PERCEPTION IS REALITY

On a similar note, how a health professional describes a person's contribution to their own health needs can affect how people perceive that person. Much of the literature concerned with health professional–client communication issues focuses on getting the client to cooperate with the health professional's treatment goals or compliance. The word 'compliance' seems to be used without consideration of how it might shape a health professional's attitude and relationship with people receiving care. Compliance suggests passivity. In health care this would reflect a person following healthcare directives with complete acceptance and without question. If a person is not willing or able to do what is requested of them at a particular time, they may be described, both verbally and in healthcare records, as noncompliant, even being perceived as rebellious or incapable of following instructions. The problem with this is that such a judgemental descriptor can frequently be taken up by other members of the healthcare team, often without any thought or questioning of its origins.

Consequently, the danger is the strong possibility of a client being perceived as such for the rest of their treatment history. It can become a self-fulfilling prophecy, where other health professionals expect a person to have a particular attitude to treatment and relate to them in such a way that leads the client to demonstrate that attitude.

Health professionals may possibly describe a client as noncompliant because they present a challenge of some sort. This usually involves not wishing to accept a particular form of treatment that has been prescribed for them. Other frequent situations when this occurs are when a client speaks very little English and does not understand what the health professional is expecting of them or a well-educated person simply questions what is being done to them. Similarly, it might also be a client with poor health literacy as discussed in Chapter 8.

TERMINOLOGY

The term '**compliance**' itself has been criticised because of its paternalistic or even coercive implication that all medical advice or treatments should be followed without question. Often health professionals can be quick to assume a client is being uncooperative or disobedient if they choose not to follow the recommended treatment regimen. But this noncompliance is at times unintentional, such as a person with significant memory problems who frequently forgets to take their medication or a person being unable to afford the prescribed treatments. On the other hand, the client may intentionally be noncompliant due to their health beliefs or concerns about side effects—for example, a client who decides to stop taking their steroid medication due to weight gain.

An alternative term, '**adherence**', has since been introduced into the healthcare literature to replace that of compliance, aiming to signify a stronger implication of choice by having the opportunity to decide whether to adhere to the recommended treatment or advice. This signifies a person is free to decide whether to follow the recommendations but that failure to do so does not reflect poor behaviour on the part of a person and therefore no blame is attached to their decision. But it is debatable as to whether this is an improvement; for instance, adherence also has the implication of following instruction or direction. Both compliance and adherence focus on the client's behaviour in following treatment regimens, whereas in the mid-90s the United Kingdom introduced the term '**concordance**' with the purpose of defining the relationship, rather than the behaviour between a health professional and a client. Concordance is based on a mutual understanding, collaboration and respect for each other's contributions (Chapman 2018; European Patients Forum 2015). It embraces the relationship between the recipient of care and the clinician as a partnership. It involves clients having a voice in decisions about their own health care, whether related to prescribed medication or treatment plans, by listening to their views and beliefs with the aim of reaching a shared agreement. Despite the various labels, one could argue it is better for none to be used but to instead focus on the engagement process. Exploring the relationships between health professionals and those experiencing chronic illness provides an effective starting point to explore partnerships further.

Chronic conditions

To first understand the complexity of **chronic conditions**, it helps to understand the terminology used nationally and internationally. The Australian Department of Health defines chronic conditions as 'a broad range of chronic and complex health conditions across the spectrum of illness, including mental illness, trauma, disability and genetic disorders' (Australian Institute of Health and Welfare 2022). New Zealand refers to such conditions as 'long-term conditions' (Ministry of Health – Manatu Hauora 2020), whereas internationally, 'non-communicable disease (NCD)' is the term frequently used. NCD differs slightly since it refers to a disease that has not been transmitted person to person, and while factors such as risk and longevity of illness are common in NCD, the term fails to include those diseases that are both long term in nature and also communicable. An example of this would be a person with HIV or hepatitis.

Chronic conditions are a leading cause for concern worldwide, accounting for 71% of deaths, with 77% of these taking place in low–middle income countries before the age of 60 (World Health Organization [WHO] 2021a). The social context of a person's life, lifestyle risk factors and behaviour such as poverty/inequality, poor nutrition/diet, inadequate environmental health conditions, physical inactivity, alcohol misuse and tobacco smoking can greatly contribute to the onset, poor outcome and overall burden of chronic disease in today's society yet remain common throughout the world (WHO 2021a).

The cost of delivering health care for health concerns that are preventable makes the issue a forerunner in debate, policy and practice when planning future health services. With a predicted ageing population, a decrease in mortality and advanced practice regimens extending life expectancy (WHO 2021b), there seems little expectation that things will change in the near future. In light of expected continuing rising costs and apprehension about how healthcare services will manage escalating figures, chronic conditions are a priority worldwide.

Chronic illness remains complex and difficult to define. It commonly refers to any illness or disability that a person may endure permanently or over a prolonged period. A significant number of conditions can be termed chronic, with coronary heart disease, stroke, lung cancer, colorectal cancer, depression, type 2 diabetes, arthritis, osteoporosis, asthma, chronic obstructive pulmonary disease, chronic kidney disease and oral disease identified as major concerns for the healthcare system in developed countries. Other conditions include epilepsy, fibromyalgia, other cancers, chronic fatigue syndrome, hypertension and multiple sclerosis. Some chronic conditions worsen over time (e.g. Alzheimer's disease), while others such as cancer may have periods of remission. For some people a complete recovery is achievable, whereas for others, death is an inevitable outcome. In attempting to define chronic conditions the Australian Health Ministers' Advisory Council (2017) identify the following shared characteristics:

- complex and multiple causality
- gradual onset but can have sudden acute episodes

- can occur across the lifespan but most prevalent in later age
- multiple risk factors
- a prolonged and persistent course of illness
- functional impairment or disability compromising quality of life
- gradual deterioration of health
- not immediately life-threatening but a leading cause of premature mortality.

In any of these given situations, it can be true to say that having a chronic illness will certainly have a lasting effect on the person's quality of life, affecting the emotional, physical, psychological and behavioural aspects of their daily living.

In health psychology, understanding how the biological, behavioural and social factors can influence chronic illness allows us to explore the human dimension of how a person lives with the chronic health issue and how this may influence their health behaviour and the behaviour of those around them. Larson (2021, p. 2) describes this as how the illness is 'perceived, lived with and responded to by others'. She goes on to say that, as health professionals, we shouldn't necessarily think about disability only in terms of severity or physical deterioration but to also think about how it can be affected due to a person's perception of the illness. The implications of how much a person's lifestyle is altered are very much related to their own understanding and health beliefs about the onset of the illness, its treatment and the outcomes (Larson 2021). As already identified, there are numerous biological, psychological, social and environmental risks associated with chronic illness, but with the appropriate behavioural strategies implemented before the onset of problems being evident, these illnesses can be prevented. Areas to be targeted in health promotion, prevention and education include exercise, nutrition, cessation of smoking and alcohol moderation to name a few (see also Chapter 13). Alongside these preventative support mechanisms, the access to resources also needs to be improved if we hope to see any tangible long-term impact of enhancing a person's health and reducing the pressure on the health system.

Factors influencing partnerships

People with an existing chronic illness or disability can offer valuable insights into how the illness has affected them and how they best manage their health issue; therefore, as part of a partnership it is important to listen to the person as an expert in their own health care (Australian Commission on Safety and Quality in Health Care 2021). That being said, there are a variety of reasons why at least 50% of clients do not carry through with treatment prescribed for them. These include: side effects and costs; treatment difficulties; fatalism or resistance to control; forgetting to take medication; and little external support. For example, when the symptoms begin to subside they may see no need to complete their medication; they may cease because there may be no sign of improvement; they may decide that if a little works then a lot will be even better; or if enduring long-term illness, a client may tire of taking medication or other treatment. Sometimes when the client refuses, health professionals may see them as a problem client (i.e. someone who does not passively accept treatment), as uncooperative or constantly complaining, perceiving the client negatively without attempting to understand why it is happening by listening to the person's expertise in their own lived experience of illness. Should we then accept there is no such thing as a non-adherent client? Haven't we all been non-adherent at some point in our lives? Rather than attempting to identify a person on factors such as behaviour, sociodemographics and dispositional characteristics, it would be far more person-centred for a health professional to focus time and energy on understanding the person and their health issue.

Challenges for health professionals

A natural outcome of easy and accessible information online is a shared knowledge base and expertise developed by various client interest groups, particularly those with disability or chronic illness in common. Individuals such as those suffering conditions known as contested illnesses (e.g. fibromyalgia, chronic fatigue syndrome, Lyme disease and Gulf War syndrome) are particularly evident. Members can be seen to empower each other, share knowledge and research findings, and to not only validate the disorder but also challenge the expertise of clinicians. For some health professionals, unexplained pain, symptoms with no **biomedical** explanation and illnesses with little social and medical legitimacy can become a cause for frustration, hostility, helplessness and impatience when presented in clinic. Working with people who are more knowledgeable about a health condition than the consulting practitioner can be challenging and even threatening. Such clients may contest the health professional's directions and decisions, using a valid evidence base to support their viewpoint. This, of course, must be balanced with the fact that not all information on the internet is reliable and people may have completely inaccurate, false information about their illness from reading various websites, as discussed in Chapter 8. Either way, patience is often required on the part of health professionals to listen and ensure clients understand all available information. It may be that further questioning is needed to address the concerns or decide on the best treatment options. As Stone (2014) points out, validating a person's feelings, supporting them to consider possible explanations and using the skills of empathic active listening will maintain the relationship over time. If required, it may also be necessary to offer the client an opportunity to see another health professional without taking this as a personal failure but instead reframing it as doing what's best in the interests of the client (see Box 12.1).

Person-centred practice

Person-centred practice (PCP) is not a new concept and though significantly different from the health professional–led biomedical model, it has been in the literature for many years, exerting significant influence on policy, practice and care delivery. Definitions vary between identifying the elements needed for individualised client care and looking at it from an organisational perspective to provide the best possible care. Either way, at the heart of PCP is the person receiving care. It provides a model of care based on mutually beneficial partnerships among health professionals, clients and families, and is the foundation from which person-centred communication stems (Chapter 8). In PCP, attention is paid to all elements of the person (the 'whole'),

Box 12.1 Managing contested illnesses

- Validate the subjective experience of illness (e.g. 'I can see you are experiencing a lot of pain, and the constant fatigue must be getting you down').
- Use the patient's words and frameworks if you can. For instance, if a patient believes they have fibromyalgia, their symptoms are consistent and they are feeling supported by the diagnosis, you may wish to use the term.
- Use their language to broaden the agenda to include physical, psychological and social strategies for management (e.g. 'Patients with fibromyalgia seem to respond best to a combination of treatments. I'd like to look at strategies to address the pain but also see if we can help you manage stress, because stress seems to make fibromyalgia pain worse.').
- Involve a multidisciplinary team.
- Keep a focus on active intervention (e.g. 'I know you are often quite tired, but fibromyalgia patients do better if they undertake some regular light exercise. What exercise can you do at the moment?').
- Explain that different strategies work for different people, so you will have to try a number of strategies to see what works in their particular case.
- Work out what you agree and disagree on. For instance, you may have to explain that some treatments your patient has sourced over the internet are unproven, expensive or risky.
- Harm minimisation: maintaining a non-judgemental, open relationship will allow your patient to discuss alternative treatments that have the potential for harm.
- Keep an eye out for other diseases. Patients with medically unexplained symptoms often have comorbid physical illnesses. A regular physical health assessment can help screen for unexpected comorbidity.

Adapted from Stone 2014

taking into account the wider context of the person's lifestyle such as those social, environmental and psychological factors that may contribute to assessing and managing the health issue. Collaboration, therapeutic alliance, sharing power and responsibility for decision making, and the freedom of choice and autonomy become central to delivering care and require commitment and considerable effort on the part of health professionals and organisations. In Australia and New Zealand many healthcare organisations have now started to encourage clients, particularly those with a chronic illness, to adopt personalised care plans or self-management plans. These offer an opportunity for health professionals to collaborate with clients and develop a formal written record that respects the client's opinions so that control and ownership of care is held by the client rather than the professional.

A successful partnership between a health professional and client can go a long way to achieving PCP, yet several barriers are often cited as reasons for being unable to establish the partnership or deliver PCP. Time constraints, lack of resources, differing agendas, organisational constraints and a belief they 'know best' are common reasons presented by health professionals when unable to deliver PCP (Lloyd et al. 2018). Although some of these may seem inevitable, particularly in light of the increasing pressure to undertake a growing number of tasks, administration duties and staff shortages, you need to question if this is truly saving time and money in the longer term when evidence suggests a negative impact on health outcomes including engagement in treatment regimens, pain management and client and carer satisfaction in the absence of PCP (McCormack & McCance 2016; McCormack 2020).

While acknowledging these barriers, as a health professional there are several features of establishing a partnership that can be undertaken in practice to support PCP. These include:

- getting close to the person
- providing care that is consistent with the person's values
- taking a biographical approach to assessment
- focusing on ability rather than dependency.

Since the initial development of a nursing framework to reflect PCP in aged care (McCormack & McCance 2006), the framework based on empirical evidence has evolved to be used in various health contexts and across various disciplines resulting in developing a PCP framework alongside a revised and updated person-centred nursing framework (McCormack & McCance 2019). The multidisciplinary person-centred framework provides an excellent tool to support the delivery of person-centred care within a team, an organisation, in policy development and healthcare planning. It enables health professionals to explore what person-centred care looks like, how it occurs in the context of their own practice and in turn how it can be operationalised, evaluated and improved for future practice and successful health outcomes (see Figure 12.1).

CASE STUDY: PATRICK

Patrick is a 19-year-old male who has recently been diagnosed with schizophrenia after a short period of hospitalisation for an acute psychotic episode. One nurse has informed him that it is highly likely he will need to take neuroleptic medications for the rest of his life. This has greatly upset him because he has found he has an increased appetite and therefore put on weight as a side effect of the medication. He describes feeling helpless and unable to see a future while living with his illness. His weight is a major issue for him because he believes it will reduce his chances of finding employment in the hospitality industry and affect his chances of finding a girlfriend.

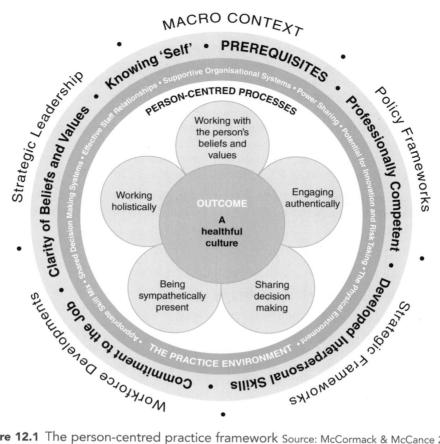

Figure 12.1 The person-centred practice framework Source: McCormack & McCance 2019.

Student activity

Discuss the following in small groups.

1. As a health professional listening to Patrick, how would you respond?
2. What will you do to demonstrate PCP?
3. What are the enablers and barriers to delivering person-centred care to Patrick?

Recovery-oriented care

As health care moves away from an exclusive biomedical-focused model and embraces psychosocial aspects of care, healthcare services similarly have begun the process of examining how they deliver fundamental services. Parallel with the PCP philosophy of care is the concept of a health system with **recovery-oriented care**, which can have major implications on care delivery.

The concept of 'recovery' in health usually has an emphasis on regaining or restoring something that has been lost. For example, we often describe people as recovered after a bout of illness, implying they have regained their full strength and returned to the state of being healthy once more. But this is a limited understanding. What happens to the person who as a consequence of trauma loses a limb or the person who is diagnosed with type 1 diabetes? Some of these issues have already been discussed in previous chapters when exploring the concept of 'health' and whether people who have not returned to a previous health status are now not 'healthy'. For each individual, recovery will be a different personal experience. If we accept there are other dimensions of health, then the notion of recovery likewise should support internal and external factors that may contribute to a person's journey of recovery.

Since the 1980s, when people with a lived experience of mental illness began to challenge the biomedical-driven model of care, the concept of recovery-oriented health has grown remarkably to the point that it now guides and underpins all mental health reform in policy and practice in Western countries (O'Keeffe et al. 2018). Within the context of mental health, 'recovery' refers to a person being able to live a full and meaningful life, despite having an ongoing mental illness. It embraces notions of hope and setting goals for the future—not just symptom management. For health professionals, working in a recovery framework involves not only working with a consumer to manage the symptoms of their mental illness but also working with the person to enable them to live a fulfilling life (O'Kane 2021). Arguably, this philosophy should not be thought of as a model of care for mental health practice only. The guiding principles of recovery-oriented health care are universal and can be applied to a range of healthcare settings, particularly for those with the lived experience of a chronic illness and who plays a significant role in managing their illness.

RECOVERY PRINCIPLES

The principles of recovery in health care are not difficult to understand, though the reality of its implementation may prove more difficult in a biomedically driven healthcare system. The philosophy of recovery encompasses a range of factors that require individual, organisational and systematic change. Therefore, rather than a model in its own right, recovery should be seen as a flexible process or framework to guide health professionals in their practice. While recovery from illness and/or disability continues to be perceived as synonymous with cure or symptom relief, then those elements that also contribute to a person's health, including personal, social, vocational, family and education, become largely ignored. These elements, alongside others such as service provision, access/funding, human rights and social inclusion, can all have an impact or be affected as a consequence of illness or poor health. It is therefore important that they are not pushed aside when we consider a person's journey to recovery. Collectively, these factors constitute an individual's 'lived experience' of recovery and are the foundation to guide health professionals in delivering care to support someone to understand and come to terms with their illness. People who have experienced chronic mental illness often describe their recovery in terms of having the ability to live a satisfying and meaningful life despite their serious illness or the lasting effects the illness may have on them.

RECOVERY-ORIENTED PRACTICE

The past decade has seen a growing international body of literature from researchers, service providers, clinicians and service users that has developed, refined and operationalised the concept of recovery-oriented health care in an attempt to find commonalities that can be used to facilitate and promote recovery-oriented practice in different healthcare systems. In terms of what can be done as a health professional, if the aim of recovery is for people with chronic illness or disability to develop new meaning and purpose in their lives, not just the alleviation of symptoms, then it is up to health professionals to assist in this process by developing and maintaining a collaborative partnership, not just with the identified client. Family, carers, teams or agencies may need to be involved in different aspects of care and resource provision. From listening to people's stories of how they accepted and overcame the challenges of their illness or disability, several key facilitators have been identified as underpinning the philosophy of recovery and supporting clients in their journey. These include taking control of one's life through hope, empowerment, support, education, medication management, spirituality, choice, advocacy and autonomy to name a few (Deegan 1996; Glover 2012; O'Hagan 2012; Shepherd et al. 2008). Health professionals can work towards supporting a person with their health issue by helping them identify their strengths and the protective factors that promote recovery rather than focus on the changes, limitations and losses that may have occurred as a result of the illness or disability.

Shepherd and colleagues (2008) provides 10 top tips for recovery-oriented practice in mental health that could easily be applied in other healthcare settings by guiding health professionals in promoting person-centred care. See Box 12.2 for how Shepherd's tips can be applied to general health issues.

Table 12.1 illustrates the many similarities between the philosophy of recovery and that of PCP. Ultimately, the partnership established between the person receiving

---

Box 12.2 '10 top tips' for recovery-oriented practice

After each interaction, the health professional should ask, did I...?

1. Actively listen to help the person to make sense of their health problems?
2. Help the person identify and prioritise their personal goals for recovery—not professional goals?
3. Demonstrate a belief in the person's existing strengths and resources in relation to the pursuit of these goals?
4. Identify stories of individuals' experiences of illness that inspire and validate hope? (Be aware, though, of confidentiality when telling another client's story and, if you recount a story of your own, be mindful of whose interests are served in telling the story, i.e. the client's not your own.)
5. Pay particular attention to the importance of goals that take the person out of the 'sick role' and enable them to actively contribute to the lives of others?
6. Identify non-health resources—friends, contacts, organisations—relevant to achieving their goals?

Box 12.2 '10 top tips' for recovery-oriented practice—cont'd

7. Encourage self-management of health problems (by providing information, reinforcing existing coping strategies, etc.)?

8. Discuss what the person wants in terms of therapeutic interventions such as biomedical and psychological treatments, alternative therapies and joint crisis planning, respecting their wishes wherever possible?

9. Behave at all times so as to convey an attitude of respect for the person and a desire for an equal partnership in working together, indicating a willingness to 'go the extra mile'?

10. While accepting that the future is uncertain and setbacks will happen, continue to express support for the possibility of achieving these self-defined goals—maintaining hope and positive expectations?

Adapted from Shepherd et al. 2008

Table 12.1

COMPARABLE PRINCIPLES IN RECOVERY-ORIENTED PRACTICE AND PERSON-CENTRED CARE

Recovery-oriented practice	Person-centred care
Recovery is fundamentally about a set of values related to human living applied to the pursuit of health and wellness.	A value base that asserts the absolute value of all human lives regardless of age or cognitive ability.
The helping relationship between clinicians and clients moves away from being expert–patient to clinicians being 'coaches' or 'partners' on an individual's journey of discovery.	The need to move beyond a focus on technical competence and to engage in authentic humanistic caring practices that embrace all forms of knowing and acting, to promote choice and partnership in care decision making.
Recovery is closely associated with social inclusion and being able to take on meaningful and satisfying roles in society.	Provides an enriched environment that can foster opportunities for personal growth.
People do not recover in isolation. Family and other supporters are often crucial to recovery and should be included as partners wherever possible.	Recognises that all human life is grounded in relationships.
Recovery approaches give positive value to cultural, religious, sexual and other forms of diversity as resources and supports for wellbeing and identity.	An individualised approach—valuing uniqueness. Accepting differences in culture, gender, temperament, lifestyle, outlook, beliefs, values, commitments, taste and interests.

Source: Hill et al. 2010

a healthcare service and the health professional delivering it is based on the premise that the recipient of care knows themselves better than anyone else and hence is an 'expert by experience'. The health professional, while acknowledging and valuing the person's contributions, can offer advice and guidance via their own knowledge and experience gained through professional training to help support the person in managing their own healthcare needs (Roberts & Boardman 2013).

If you think about the role of a health professional working with someone who has type 1 diabetes, the partnership would incorporate advice on exercise, dietary intake, medication management/administration, support groups and education regarding risk factors related to the illness. However, you need to remember that not everybody will require the same amount of support and guidance; for instance, a 19-year-old newly diagnosed person with diabetes may want very different things from the partnership compared with a 55-year-old who has managed their diabetes over several years. The partnership, therefore, initially needs to establish the goals for each party through an open and trustworthy relationship based on transparency and respect for each other's contributions.

Student activity

Complete the following in small groups.

1. Using the 10 top tips identified by Shepherd and colleagues (2008), identify other areas of healthcare practice in which tips could be used when working with a client diagnosed with:
   » juvenile arthritis
   » chronic obstructive pulmonary disease
   » Alzheimer's disease
   » type 2 diabetes
   » motor neurone disease.
2. How would the client benefit?
3. How do you foresee yourself using these tips in daily practice?

HEALTH PROFESSIONALS FROM A DIFFERENT CULTURE

Aspects of cultural safety and how to communicate with clients from various cultures have been explored in Chapter 8. We will now look at working with a health professional from another culture and how this may affect partnerships of care. As the healthcare workforce continues to become multicultural in nature, expectations about the client and the different roles and responsibilities of each team member may be quite different from the usual Western individualist tradition for some healthcare graduates from non-Western collectivist cultures.

What constitutes a partnership and the attitudes a health professional has about this health professional–client partnership can be very different from the client's perspective, particularly if there was an emphasis on a biomedical approach with little focus on the psychosocial aspects of treatment in a health professional's education. For instance, some cultures differ on the client's entitlement to consent to treatment. Based on gender dynamics, community status or family leadership, families may perceive there is no freedom of personal choice in health issues but instead it is their responsibility for decisions about an individual's health care (Ekmekci & Arda 2017). In other cultures, it is not acceptable for a health professional to challenge or confront a doctor's decision-making process but instead unquestioningly agree with all given medical directives (Mao & Ahmed 2018). Australian research has found it is frequently a culture shock for non-Western healthcare workers to encounter such differences and so do nothing to embrace the partnership model and true shared care in practice (Mao & Ahmed 2018). To overcome potential issues and maintain partnerships with other work colleagues, clients and carers, workplaces can offer acculturation programs to support the international workforce. Such programs can address concerns, reduce misunderstandings and identify and/or resolve potential cross-cultural issues. What may be required is not simply assistance with the English language and its colloquialisms but how to relate to clients from another culture.

Making decisions about one's own health

Becker and Rosenstock's (1984) work that resulted in the health belief model (see Chapter 7) was concerned with how people make decisions about their health. They concluded that a person's motivation to engage in healthy behaviours depended on how severe they saw their problem to be, how susceptible they perceived themselves to be and whether they believed that making a change would make a difference to their health. Over time, the health belief model was developed and extended by social psychologists seeking to promote better preventive health (Janz & Becker 1984; Rosenstock 1974). It remains a common and widely used model of health behaviour change in practice today, being implemented to measure individuals' likelihood of changing their health behaviours. Its basis is that preventive health behaviour in an individual is influenced by five factors: (1) any barriers they perceive to carrying out a particular response; (2) perceived benefits of performing the recommended response; (3) their perceived susceptibility to a health threat; (4) perceived severity of a health threat; and (5) cues to the person taking action in response (Becker & Rosenstock 1984). So it follows that it is what the client thinks is important in influencing their decision about the health behaviour (see also Chapter 7).

The health belief model raises the important question of how much health professionals should honestly and carefully explain to clients about their health status. It also implies the importance of having to consider the person's capacity and ability to cope with these facts, understand them and to then act on them. This can often be an issue. It is important, therefore, for health professionals to attempt to engage clients in a working partnership, or alliance, while also recognising that this may at times be a challenge due to the client having a variety of reasons for not wishing, or being able, to cooperate. Such factors include: not experiencing a significant degree of distress from the illness, not accepting the fact of being ill, having poor communication skills, the regimen of treatment being too complex, associated costs of treatments, feeling embarrassed, possible side effects and the possible gains from being seen as ill. All of this reinforces the need for good communication skills, easy-to-comprehend treatment plans with clear instructions, emphasising the positive gains of following treatment and, following from this, the client experiencing shared decision making and treatment success. Of course, there will be times in practice when communication is not as successful as one would hope. For example, even given the best health professional communicator, the client may not have the communication skills or understanding to let their opinion be known. In cases such as this, the health professional may need to use other tools and resources to support the voice of the client and provide the opportunity for them to feel informed and involved in decisions about their care.

THE HEALTH PROFESSIONAL'S ROLE

In spite of the above challenges, it still remains the aim of health professionals to work successfully with their clients. Viewing treatment as a partnership rather than a battle of wills or a procedure to be done is one way to achieve collaboration. It should be seen as entering into interactions with clients with the goal of seeking to form a working alliance. While bearing in mind a client's diagnosis and treatment plan, it is important to remember the following: What are the client's needs here and now? How may they be assisted in making informed decisions about their treatment? How could their needs be incorporated into a treatment plan?

Many health professionals nevertheless still do not follow this approach. Unfortunately, the healthcare service industry is still largely based on medical diagnosis and treatment of disorders, rather than the client. In spite of this medically driven model still being common, research now seems quite conclusive that where health professionals use a person-centred approach to care rather than a diagnosis basis, clients are more likely to cooperate in their care (Care Quality Commission 2016). Although some clinicians may be excellent at involving people in their care, others can become so focused on developing a treatment plan they lose sight of the main agenda, resulting in the client having a passive role and taking little responsibility for decisions about their own health. Ultimately, how a health professional responds to a client will influence the overall interaction and relationship.

'UNCOOPERATIVE' CLIENTS

All of this is not to deny the existence of those few clients who do not cooperate with any form of treatment regimen, no matter how much a health professional attempts to explore their reasons and to empathise with them. Not all clients want to be active in their treatment, and some may simply require the health professional to make them better, with no ability or motivation to change behaviours that are harmful to their health. Others have no desire to improve their health status. Some may have previously been treated by health professionals who did not explain about their condition or who did not emphasise a working alliance with them, or were disinterested or even rude to them. Some clients may be actively antagonistic to accepting treatment that the evidence has shown is best for them. It can sometimes require a great deal of explanation and education to enlist the client's cooperation though patience, perseverance and ongoing attempts will potentiate the desired outcome of establishing a relationship that reflects person-centred care.

BELIEFS AND PERCEPTIONS

At this point it may be worth thinking about how a person's belief system may influence their behaviour in developing partnerships with health professionals and how willing they are to change health behaviours. As already discussed in Chapter 7, how a person perceives illness and health will affect their ability to cope and manage their own health behaviour; therefore, one model worth exploring further is the **health locus of control** (HLOC). This model allows us to examine a person's perception of the degree of control they possess over their personal health, which in turn affects their behaviour, beliefs and attitudes towards their health. Though Julian Rotter originally developed the social learning theory of locus of control in the 1950s, it was in the 1970s that the concept developed significantly in healthcare practice, with various tools emerging that had been specifically designed to measure a person's HLOC in areas such as drug dependency, mental health and chronic pain (Wallston et al. 1976).

HLOC is concerned with how much a person believes their health is controlled by internal factors or external factors. For instance, if a person believes their personal health is the result of their own behaviour and sees themselves as having control of their lives, internal factors are said to be at play. On the other hand, an external explanation results when the person believes their personal health is controlled by other causes such as health professionals, social forces or even plain luck. Research such as Rizza and colleagues 2017 and Stewart and colleagues 2018 shows that assessing a person's perception of control over their health helps to better understand their engagement in healthcare practice. The higher a person's internal HLOC, the more likely they are to see themselves as able to manage their own health and bring about change independently, whereas those with a lower internal HLOC see themselves as powerless to bring about any change, believing their health is being influenced by things beyond their control (Wallston et al. 1976).

Whatever model is used, the importance of a person being assisted to make an informed decision and take as much responsibility as possible for their own health reinforces the concept of the client as an active participant in the healthcare team. This is now an accepted aspect of most health service policies.

A rather different way of seeing the issue of client engagement argues that not engaging in treatment may sometimes seem like the sensible thing to the client—that is, it is a rational decision. When looking at the health belief model (Becker & Rosenstock 1984), the client may not, for instance, believe that what the doctor has suggested is in their best interest and have what they see as a reasonable explanation for their belief. This is called *rational* or *intentional non-adherence* (Usherwood 2017). The main reasons for rational non-adherence are side effects that are worrying, unpleasant or reduce the quality of life, practical barriers such as cost or changes to lifestyle, and confusion about when and how much of the treatment to take. Others may choose not to accept treatment on philosophical, religious or cultural grounds.

Research focus

Source: Laba et al. 2015

ABSTRACT

Background

Adherence to medications for chronic disease is suboptimal. Current adherence-enhancing strategies do not seem to adequately address the fundamental need to sustain adherence or prevent non-adherence. Intentional non-adherence, involving active medication-taking decisions, is not well described within the Australian community setting. Understanding if, how and why non-adherent decisions are made may help develop strategies to sustain adherence in chronic disease.

Objective

This study aimed to describe intentional non-adherent behaviour in chronic disease within the Australian community setting and identify the factors that promote and prevent non-adherent decisions.

Methods

In-depth, semi-structured interviews were conducted with 21 patients (12 rural, nine metropolitan in New South Wales) prescribed medications for a diverse range of chronic conditions. Using the theory of planned behaviour as the theoretical framework, an iterative thematic framework analysis method was used to characterise the intentions and the decisions underlying non-adherent behaviour. Data were indexed and charted within the thematic framework using Excel, and linked themes were combined, and associations and explanations drawn.

Results

Although there was a strong intent to follow prescribers' recommendations, most patients described instances of intentionally non-adherent behaviour. Trading between perceived treatment inefficacy, unfavourable side effects and unaffordable medication costs promoted non-adherent decisions; trusting prescriber–patient relationships, positive family values and lack of perceived control over treatment choice maintained adherent intentions. Intentional non-adherence was mostly temporary.

Conclusions

Intentional medication non-adherence in chronic disease appears reversible and amenable to interventions that address treatment-related barriers such as medication affordability. Strategies that strengthen patient–prescriber relationships and empower patients as informed decision-makers may help maintain adherence intentions. Crucially, regular and sustained interventions that are refreshed to meet the changing needs of patients are needed to curb the temporal decline in adherence to chronic disease medications.

Critical thinking

- Reflect on a time when you have been prescribed medication or some other treatment. Did you remember all the health professional's instructions? Did you do everything the health professional told you to do? If you didn't, what were your reasons?

- Following from this, imagine if you were concerned about a client of yours. How would you attempt to ensure they followed the treatment that was ordered for them? If you looked at it from their point of view, could there be possible reasons for their attitude and behaviour?

- Thinking about the concept of HLOC, what internal and external factors may impact on a client who has decided to not accept treatment? How might you as a health professional attempt to engage with them?

The context of the health professional–client partnership

It follows from the preceding discussion that another factor to be considered is the treatment context. Usually most health professionals are employees of a health service or organisation. It is possible that an employer may disagree with your values or that their actions contrast with their stated policy. Words spoken and printed claiming that holistic, person-centred care will be provided may not, unfortunately, always fit with actual practice. A service may state that these concerns underpin their care, but there might not be adequate funding or facilities for such quality of care to be provided. There is a danger that services and health professionals can be consumed with more efficient, quicker, more economical approaches to treating clients and lose sight of the person. Diagnostic-related categories and treatment/care plans, where interventions are planned according to type and length of treatment usually required for a particular disorder, are useful to assist the efficient management of care in health agencies. But the risk is of quality of care being dependent on a budget that emphasises the number of clients treated rather than the quality of care delivered.

So, given this, how should a healthcare student or recent graduate approach their professional practice? It can be somewhat disillusioning for people who have a passion for helping others to encounter colleagues who are cynical or seem to lack any ability to care for their clients. In spite of these problems, there are many individual health professionals and agencies that are genuinely committed to the importance of PCP and building partnerships. It is therefore important for individual health professionals to consider what they believe about the helping relationship and how they wish to practise their profession. As you begin to practise your profession, you will begin to discover the challenges and rewards of helping people in a variety of situations.

CASE STUDY: SYLVIA

Sylvia is an 80-year-old widow who is soon to be discharged from hospital after a recent hip replacement operation. She lives alone and has no family members living in the local area. She was previously living independently but will require some short-term support for the first few weeks after discharge. Sylvia is frightened that a decision will be made to place her in a residential nursing home.

Critical thinking

You are the health professional who is responsible for Sylvia's discharge planning.

- What support do you think Sylvia will need?
- Who do you need to establish a partnership with? Provide your rationale for this.
- How will you establish and maintain the partnerships?
- What do you foresee your role to be as a health professional?
- What obstacles do you think may prevent the partnerships being effective? How would you overcome these?

Partnerships and collaborative practice

The chapter has largely focused on the partnership between two key parties—the client and the health professional. Yet for effective and quality care to be delivered, health professionals are often not working alone. Person-centred care packages for people with chronic or complex issues will need to rely on other disciplines, services and organisations to play a vital role in the care delivery if they are to achieve optimal health care that allows the person to function to the best of their ability. With this in mind, partnerships need to be initiated and sustained with people other than the client at the centre of care. Essential to an effective partnership with others is the skill of working in a cooperative and integrated way through professional collaboration in a multi- or interdisciplinary healthcare team. Yet despite the assumption that interdisciplinary working leads to success, evidence has shown several barriers that hinder partnerships, with the most common being miscommunication and misunderstanding of each other's role and responsibility. Others include lack of trust, rivalry, stereotyping of professionals, conflicting opinions and role insecurity (Ndoro 2014). Partnerships that promote collaborative care require time and effort on the part of all key parties. It may be that, as a health professional, terms commonly used in one service are unfamiliar or are misunderstood due to the same word being used in a different way in another service. In this situation, as in all situations when working with other professionals, clarification needs to be sought so that mutual understanding can occur, just as each key player in the partnership needs to clarify their role and what they perceive their responsibility in the care package to be. Clear direction of who will do what task, expectations of each other, time management and the overarching aim of the care package, if communicated clearly to all parties, will go some way to avoid the previously mentioned barriers. Recent evidence from WHO suggests that one way of achieving effective partnerships and **collaborative practice** is by delivering interprofessional education. By different professionals learning together, they can learn 'from and about each other' (WHO 2010, p. 7); this, in turn, will enhance their partnerships in practice, leading to improved health outcomes for the person at the centre of care.

Chapter summary

This chapter has considered the various issues involved in relationships between health professionals, clients and others. Successful health outcomes depend on the key people involved in care, including health professionals, families, carers and communities working together to create an effective partnership. We discussed the meanings and implications in the terms health professionals use on a daily basis and the importance of the client being involved in their own care based on the philosophy of person-centred practice and recovery-oriented care, particularly in chronic and complex health issues. Similarly, creating partnerships with other disciplines can offer opportunity for better health outcomes. An understanding of the factors involved in healthcare partnerships helps identify possibilities health professionals can use to create and maintain effective partnerships throughout their career.

KEY POINTS

- Successful health outcomes require a partnership between health professionals and clients.
- Terms such as compliance/adherence versus partnership, and patient/client versus consumer/service user impact differently on the health partnership relationship.
- A partnership approach enables a person to be involved in their own health care. This can be achieved by embracing philosophies such as person-centred and recovery-oriented practice.
- Clients may not always 'comply' with or accept the advice of a health professional.
- Factors in the healthcare agency may raise challenges in establishing effective partnerships.

Further reading

Australian College of Nursing (ACN). 2019, 'Person-Centred Care', ACN, Canberra.

Jesus, T., Bright, F., Kayes, N., et al., 2016. Person-centered rehabilitation—what exactly does it mean? Protocol for a scoping review with thematic analysis towards framing the concept and practice of person-centered rehabilitation. BMJ Open 6 (7).

McCormack, B., McCance, T., Bulley C., et al. 2021. Fundamentals of Person-Centred Healthcare Practice. Wiley-Blackwell. Oxford.

Santana, M.J., Manalili, K., Jolley, R.J., et al., 2018. How to practice person-centred care: a conceptual framework. Health Expectations: An International Journal of Public Participation in Health Care and Health Policy, 21 (2), 429–440.

Slusser, M., Garcia, L., Reed, C., et al., 2018. Foundations of Interprofessional Collaborative Practice in Health Care. Elsevier. Sydney.

Weblinks

Encouraging Adherence to Long-Term Medication, Australian Prescriber

www.nps.org.au/australian-prescriber/articles/encouraging-adherence-to-long-term-medication

Adherence is considered in this research, exploring the effectiveness of strategies suggested to increase adherence by patients in taking long-term medication.

Health Issues Centre—Patient-Centred Care

www.healthissuescentre.org.au/subjects/list-library-subject.chtml?subject=35

This site is a resource library with publications and presentations linked to patient-centred care.

Department of Health, a National Framework for Recovery-Oriented Mental Health Services: Guide for Practitioners and Providers

https://www.health.gov.au/resources/publications/a-national-framework-for-recovery-oriented-mental-health-services-guide-for-practitioners-and-providers

An excellent document providing guidance to mental health practitioners and services on recovery-oriented practice and service delivery.

Advance Care Planning Australia

www.advancecareplanning.org.au

Information for clients and health professionals on advance care planning.

Patient-centred care—Indigenous health

www.racgp.org.au/afp/200812/200812nguyen1.pdf

This is an excellent resource to consider cultural safety in Indigenous health.

The Health Foundation—Person Centred Care Resource Centre

http://personcentredcare.health.org.uk/overview-of-person-centred-care/overview-of-person-centred-care/overview-of-person-centred-care-0

This site offers useful resources for health professionals who have responsibility to improve the experience of those using a health service.

The Health Navigator: Person Centered Care

https://www.healthnavigator.org.nz/videos/p/patient-centred-care/person-centred-care/

This resource introduces the concept of person-centred care in New Zealand, offering a variety of videos to support understanding of the key elements.

References

Albury, C., Strain, W.D.,' Brocq, S.L., et al., 2020. Language Matters working group. The importance of language in engagement between healthcare professionals and people living with obesity: a joint consensus statement. Lancet Diabetes Endocrinol. 8 (5), 447–455.

Australian Commission on Safety and Quality in Health Care, 2021. Partnering with consumers in National Safety and Quality Health Service Standards (second edition). Australian Commission on Safety and Quality in Health Care. Sydney.

Australian Health Ministers' Advisory Council, 2017. National Strategic Framework for Chronic Conditions. Australian Government, Canberra.

Australian Institute of Health and Welfare, 2022. National Strategic Framework for Chronic Conditions, reporting framework: indicator results, catalogue number PHE 299, AIHW, Australian Government.

Becker, M.H., Rosenstock, I.M., 1984. Compliance with medical advice. In: Steptoe, A., Mathews, A. (Eds.), Healthcare and Human Behaviour. Academic Press, London.

Care Quality Commission, 2016. Better care in my hands, CQC, London.

Chapman, H., 2018. Nursing theories 4: adherence and concordance. Nursing Times; 114 (2), 50.

Costa, D., Mercieca-Bebber, R., Tesson, S., et al., 2019. Patient, client, consumer, survivor or other alternatives? A scoping review of preferred terms for labelling individuals who access healthcare across settings. BMJ Open, 9, e025166.

Deegan, P., 1996. Recovery as a journey of the heart. Psychiatric Rehabilitation Journal 11, 11–19.

Ekmekci, P.E., Arda, B., 2017. Interculturalism and informed consent: respecting cultural differences without breaching human rights. Cultura (Iasi, Romania), 14 (2), 159–172.

European Patients Forum, 2015. Adherence and concordance. Available: https://tinyurl.com/yyzmodr7 (accessed 8 April 2022)

Glover, H., 2012. Recovery, lifelong learning, social inclusion and empowerment: is a new paradigm emerging? In: Ryan, P., Ramon, S., Greacen, T. (eds.), Empowerment, Lifelong Learning and Recovery in Mental Health: Towards a New Paradigm. Palgrave Publishers, London.

Granello, D.H., Gibbs, T.A., 2016. The power of language and labels: 'The mentally ill' versus 'people with mental illnesses'. Journal of Counseling & Development 94 (1), 31–40.

Janz, N., Becker, M.L., 1984. The health belief model: a decade later. Health Education Quarterly 11, 1–47.

Laba, T.L., Lehnbom, E., Brien, J.A., et al., 2015. Understanding if, how and why non-adherent decisions are made in an Australian community sample: a key to sustaining medication adherence in chronic disease? Research in Social and Administrative Pharmacy 11 (2), 154–162.

Larson, P., 2021. The illness experience. In: Lubkin, I., Larson, P. (Eds.), Chronic Illness. Impact and Intervention, 11th edn. Jones and Bartlett, Burlington.

Lloyd, B., Elkins, M., Innes, L., 2018. Barriers and enablers of patient and family-centred care in an Australian acute care hospital: perspectives of health managers. Patient Experience Journal 5 (3), 55–64.

Mao, Y., Ahmed, R., 2018. Culture, Migration, and Health Communication in a Global Context. Routledge, NY.

McCormack, B., 2020. The person-centred nursing and person-centred practice frameworks: from conceptual development to programmatic impact. Nursing Standard, 35(10), 86–89.

McCormack, B., McCance, T., 2019. The Person-Centred Nursing Framework. Available: http://www.cpcpr.org/resources (accessed 10 April 2022)

McCormack, B., McCance, T., 2016. Person Centred Practice in Nursing and Health Care Theory and Practice, 2nd edn. John Wiley & Sons, Chichester.

McCormack, B., McCance, T.V., 2006. Developing a conceptual framework for person-centred nursing. Journal of Advanced Nursing, 56(5), 472–479.

Ministry of Health – Manatu Hauora, 2020. Long-term conditions. New Zealand. Available: https://www.health.govt.nz/our-work/diseases-and-conditions/long-term-conditions#:~:text=LTCs%20include%20conditions%20such%20as,chronic%20kidney%20disease%20and%20dementia. (Accessed 9 April 2022).

Ndoro, S., 2014. Effective multidisciplinary working: the key to high-quality care. British Journal of Nursing 23 (13), 724–727.

O'Hagan, M., Reynolds, P., Smith, C., 2012. Recovery in New Zealand: An evolving concept? International Review of Psychiatry, 24 (1), 56–63.

O'Kane, D., 2021. Mental Health. A pocket guide. Elsevier, Sydney,

O'Keeffe, D., Sheridan, A., Kelly, A. et al., 2018. 'Recovery' in the real world: service user experiences of mental health service use and recommendations for change 20 years on from a first episode psychosis. Administration and Policy in Mental Health 45, 635–648.

Rizza, F., Gison, A., Bonassi, S., et al., 2017. 'Locus of control', health-related quality of life, emotional distress and disability in Parkinson's disease. Journal of Health Psychology 22, 844–852.

Roberts, G., Boardman, J., 2013. Understanding recovery. Advances in Psychiatric Treatment 19, 400–409.

Rosenstock, I., 1974. Historical origins of the health model. Health Education Monographs 2, 328–335.

Shepherd, G., Boardman, J., Slade, M., 2008. Making Recovery a Reality. Sainsbury Centre for Mental Health, London.

Stewart, J.A., Aebischer, V., Egloff, N., et al., 2018. The role of health locus of control in pain intensity outcome of conservatively and operatively treated hand surgery patients. International Journal of Behavioral Medicine, 25 (3), 374–379.

Stone, L., 2014. Blame, shame and hopelessness: medically unexplained symptoms and the 'heartsink' experience. Australian Family Physician 43, 191–195.

Usherwood, T., 2017. Encouraging adherence to long-term medication. Australian Prescriber, 40, 147–150.

Wallston, B.S., Wallston, K.A., Kaplan, G.D., et al., 1976. Development and validation of the health locus of control (HLC) scale. Journal of Consulting and Clinical Psychology, 44 (4), 580–585.

World Health Organization (WHO) 2021a. Noncommunicable diseases. Available: https://www.who.int/news-room/fact-sheets/detail/noncommunicable-diseases. (Accessed 10 April 2022).

World Health Organization (WHO) 2021b. Ageing and Health. Available: https://www.who.int/news-room/fact-sheets/detail/ageing-and-health#:~:text=At%20this%20time%20the%20share,2050%20to%20reach%20426%20million. (Accessed 29 March 2022).

World Health Organization (WHO), 2010. Framework for action on interprofessional education and collaborative practice. Available: https://www.who.int/publications/i/item/framework-for-action-on-interprofessional-education-collaborative-practice (Accessed 10 April 2022).

Chapter 13

Health promotion

LOUISE BALDWIN

Learning objectives

The material in this chapter will help you to:

- describe the contribution of the discipline of psychology to health promotion
- distinguish between health promotion and illness prevention
- identify the social determinants of health
- describe protective factors for health
- describe risk factors for illness
- identify settings for health promotion
- understand population approaches to health promotion.

Key terms

- Health promotion (360)
- Wellbeing societies (360)
- Social determinants of health (361)
- Salutogenesis (361)
- Illness prevention (365)
- Primary prevention (369)
- Secondary prevention (370)
- Early intervention (370)
- Tertiary prevention (370)
- Recovery (370)
- Population-focused approaches (373)
- Settings approach (373)

Introduction

Health promotion is the process of enabling people to take control over and improve their health and its determinants. Health promotion is about creating the conditions and conducive environment for healthy choices for all and where people live, work, age and play.

(World Health Organization 2022b)

The term '**health promotion**' encompasses a broad set of approaches focusing on people, communities, places and policies to ensure factors that impact on people's health can be controlled for the greatest possible health outcomes. It forms part of the broad landscape of public health and sits firmly in the continuum of care cycle focusing on different levels of prevention and early intervention. Health promotion stemmed from the recognition that some causes of premature death, illness and injury could be prevented with lifestyle changes. This knowledge grew to the impacts of other determinants in society and the environment that also have an impact on health. There is now a wealth of history and evidence behind health promotion that has brought it to be the dynamic discipline that it is today. It is important to acknowledge at the outset that health promotion is not just about education or the 'promotion' of health messages. Education, awareness and health literacy are core to health promotion, yet it is not about promotional communication and marketing. The term 'promotion' in this instance means to enhance or enable health. Today health promotion is an evidence-based discipline focusing on policy, supportive environments, advocacy and systems change.

In this chapter we will explore these concepts, underpinned by an understanding of the social determinants of health. Examples and case studies of health promotion in action are provided along with links to the foundations of psychology and a connection to the role of prevention and health promotion in the continuum of care.

Definitions of health promotion have changed over time from an individual behaviour change focus to a more multidimensional approach recognising the number of factors that determine health. Previous definitions of health promotion range from those that focused more on the individual and their personal responsibility for their health outcomes to definitions that take account of the wider social, political and economic forces that influence the health of individuals, communities and wider society with the development of the Geneva Charter for Well-being in 2021, which calls for sustainable **wellbeing societies** (Traina 2019).

Looking back at original definitions, O'Donnell (2009), the editor of the *American Journal of Health Promotion*, for example, defines health promotion as:

... is the art and science of helping people discover the synergies between their core passions and optimal health, enhancing their motivation to strive for optimal health, and supporting them in changing their lifestyle to move toward a state of optimal health. Optimal health is a dynamic balance of physical, emotional, social, spiritual, and intellectual health. Lifestyle change can be facilitated through a combination of learning experiences that enhance awareness, increase motivation, and build skills and, most important, through the creation of opportunities that open access to environments that make positive health practices the easiest choice.

Cont... ▶

The World Health Organization (WHO), however, defines health promotion more broadly as:

A comprehensive social and political process [that] not only embraces actions directed at strengthening the skills and capabilities of individuals, but also action directed towards changing social, environmental and economic conditions so as to alleviate their impact on public and individual health. Health promotion is the process of enabling people to increase control over the determinants of health and thereby improve their health.

(WHO 2022b)

We also see these contemporary approaches to health promotion supported by a call for an urgency to act to create wellbeing societies, with WHO saying that '(r)esponses require investments that integrate planetary, societal, community and individual health and well-being, as well as changes in social structures to support people to take control of their lives and health. Fundamental redirection of societal values and action consistent with the 2030 Agenda for Sustainable Development are required' (United Nations 2022).

Although seemingly disparate, these explanations are both valid because they offer definitions that are applicable in different contexts. O'Donnell's older definition is a selective approach and can be applied to health promotion for specific people with a specific purpose—for example, diabetes education for a newly diagnosed person with diabetes or antenatal classes for prospective parents. This can be useful in a clinical or primary health setting. The WHO definition, on the other hand, is comprehensive and applies to population-focused health promotion in which the **social determinants of health**, like housing, employment and education, are addressed in order to improve the health of individuals and communities (WHO 2022b). More contemporary approaches combine focusing on determinants of health and reducing inequities such as policy and changes to environments, programs and services to contribute more sustainably to wellbeing of communities.

Focusing on a salutogenic approach to health promotion is also relevant in the fields of psychology and health promotion, focusing on factors that support health rather than factors that cause disease. Barry (2022) notes that, '**Salutogenesis** provides a guiding theory for the field of health promotion as it is concerned with positive health, creating coherent living environments, strengthening socio-ecological health resources, and strengthening the sense of coherence of individuals and groups'.

When we think about heath it is important to think beyond 'being sick' and 'being healthy'. It is important to think about what 'sick' or 'unwell' might mean and what 'being healthy' or 'wellbeing' actually means in the broadest sense. Think about health in its broadest form while reading this chapter. To help with this, consider the determinants of health.

SOCIAL DETERMINANTS OF HEALTH

It's important when looking at health promotion to revisit the social determinants of health (discussed in Chapter 6). Determinants of health are often referred to as social, economic, environmental, cultural or commercial determinants of health.

These considerations highlight the interplay of factors at the individual, community and systems levels that impact on health. These are often referred to as the 'non-medical' factors that influence health. They are the factors that also impact on equity, which is inextricably linked to health outcomes. WHO notes that the determinants are 'the conditions in which people are born, grow, work, live, and age, and the wider set of forces and systems shaping the conditions of daily life. These forces and systems include economic policies and systems, development agendas, social norms, social policies and political systems' (WHO 2022c).

The wide range of determinants are often grouped under the collective term of 'social determinants' to include factors such as income, education, employment, housing, food access and security, conflict, and access to health services (WHO 2022c).

It may seem like an extended link to associate a person in hospital with heart disease and their housing or employment. In Australia, for example, it may seem on the surface that hospitals and health care are accessible, there is awareness and education about heart disease and that data shows survival is relatively strong. But let's think about this example in an Australian context. In 2020 the Australian Institute of Health and Welfare (AIHW) reported that rates of death varied by level of education, with lower education rates directly relating to greater probability of dying. Similarly, babies born in lower socioeconomic areas were more likely to have a lower birthweight, while smoking was higher among unemployed populations. Using our heart disease example, the incidence of both heart attack and strokes increased with increasing socioeconomic disadvantage (AIHW 2020b).

Student activity

Search the social determinants of health and consider these in a community that you know. Think about housing—what link does housing have to health? Think about basic public health issues such as sanitation, clean water and air circulation. Then think about access to affordable housing and where these houses are located in comparison with local services. You may also like to consider the effect of stress of unstable housing and what other health behaviours this may instigate, all of which collectively impact on a person's health.

HEALTH INEQUITIES

Health is essential to wellbeing and quality of life; therefore, health inequities further disadvantage groups of people who are already socially disadvantaged due to poverty, gender or being a member of a disenfranchised racial, ethnic or religious group. Furthermore, equity is a social justice principle and closely related to human rights (McKay & Taket 2020).

In a 2018 publication on achieving health inequities, VicHealth (2018) defines health inequity as the 'differences in health status between population groups' that are 'socially produced, systematic' in that there is 'unequal distribution across the population, [which is] avoidable and unfair'. VicHealth identifies three dimensions of inequality, all of which need to be addressed to overcome health inequalities:

1. *Inequality of access*—as a result of barriers to support services required for health and wellbeing. This can result from costs of the service, lack of transport to the service, services that are inaccessible for people with special needs and services that are culturally inappropriate for some population groups.

2. *Inequality of opportunity*—as a result of social, geographic or economic resources for health including education, employment and suitable housing.

3. *Inequality of impacts and outcomes*—differences in health outcomes between groups and populations such as mortality and morbidity rates or self-reported health rates.

Accompanying visionary work by Backholer and colleagues (2021) set out a pathway for Australia to achieve greater health equity by 2030. The team of authors call on a mix of approaches looking at the social determinants of health; stronger individual and collective wellbeing for Indigenous communities; issues surrounding built and natural environments including planetary health; a focus on commercial determinants of health, which means reducing the impact of commercial drivers for unhealthy products such as junk food and tobacco; and the need for digital transformation as the basis of governance for wellbeing futures.

Redressing health inequities for indigenous people

Indigenous Australians and New Zealand Māori experience poorer health outcomes than the non-Indigenous people of these two countries. In addition to health inequities, many Indigenous people also experience disadvantage in education, employment status, economic status, housing and lack of appropriate environmental infrastructure (AIHW 2021; Finlay et al. 2021).

Therefore, when planning and implementing health promotion with Indigenous peoples it is essential that social justice and human rights be incorporated because social conditions, health equity and human rights are interrelated. Furthermore, a research study by Wilson and colleagues (2020) found cultural safety and trust must be built on an unwavering foundation of relationships, an awareness of Aboriginal history, communication, commitment, flexibility, humility, honesty and persistence.

In New Zealand, health promotion practice takes account of the 1840 Treaty of Waitangi, which is the country's founding contract between Māori and the Crown and the 1986 Ottawa Charter for Health Promotion. Māori health is understood as a holistic concept in which health is recognised as being dependent on a balance of factors that influence wellbeing. These contributing factors include spiritual (wairua), mental (hinengaro), physical (tinana), language (te reo rangatira) and family (whanau), which interact to enable wellbeing, as does the environment (te ao tūroa). Therefore, in understanding Māori health, it is evident that the social, economic and cultural position of Māori must be taken into account, and that for Māori, health promotion means taking control of their own health to determine their own wellbeing (Health Promotion Forum of New Zealand 2018).

History of health promotion

Health promotion emerged in the 1970s after identifying lifestyle as a major contributor to health and illness (Adhikari 2021) and the development of psychological models for understanding and changing health behaviours. The health belief model (see also Chapter 7) was especially influential in early health promotion campaigns and was seen as the way forward in changing unhealthy lifestyle practices, particularly in relation to diet, physical activity, tobacco smoking and alcohol consumption. At this time, health promotion initiatives mainly consisted of health education and counselling of people about lifestyle, illness prevention strategies (e.g. mass vaccination and screening initiatives) and lifestyle education programs (e.g. stress management).

Initially, health promotion programs in the 1970s sought to improve health by encouraging individuals, through health education and counselling, to make behavioural and lifestyle changes. Through the 1980s, health professionals became aware that broader social, political and economic forces also played a role in health outcomes, and health promotion activities expanded to reflect this. Consequently, contemporary health promotion has evolved to include population-focused models that use interdisciplinary, intersectoral and partnership approaches to lead to greater systems change for longer term better outcomes.

PSYCHOLOGY AND HEALTH PROMOTION

Contributions to the field of health promotion by the discipline of psychology have been significant since the 1970s when psychological theories like the health belief model, the transtheoretical model and the health action process approach were first used in health education and counselling to bring about targeted individual behaviour and lifestyle changes. Contemporary examples of psychological approaches to health behaviour change include positive psychology, motivational interviewing and acceptance commitment therapy. However, in recent years the rise in the prevalence and burden of chronic illnesses in Western countries has shifted the focus of health promotion efforts from reducing mortality to reducing morbidity or the burden of disease (Budreviciute et al. 2020; Marthias et al. 2021). Also, psychological research that had initially focused on identifying risk factors now shifted to understanding and facilitating 'protective' factors for health like resilience (Nutbeam & Muscat 2021) and to acknowledging and responding to the social determinants of health and a salutogenic, or strengths-based, approach (Mittelmark et al. 2022).

In contemporary health promotion, psychological theory contributes to an interdisciplinary approach across the range of activities at all levels of intervention from that of the individual to that of the wider population. Motivational interviewing, for example, is a psychologically based counselling intervention aimed at changing unhealthy behaviours. It uses a client-centred, semi-directed approach and focuses on reasons for and against the change to motivate the person to change to a healthier lifestyle (see also Chapter 7). In larger scale health promotion interventions, behavioural and cognitive principles that come from psychological theory are incorporated in mass media health education campaigns, particularly those targeting lifestyle.

PRIMARY HEALTH CARE MOVEMENT AND HEALTH PROMOTION

During the 1980s, it became apparent that health education and counselling approaches, on their own, were insufficient to bring about the required changes in many instances because people's behaviour is also shaped by the social, political and economic environments in which they live (AIHW 2020a). It was at this time that WHO released its seminal document, the Ottawa Charter for Health Promotion (see Chapter 5), which subsequently became the cornerstone of the health promotion movement worldwide. The Charter shifted the emphasis of health promotion from the individual and called on governments and health services to address the wider social, political and economic drivers of health. As a consequence, health promotion became located in, and was central to, the emerging primary healthcare movement.

The shift from an individual to a societal and population focus precipitated a change in perceptions of responsibility for health away from the individual to wider society and the environments in which people live. Although both individual and population-focused approaches have a role to play in contemporary health promotion practice, a population approach that addresses the social determinants of health offers greater opportunity to influence health outcomes for a greater number of people. Nevertheless, individual approaches do continue to play a role in assisting people to engage in healthy lifestyle practices and can facilitate the use of strategies contained in the Ottawa Charter in healthcare practice—for example, developing personal skills through health education and counselling. Despite originating in the 1980s, the Ottawa Charter remains relevant in the 21st century (Thompson et al. 2017) as a framework for health promotion, as evidenced by its frequent citing in the literature and its widespread use in healthcare practice and programs.

What is health promotion?

The approaches of health promotion have continued to be refined by charters and frameworks from major global conferences. The first of these was the Ottawa Charter, developed some 30 years ago in one of the first health promotion conferences. This charter shows, as we discussed before, that health promotion is far more than just 'promotional' messages and education. The five areas of the Ottawa Charter are: building healthy public policy; creating supportive environments; strengthening community action; developing personal skills; and reorienting the health system. These essential elements for health promotion are underpinned by actions of enabling, mediating and advocating. An example is provided in Table 13.1.

Health promotion is a broad, multiarmed discipline that forms part of public health. Its approaches can be applied as part of health disciplines such as psychology and nursing, while it is also relevant to broader disciplines that impact on social determinants such as education and housing. It can be applied to a variety of healthcare practices and research activities that range from promoting wellbeing and preventing illness through to rehabilitation and recovery from illness. Also in this chapter, health promotion will be presented as distinct from illness prevention. Health promotion is defined here as being concerned with fostering *protective* factors for health, while **illness prevention** is concerned with identifying, reducing and responding to the *risk* factors for illness.

Table 13.1	
APPLICATION OF THE OTTAWA CHARTER FOR HEALTH PROMOTION	
Element	Application
Building healthy public policy	Healthy food policies in early childhood centres, supported by overarching policies within childcare accreditation requirements
Creating supportive environments	Affordability and access to fresh fruit and vegetables; creating well planned local built environments to encourage community connection and social cohesion including walkability, connection to services, well planned shade, connected public transport
Strengthening community action	Community engagement and collaboration for change to improve health outcomes
Developing personal skills	Focus on health literacy strategies and understanding health information and education
Reorienting health services	Supporting prevention and early detection in primary care settings; considering movements such as social prescribing for physical activity and healthy eating to reduce risk of lifestyle-related diseases; supporting mental health promotion as opposed to only treatment of illness

Source: Baldwin 2020

PROTECTIVE AND RISK FACTORS

Factors that contribute to a person's risk of developing a disease or contributing to their poorer health status are often discussed as being either 'risk factors' or 'protective factors'. These factors can be modifiable or non-modifiable—meaning a person can change or have an impact on changing a factor, or not. Those that can't be changed are usually referred to as genetic or biological. This doesn't mean these factors can't be managed with some form of clinical or social intervention. These factors are well cited for chronic disease prevention. For example, evidence shows that physical activity and healthy eating can impact on a person's risk for heart disease and some cancers (Guthold et al. 2018). Therefore adequate physical activity and maintaining a healthy diet are seen as protective factors against heart disease, whereas an unhealthy diet and a lack of physical activity is seen as a risk factor—so the person's risk of developing heart disease increases. Of course, these factors are not considered alone. In a review of non-genetic risk factors and protective factors for neurological disorders, Mentis and colleagues (2021) undertook a comprehensive systemic review. They found, for example, that a Mediterranean diet was associated with a lower risk of dementia, Alzheimer's disease and stroke, while smoking was associated with an elevated risk of multiple sclerosis and dementia.

Protective factors assist people to maintain physical, emotional and social wellbeing and to cope with life experiences including adversity. They can provide a buffer against stress as well as being a set of resources to draw upon to deal with stress. Factors that have been identified as protective for healthy development in children include easy temperament, family harmony/stability, positive social networks (e.g. peers, teachers, neighbours), academic achievement and strong cultural identity and pride (AIHW 2019).

Risk factors increase vulnerability to illness and injury and work against recovery from the illness or injury. Developmental risk factors in children have been identified as poor bonding with parent(s), family disharmony, peer rejection and/or bullying, emotional trauma and socioeconomic disadvantage (AIHW 2019).

It cannot be assumed, though, that identifying protective and risk factors can lead to accurately predicting who will or will not be healthy. Demographic data, epidemiological data and research findings merely indicate levels of risk and vulnerability in certain populations, or the increased likelihood of some people for particular illnesses—and their interaction is complex. The significant contribution made by health promotion research findings is that it provides evidence for health professionals and policymakers about opportunities for intervention to promote health and wellbeing, and to prevent illness for individuals and populations.

Student activity

1. In small groups, identify risk and protective factors for the following health issues:
   » HIV/AIDS
   » depression
   » cardiovascular disease
   » unplanned parenthood
   » obesity.
2. If funding was available for a health promotion initiative to address *one* of these issues, which one would you pick? Why? Think about how you would ensure an equitable approach.
3. Pair up with another student who selected a different issue from you and explain the reasons for your choice to each other.
4. In small groups, identify and discuss the challenges faced by health planners when allocating funding for health promotion initiatives.

Levels of intervention

Theories and models for health promotion offer opportunities for three levels of intervention: the individual level, the community level and the population level. These are also referred to as downstream (individual), midstream (community) and upstream (population) levels, as outlined in Table 13.2.

Table 13.2

LEVELS OF INTERVENTION

	Health promotion: intervention levels			
Upstream	**Midstream**		**Downstream**	
Primary			*Secondary*	*Tertiary*
Enduring social, political change and policy about: • health • social • welfare • environment				
Services/programs for: • health • social • welfare • environment	Services/programs to: • prevent illness • eradicate health risks in at-risk groups	Services/programs to: • prevent illness • eradicate health risks for at-risk individuals	Services/programs for illness: • diagnosis • treatment • management	Services/programs for: • recovery • rehabilitation • management
Outcomes	**Outcomes**		**Outcomes**	
Healthy society and members Individual behaviour change Sustainable environments for health Health promotion	Healthy community and individuals Individual behaviour change Environmental change Illness prevention		Healthy individuals Individual behaviour change Illness management Recovery	

The upstream/midstream/downstream distinction is best illustrated by a popular analogy. The physician jumped in the water and rescued the man. However, no sooner had the physician rescued the man when another drowning person came by. Repeatedly, the physician rescued and resuscitated drowning people as they floated past. In fact, the physician was so busy rescuing the drowning people that he did not have time to go upstream to see who was pushing them in (James 2020; McMahon 2021). This frequently repeated scenario is now an enduring primary health care metaphor illustrating that while downstream interventions are effective in responding to a health problem, they do nothing to address the actual upstream cause of the problem.

The medical model operates primarily as a downstream approach in which people with health problems seek assistance from their general practitioner (GP) or the healthcare system. An exception is mass immunisation programs, which are a biomedical intervention with an illness prevention focus. Downstream approaches also occur mainly at the individual level. Downstream approaches are generally limited to disease-specific interventions such as dietary advice to lower cholesterol. Midstream interventions operate at the local community level and use education and intervention strategies to prevent illness. Upstream interventions operate at the societal level, whereby social policy and planning is used to address the social determinants of health and to redress social inequities.

Student activity

In small groups identify upstream, midstream and downstream interventions for the following health issues:

- tobacco smoking
- cancer
- type 2 diabetes
- not having a child immunised
- unsuitable housing
- polluted waterways.

Primary, secondary and tertiary interventions

The terms primary, secondary and tertiary prevention are used to distinguish between levels of intervention that foster wellness, treat illness and restore function following illness (recovery). Combined, these strategies both focus on the prevention of disease and illness but also improve complications of a diagnosis or improve survivorship (Kisling & Das 2020).

PRIMARY PREVENTION

Primary prevention aims to foster wellbeing and prevent the occurrence of illness. It includes both midstream and upstream strategies. Midstream strategies focus on 'at-risk individuals' and 'at-risk groups', with the goal of changing the individual's risky behaviour, like ceasing tobacco smoking or reducing risk in the community (e.g. by improving access to healthcare services for people who live in regional areas). Other examples of population-focused primary prevention include mass vaccination programs, sanitation and clean water, legislation to protect vulnerable members of the society such as antidiscrimination laws, social inclusion policy and economic policies to fund health screening and public housing.

SECONDARY PREVENTION

Secondary prevention refers to interventions that are, in the main, delivered downstream when symptoms, injury or illness are identified and treated as early as possible to restore health. It includes the range of health services that the general public will be most familiar with—for example, attending an emergency department when injured or visiting a GP when symptoms present.

In addition to treating illness and health problems, a further goal of secondary prevention is **early intervention**. Hence, some interventions will occur midstream, such as health screening like mammograms, or hearing tests for infants. In this instance, the purpose of early intervention is to identify and address health issues before they become a problem or to minimise the impact of an illness or disability on the person. For example, breast cancer screening at the recommended screening intervals has been shown to reduce the morbidity and mortality of breast cancer.

TERTIARY PREVENTION

Tertiary prevention is also a downstream approach and is implemented when the disease cannot be cured or the illness process is prolonged. Its aim is to assist individuals (and their family and carers) to cope with a change in their health status, to limit disability from the health problem and to promote health and quality of life (**recovery**). Interventions include: treatment programs for chronic illnesses like emphysema and irritable bowel syndrome; rehabilitation and recovery programs for conditions like mental illness, post-coronary heart disease and post-stroke; and palliative care for chronic illnesses like cancer and dementia.

Recovery, which is a goal of tertiary prevention, is a concept that evolved as part of the reform of mental health services that has occurred in Western countries over recent decades. A recovery approach has subsequently become an integral component of mental health clinical practice (Slade 2013). Recovery for the client refers to living well with a chronic illness or disability. It may include learning about the condition and what triggers episodes, and making lifestyle changes. In this model the client is viewed as the expert about their own condition. For health professionals it means not only working with clients to manage the symptoms of health problems but also to work in collaboration with clients to manage a life lived well despite illness or disability. The approach acknowledges that lifestyle and the social context of people's lives can positively or negatively influence the course of the ongoing illness. Hence, a recovery approach encompasses more than merely treating or managing the symptoms of the illness. It also includes recognition of and attention to social, economic and political aspects of people's lives. In a recovery-focused model of care, health professionals and clients work together in partnership to maximise the quality of life for the person living with the ongoing illness (see also Chapter 12).

While, to date, the recovery model has mainly focused on minimising the disability from mental illness and to enable people with mental illness to live a fulfilling life despite their condition, the approach does have wider applicability for people who live with other chronic illnesses and for those health professionals who work with people living with a chronic illness or disability. An example of a recovery-focused tertiary intervention that has a broad application is the Flinders Program of chronic disease self-management developed by health professionals and researchers at Flinders University, Adelaide. The model is underpinned by cognitive behavioural therapy principles. It uses a partnership approach in which health professionals and clients collaborate on problem identification, goal setting and developing an individualised care plan. The model has proved to be effective in facilitating self-management among people with chronic health conditions and improves health-related behaviour and health outcomes (Battersby et al. 2013).

In summary, health promotion can be implemented at the primary, secondary or tertiary level to target individual, community or population health needs. Secondary and tertiary approaches are effective in diagnosing, treating and managing illness. However, as McKinlay's (1974) primary health care metaphor tells us, responding to health problems with a treatment response will deal with the symptoms but not necessarily the cause of the health problem. Therefore, to address the cause of a health problem, it is evident that primary intervention, alongside treatment and recovery models, is required. Table 13.3 summarises the health promotion levels of intervention using real-life examples.

Student activity

Mental health is core to health and wellbeing. However, it is often noted that mental health programs and services focus on treatment while prevention programs and services remain scarce. Consider this issue and list some reasons for this. Now that you know of the social determinants of health and upstream thinking, consider how a more preventative focus for mental health could occur within our communities.

Table 13.3

ADDRESSING POOR NUTRITION TO PROMOTE HEART HEALTH

Upstream	Midstream	Downstream
Policy change to improve nutritional value of food (similar to tobacco legislation)	Workplace weight-reduction programs and education	Dietary education to assist individuals to eat healthy food
Tax unhealthy foods	Improve access to healthy foods by offering healthy options in workplaces and school canteens	Shopping advice for choosing healthy food

Health promotion approaches are delivered through interdisciplinary and intersectoral activities that are influenced and driven by the underlying values, theories and research findings of the relevant discipline. Interventions, therefore, vary enormously depending on the disciplinary approach and whether the interventions target individuals, communities or whole populations. Biomedical approaches, for example, identify causative factors within the individual and their environment to prevent illness (e.g. clean water supply and immunisation) or early identification and intervention (health screening). Psychological theories of behaviour change, as discussed in Chapter 7, are used in health education and counselling approaches to assist people to engage in behaviours that contribute to a healthy lifestyle. A social determinants approach incorporates primary health care values and practices, is underpinned by social justice principles and aims to reduce health inequities and thereby improve the health of a population and its members.

SOCIAL DETERMINANTS / HEALTH INEQUITIES APPROACH

As discussed above and in Chapter 6, social determinants refer to a range of factors that have an impact on health. These include education, employment, housing and access to services. A social determinants approach to health promotion addresses health inequities and is, therefore, underpinned by the principles and values of social justice, equity and respect for the rights of others. There is recognition that drivers outside the health arena influence health outcomes and a commitment to working in partnership with individuals and communities. The WHO Commission on the Social Determinants of Health report advocated strongly for a social justice approach to health that includes recognising and addressing health inequities. This has been actioned by WHO, first through establishing Millennium Development Goals, and followed by the United Nations in developing the Sustainable Development Goals, which recognise that ending poverty and other deprivations must go hand-in-hand with strategies that improve health and education, reduce inequality and spur economic growth—all while tackling climate change and working to preserve our oceans and forests (United Nations 2022).

The United States strategy 'Healthy People 2020' (Office of Disease Prevention and Health Promotion n.d.) embraces this approach as they work towards their goal of Healthy People 2030. This is being achieved by two key approaches:

- developing objectives that address the relationship between health status and biology, individual behaviour, health services, social factors and policies
- emphasising an ecological approach to disease prevention and health promotion (an ecological approach focuses on both individual-level and population-level determinants of health and interventions).

POPULATION HEALTH PROMOTION APPROACHES

Population refers to a group of people who are bound by a common theme. This may be ethnicity, culture, geographic location, workplace or demographic characteristics like age, gender or socioeconomic status. Disparities in health exist between different populations, so the goal of a population approach to health promotion is to reduce difference in health status and to reduce inequities and improve the health of the whole population. This approach developed following the growing awareness that factors outside an individual's control, and drivers outside the health arena, influence health outcomes. Consequently, models and approaches to health promotion shifted from being individual- to population-focused.

Population-focused approaches target the whole of the population through: interventions that target individual behaviour (e.g. through health information social marketing campaigns); structural mechanisms and macroeconomic policies (e.g. through public housing or tobacco taxation); or interventions that address the causes of poor health (e.g. healthy eating initiatives). Population approaches aim to improve the health of members of the group by facilitating protective factors and reducing risk factors by addressing health inequities.

Populations in Australia, for example, that have been identified as experiencing the greatest health inequities and therefore the greatest need for intervention include Indigenous peoples; newly arrived migrants and refugees; people living with disabilities; people from low socioeconomic backgrounds; people living in rural and remote areas; and people living with mental illness (AIHW 2018; Murray et al. 2021).

SETTINGS FOR HEALTH PROMOTION

A **settings approach** to health promotion was advocated in the Jakarta Declaration as the 'organisational base of the infrastructure required for health promotion' (WHO 1997). It is based on the structures and ways of working within settings as a basis to integrate health promotion. Settings such as schools provide policy structures, environments, learning opportunities and access to the wider community.

A settings approach to health promotion facilitates the nurturing of human and social capital. It is based around where people spend their time and the systems and structures that they are part of where they live, where they work, where they play and where they learn. Bauer (2022) also reminds us that these are places where people thrive.

Health promotion settings: schools

WHO has a vision for every school to be a health-promoting school. As we learned earlier, this means the most health-enhancing and health-enabling school, across the broadest view of health and its determinants. The Health Promoting Schools program strives to develop the capacity of schools as a healthy setting for living, learning and working, with a focus on: caring for oneself and others; making healthy decisions and taking control over life's circumstances; creating conditions that are conducive to health (through policies, services, physical/social conditions); building capacities for peace, shelter, education, food, income, a stable ecosystem, equity, social justice and sustainable development; preventing leading causes of death, disease and disability (e.g. helminths [worms], tobacco use, HIV/AIDS/STIs, sedentary lifestyle, drugs and alcohol, violence/injuries and unhealthy nutrition); and influencing health-related behaviours (e.g. knowledge, beliefs, skills, attitudes, values and support). To enable this, WHO (2022a) provides 13 levers for action:

1. Multistakeholder coordination
2. Develop or update policy
3. Strengthen school leadership and governance
4. Allocate resources

5. Use evidence-informed practices

6. Strengthen school and community partnerships

7. Invest in school infrastructure

8. Develop the curriculum and associated resources and ensure implementation

9. Ensure access to teacher training and professional learning

10. Ensure access to comprehensive school health services

11. Involve students

12. Involve parents, caregivers and the local community

13. Monitor and evaluate.

Health promotion settings: workplace

The principle or levers for action for Health Promoting Schools can equally be adapted to create health-promoting workplaces. Like other settings, workplaces provide a structure and processes in which health-promoting actions can be integrated, continuing towards health-promoting places.

The Ottawa Charter for Health Promotion states that work has 'a significant impact on health' and can be 'a source of health for people' because 'the way society organizes work should help create a healthy society' (WHO 1986, p. 2). Yet, despite this social framework for action provided by the Charter, workplace health promotion has concentrated more on programs that aim to bring about individual behaviour change for healthy lifestyles, or the screening of 'at-risk' populations—that is, illness prevention, rather than promoting health and wellbeing. Robroek and colleagues (2021) note that many workplace health promotion initiatives have shown little effect and so call for programs that focus on the determinants of health rather than 'intervention' and 'campaigns' that are tacked onto the daily activities of workers. The authors also note the need for strong evaluation of workplace health promotion initiatives and inclusion of lower socioeconomic workforces given clear links to inequity and disparity of health outcomes.

Also, despite the introduction of legislation and workplace policies, structural changes have been unsuccessful in bringing about environmental modification, which fosters mental wellbeing. Bullying continues to be endemic in work settings, recognised as an 'international plight that transcends geographic and cultural boundaries. Its pervasiveness in all environments is reflected in the research literature that documents the problem in both the private and public sectors' (Busby et al. 2022, p. 1).

Nevertheless, while mental health promotion is appealing, there are challenges to implementing it in the workplace. These include difficulties in demonstrating the efficacy of interventions and competition for the health dollar. Also, entrenched institutional structures may work against change when institutions have an investment in maintaining the status quo or fear the uncertainty of change.

Social network and technologies approaches

In recent years, health education and health promotion has embraced social network technologies like Twitter and Facebook to increase the effectiveness and reach of public health initiatives. Simple examples include SMS messages sent out by health departments during a heatwave to encourage people to stay hydrated.

More sophisticated examples include Facebook pages that provide support and information about particular health issues. The appeal of social networking is the ease of access to information and the potential to provide education and immediate support to users. However, research conducted by Balatsoukas and colleagues (2015) found that using social media as a single strategy might not be sufficient to bring about health behaviour changes or sustained engagement in health promotion activities. Also, the researchers suggest that these technologies have the potential to provide inaccurate or misleading information, which may actually cause harm. Therefore, they conclude that further studies are required to determine if social networking is an effective strategy and/or how best to use these technologies in health promotion.

HEALTH EDUCATION: A POPULATION APPROACH

Australia has the highest rate of skin cancer in the world, mostly caused by overexposure to ultraviolet (UV) radiation. By the age of 70 years, two out of three Australians will be diagnosed with skin cancer (SunSmart Victoria 2018). In 1981, in response to the alarming incidence of skin cancer in the population, Australia introduced a social marketing health campaign titled 'Slip! Slop! Slap!', which was led by a seagull named Sid. Australians were encouraged to 'slip on a shirt, slop on sunscreen and slap on a hat' before venturing outdoors to prevent sunburn and skin cancer. The campaign included print and television media advertisements, a jingle, education resources for school teachers and visits by the mascot, Sid Seagull, to schools and public events. A similar campaign was undertaken in New Zealand where the mascot was a lobster (SunSmart New Zealand 2018). In subsequent years, seeking shade and wearing sunglasses were added to the health message and people are now encouraged to 'Slip, Slop, Slap, Seek [shade] and Slide [on sunglasses]'.

Following this public health campaign, the incidence of basal cell carcinoma and squamous cell carcinoma, the most common forms of skin cancer, were reduced. However, the incidence of melanoma, which is the most fatal form of skin cancer, was not affected. This is most likely because the use of sunscreen does not prevent the development of melanoma, whereas sunscreen prevents basal cell carcinomas and squamous cell carcinomas by preventing sunburn (Planta 2011). It is therefore a false confidence for a person to believe that applying sunscreen will provide protection against all forms of skin cancer.

Furthermore, despite the overall decrease in skin cancer rates, another health issue related to reduced sun exposure has arisen. Vitamin D deficiency is now a global pandemic (Holick 2017). It predisposes individuals to increased risk of bone fractures, particularly in later life, and has been observed in some sections of the population, especially the elderly, people with dark skin and people who cover their body in clothing for religious or cultural reasons. The deficiency is linked to insufficient sun exposure because sunlight is the major source of vitamin D (Holick 2017). In this case, the prevention of one health problem may predispose a person to another.

These findings highlight the importance of evaluating health promotion interventions to ascertain that the intervention has the required outcome, and that other unwanted effects do not occur. Even interventions that have intuitive appeal and can show positive health outcomes (e.g. the SunSmart campaign) may not be effective for all people or all forms of skin cancer. And for some population groups, like the elderly, the intervention may have other unwanted side effects (e.g. reducing uptake of vitamin D).

Finally, considering the inconclusive results from health education initiatives to promote health, research suggests that for health education to be effective it must move beyond the advice-giving–knowledge-transfer–symptom-control model to one of empowerment that is inherent in a social determinants approach.

Student activity

1. In small groups, make a list of common health education messages such as quit smoking, and slip, slop, slap, seek and slide.
2. Discuss the following in pairs.
   » What impact do such messages have on you?
   » Have you ever changed a health behaviour in response to a health education message?
3. In small groups, discuss whether you think such messages influence people in general. Why or why not?
   » What are some of the underlying assumptions of health education?
   » In what circumstances might health education have a negative impact?

Evidence for health promotion

There is now a growing and convincing body of evidence that shows that the health of individuals, communities and populations is influenced by a broad range of factors, many of which are outside the health sector. Research findings also show that social and economic factors have more influence on health outcomes than lifestyle or health care. The evidence on effectively using health promotion to improve population health is also strong. A recent review by Howse and colleagues (2021) showed the value of prevention across four risk factors in an Australian context. These risk factors were overweight and obesity; an unhealthy diet; physical inactivity; and use of tobacco. The review found that tobacco represented the highest burden on disease, yet the four risk factors combined cause tens of thousands of premature deaths every year in Australia and what the researchers referred to as 'years lived in poor health'. The team also identified that multicomponent approaches to health promotion were most effective including at the systems and setting levels. They also noted that the cost-benefits were high. Some strategies also had co-benefits; for example, strategies to improve the built environment may have benefit for physical activity, social connection and mental health (Howse et al. 2021).

One of these specific interventions—reduction of tobacco smoking—will now be examined.

EVIDENCE FOR HEALTH PROMOTION: TOBACCO SMOKING

Tobacco smoking is the leading preventable cause of death and disease in Australia and a leading risk factor for many chronic diseases (AIHW 2020c). Although daily smoking rates have declined to just over 11% of the population (compared with 25% in 1991), smoking remains a serious public health issue despite the success of health promotion approaches (AIHW 2020c). Illnesses for which smoking is a major risk factor include cancer, respiratory disease and coronary heart disease. Since the 1980s, public health programs with a whole-of-population focus have targeted tobacco smoking cessation and successfully reduced smoking rates in developed countries (Greenhalgh et al. 2022).

This outcome has been achieved by not just one strategy but several interventions interacting together to achieve the reduction in the percentage of the population who smoke tobacco. Health promotion strategies to reduce tobacco smoking have included a range of activities such as increased taxation, restriction of advertising, health education in schools, social marketing in the mass media that uses both education and fear appeal principles (graphic images on tobacco products), legislation (the banning of smoking in public places) and access to 'quit' programs and other supports for smokers who wish to give it up. In summary, several Ottawa Charter strategies have been used concurrently to reduce smoking.

Research focus

Source: Blackford et al. 2016

ABSTRACT

The presence of metabolic syndrome (MetS) increases the risk of developing type 2 diabetes and cardiovascular disease. Targeted interventions to reduce MetS for high-risk populations are crucial for preventing these chronic diseases.

This study evaluated the effectiveness of a 6-month home-based physical activity and diet intervention for rural adults with, or at risk of, MetS. The randomised controlled trial was conducted in Albany and surrounding towns in Western Australia over 2014–2015. Participants were screened for MetS using the International Diabetes Federation criteria, and eligible participants were randomly assigned to the intervention ($n = 201$) or control ($n = 200$) group.

The intervention group received printed and online program materials and motivational support, and the control group was waitlisted to receive the program after post-test data collection. Anthropometry, lipid profiles, glycaemic status and blood pressure were measured at baseline and 6-months post-test. In total, 312 (77.8%) participants completed post-test data collection and were included in the anthropometric analysis, and 274 (68.3%) participants were included in the blood sample analysis.

After controlling for confounders, the intervention group significantly improved their triglyceride (-0.10 mM, $p = 0.002$), total cholesterol

Cont... ▶

$(-0.09$ mM, $p = 0.02$) and non-HDL cholesterol (-0.08 mM, $p = 0.02$) concentrations compared with the control group. Waist circumference (-2.11 cm, $p = 0.03$), waist-to-hip ratio (-0.01, $p = 0.04$), weight (-0.70 kg, $p = 0.01$) and body mass index (-0.20 kg/m^2, $p < 0.001$) also improved.

These findings suggest that comprehensive home-based prevention programs that include a combination of dietary and physical activity interventions are a promising means to prevent the onset of chronic disease in rural adults.

Critical thinking

- Identify other health problems to which population-focused health promotion could be applied.
- Suggest strategies that could be implemented to address these problems.

Population approach: healthy cities

Healthy Cities is a global movement that originated out of the WHO European office, with the aim of implementing the Ottawa Charter at the city level. There are now Healthy Cities in the six WHO regions, namely, Africa, East Mediterranean, Europe, the Americas, South-East Asia and the Western Pacific. The movement encourages local governments to engage in health development through political commitment, institutional change, capacity building, partnership-based planning and innovative projects. Projects strive to be broad-based, intersectoral, ecological and political. They are innovative and encourage community participation.

Healthy Cities promotes an approach to policy and planning that is comprehensive and systematic and emphasises the importance of addressing health inequalities and urban poverty (the needs of vulnerable groups). Its approach encourages participatory governance and takes account of the social, economic and environmental determinants of health. Healthy Cities also strives to put health issues on the agenda regarding economic policy and urban development efforts such as establishing dedicated bikeways to improve safety for cyclists and to facilitate community members' engagement in physical activity.

Student activity

In recent years the concept of an age-friendly city has been developed in response to the world's ageing population needs and the need to create environments that support healthy ageing. Search for some examples of healthy ageing in your country. Map these against the elements of the Ottawa Charter.

- Which elements of the Ottawa Charter are prominent in healthy ageing initiatives?

Cont... ▶

- How could healthy ageing initiatives be better integrated into policy?
- Think about the social determinants of health—how can access and equity be considered in healthy ageing approaches as part of a Healthy Cities framework?

Challenges of a health promotion approach

Despite health promotion having intuitive appeal to policymakers, health professionals and laypeople (as evidenced by colloquial sayings like 'prevention is better than cure'), and research findings that show the effectiveness of health promotion, there are still challenges in the implementation and effectiveness of health-promoting initiatives. These include blaming individuals for lifestyle and health outcomes and issues in translating research findings into healthcare practice.

Strategies that target people's health behaviour, such as health education and social marketing, have the potential to lead to 'victim blaming' should the person not alter their behaviour after the intervention. Attributing responsibility for the health problem solely to the individual overlooks the social and external forces that also contribute to the continuation of the behaviour and stigmatises the person whose health problems are deemed to be their own fault. Furthermore, making the person responsible for their own health may absolve the state and health services of responsibility in addressing the health issue or the social and political factors that contribute to it.

Population approaches, too, can be problematic. The lead time for demonstrating the effectiveness of population-focused interventions is long and complex—often many years or even decades. Given that decisions about health funding allocation are made in a political environment in which the term of the governing political party that allocates the funding is only 3–5 years, funding decisions may consequently be made that favour initiatives that deliver shorter term outcomes, and these tend to focus on treatment rather than on prevention or promotion.

A further issue with the long lead time to demonstrate effectiveness is the range and complexity of intervening factors that may contribute to the health outcome. The breadth of contributing factors poses a challenge in deciding which factors should be addressed and which factors will or will not receive funding. Moreover, the allocation of funding may be made on the magnitude of community demand, which may only be the most vocal need rather than the most pressing one.

CASE STUDY: HEALTH FUNDING

Southwood is a fictional suburb located on the outskirts of a major city. For several years a community group has lobbied the health minister seeking an intensive care unit at the local hospital, despite such facilities being available at

Cont... ▸

a university teaching hospital approximately 15 kilometres away. Meanwhile, in the same community, there is a shortage of supported accommodation for people with schizophrenia. The minister is aware of this housing shortage and of a report that identifies suitable housing as an important component for recovery following a psychotic illness; however, no formal requests have been received at the electoral office to fund supported accommodation for people with mental illness.

Critical thinking

- Imagine funding was available to fund only one of these initiatives. Which initiative would you choose, and why?
- What are the social justice implications for the initiative you did not select for funding?
- If there was to be an election in 6 months, which initiative do you think the minister would select and why?
- What are the social justice implications for the initiative you predicted that the minister would *not* select?

Chapter summary

Health and health outcomes are influenced by a range of factors that are located both within the person and within the contexts and environments in which people live. In this chapter, health promotion was presented as an interdisciplinary field of endeavour that seeks to influence health outcomes by facilitating wellbeing, preventing illness and fostering recovery for individuals and communities, and to thereby enable people to take control of and to improve their health and quality of life. Values that underpin a social determinants approach to health promotion, such as social justice and health equity, were also identified, as were strategies for primary, secondary and tertiary intervention.

The contribution made by psychology and other disciplines was highlighted and the effectiveness of interdisciplinary and intersectoral interventions was emphasised. Finally, contemporary health promotion was located within a social justice and equity framework that sees 'health for all', as articulated in the Ottawa Charter for Health Promotion (WHO 1986), as a basic human right.

KEY POINTS

- Health promotion is the process of enabling people to take control of and improve their health.

- The purpose of health promotion is to facilitate wellbeing and improve quality of life.
- Health promotion originated from psychological models of behaviour change and health education in the latter half of the 20th century.
- Contemporary health promotion has shifted from an exclusively individual focus to also address social determinants of health and a focus on populations and social equity.
- Effective health promotion requires input from within and outside the health sector.

Further reading

Australian Institute of Health and Welfare, 2022. Australia's Health 2020, Commonwealth of Australia, Canberra. Available: www.aihw.gov.au/reports-data/australias-health.

Department of Health, 2021. National Preventive Health Strategy 2021–2030, Commonwealth of Australia, Canberra. Available: https://www.health.gov.au/resources/publications/national-preventive-health-strategy-2021-2030.

Weblinks

Australian Health Promotion Association

www.healthpromotion.org.au

The Australian Health Promotion Association's aim is to provide knowledge, resources and perspectives to improve health promotion research and practice.

International Union for Health Promotion and Education

www.iuhpe.org/index.php/en/

The International Union for Health Promotion and Education aims to support everyone committed to advancing health promotion and achieving equity in health globally. The website contains information about health promotion research, publications and conferences.

Public Health Association of Australia

https://www.phaa.net.au/

As the leading national peak body for public health representation and advocacy, PHAA aims to drive better health outcomes through increased knowledge, better access and equity, evidence-informed policy and effective population-based practice in public health.

Runanga Whakapiki Ake I Te Hauora O Aotearoa / Health Promotion Forum of New Zealand

https://hauora.co.nz

The Runanga Whakapiki Ake I Te Hauora O Aotearoa / Health Promotion Forum of New Zealand is the national umbrella organisation for health promotion in New Zealand. The forum's mission is 'Hauora—everyone's right—our commitment'.

References

Adhikari, B., 2021. History of health promotion in global context. Available: https://publichealthglobe.com/history-of-health-promotion-in-global-contexthistorical-development-of-health-promotion/ Accessed 1 July 2022

Australian Institute of Health and Welfare (AIHW), 2018. Australia's health 2018. Available: https://www.aihw.gov.au/reports/australias-health/australias-health-2018-in-brief/contents/about Accessed 1 July 2022

Australian Institute of Health and Welfare (AIHW), 2019. Risk Factors. Available: https://www.aihw.gov.au/reports-data/behaviours-risk-factors/risk-factors/overview Accessed 1 July 2022

Australian Institute of Health and Welfare (AIHW), 2020a. Health Promotion Available: https://www.aihw.gov.au/reports/australias-health/health-promotion Accessed 1 July 2022

Australian Institute of Health and Welfare (AIHW), 2020b. Social determinants of health. Available: https://www.aihw.gov.au/reports/australias-health/social-determinants-of-health Accessed 1 July 2022

Australian Institute of Health and Welfare (AIHW), 2020c. Tobacco Smoking snapshot. Available: https://www.aihw.gov.au/reports/australias-health/tobacco-smoking Accessed 1 July 2022

Australian Institute of Health and Welfare (AIHW), 2021. Regional Insights for Indigenous Communities. Available: https://www.rific.gov.au Accessed 1 July 2022

Backholer, K., Baum, F., Finlay, S., et al. 2021. Australia in 2030: what is our path to health for all? Medical Journal of Australia, 214 (8 Suppl), S1–S40.

Balatsoukas, P., Kennedy, C.M., Buchan, I., et al. 2015. The role of social network technologies in online health promotion: a narrative review of theoretical and empirical factors influencing intervention effectiveness. Journal of Medical Internet Research, 17(6), e141.

Baldwin, L., 2020. Planning and implementing health promotion programs in Fleming ML and Baldwin L (eds) Health promotion in the 21st century: new approaches to achieving health for all. Sydney: Allen and Unwin.

Barry, M., 2022. Foreword. In: Mittelmark, MB, Bauer, GF, Vaandrager, L, et al. (2022) The Handbook of Salutogensis, 2nd edn. Cham (CH): Springer.

Battersby, M., Beattie, J., Pols, R., et al., 2013. A randomized control trial of the Flinders Program in Vietnam veterans with co-morbid alcohol misuse, and psychiatric and medical conditions. Australian and New Zealand Journal of Psychiatry 47 (5), 451–462.

Bauer, G.F., 2022. Salutogenesis in health promoting settings: a synthesis across organizations, communities, and environments. In: Mittelmark, M.B., Bauer, G.F., Vaandrager, L., et al. The Handbook of Salutogenesis, 2nd edn. Springer, Cham.

Blackford, K., Jancey, J., Lee, A., et al. 2016. Home-based lifestyle intervention for rural adults improves metabolic syndrome parameters and cardiovascular risk factors: a randomized control trial. Preventive Medicine 89, 15–22.

Budreviciute, A., Damiati, S., Sabir, D.K., et al. 2020. Management and prevention strategies for non-communicable diseases (NCDs) and their risk factors. Frontiers in Public Health (8), 574111

Busby, L., Patrick, L., Gaudine, A., 2022. Upwards workplace bullying: a literature review. SAGE Open, 12(1).

Finlay, S.M., Canuto, K., Canuto, K., et al., 2021. Aboriginal and Torres Strait Islander connection to culture: building stronger individual and collective wellbeing. Medical Journal of Australia 214 (8 Suppl): S12–S16.

Greenhalgh, E.M., Scollo, M.M., Winstanley, M.H., 2022. Tobacco in Australia: Facts and Issues. Melbourne: Cancer Council Victoria.

Guthold, R., Stevens, G.A., Riley, L.M., et al. 2018. Worldwide trends in insufficient physical activity from 2001 to 2016: a pooled analysis of 358 population-based surveys with 1·9 million participants. Lancet Global Health, 6 (10), e1077–e1086.

Health Promotion Forum of New Zealand – Runanga Whakapiki Ake I Te Hauora O Aotearoa, 2018. Available: https://hauora.co.nz. Accessed 1 July 2022.

Holick, M., 2017. The vitamin D pandemic: approaches for diagnosis, treatment and prevention. Reviews in Endocrine and Metabolic Disorders 18 (2), 153–165.

Howse, E., Crosland, P., Rychetnik, L., et al. 2021. The value of prevention: An Evidence Check rapid review brokered by the Sax Institute for the Centre for Population Health, NSW Ministry of Health. Sydney: The Australian Prevention Partnership Centre.

James, T., 2020. What is upstream healthcare? Available: https://healthcity.bmc.org/population-health/upstream-healthcare-sdoh-root-causes Accessed 1 July 2022

Kisling, L.A., Das, J.M., 2021. Prevention Strategies. StatPearls Publishing, Treasure Island, FL. Available: https://www.ncbi.nlm.nih.gov/books/NBK537222/ Accessed 1 July 2022

Marthias, T., Anindya, K., Ng, N., et al. 2021. Impact of non-communicable disease multimorbidity on health service use, catastrophic health expenditure and productivity loss in Indonesia: a population-based panel data analysis study. BMJ Open, 11 (2), e041870.

McKay, F.H., Taket, A.R., 2020. Health equity, social justice and human rights. 2nd edn. New York: Routledge.

McKinlay, J., 1974. A Case for Refocusing Upstream: The Political Economy of Illness. Applying Behavioural Science to Cardiovascular Risk. American Heart Association, Washington.

McMahon, N.E., 2021. Working 'upstream' to reduce social inequalities in health: a qualitative study of how partners in an applied health research collaboration interpret the metaphor, Critical Public Health, 32 (5), 654–664.

Mentis, A.F.A., Dardiotis, E., Efthymiou, V. et al. 2021. Non-genetic risk and protective factors and biomarkers for neurological disorders: a meta-umbrella systematic review of umbrella reviews. BMC Medicine 19, 6.

Mittelmark, M.B., Bauer, G.F.,Vaandrager, L., et al. 2022. The Handbook of Salutogensis, 2nd edn. Cham (CH): Springer.

Murray, K., Khawaja, N., Schweitzer, R., et al. 2021. Provider perspectives on services for people seeking asylum in Australia: best practices and challenges. Australian Psychologist, 56 (4), 289–298.

Nutbeam, D., Muscat, D., 2021, Health Promotion Glossary, Health Promotion International, 36 (6), 1578–1598.

O'Donnell, M., 2009. Definition of health promotion 2.0: embracing passion, enhancing motivation, recognizing dynamic balance, and creating opportunities. American Journal of Health Promotion 24 (1), iv.

Office of Disease Prevention and Health Promotion, n.d. Healthy People 2020. Available: https://health.gov/our-work/national-health-initiatives/healthy-people/healthy-people-2020 Accessed 1 July 2022

Planta, M., 2011. Sunscreen and melanoma: is our prevention message correct. Journal of American Board of Family Medicine 24 (6), 735–739.

Robroek, S.J., Coenen, P., Oude Hengel, K.M., 2021. Decades of workplace health promotion research marginal gains or a bright future ahead. Scandinavian Journal of Work, Environment & Health, 47 (8), 561–564.

Slade, M., 2013. 100 ways to support recovery: a guide for mental health professionals. Second edition. Rethink Mental Illness, London. Available: www.rethink.org/media/704895/100_ways_to_support_recovery_2nd_edition.pdf. Accessed 1 July 2022

SunSmart New Zealand, 2018. SunSmart. Available: www.sunsmart.org.nz Accessed 1 July 2022

SunSmart Victoria, 2018. Sun protection. Available: www.sunsmart.com.au Accessed 1 July 2022

Thompson, S., Watson, M., Tilford, S., 2017. The Ottawa Charter 30 years on: still an important standard for health promotion. International Journal of Health Promotion and Education 56 (2), 73–84.

Traina, G., Martinussen, P.E., Feiring, E., 2019. Being healthy, being sick, being responsible: attitudes towards responsibility for health in a public healthcare system. Public Health Ethics, 12 (2), 145–157.

United Nations, 2022. Sustainable Development – the 17 Goals. Available: https://sdgs.un.org/goals Accessed 1 July 2022

VicHealth, 2018. Health equity: health inequalities and health inequities. Available: www.vichealth.vic.gov.au/our-work/health-equity-health-inequalities-health-inequities. Accessed 1 July 2022

Wilson, A.M., Kelly, J., Jones, M. et al. 2020. Working together in Aboriginal health: a framework to guide health professional practice. BMC Health Services Research, 20, 601.

World Health Organization, 1986. The Ottawa Charter for Health Promotion. WHO, Geneva.

World Health Organization, 1997. The Jakarta Declaration on Leading Health Promotion Into the 21st Century. WHO, Geneva.

World Health Organization (WHO) 2022a. Health promoting schools. Available: https://www.who.int/health-topics/health-promoting-schools#tab=tab_1 (Accessed 1 July 2022).

World Health Organization (WHO) 2022b. Health Promotion. Available: https://www.who.int/teams/health-promotion/enhanced-wellbeing/first-global-conference/actions Accessed 1 July 2022

World Health Organization (WHO) 2022c. Social determinants. Available: https://www.who.int/health-topics/social-determinants-of-health#tab=tab_1 Accessed 1 July 2022

Section 3
Application of psychology in healthcare practice

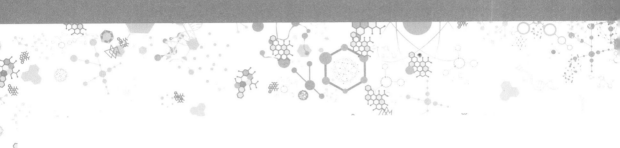

Chapter 14
Psychology in practice

DEB O'KANE

 Nursing

Themes

Health belief model | Mental health | Nexus of mental and physical health

Scenario

Rachel is a woman in her early 20s who has been referred to you as a general practice mental health nurse for counselling because, although she is very bright and excelled at school, subsequently gaining a place at university in health sciences, she dropped out without attending a class and lost her part-time job because she was 'too tired to go'. A year ago, she took an overdose of paracetamol but was found in time and taken to hospital. During the admission doctors discovered that Rachel had low thyroid function and very low blood pressure. She commenced thyroxine 0.50 mg in the morning, but her GP has become concerned with Rachel 'missing' medication doses and when she is asked about this, says 'I don't believe taking the medication is necessary'. Rachel now describes herself as 'more depressed', saying 'I'm too tired to bother with this'.

Questions

1. Which behaviour change model may best explain the circumstances in the case study? Give a rationale for your answer.
2. What techniques may be useful to facilitate behaviour change to motivate Rachel in taking her medication as prescribed?
3. The nexus of mental and physical health is well established in the literature. How can nurses and other health professionals best inform themselves about these links to address a person's needs from a biopsychosocial perspective?

Nursing—clinical scenario 2

Themes

End-of-life care | Advanced care directives | Dementia

Scenario

As part of your role as a specialist dementia nurse you have regular appointments with Sue, an 80-year-old woman who was diagnosed with dementia 2 years ago. The dementia has been slowly progressing and although she is still cognisant and can have conversations about her life, health and family most of the time, she has become concerned that things are changing. Sue wants to organise her advance care directives, including her funeral and end-of-life medical care with a clear indication that no heroic measures be taken should she become ill. Sue says she wants her wishes to be honoured and does not want to leave the decision to her husband, Stan, when the time arrives. Stan is also 80 and refuses to discuss this with her, saying: 'If we discuss this, it will make it real and it's not. There is nothing wrong with you. The doctors don't know anything.'

Questions

1. What grief-related factors may be influencing Stan's unwillingness to discuss his wife's advance care directives? Give a rationale for your answer.
2. Anticipatory grief can be a source of significant long-term stress where a loved one is suffering from a chronic and enduring illness or dying. In what ways can health professionals assist someone with managing these feelings?
3. What role do advance care directives play in end-of-life care? Why would health professionals need to understand these directives?

Nursing—clinical scenario 3

Themes

Attachment disorders | Parenting | Hospitalisation of infants

Scenario

Skylar is a 2-year-old girl who was born prematurely at 28 weeks weighing 1200 g. She has been admitted to the paediatric ward today with a respiratory infection. Skylar was brought to hospital by foster carers Shannon and Joe, who have had Skylar in their care for 3 months. They appear to be loving foster parents, though they do report being overwhelmed by Skylar's need 'for affection and attention all the time'. Skylar was initially discharged from the neonatal intensive care ward at 3 months old (corrected birth date) in apparent good health, having emerged from her premature delivery in 'apparent good health' to her biological mother and father's care. At

Cont... ▶

4 months old, Skylar's mother voluntarily relinquished her care to the father. Skylar's mother hasn't seen Skylar since that time, and her whereabouts are currently unknown. At the age of 6 months, Skylar was removed from her father's care due to serious neglect. Skylar's father visited her monthly for the first year she was in foster care, completing parenting classes as well as drug and alcohol rehabilitation, and appeared to be engaging well with a return-to-home plan. For the past 4 months, however, her father has seen her only once. Her father now says 'she is better off in care' and has declined to be involved. Skylar has been diagnosed with a disinhibited social engagement disorder, specifically showing indiscriminate attachment to 'any' male she encounters. In your role as a paediatric nurse, you and other staff notice that Skylar does not appear distressed by her carers leaving the ward and shows no emotional reactions to the insertion of an intravenous cannula or other interventions.

Questions

Use the information on attachment theories to answer the following questions.

1. What factors may have contributed to this outcome for Skylar? Provide a rationale for your answer.
2. What are the possible flaws in using theories of attachment? You may need to expand your reading to explore the criticisms of attachment theories.
3. What are the possible limitations of attachment theory in relation to cultural practices of child rearing?
4. What actions can health professionals take to reduce the likelihood of separation issues for children in hospital?
5. How can nurses support children and their families to ensure a thriving, healthy development in mental, emotional and social adjustment developmental tasks while in hospital?

Nursing—clinical scenario 4

Themes

Adolescent behaviour and the effects of bullying in schools | Indigenous health | Identity development in adolescents

Scenario

As the nurse educator in a local endocrinology and diabetes outpatient clinic, you see Jon on a regular basis to help him manage his type 2 diabetes. Jon is a 15-year-old Indigenous boy who stopped going to school 3 months ago. He now refuses to return due to bullying by a group of teenagers at his school. Prior to him refusing to go to school, his grades had been falling and he had not engaged with the youth and diabetes program at the outpatient clinic. His last three visits to the clinic have revealed rising blood glucose levels and increased weight gain. Jon has also been refusing to manage his medications for his diabetes.

Cont... ▶

At today's consultation, you decide to talk with Jon about the events of the past 3 months and provide further education about the importance of managing his diabetes. Jon tells you he is feeling anxious whenever he leaves his room and 'feels weird' about the diabetes. Despite education on the importance of managing his diabetes, he continues to refuse to take his medication saying, 'I don't want to take it. I want to be like everyone else. I know what I'm doing. It's my life anyway.'

Questions

1. How might bullying affect Jon's identity formation and peer relationships?

2. What developmental explanations might there be for Jon's insistence on 'being just like anyone else' and declarations of 'it's my life anyway'? Give a rationale for your answer.

3. How might developmental approaches to managing chronic illness differ between adults and adolescents? Give a rationale for your answer.

4. How will you 'accommodate' your language and communication style when working with Jon and other young people? As a nurse, what skills will you require to develop a partnership between yourself and Jon?

Nursing—clinical scenario 5   (N)

Themes

Maternal and child health | Social determinants of health | Stress and coping

Scenario

Jules gave birth to a baby boy, Kane, 6 weeks ago. Jules's husband, Connell, had to return to his job as a *National Geographic* photographer and is now working away from home for the next 7 weeks, although he talks to Jules and the baby every night via Zoom. The baby had some early difficulties with mild respiratory distress due to a prolonged and difficult labour culminating in an emergency caesarean delivery. Jules had taken maternity leave from her career as a court stenographer and was very much looking forward to being at home with her baby.

You are a child and family health nurse and visit Jules at home today. Jules is usually very organised and welcomes these visits, but today she is reporting feeling 'stressed all the time' and that she 'just isn't coping' with Connell away. The house is in disarray, with baby clothes scattered about, dishes in the sink and baby toys on the floor, which is unusual for Jules. She says: 'I'm a very organised person. I managed an entire office of 25 people. I don't know why I can't manage one baby.'

Questions

1. Using the transactional model of stress and coping, discuss what may be occurring for Jules. Provide a rationale for your answers.

Cont... ▶

2. As a health professional, how would you discuss coping skills with Jules? What words would you use?
3. Identify and discuss Jules's strengths and resources and how they can be used in a healthcare plan.
4. Child and family health nurses perform regular 'well-baby checks' throughout the first year. Discuss why these visits are essential and what factors the nurse may assess.
5. Maternal and child health is a key health priority area in Indigenous Australian and New Zealand Māori groups. What social determinants of health may be affecting these communities? Explain your response.

Paramedics

Paramedics—clinical scenario 1

Themes

Personality and human behaviour | Stress

Scenario

Paramedics have been called late on a Friday night to a 16-year-old male, Corey, who has been in a fight with others at the park not far from the local pub. He is sitting with friends when the police arrive after being called by a local resident. After a brief talk to Corey and bystanders, the police decide to call an ambulance because they suspect that Corey lost consciousness during the fight and he appears to have a swollen and bruised face.

Corey is angry and flatly denies he started the fight, even though bystanders at the scene tell police and paramedics he was verbally abusive and physically threatening to others involved. Corey's friends tell paramedics they don't know what caused Corey to become so angry and that they held Corey and tried to prevent him getting into the fight but couldn't stop him.

Corey is reluctant to let paramedics check the injuries on his face and head. He insists that he is fine, saying 'just leave me alone'. Corey doesn't believe he lost consciousness and yells that it is 'everyone else's fault' and they were 'getting in my face and threatening me'.

Paramedics notice as they are trying to calm and talk to Corey that he has old cigarette burns on his upper arms and scars on his wrists. The

Cont... ▶

paramedics ask Corey in a gentle manner about the scars on his arms and wrists and about his home life, his support networks and family relationships. Corey immediately gets up and starts to walk away from the paramedics but stops when the police start to move towards him to prevent him leaving. He goes back and explains the scars were just a joke from a year ago and that he intends to get them covered with a tattoo when he has enough money.

Questions

1. What might be Corey's physiological response to the stress and situation he finds himself in?
2. Why might Corey be responding with increasing anger in this situation?
3. Explain Corey's actions using the flight or fight model of stress.
4. How might his behaviour affect his relationship with his friends, family or others that he comes across in his life?
5. How might you respond to Corey if you were the paramedic in this case?

Paramedics—clinical scenario 2

Themes

Lifespan development | Communication | Social and family context

Scenario

The ambulance has been called to a residential address at 7.30 am to a single-parent family with a 4-year-old girl called Jemma. Jemma's mother has called the ambulance because she heard Jemma cry out and was concerned that Jemma had hurt herself. As the paramedics enter the property, they notice an overgrown garden and broken toys on the path. The door is opened by Jemma's mother, who is dressed in a clean T-shirt and shorts and is holding Jemma, with a 6-month-old baby in the rocker in the lounge room.

The mother lets the paramedics into the house and explains that Jemma had a fall as she was climbing the little swing out in the backyard. The mother is worried that she has potentially broken her wrist.

Paramedics gain permission to check Jemma to see if she has any injuries. Jemma is being held by her mother, appears to be comfortable in her mother's arms and points to an old toy that is on the ground in the lounge room. The left arm looks swollen. One of the paramedics gently approaches and starts to play with Jemma while she is in her mother's arms and begins to talk to her. They notice she seems slow to speak and uses single words and gestures.

Cont... ▶

Questions

1. Discuss what immediate assumption/impressions on socioeconomic status and family supports might be made on entering the property.
2. Would initial impressions and assumptions change the way the paramedics communicate with the mother and Jemma? If so, how and why?
3. Discuss what stage of cognitive development you think Jemma is displaying and why.
4. Discuss what social and environmental factors might influence Jemma's development and why.
5. How might you communicate/interact with Jemma?

Paramedics—clinical scenario 3

Themes

Lifespan development middle and later years | The social, family and environmental influences on the health of older people

Scenario

Micky is an 81-year-old who lives independently at home. His wife of 53 years has been recently admitted to a residential aged care facility due to increasing care needs related to dementia. Micky has spent the past 5 years caring for his wife at home with the support of his son and his daughter-in-law and found placing his wife in care a very difficult decision. However, he acknowledges that it was the right thing to do because he was not able to cope with her increasing wandering, providing meals and assisting his wife with activities of daily living. He tries to visit his wife on a regular basis.

Paramedics were called this afternoon by Micky's son to assist after Micky had a fall in the backyard. Micky is sitting on the back step as paramedics arrive and is slightly dazed and bruised but with no obvious serious injuries or evidence of a cardiac event or head injury. The son is concerned because he feels his dad is struggling to manage independently, has lost his interest in life since his wife went into care, has appeared to lose weight recently and is not engaging with his friends and social circle.

Paramedics ask Micky and his son about his life and how he is coping, finding out that Micky was the regional tenpin bowling champion and has generally experienced good health throughout his life. Recently he has been ill with a chest infection and finds he has less energy than he used to and wants to 'just stay home more often'.

Cont... ▸

Questions

1. Consider Bronfenbrenner's model of human development and discuss what individual and microsystem (family and social/cultural groups) factors might be affecting Micky's ability to remain in his home and live independently.

2. Discuss what role the relationship between Micky and his son has on his wellbeing and the potential need for further health services.

3. What other health and support services might you discuss with Micky and his son?

4. How might social and cultural understandings of age and aged care affect how Micky feels about placing his wife into an aged care facility?

5. Discuss Micky's current resources (his personal resilience, health, skills, social and structural networks) and identify, where possible, conflict between what he wants and his current resources.

Paramedics—clinical scenario 4

Themes

Biomedical and biopsychosocial models of health

Scenario

Samantha is a 28-year-old female attended to by paramedics at a local café for severe anxiety and what appears to be a panic attack. Paramedics attending to Samantha record her pulse at 120 beats per minute (high), respiratory rate at 28 breaths per minute (hyperventilating), blood pressure at 125/85, noting she has a feeling of pins and needles in her hands and feet. She is speaking in short sentences and sitting at the table with a friend, with café staff providing support.

Samantha has suffered anxiety for the past 8 years since the loss of her younger brother from cancer when she was 20. She had support from her long-term partner and family and continues to regularly see her GP and psychologist when she feels the need. She tells the paramedics that, over the past 2–3 years, she has been able to manage her anxiety effectively but recently has been thinking about the loss of her brother and her fear that she will lose another family member or someone close to her. She describes the feeling as being totally helpless and unable to stop the continual thoughts and fear of being left alone.

Questions

1. Discuss the aspects of Samantha's presentation that would be related to the biomedical model of health.

2. Discuss the aspects of Samantha's presentation that would be related to the biopsychosocial model of health.

Cont... ▶

3. What does Samantha's story suggest or tell you about her locus of control, her resilience and her self-efficacy?

4. How might you use Samantha's own understanding and help-seeking behaviour to help reduce her anxiety?

Paramedics—clinical scenario 5

Themes

Social determinants of health

Scenario

Kim-Ly is a 75-year-old pensioner who lives in a small unit in the southern suburbs of the city. The unit is part of a community housing project developed in the early 1980s, and she has lived there independently for the past 25 years. Kim-Ly is originally from Vietnam but has lived in New Zealand since she was in her mid-20s. She migrated with her family and worked with her brother in a local restaurant until she was 70, when arthritis and frequent chest and upper respiratory infections made working the long hours increasingly difficult. She has never married and her only remaining family is her brother and his children, her niece and nephew. She misses the regular coffee with her friends in the local café and the time spent with her brother and family.

Her niece has come to visit this morning and found her aunt sitting in the loungeroom coughing and struggling with shortness of breath. The niece called the ambulance service because she could not get an urgent appointment with her local medical clinic. When paramedics arrive, they find Kim-Ly very short of breath. After conducting an assessment they believe she has a chest infection and might require intravenous antibiotics. The paramedics talk to Kim-Ly and her niece, recommending she be taken to hospital and seen by medical staff to manage the suspected chest infection. Kim-Ly is very reluctant to go to hospital and insists that she will go and see her own doctor as soon as she can.

Questions

1. Discuss personal, family and cultural factors that could affect Kim-Ly's health and her reluctance to go to hospital. Outline why these factors might be important.

2. Consider and discuss economic factors that might affect Kim-Ly's health and her medical decisions. Outline why these factors might be important.

3. What structural (access to and availability of health care) and social factors might influence how Kim-Ly views and seeks health care?

4. As a paramedic, how would you address the needs of Kim-Ly so she receives the care she needs to treat her suspected chest infection?

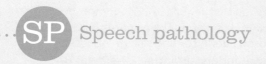

SP Speech pathology

Speech pathology—clinical scenario 1

Themes

Social cognition model | Self-efficacy | Helplessness

Scenario

Macy is a 22-year-old woman who has a two-and-a-half-year-old son, Justin. Justin was referred for speech pathology assessment by his GP, who was concerned that he wasn't using many words. During your first appointment together, you observe that Justin chooses only to play with a truck, despite being offered various other toys. Justin says 'boom boom' to mimic the truck while playing, but he becomes distressed when you try to play with him, throwing the truck away. When you speak with Macy about this, she reports: 'I can't control him'. When you ask her about how she communicates with Justin, she says: 'I try to understand him, but I can't. So I give up and let him do what he wants'. Macy discloses that she left her husband 6 months ago because their relationship was abusive, and she and Justin are now living with her mother until she can afford to rent a house.

Questions

1. Macy's relationship with Justin is critical to support his developing communication skills. What are the important features of this case that provide you with information about their relationship?

2. Several theories have helped to conceptualise how factors (both internal and external) shape how we learn about and understand our world. How could you apply theories proposed by Bandura, Beck and Seligman to help explain Macy's relationship with Justin?

3. What steps or goals might help to enable Macy to develop greater self-efficacy about how she relates to Justin, and be more confident in her communication with him?

4. Who else might be important as a source of support for Macy and Justin? Consider people in Macy and Justin's social and community environments, and the role of other health and education professionals.

Speech pathology—clinical scenario 2

Themes

Determinism | Sensorimotor development | Causal and contextual factors | Scaffolding

Scenario

Kaia is a 2-year-old girl who you are seeing as part of a premature birth follow-up service. She was born at 29 weeks' gestation and spent her first 15 weeks in a neonatal intensive care unit. When she was discharged from hospital to home, Kaia still needed feeds of breast milk from a gavage tube in her nose but had started to take small amounts of breast milk orally via bottle. Your review with Kaia is just after her second birthday, and attended by both her mother and father, who appear very worried. They report being very concerned that Kaia isn't eating well, saying she only eats a small range of bland, pureed foods, and she continues to get most of her nutrition from milk formula via her bottle. Kaia's mother says that Kaia becomes distressed when she is presented with unfamiliar foods and any liquids other than formula. She spits out any foods that have lumps. Kaia's mother and father also report feeling concerned about her communication. While Kaia understands what is being said to her, she is only saying a few words that can be understood by others.

Questions

1. Kaia is demonstrating signs of oral aversion and sensitivity that are affecting her ability to manage the broad range of foods, flavours and textures that are expected for children her age. What are the important issues for you to attend to in Kaia's case?

2. How may her current issues with eating be determined by her early experiences?

3. What causal and contextual factors might help to explain the eating and communication behaviours that Kaia is demonstrating now at 2 years?

4. How might Piaget's sensorimotor stage and Erikson's infancy stage help to explain the eating and communication behaviours that Kaia is presenting with at 2 years?

5. Using concepts described by Piaget, Erikson and Vygotsky, how might you work with Kaia and her parents to start to address and scaffold her eating and communication difficulties?

6. What other health professionals would be important to involve in Kaia's case? Why?

Speech pathology—clinical scenario 3

Themes

Erikson's developmental stages | Lifespan model of developmental challenge | Person-centred care | Goal attainment

Scenario

Mateo is a 22-year-old carpentry apprentice who is an inpatient at a brain injury rehabilitation centre, following a car accident in which his best friend was killed. Mateo has a brain injury and is having difficulties with mobilising independently, self-care and communication. He has been referred for speech pathology because he has difficulties with following instructions, has word-finding problems and is demonstrating short-term memory impairment. While Mateo is initially motivated to work on communication goals with you, he quickly becomes disinterested and starts to refuse appointments. He states that 'there is no point' and he 'can speak just fine'. When you explore this further with Mateo, he says 'no one visits me anyway' and that he 'just wants to go back to work with my mates'.

Questions

1. Erikson's theory describes the concept of 'intimacy and isolation', which is critical to Mateo's phase of development. How might these ideas be integrated into his communication goals?
2. What social supports are important to consider in planning for Mateo to return home to prevent him becoming socially isolated?
3. What factors might be causing Mateo to disengage from his communication therapy? How could you work with Mateo to identify authentic, meaningful goals?
4. Mateo has said that his work is important to him. According to Kloep and Hendry's lifespan model of developmental challenge, what factors might be important to consider in helping Mateo to achieve his goals to return to work?

Speech pathology—clinical scenario 4

Themes

Primary and preventative healthcare | Self-efficacy | Locus of control | Biopsychosocial models | Cultural safety

Scenario

You are a speech pathologist employed by a large network of community childcare centres that are located in low socioeconomic status regions. The children you work with are from diverse social and cultural backgrounds.

Cont... ▶

Through your initial screening of their communication skills, you understand many more of the children would benefit from strategies to improve their communication than you have resources to provide a service for.

Rather than seeing the children individually, you decide instead to work with the early childhood educators (ECEs) who are employed at each centre to provide care and education for the children, and who come from similar social and cultural backgrounds to the children they work with. You provide education and training to the ECEs to develop their skills to facilitate all children's communication skills development during their incidental work during the day. Your training focuses on modelling opportunities to enhance children's communication during group time, mealtimes, nappy changing and outdoor playtime. You also provide education to increase the ability of ECEs to identify children at risk of developmental difficulties with speech and language.

You observe many ECEs successfully implementing the strategies with the children, and you provide modelling and elaboration to support those finding it more difficult to implement the strategies consistently. The communication environment in the childcare centres is conducive to supporting all children's communication development, and the ECEs show they can appropriately identify those children who need referral to the speech pathologist for specialist communication support.

Questions

1. How does this model of communication service provision relate to the principles of the Ottawa Charter for Health Promotion, and of primary health?
2. Preventative and health promotion services are important ways to prevent illness in target populations. What are some of the advantages and disadvantages of the speech pathologist providing a whole-of-population preventative approach in this case? Consider the needs of children with severe difficulties with communication and discuss the implications for using such a strategy.
3. How does developing the ECEs' skills to work on children's developmental communication goals relate to their own self-efficacy and locus of control?
4. Why might delivering communication interventions for these diverse children be more appropriately delivered by ECEs who work with the children every day, and come from similar social and cultural backgrounds?

Speech pathology—clinical scenario 5

Themes

Cultural safety | Social determinants of health | Communication | Social and cultural capital | Structural determinants of health inequity

Scenario

You are working in a busy hospital outpatient department where patients who have been recently discharged from hospital come to see you for

Cont... ▶

follow-up appointments about their communication and swallowing. A 52-year-old Indigenous man called Fred comes for his first appointment with you a week after his discharge from hospital following a stroke. He is accompanied by many family members, but you feel it will be too difficult for Fred to concentrate on your assessment if they're all in the small clinic room with you. You tell Fred that only one person can be with him for the appointment.

Fred enters the room with his wife, Aisha. She speaks with him in an Indigenous language that you don't recognise. You realise, too late, that the discharge report contains no information about Fred's language history. When you ask about language, Aisha confirms that Fred learned English as an adult, but prefers to speak in his language, Kaurna. The discharge report suggests that a standardised aphasia screening test had been conducted to assess Fred's language during his admission. When you ask about how this testing went, Aisha says 'it must have been done when family wasn't around', and that she doesn't know anything about it. You wonder if it had been conducted in English.

During your time in the clinic room with Fred and Aisha, it has been Aisha who answers your questions. Fred has kept his eye gaze lowered and has not responded verbally to any of your questions.

Questions

1. Structural barriers that impede Indigenous people from accessing culturally safe health care include assumptions about how services should be provided, including routines such as timing and location of services, conducting assessments and orienting services to individuals. What are the structural barriers that might present difficulties for Fred and his family in accessing appropriate services to meet their needs?

2. What are the important elements of this case that inform you about the experience Fred and his family have had during his hospital admission and follow-up appointment?

3. What is culturally safe healthcare practice? What elements of this case would you change to enable Fred and his family to have a culturally safe healthcare experience?

4. Why are language, culture and family important to consider in this case?

 Midwifery

Midwifery—clinical scenario 1

Themes

Communication | Disenfranchised loss | Stress

Scenario

Julia is a 30-year-old married woman who presents to you in early pregnancy at 10 weeks with some slight vaginal bleeding. She is a G5 P2 (five pregnancies and two deliveries). She has previously had two miscarriages, one at 12 weeks and one at 9 weeks. Both of these were complete expulsion of the fetus and she did not need any further treatment. She has had two previous caesareans. The first was 6 years ago and the indication was a low-lying placenta. The second was 3 years ago and was done because of the previous caesarean.

At this visit, the doctor ascertained that the bleeding was slight and had settled with no further bleeding. It was established that the bleeding was following sexual intercourse the night before. Julia is discharged home. You take over the care of Julia because you work in a continuity of care model and make a time to see her in 6 weeks unless there are problems. Julia comes back at 16 weeks for her first visit with you, as the midwife. You spend time with her undertaking her first history visit and in the course of the interview with Julia she tells you that she is really worried that this pregnancy will result in another miscarriage even though she knows she will probably be okay. She also informs you that she wants to have a VBAC (vaginal birth after caesarean) and that her husband is now too frightened to be intimate with her. She tells you that her mother-in-law and her mother are telling her that a VBAC will be too risky even though she has tried to tell them that she has done some research and knows that the previous caesarean should not stop her from trying to have a vaginal birth. She feels that she is sick of the conversation with them. Her husband is supportive, but she is missing the intimate contact that they used to have. She tells you that she has shed some tears over her situation. Julia says that she is feeling anxious, depressed and unloved.

Questions

1. Identify the key psychological issues for Julia regarding this pregnancy. How do they relate to any of the key theories of health psychology within the book?
2. Which of Julia's issues would you prioritise and deal with given that you only have a 30-minute time slot for her visit?
3. How can you support Julia's husband to overcome his own anxiety with the intimacy of their relationship?
4. In what ways could you assist Julia's feelings of anxiety, depression and feeling unloved?

Midwifery—clinical scenario 2

Themes

Communication | Person-centred care | Stress

Scenario

Bridget is 42 years of age and pregnant with her first child. She is married and in a stable relationship. She is due for an elective caesarean in 3 days' time. Bridget has already shared with you throughout the antenatal period that she has suffered extensive sexual abuse since childhood, initially facilitated by her own mother. She has had multiple reconstructive genitourinary operations and hence the elective caesarean. While you have had lots of discussions with Bridget about her situation, at this visit she is adamant that she wants you to support her throughout the caesarean to make sure that she can facilitate skin-to-skin contact with her baby immediately following the birth and that you be with her while she attempts to breastfeed her baby as soon as possible. Bridget specifically requests that you do not touch her when you assist her with positioning and latching because she wants to foster a nurturing, non-sexual relationship with her unborn daughter.

Questions

1. How will you respond to Bridget's request?
2. Discuss how Bridget's past traumatic experience may affect her beliefs, perceptions and behaviour regarding her relationship with her unborn daughter.
3. How will you facilitate person-centred care for Bridget?
4. Why is communication a vital part of your ongoing relationship with Bridget?
5. How can the support that Bridget needs be provided?

Midwifery—clinical scenario 3

Themes

Health education | Social connectedness | Pain | Stress

Scenario

Binh is a 27-year-old woman from Vietnam who has been living in Australia for 3 years. She married an Australian man 2 years ago and they have been living in a small coastal town in a rural area (population 2000 people). Her husband, Mark, has a small café and they run the business together. Binh has no family in Australia, and she is the only Vietnamese person living in the community. She has several close women friends who meet for coffee once a week. Binh has been having her antenatal care in a shared-care model with the GP in her town and a midwife in a larger town

Cont... ▶

40 km from where she lives. There is a small hospital in Binh's town, but as with many rural services the midwifery service has been closed. There is a large maternity service 2 hours' drive from where Binh and Mark live.

Binh comes to see you as the midwife at 32 weeks' gestation. Her pregnancy has presented no problems and Binh has loved being pregnant and getting some attention when people come to the café. All her measurements are within normal parameters and you and the GP have documented her care well and shared this information. Binh is feeling very special about having her first baby. Mark's family live 250 km from them and Binh talks to her mother-in-law every week. Binh's friends are excited about the pending birth and are planning a baby shower for her. Binh has a good command of English but speaks quite slowly. At this visit you undertake all the antenatal checks and then have a discussion with Binh about labour and birth.

Binh says to you: 'I want a caesarean please. I'm too scared to have labour'.

Questions

1. Identify the key psychological and social issues Binh is facing.
2. How does Binh's fear of labour link to perceptions of pain and fear avoidance?
3. What strategies can you put in place to alleviate Binh's fear of labour and ensure she can prepare for the birth?
4. Why is social/community support an important element in this case? How will you use Binh's network of friends and Mark's family to support her?

Midwifery—clinical scenario 4

Themes

Health beliefs | Evidence-based practice | Health literacy

Scenario

You are a midwife working in private practice. You have been endorsed to prescribe medicines and you are successfully working to the full definition of the scope of practice for a midwife. You have a very successful practice and women seek your services for their women's health issues long after they have had their babies.

Asher is a 42-year-old woman who you have cared for in four pregnancies. She has had three singleton births and one multiple birth. The birth of her twins was her third pregnancy and, with that pregnancy, she told you that she hated her body and that she had a saggy and unsightly tummy and that her skin was loose and horrible. She also told you that she would not let her husband see her naked. You spoke to her about this at the time and Asher said she would just exercise. Asher was doing well and then found she was pregnant for the fourth time. When

Cont... ▶

she sees you, she is emotional about her tummy and comments about how it would just be worse after this pregnancy. She tells you that she saw an article in the paper about women having a 'tummy tuck' after they have a baby. She says that the researchers say that women can have significant emotional, psychological and relationship distress when they have a saggy tummy. She tells you that this is what is happening to her and asks whether she can have a tummy tuck. You tell Asher that you do not know about this research.

Questions

1. How does Asher's level of health literacy impact on her understanding of her body postpartum?
2. What strategies will you use to find out more about this research?
3. What are your personal beliefs about surgery for a saggy tummy? How might your beliefs influence your care of Asher? Give reasons for your response.
4. How will you disseminate evidence-based information to Asher so she can make an informed decision?

Midwifery—clinical scenario 5

Themes

Communication | Professional relationship/boundaries

Scenario

Jenny comes to visit you in your private midwifery practice. She is the mother of one of the women you care for in a continuity of care model. She tells you that her daughter, Hannah, has been living with a partner who has been seriously abusive towards her, both physically and verbally. He had bruised her, kicked her and hit her. She tells you that Hannah's self-esteem is so low that she doesn't see or believe she can have a different life. Hannah had been seeing you intermittently for her antenatal care and at the last visit at 28 weeks you did notice some bruising on Hannah's abdomen. She explained that she fell at home onto a table and that was what caused the bruise. You did note this in your cares notes, and you also asked her whether there was anything that she wanted to talk to you about. Her partner, Josh, attended the last visit with her.

Jenny tells you that Josh is currently in jail for drug offences, but he could be released on parole in a few weeks. Jenny expresses that she is scared that on his release he will get back with Hannah and that he will give her drugs again and eventually kill her. She also tells you that Hannah keeps saying that she will take her own life because she doesn't want to live anymore. Jenny tells you that Hannah does not know that she has come to see you and she knows that Hannah is planning to come to see you in 2 weeks' time.

Cont... ▶

Questions

1. How will you deal with this situation given what Jenny has disclosed to you?
2. What are the ethical considerations when communicating with Jenny and Hannah?
3. How will you maintain a collaborative and effective relationship with Hannah knowing Jenny has been in contact with you?
4. What other services need to be involved to ensure Hannah maintains her health and safety?

Nutrition and dietetics

Nutrition and dietetics—clinical scenario 1

Themes

Health behaviours | Loss

Scenario

Sasha is a 21-year-old female admitted to the intensive critical care unit for diabetic ketoacidosis related to poorly controlled type 1 diabetes. She recovers relatively quickly after treatment in the unit and is transferred to a general medical ward where she will soon be discharged home. You have been referred to provide dietary education to help manage diabetes. After reading her case notes, you discover Sasha has had diabetes since she was 4 years old and had been self-managing well at home until 6 months ago when her mother suddenly died in a car accident. Sasha was previously living with her mother who did most of the cooking and supported Sasha in carbohydrate counting and insulin dosing. Since her mother died, Sasha has had to move into a rental with housemates from university. She tells you she has been struggling to cope with her diabetes management since this and has been skipping meals, eating a lot of takeaway food and missing insulin doses.

Questions

1. What are the key health and social issues for Sasha?
2. Consider how the loss of her mother and grieving process might have affected the way Sasha manages her diabetes.
3. What other members of the multidisciplinary team could you refer Sasha to in order to ensure a holistic approach and empower Sasha in managing her diabetes?

Nutrition and dietetics—clinical scenario 2

Themes

Loss | Stress and coping | Evidence-based practice

Scenario

You are working in a regional community healthcare centre with limited funding and resources. Bob is a 67-year-old male who has been referred to you for malnutrition on a background of tonsil malignancy. He was diagnosed 3 months ago, following a surgical resection. He is now scheduled for radical chemo and radiotherapy in the coming months. Bob's surgery caused permanent damage to his swallowing ability and currently he is only safe to consume foods that have been pureed to a smooth consistency. Bob hates his new modified texture diet, describing it as 'slosh' and has been eating less and less because of this. After performing a full nutritional assessment, you recommend nutritional supplement drinks for Bob in order to meet his nutritional needs and prevent further malnutrition while he undergoes further cancer therapies. Bob declines this, believing processed food and drinks are carcinogenic and will cause his cancer to return.

Questions

1. Identify losses and stressors for Bob.
2. What coping strategies is Bob using?
3. How would you respond to Bob's concerns?
4. How could you investigate the evidence base for this clinical area?

Nutrition and dietetics—clinical scenario 3

Themes

Health behaviours | Health beliefs

Scenario

Jimmy is a 43-year-old Indigenous man who moved from a remote Aboriginal community to a regional country town about 5 years ago. He is working at the local bakery and lives with his friend. When he was living in the remote Aboriginal community, he was consuming a lot of bush tucker. Since moving to your country town his diet has changed significantly. He tells you he is now eating a lot of pastries from the bakery where he works, as he is allowed to eat during his shift free of charge. He recently attended a GP appointment where he was diagnosed with high cholesterol. Jimmy's GP told him he would need to be on cholesterol-lowering medication for the rest of his life. Jimmy was then referred to you for dietary education to assist in managing his

Cont... ▶

cholesterol. He attends your appointment and tells you that he is very resistant to negotiating any dietary changes. He questions you about why he needs to make these changes if he is going to be on medication for the rest of his life anyway.

Questions

1. What are the key health and social issues for Jimmy?
2. What social and cultural factors are influencing Jimmy's dietary choices?
3. How would you respond to Jimmy's question?
4. Consider the possible cognitions and beliefs influencing Jimmy's health behaviours.

Nutrition and dietetics—clinical scenario 4

Themes

Health beliefs | Behaviour change

Scenario

Isabella is a 73-year-old woman living in a retirement village. She goes to a dance class twice weekly with her husband and it is the highlight of her week. Isabella has won many awards over the years for her dancing, and she is very proud of this. Recently, Isabella had a bone density scan that showed she has osteopenia. Her GP has referred her to you for dietary education for bone health. During your consult, Isabella tells you she avoids all dairy products because she believes she is lactose intolerant. She has been avoiding dairy for nearly 50 years after an episode of severe cramping and diarrhoea she had after drinking a big glass of milk. She has never had formal testing for lactose intolerance. Isabella uses rice milk as a replacement in her tea and coffee. Isabella isn't sure why she has been referred to see you and asks you why she needs to make changes to her diet because she has always been very healthy.

Questions

1. What are the key health and psychological issues for Isabella?
2. Consider how Isabella has associated an acute episode of pain to dairy food and how this has affected her long-term bone health.
3. Which theory of health behaviour can explain Isabella's dietary choices and how?
4. How would you respond to Isabella's question? Consider what stage of behaviour change she is in.

Nutrition and dietetics—clinical scenario 5

Themes

Social determinants | Communication

Scenario

Jasmine is a 2-year-old girl who has been referred to you for iron deficiency due to a diet high in cow's milk and low in iron-rich foods. She lives with her mother, Anna, and three older siblings. Before you meet with Jasmine and Anna, their social worker contacts you to say that Anna and her four children have recently moved into government housing after a separation from her abusive partner. On top of this, Anna has a history of chronic pain due to a previous back injury. During the appointment Anna appears to be withdrawn, responding with mostly one-word answers.

Questions

1. What are the key health and social issues for Jasmine?
2. What are the key social and psychosocial stressors for Anna in this situation?
3. What communication principles would you consider when discussing Jasmine's iron deficiency with Anna?
4. Consider the social model of health. What social determinants are influencing Jasmine's health?

Exercise physiology

Exercise physiology—clinical scenario 1

Themes

Coping strategies | Resilience | Social support

Scenario

Jonah is a 21-year-old elite swimmer who has recently returned from the Youth Olympic Games, where he placed third in the final of the 100 m freestyle. He loves the intensity of training and since he was 3 years old has only ever wanted to represent Australia as an Olympic swimmer. While competing in the Youth Olympics, he suffered some chest pains and shortness of breath that he shrugged off as excitement coupled with a high training load. On return, the team sports doctor advised Jonah to have the chest pains examined, and an ECG revealed that he has hypertrophic cardiomyopathy (HCM). Jonah is prescribed medication to

Cont... ▶

help with his HCM but given that death from HCM is most prevalent in young people (Gregor 2015), he is concerned and anxious about training and his future in competitive swimming.

Questions

1. Find evidence on HCM and exercise and provide:
   a. advice to Jonah about his future exercise regimen
   b. strategies for Jonah to overcome his anxiety about training.
2. In the event that Jonah's condition worsens, how would you then counsel him given that it is likely he may not be able to compete at the elite level again?
3. What other people, including health professionals, could you work with on Jonah's case?

Exercise physiology—clinical scenario 2

Themes

Personal control | Self-efficacy | Locus of control | Resilience

Scenario

Joy is an 87-year-old woman who has recently had a stroke. Until the stroke, Joy lived independently (in her house) and enjoyed life. She regularly met with other ladies, looked after herself with make-up and hair appointments and drove some of her less able friends to the movies and the local café. Her stroke was debilitating; she lost the use of her left side, could no longer shower or bathe herself without help, could not walk or talk properly, and had some cognition issues. Joy had to stay in hospital for several weeks and did not like being there. When Joy was well enough, she moved from hospital into assisted living because she could no longer look after herself in her home. While in the assisted living facility, Joy started taking exercise classes run by the exercise physiologist and started regaining some of her ability to walk, but with the help of a mobile walker. She is also making new friends.

Questions

1. From this case, you can assume that Joy was very social and independent but lost most of that when she suffered her stroke. However, she is starting to regain some of her ability with exercise. Explain how the exercise physiologist can use the concept of self-efficacy to support Joy's rehabilitation.
2. Using the statement in Question 1, explain locus of control and how Joy's belief in herself may or may not affect her locus of control in her rehabilitation.
3. Discuss the case in relation to coping and resilience and what this may mean for Joy and people who have experienced a stroke.

Exercise physiology—clinical scenario 3

Themes

Stress and coping | Coping strategies | Social support | Behaviour change theory

Scenario

Meg is 34 and has been diagnosed with coronary heart disease, high cholesterol and a BMI of 30 (this is considered obese). Recently, Meg had a blood test, and the results showed that she has type 2 diabetes. Meg has tried on numerous occasions to exercise and eat healthier, but she often feels 'stressed' because she is overweight and wonders what other people think of her. She feels embarrassed about how she looks and as a result is not very confident. The stress she feels stops her from participating in regular physical activity and often causes her to snack. She has a husband and two young children and has been referred to you due to this recent diabetes diagnosis.

Questions

1. Using the Diabetes Australia website (www.diabetesaustralia.com.au) as a guiding resource, write a plan that will help Meg and her family live with Meg's diagnosis of diabetes. Take into consideration what sort of support Meg will need in her management.
2. Discuss the word 'stress' and how it is used by Meg; think about the different types of stress and how they can be distinguished.
3. What behaviour change theory could be used to understand Meg and help change her current practices? Also think about the rest of her family.

Exercise physiology—clinical scenario 4

Themes

Loss | Responses to grief | Grief counselling

Scenario

You are a recent exercise physiology graduate working in a rural clinic and your client, Pio, is a 40-year-old man who was recently involved in a horrific cycling accident. The accident was so severe that Pio underwent multiple surgeries to repair a punctured lung, fractured ribs, a shattered fibula and a brain injury. Pio, who was a competitive triathlete and had been training for the Hawaii Ironman event when he was hit, maintains that he will one day 'get well enough to compete in Hawaii'. He has come to you so you can work with him in his exercise rehabilitation.

While Pio is showing good signs of responding to a moderate exercise program, he is unlikely to regain full use of his leg to enable him to

Cont... ▶

compete at the level he was used to. Pio is generally upbeat but does have feelings of physical and mental anguish over what happened. He discusses his accident in depth with you during most exercise sessions.

Questions

1. Given Pio regularly discusses his accident with you, what appropriate responses could you make to Pio to acknowledge his loss and show your understanding of that loss? Write out three possible responses.

2. As a newly graduated exercise physiologist, what strategies would you use to protect yourself from becoming too invested in Pio's anguish, yet still maintain your role as a health professional?

3. Explain further support for Pio in both his grief of no longer being a high-level triathlete and his thoughts that he will one day 'get well enough to compete in Hawaii'.

Exercise physiology—clinical scenario 5

Themes

Loss | Grief | Mourning

Scenario

Marg's mother died of breast cancer when she was young. She was very close to her mum and struggled with the loss. Even though Marg had no symptoms, she was recently also diagnosed with breast cancer, which was picked up during her yearly mammogram and then confirmed with the diagnostic test (biopsy). Due to her family history, Marg opted for surgery and underwent a mastectomy. After surgery, Marg started seeing an exercise physiologist because evidence indicates that exercise can help in the treatment and prevention of cancer (Kraschnewski & Schmitz 2017). While Marg is fine at first with undertaking the prescribed exercise program, she cannot shake the feelings of loss and grief that she is starting to feel on a daily basis. The exercise physiologist believes that this sense of loss is due to the memory of her mother's death and then Marg's diagnosis. As time goes on, Marg becomes less available to exercise and eventually stops attending the sessions.

Questions

1. As an exercise physiologist, you need an understanding of loss and its impact on a situation. Using Weenolsen's (1988) classifications of loss, identify what classification would apply to Marg's story and why.

2. How would you describe Marg's level of loss? Use Weenolsen's five levels of loss as your framework. Why would knowing this be important to an exercise physiologist?

3. What other people, including health professionals, could the exercise physiologist work with on Marg's case?

References

Gregor, P., 2015. Hypertrophic cardiomyopathy and sports. Cor et Vasa 57, e12–e15.

Kraschnewski, J.L., Schmitz, K.H., 2017. Exercise in the prevention and treatment of breast cancer: what clinicians need to tell their patients. Current Sports Medicine Reports 16 (4), 263–267.

P Physiotherapy

Physiotherapy—clinical scenario 1

Themes

Coping strategies | Social aspects of pain | Patient's expectations

Scenario

Amy is a single 35-year-old female who lives by herself. Amy presented to the physiotherapy clinic with a 7-month history of persistent low back pain. Amy reported that she works at a call centre Monday to Friday and she usually can manage to get through a full day of work. Amy is more concerned with the debilitating pain at the end of a busy day of domestic duties. On occasions Amy has had to call in sick on Monday to recover. Amy described her pain as 'annoying', 'not able to be fixed' and repeatedly stated that her back is 'stuffed'. Amy stated: 'I know it will be painful, but I just have to get it done'. When asked what she did to ease her pain Amy replied 'nothing, just resting in bed for 2 to 3 hours'. When asked if she could take a break from doing her home duties, Amy replied, 'I have no one else to help and I only have the weekend to do all the chores'.

Questions

1. Which coping strategy may best explain the circumstances in this case study? Give a rationale for your answer.
2. How would you incorporate the social implications of pain management evident in this case study, such as marital status, living arrangement and support network, into your management of this client?
3. Managing the expectations of a patient is important for a successful outcome. State one of Amy's unrealistic expectations from this case study and give examples of how you would attempt to change it.

Physiotherapy—clinical scenario 2

Themes

Coping strategies | Psychosocial barriers | Behaviour management

Scenario

Peter, a 75-year-old male, requested a home visit from a physiotherapist to assist with his ability to ambulate independently. Four months ago, Peter fell and broke his right radius while performing his daily walk to the local shop to buy the newspaper. Peter came out of his cast 1 month ago and is now experiencing shortness of breath, has a reduced ability to ambulate around the house and is suffering from disrupted sleep. When asked about his current level of exercise, Peter said he rarely leaves the house because he doesn't want to fall again. Peter reported that his wife 'has been great and she does everything for me including going to get the newspaper'. When asked about getting the paper himself, Peter said, 'I would never have the balance to be able to get the paper again'.

Questions

1. Which coping strategy may best explain the circumstances in this case study? Give a rationale for your answer.
2. Identify the psychosocial barriers that are preventing Peter's recovery.
3. Behaviour management is a key factor for a successful rehabilitation program. Give examples of how you would use education and functional exercise to facilitate a change in Peter's behaviour towards activities of daily living and the fear of falling.

Physiotherapy—clinical scenario 3

Themes

Psychosocial risk factors | Beliefs | Education

Scenario

Isaiah, a 25-year-old male, presents to the physiotherapy clinic with extreme low back pain. Isaiah shuffles into the treatment room holding his back and is not willing to sit down. Isaiah exhibits a very shallow, fast breathing pattern, is sweating and finds it hard to complete a full sentence. He mentions the pain started a few weeks ago when he was loading his car for a weekend away. Isaiah says it was the first time he had hurt his back and describes the pain as if he had 'popped his disc out'. Isaiah goes on to explain that his mother has suffered from 'crippling' low back pain for more than 20 years and he is worried that now his back will restrict him from working and earning a living. When you ask Isaiah about his current financial situation, he begins to cry. After hearing Isaiah's story,

Cont... ▶

you are concerned his level of depression may be affecting his ability to process the injury and begin rehabilitating, so you conduct a K10 (Kessler) questionnaire. Isaiah scores 26/30.

Questions

1. Identify Isaiah's psychosocial risk factors. Give a rationale for your answers.
2. What would you incorporate into your rehabilitation program to assist in changing Isaiah's beliefs?
3. Based on Isaiah's current K10 score, explain the role of education. If Isaiah's K10 score was at 25/30 in 2 weeks' time, what would be a consideration to progress treatment? Review the K10 at www. blackdoginstitute.org.au/docs/default-source/psychological-toolkit/k10. pdf?sfvrsn=4.
4. What other resources and health professionals could you refer Isaiah to?

Physiotherapy—clinical scenario 4

Themes

Stress and anxiety | Pain

Scenario

You are a new graduate physiotherapist who accepted a job servicing rural Australia 6 months ago. As a part of your role, you are involved in an outreach program for young farmers. One of your patients, Ryan, is a 22-year-old farmer who has returned to the family farm after completing an agriculture diploma. Ryan is expected to take over the farm. During an early session, Ryan discussed the increase in stress and anxiety he has been feeling since he returned home. Of late, Ryan has started to miss appointments, and when you ask why, he cannot give rational reasons. You notice his demeanour is becoming more and more withdrawn. You are treating Ryan for low back pain that has been radiating down his right leg. It has been affecting his ability to work on the farm with tasks of driving and lifting. The pain has been persistent over the past 3 months. You are not happy with his progress and feel that the natural healing timeframes of his injury are not being met. You are starting to contemplate referring Ryan to a senior physiotherapist at the clinic. When you discuss this with Ryan, he is reluctant to see a new practitioner.

Questions

1. Identify the psychosocial factors that may be contributing to Ryan's persistent pain.
2. Discuss how Ryan's emotional stress can affect his physical recovery.

Cont... ▶

3. How do you adapt your approach to treatment to reflect the presence of stress and anxiety?

4. What other resources are available to you to assist this client in progressing through his rehabilitation?

Physiotherapy—clinical scenario 5

Themes

Recognising stressors and signs of stress | Implementing support mechanisms | Professional boundaries

Scenario

You and Taylor graduated physiotherapy school together and developed a strong friendship. You were both offered jobs at a big chain physiotherapy clinic. This particular clinic has 10 physiotherapists, all with varying levels of experience. Taylor is the newest employee with the least experience and has found it hard to settle in. She has been asked to work the late shifts, which finish at 8 pm. A couple of the other physiotherapists at the clinic have been sick and away on annual leave. Due to their absence, Taylor has been asked to cover some of their morning shifts. You are starting to notice Taylor acting differently. She has been cancelling plans with you because she has been too tired or not in the mood to socialise. When you have tried to talk to her about your concerns she has cut you off abruptly, denied there being anything wrong and suggested it is all a misunderstanding. Recently at work, Taylor has been running late with clients, and a few clients have left complaints about Taylor's poor explanation and her not listening to their concerns. The next day Taylor is called in to the principal physiotherapist's office to discuss her time management and the latest feedback from her clients.

Questions

1. What are some of the key signs Taylor is suffering from stress?
2. What do you think are the main factors behind Taylor's behavioural changes?
3. Consider Taylor's behavioural changes and the likely factors causing them. As a friend, how could you offer support to Taylor?
4. How will you manage professional boundaries?

R Radiography

Radiography—clinical scenario 1

Themes

Loss | Grief | Coping

Scenario

Alec is a 35-year-old man who has been suffering from depression for several years. He has no siblings and his parents are deceased. Recently, Alec's health has worsened after he lost his job. He had trouble paying bills and needed to find alternative accommodation in a smaller unit, forcing him to relinquish many of his belongings and his cat, which he misses immensely.

Alec attends the local mental health unit on a weekly basis where he is prescribed medication to help manage his depression and anxiety. Money is tight, his motivation is low and his anxiety prevents him from going outside unless necessary. The medication makes him drowsy and unsteady. He is concerned that he will be forced onto the street. Sometimes he has to choose between food and medication. Although a social worker has been helping him, it's proving difficult to get the financial and personal support that he needs.

An unending series of colds and bouts of the flu add to Alec's morose state. His joints ache and it takes a long time for him to get to sleep at night. He presents to an emergency department after falling at home and hurting his wrist. An x-ray confirms it is broken. Alec's speech is slurred and he is having trouble keeping his eyes open. It is also noted that he has a bad cough and he is sent for a CT scan.

The radiographer performing the CT scan notes that Alec has a very fine chain around his neck, which needs to be removed before imaging. Alec does not want to take it off, concerned that it may be lost. He tells the radiographer that the chain belonged to his mother; it's one of the few belongings he cannot face losing. The radiographer assures Alec that it will be put on again as soon as the x-ray is complete. He agrees to the chain being removed for the scan and it is returned immediately after.

Questions

1. Alec has suffered several losses. What are the types of losses he has experienced?
2. Alec has lost much of his connection to others. What prevents him from reconnecting with others or making new connections?
3. The methods that Alec has used to adjust to his new situation have required him to make some difficult decisions. Consider his choices and discuss their relative benefits and drawbacks.
4. Consider the social supports available to Alec. What benefits him and what is lacking?

Radiography—clinical scenario 2

Themes

Communication | Multidisciplinary teams

Scenario

Maya is a radiographer working the evening shift in the emergency department of a hospital. Although there is a designated after-hours imaging protocol, she generally makes an effort to complete as much non-urgent work as possible after hours.

She receives a request for a CT scan of the ankle of a patient on the orthopaedic ward, seeking clinical delineation of damage to the talus. The patient is stable, and the department's protocol is to only perform urgent imaging after hours. The orthopaedic registrar, Pavin, pressures Maya to perform the scan. Maya explains that she is busy with emergency work for a while but will take a look when she catches up.

Pavin argues that the patient is scheduled for surgery the following morning and wants his patient scanned first. Maya explains that other examinations take priority and his will need to wait. Pavin is annoyed and leaves, telling Maya that the surgery will be delayed and that if anything goes wrong it will be her fault. As he leaves, Maya thinks she could try to complete the scan before her shift ends if the workload eases, but she does not want to reinforce the aggressive behaviour of the registrar.

The next afternoon, Maya's supervisor, Andrew, asks about the patient who needed the CT scan of the ankle. Andrew has received a complaint from Pavin, who is indicating that the patient's surgery has been delayed due to the inability to complete the scan overnight. Maya explains that Pavin attended in the early evening and was intimidating and harassing. Andrew reviews the examination and request and acknowledges that Maya's decision was correct. She says that this is not the first time that Pavin has behaved in such a manner and that she no longer wishes to be the subject of his antagonism.

Having spoken with Pavin's consultant, Andrew arranges a meeting between Maya and Pavin. Pavin does not realise that his behaviour is being perceived poorly. He concedes that his throwaway comment blaming Maya for delayed surgery was unwarranted. He admits that he had been ill-prepared for the surgery due to his own large workload and because he had been trying to capitalise on an unexpected cancellation on the operating theatre list.

Questions

1. What communication strategies did Maya use in this scenario?
2. Why did Pavin's efforts cause friction? How could he modify his communication to better advocate for his patient?
3. What means did Andrew use to address the communication problems so they did not recur? What else could be done to improve relations?

Radiography—clinical scenario 3

Themes

Personality | Health behaviours | Health psychology

Scenario

Spiro is an ambitious 45-year-old businessperson who has recently experienced palpitations. His father suffered a heart attack at the same age. Spiro is very fit and body conscious. He works out at the gym every day and parties on the weekends. Sometimes he indulges by taking cocaine. Recently one of his close friends died after shooting up.

Following a review by a cardiologist, Spiro is sent for a CT scan to examine his coronary arteries. His appointment is at 10 am and when he arrives he is taken straight through, where he is asked to change into a gown and lie on a trolley. Spiro's vital signs are checked and it is found that his heart rate is too fast for the scan. He is administered beta-blockers to reduce his heart rate.

Ngoc is also having a coronary CT scan and, when checked, his heart rate is within the ideal range. No beta-blockers are required and the staff prepare to take Ngoc through for his scan.

Spiro is incensed that he is being forced to wait. He argues that his appointment is before Ngoc's and that he does not have time to wait.

Emily is a CT radiographer who tries to explain to Spiro that in order to get the best possible scans, his heart rate must be below 60 beats per minute. Without this, the scan will be compromised. Spiro does not accept the reason and decides that he is going to leave and will complain to his cardiologist.

Spiro presents to an emergency department after another attack of palpitations while working out at the gym, this time accompanied by chest pain. An ECG shows signs suggestive of a heart attack. He is sent for a coronary CT scan. It shows that a section of his myocardium has been damaged and that one of the coronary arteries is blocked. He is sent straight to the cardiac catheter lab where the blockage is reversed and a stent placed in one of the arteries to ensure it stays open.

Questions

1. How would you describe Spiro's personality?
2. Identify Spiro's health locus of control. How does it shift?
3. How can Spiro's use of cocaine be reconciled with his body-conscious image?
4. What social determinants may be influencing Spiro's behaviour?

Radiography—clinical scenario 4

Themes

Evidence-based health care | Quantitative research | Ethics

Scenario

You are a radiographer working in magnetic resonance imaging (MRI) scanning the brain of a patient, Georgia, with a first presentation of optic neuritis and a clinical diagnosis of multiple sclerosis. Because this is Georgia's first scan for this condition, the radiologist approves the use of contrast. You explain the procedure to Georgia including the use of an intravenous contrast medium and seek her approval to administer the drug during the scan.

Georgia indicates that she is a nurse. She asks about the risks of contrast uptake in her tissues; she has heard the MRI staff talk about new research showing that gadolinium accumulates in the brain and she has also heard about nephrogenic systemic fibrosis (NSF).

You explain that NSF occurs only in patients who are suffering end-stage renal disease. You tell her that you have reviewed her pathology and that her renal function is normal, so she is not at risk of NSF.

You go on to explain that there are several different types of gadolinium-based contrast agents. Each has a different molecular makeup. A paper in 2014 by a team led by Kanda showed that a single dose of the contrast was not enough to result in signal change in the brain, but six or more doses of some contrast agents seemed to result in increased signal on non-contrast images in some areas of the brain. The mechanism behind this effect is poorly understood and its overall significance is as yet unclear. The research since 2014 has found variability between the contrast agents used. In an effort to reassure the patient, you tell her that the contrast used for scans at your site is not implicated in the prevailing research.

Georgia asks if the scan can be performed without using contrast. You explain that it can, but the activity of her disease will be difficult to diagnose without the contrast images.

Georgia asks if she will need to have gadolinium for every scan as her disease progresses. You tell her that this may not always be the case, but to provide a complete assessment today contrast should be used. The patient decides to proceed with the scan and consents to the use of contrast.

Questions

1. Review the landmark paper by Kanda and colleagues (2014). What type of methodology has been applied to research this paper?
2. What ethical questions would Kanda and colleagues (2014) have needed to address before researching and publishing this paper?
3. What strategies has the radiographer employed to ensure an evidence-based approach?
4. Consider the decision to restrict some types of contrast by the European Medicines Agency. What reasoning applied to justify the conclusion?
5. Discuss the ethics of using gadolinium for MRI.

Radiography—clinical scenario 5

Themes

Communication | Conditioning | Evidence-based research | Ethics

Scenario

Fatima presents for x-rays of an incidental finding of a lesion seen in her bony pelvis on MRI. The request is for x-rays of the pelvis, lumbar spine and hips. She is a refugee with good English language skills. She lived in Kuwait during the Gulf War and is anxious about exposure to radiation. She has not been told of the incidental finding on the MRI and questions the reason for the x-rays.

She tells you that munitions involving radioactive components were used in the Gulf War. She is fearful of the effects of additional radiation because she saw the effects on her friends and family who developed cancer soon after the war ended.

Ralph is a radiographer and explains to Fatima that the type of radiation that will be used to take her images is different from that used in ammunition. After some discussion about types of radiation and doses, Fatima consents to the x-rays and changes into a hospital gown.

After three x-rays, Fatima questions why you are taking so many images. She tells Ralph that he is taking too many and that she wants him to stop. Ralph tries to explain that the doctor has requested images of several parts of her body and each area requires a different series of images, but she becomes more upset and tells Ralph again that she wants him to stop taking x-rays.

An exasperated Ralph tells Fatima that he has not completed all the images and that this will limit the ability of the radiologist to make a diagnosis. Fatima does not wish to continue. Ralph finds Fatima's paranoia frustrating. He documents the withdrawal of consent with a note to the radiologist.

After the patient has left, Ralph discusses the patient's manner with a colleague. They are both sceptical about Fatima's fear and decide to search the internet for information about radiation used in the Gulf War. They find several non–peer reviewed sources and news articles that discuss the use of not only nuclear munitions but also biological and chemical weapons.

Ralph notes a report of depleted uranium in Kuwait by a recognised international body. He also notes that while the report acknowledges that radioactive residue remains, it is not harmful. There is also research into the effects of exposure to various pollutants on veterans of the Gulf War and the fact that there is acknowledgment of some ill effects. There are several other non–peer reviewed articles that make stronger assertions. Ralph reconsiders his initial opinion and decides that the patient's concerns may have had some basis.

Cont... ▶

1. Is Fatima's anxiety about x-rays evidence-based or conditioned?
2. Why did Ralph not tell Fatima about the lesion seen on her MRI? Was this ethical? Should he have told her in order to gain consent to complete the x-rays?
3. How might Ralph respond to Fatima's concerns? And should she be referred for more x-rays?
4. Several factors influence Fatima's views. What are these and how are they challenged?

Reference

Kanda, T., Ishii, K., Kawaguchi, H., et al., 2014. High signal intensity in the dentate nucleus and globus pallidus on unenhanced T1-weighted MR images: relationship with increasing cumulative dose of a gadolinium-based contrast material. Radiology 270, 834–841.

Podiatry

Podiatry—clinical scenario 1

Themes

Chronic illness | Social isolation | Person-centred care

Scenario

Drew is 53 years of age and was born on the South Island of New Zealand. He has been coming to see you for the past 5 months to receive podiatric care at the high-risk foot clinic where you work. He initially presented after being hospitalised with an infected plantar foot ulcer (i.e. an open wound under his foot with associated soft tissue infection). Once the infection had resolved, he was discharged to the high-risk foot service where you work to receive ulcer management and education.

Drew has a complex medical history and sustained ulceration under his foot due to chronic diabetes complications. He knows that his feet are very numb because of years of poorly controlled blood glucose levels; however, in some ways he is relieved about this because it means the large wound under his foot does not hurt so he can continue work for hours on his feet without pain. Drew owns a dairy farm in the country. He works long hours, tending to the animals and all the other jobs around the farm. Drew hires staff locally to help because he lives alone since his youngest son left for the city a year ago. The dairy farm means the world to Drew because he

Cont... ▸

feels he has little else left in his life. His wife died suddenly over a decade ago from breast cancer and the kids have all moved away now. The farm is around 2 hours' drive away from the high-risk foot clinic so Drew needs to take half a day away from work to make his appointment. He has mentioned before that it is difficult for him to make appointments due to the distance but there is no similar service closer.

Thankfully, Drew has good blood supply to his feet, which means if enough pressure is taken off his foot ulcer it should heal in around 5 weeks. However, after 5 months the wound has become larger, despite you providing current best practice podiatric care (i.e. ulcer pressure relief with offloading padding). Drew is also becoming increasingly despondent. Lately you notice that Drew's moods are flat when he comes to see you and he has started missing appointments. When he does come, he is often grumpy or just quiet, not keen to talk to you about much at all, particularly the lack of progress with his foot. You are concerned that Drew has been removing his offloading padding when he is at work, but he gets annoyed with you when you ask. You are concerned as the offloading padding looks relatively unworn and Drew's wounds are not responding as they should. There is a real risk his foot might get infected again if things keep going like this, which might eventually lead to Drew needing to have his leg amputated. Something needs to change.

Questions

1. What are the social and psychological key issues in Drew's case?
2. How might these issues be related to the deterioration of his foot health?
3. How might Drew's rural location impact on the situation?
4. What are the challenges you face as Drew's podiatrist?
5. What factors might be contributing to Drew not following your advice?
6. How would you respond to this case? What other professionals might assist with Drew's management?

Podiatry—clinical scenario 2

Themes

Health behaviour models | Behaviour change theories | Reluctance to change

Scenario

Suresh runs a busy and successful private practice, working as a sole podiatric practitioner in a middle-class suburb in Perth. Much of his business involves caring for people in the local community, with lots of patients coming in for routine podiatric care, including general nail and callus reduction. Sandra is typical of his clientele—a friendly and hard-working

Cont... ▶

42-year-old woman who runs a busy household, works part-time in human resources at a city law firm and looks after three teenage kids with her husband. Sandra has attended Suresh's practice every 8 weeks for the past 10 years or so for routine nail care and management of painful, deep corns on the outside of both of her little (fifth) toes. She has no relevant medical history and is generally fit and well.

While Sandra's foot health is quite good, there is one sticking point with her care. Each time she comes to see Suresh for treatment, he finishes the consultation by advising Sandra that her corns would form much less quickly, and be a lot less painful, if she wore shoes that were wider around her toes. However, she simply does not take his advice. When she comes to her appointments she usually wears runners; however, Suresh has seen Sandra on the train several times going to work wearing pointy-toed, high-heel stilettos. Her shoes were clearly very tight because he could see the leather on the upper of the shoe toe box being pushed out where her little toes rubbed. Sandra's response to his advice is always the same—that she has trouble finding shoes that fit but she will try to go shopping again to see what she can find.

It doesn't surprise Suresh that Sandra dismisses his advice over and over, offering excuses each time, because this is something he experiences with many of his clients—a reluctance to make a change that would be of benefit to their health. Last year, Suresh experienced a patient who, despite the best advice, continued to smoke for years and eventually lost his leg due to complications of severe atherosclerosis. He has even seen very active people with problems such as debilitating Achilles tendinopathy, and they refuse to modify their exercise levels even though they know it will just continue to make the injury worse. Sometimes Suresh finds people being stuck in their ways very frustrating; however, he wonders if he has a right to try to make people change if they don't want to.

Questions

1. Why can some people find change so difficult?
2. What might be preventing Sandra from changing her footwear even though wearing tight shoes causes pain and reduces her foot health?
3. Use one theory of health behaviour to explain Sandra's behaviour.
4. Identify one behaviour change theory that might be used to assist Sandra and explain how this could work.
5. What is a health practitioner's role in facilitating change?
6. What strategies or resources might Suresh draw on to assist with the change process?
7. In this case, how might Suresh address his own frustration about his patients' reluctance to change?

Podiatry—clinical scenario 3

Themes

Working with culturally diverse populations

Scenario

Riya is a 60-year-old woman who was born in a small village just outside of Bangalore, India. She follows Hinduism, an Indian religion that she considers a dharma, or way of life. Riya moved to Australia in the late 1970s with her then new husband because he wanted to live with his sister who had also recently immigrated to Australia. They all lived in the Dandenong region of Melbourne. Riya was united with her husband through an arranged marriage and moving to Australia was difficult because she didn't know anyone else living there. All of Riya's family stayed in India and she missed them terribly when she was younger. Communications with her family were sparse, just an occasional letter from her mother. This aside, Riya has been mostly happy in Australia, choosing to live a fairly traditional Hindu lifestyle. Riya does not speak English because her husband takes care of things outside of the home; she spends her time looking after her three grandchildren.

Riya's daughter, Amrita, brings her mother into the podiatry clinic for her regular appointments every 8 weeks. Amrita speaks English fluently and translates for her mother. Riya's husband does not wish to attend because he feels that his wife's health is women's business; therefore, Amrita takes time off work to do this. Riya does not really approve of Amrita working and not following the old ways, but she understands that it is up to her daughter. In any case, Riya is pleased she can look after Amrita's three kids because she is adamant that they won't go to childcare and be raised by strangers. At today's visit, Amrita looks strained and you are concerned that something is wrong.

As Riya sits in the consultation chair, you see that she has some loose bandages on her ankle. Riya has a medical history of type 2 diabetes, varicose veins, hypertension and hyperlipidaemia. She knows that a balanced diet is important to her health, but she struggles to manage her diabetes around times of traditional ceremonies, given cooking and eating is such a part of her culture. She also likes to wear thongs with her sari and no shoes inside her house, although you have repeatedly advised her of the dangers of this. Riya has some numbness in her toes as a complication of her diabetes, which places her at risk of sustaining damage to her feet because she cannot feel it occurring.

You ask Amrita about the bandages and she takes them off her mother to show you. Riya has a large weeping wound on her ankle, a very red, hot and swollen leg and some weeping blisters on the top of her foot. She says she took her mother to the doctor and he believes Riya has an infected venous leg ulcer with significant venous oedema. The GP has prescribed antibiotics and would like to know if Riya can attend the wound clinic that runs at the community health centre where you work.

Cont... ▶

More concerning to Amrita, though, is that Riya has also started showing signs of memory loss and confusion. The doctor has organised further tests, but Amrita asks you what could be going on. She is very worried about her mother but also her kids while they are in her care.

Questions

1. What are the key social and psychological issues in Riya's case?
2. How does culture play an important role in Riya's health practices and health care?
3. Why is it important for health practitioners to develop cultural competency?
4. Why is Amrita concerned and what would you tell her?
5. How would you respond to this case?

Podiatry—clinical scenario 4

Themes

Communication | Social determinants | Person-centred care

Scenario

Sally was thrilled when she received the letter of appointment 3 years ago to a grade 2 podiatrist position in a large tertiary hospital in Brisbane. Although she had only just graduated at the time, the appointment was at a high level because she was going to be seeing patients with complex medical, social and psychological histories. Sally felt that she was well equipped for the job because her training and clinical placements were excellent preparation. Also, her mother experienced mental health issues when Sally was growing up, so she had first-hand experience.

The position went well for a while, but after some time Sally started to feel a bit down after work, especially after seeing some patients. There were so many people who were unwell, some with very sad stories, that it started to become challenging to deal with all the emotional aspects of the job. Sally was surprised that there was very little orientation or briefing when she started her job at the hospital, and she didn't really expect to encounter some of the serious things the patients were admitted for. She was surprised at how many people struggled with their physical and mental health, and how hard some of the patients' lives were with things like lack of money, drug and alcohol use, and sometimes even family violence. Sally was often told a lot of details too, whether she wanted to hear it or not, because patients were sitting in the treatment chair for at least 30 minutes during consultations, directly facing her. They commonly said they just needed someone to talk to. A little while ago, Sally asked around the hospital if there was a psychologist or other professional support person who she could debrief with, but no one got back to her.

Cont... ▶

More recently, something happened that Sally has been feeling pretty awful about. She had been seeing a lovely patient, Betty, for some time. Betty attends the hospital as an outpatient because she has rheumatoid arthritis (a chronic inflammatory joint condition) and requires routine nail and callus care and offloading insoles. Sally is also aware that Betty has been diagnosed with bipolar disorder but only because she asked Betty why she was taking a medication called lithium. Betty says that people treat her differently when they know about her mental health condition, so she avoids telling people. At Betty's last appointment she seemed different from usual, talking very quickly and telling Sally about all of the successes she has had this year. Betty had just been shopping and had many bags, but she was hard to talk to because her conversation jumped around a lot. Sally got angry at Betty during the consultation because she recently negotiated money for Betty's shoes and insoles through community funding. Sally sees that Betty has spent more than twice as much as that in just one day! After the consultation, Sally realises that Betty may have been experiencing a manic episode and she feels terrible for speaking sharply to her. Sally mentioned the incident to a colleague at lunch and they just said Betty shouldn't be allowed out when she is like that; the lack of empathy surprised Sally. Sally also started to wonder if her mum had to deal with stigma around having a mental health issue. The job is starting to feel too much for Sally, and she thinks she needs some help to cope better.

Questions

1. What do you think is happening here for Sally as the health professional in this situation?
2. What ways might Sally seek help for herself?
3. Why did Sally feel bad about what happened with Betty and why did her colleague's comments make it worse?
4. What is mental health stigma and how can it be minimised?
5. In hindsight, what strategies could have been implemented to facilitate person-centred care and communication?

Podiatry—clinical scenario 5

Themes

Health issues | Health beliefs and behaviour

Scenario

Casey is a 16-year-old girl who competes at an advanced level at her local gymnastics club. Her parents are optimistic that she will qualify at state or possibly even national competitions, so they make sure she always does her 20-plus hours a week of gym practice. For the past few weeks Casey has been experiencing sharp pain in the middle of her right foot when

Cont... ▶

training, although it did seem to settle a bit when she rested. She pushed on with training and rested when possible. Despite Casey's best efforts, the pain has become worse in the past few days and is now there all of the time, especially at night. Her parents are concerned that Casey's foot has not improved with ice application and taping, but they are encouraging her to 'stay strong' and just keep going in order to prepare for upcoming state championships. They have brought Casey to see you for some insoles to fix the problem.

Casey presents as a bright and friendly girl who is good at school and aims for high achievement in whatever she does. Casey explains that she had increased her training quite a lot in the past few months because the state championships are such an important event. She wants to win to please her parents because they have put so much into her success. It has been hard, though, because she often feels tired. She thinks it has helped that she has lost around 15 kg because she looks more like what everyone thinks a gymnast should look like and feels lighter on her feet. She is still not that happy with her body image, but she thinks she looks more like the other girls now. Sometimes for motivation she looks at photos of thin, fit girls online and tells herself that she can be like that too if she is disciplined enough. Casey struggled when she reached puberty and noticed her body changing, but she says she has that under control now with her diet and she has managed to get her periods to stop. Like most of the girls, she hasn't told her trainer about her diet; it's just part of the sport to 'have no curves'.

Casey currently weighs 40 kg after going on a strict low-carb, low-calorie, small-portion protein diet, which at a height of 168 cm, places her BMI at 14.4 (which is in the underweight category and bottom third percentile for her sex and age). On clinical examination of her right foot, Casey reports tenderness when you press down on the top of the navicular bone. Subsequent plain film x-rays are inconclusive, but an MRI shows that Casey has developed a navicular stress fracture (visible as a focal area of increased signal on T2-weighted sequences). You are concerned about what this means for Casey and how her parents will react.

Questions

1. What are the key social and psychological issues in Casey's case?
2. What role might parents, trainers, the gym fraternity, peers and the media play in Casey's body image concerns and dysfunctional eating behaviours?
3. What concerns do you have for Casey in the medium and longer term?
4. What are the implications of this diagnosis for Casey's upcoming competition and how might you communicate this to Casey and her parents?
5. What messages might you communicate to Casey and her parents about Casey's body image concerns and eating patterns?
6. Role-play how you would communicate your concerns for Casey, including examples of verbal microskills (e.g. clarity, tone, safe wording) and non-verbal microskills (e.g. body language, facial expressions, eye contact).
7. How would you respond to this case? What other professionals might assist with Casey's management?

Pharmacy

Pharmacy—clinical scenario 1

Themes

Stress | Communication

Scenario

Maggie is a 35-year-old working mother of three who enters the pharmacy and requests Phenergan Elixir (promethazine, a sedating antihistamine) for her 2- and 3-year-old daughters and her 6-year-old son. Upon questioning, you identify that Maggie's children do not have allergies or experience motion sickness. Rather, Maggie wants to sedate her children, hoping it will calm them down and provide her with some respite. Maggie goes on to tell you that she recently separated from her husband of 12 years, that she is financially strained and hasn't had any time for herself. Maggie feels that her children's behaviour has spiralled out of control in response to their father moving out. Maggie feels she is projecting her own stress onto her children and that she is constantly yelling at them. Maggie says she is not coping with the stress and that her asthma has become significantly worse, requiring her to use her reliever more frequently.

Questions

1. What are the key social and psychological issues for Maggie?
2. What are the neurochemical links between the nervous, endocrine and immune systems? How might this be affecting Maggie?
3. What internal and external coping resources can Maggie draw on?
4. Would you recommend Phenergan Elixir in this case? Explain your decision.
5. How might you respond to Maggie?

Pharmacy—clinical scenario 2

Themes

Pain | Behaviour change

Scenario

Evelyn is a 68-year-old retiree who suffers from chronic hip and hand osteoarthritis. Evelyn has a current BMI of 30 and her diet is one of convenience, with limited fruit and vegetables. Evelyn first presented to

Cont... ▶

her doctor 3 years ago, with increasing day and night pain and stiffness in her joints, and was prescribed both paracetamol and celecoxib (COX-2–selective inhibitor). On a subsequent visit, due to uncontrolled osteoarthritis pain, the doctor started Evelyn on oxycodone (an opioid medication). Over the past 6 months, the oxycodone dose has been gradually increased. As Evelyn's regular doctor has moved interstate, a new doctor, Dr Burnett, is now overseeing Evelyn's care. Dr Burnett would like to taper (reduce) Evelyn's oxycodone dose with the hope of ceasing the medication. Dr Burnett has written a GP Management Plan and Team Care Arrangements, referring Evelyn to allied health professionals including a dietitian, a physiotherapist and a psychologist to help manage her pain and chronic disease. Dr Burnett is hoping that a coordinated approach will see Evelyn improve her diet, lose weight, increase her physical activity and improve her coping strategies, with the overarching goal of improving pain management and her quality of life.

Evelyn speaks with you, the pharmacist, about Dr Burnett's recommendations. Evelyn expresses that she is concerned and anxious about reducing her oxycodone dosage and that she is unwilling to meet with allied health professionals because 'it seems too hard'.

Questions

1. What are the key issues for Evelyn?
2. What type of pain is Evelyn experiencing?
3. Explain what is meant by the 'biopsychosocial model' of pain.
4. What psychological strategies can be used to help Evelyn manage her chronic pain?
5. Why do you think Dr Burnett is opting for a different pain management strategy for Evelyn? What are the likely benefits to this approach? What are the likely hurdles?
6. As a pharmacist, what is your advice? And how would you respond to Evelyn?

Pharmacy—clinical scenario 3

Themes

Lifespan

Scenario

Mitchell is a 19-year-old university student attending a large music festival in Auckland. The local government and police, as part of a harm-minimisation strategy, are supporting a pill (illicit drug) testing service at the music festival. Mitchell takes his illicit drug to the pill testing service, which is staffed by analytical chemists and health professionals, including you—a pharmacist. The analytical chemist uses a mobile laboratory to assess the

Cont... ▶

composition of Mitchell's pill. As the health professional, it is your role to relay the risks associated with taking the pill that has been analysed. The analytical chemist shows Mitchell graphically the composition of his pill; it has been cut with a high percentage of 'unknown substances' and may have life-threatening impurities. You inform Mitchell that the pill is not considered safe and that it may cause him harm or even death. You provide Mitchell with an opportunity to dispose of the pill in the provided amnesty bin. Mitchell thanks you for your time and for testing the pill for him but goes on to say that 'my mates are all high so I'm going to take it anyway'.

Questions

1. With reference to Mitchell's age, what developmental stage is he in?
2. What are some of the social and psychological aspects of this developmental stage?
3. What are the key issues that influence Mitchell's behaviour?
4. What advice will you give Mitchell as he leaves?

Pharmacy—clinical scenario 4

Themes

Communication | Social determinants | Health beliefs

Scenario

Under section 100 provisions of the *National Health Act 1953* (Cth), you are visiting a very remote Aboriginal community in the Northern Territory of Australia to provide professional pharmacist support services. Support services include arranging and stocking the medicines room at the health clinic and conducting a medication review for Olga. Olga is a 42-year-old mother of six. Olga uses the local Aboriginal language as her mother tongue. Olga uses some Aboriginal English too. You are informed by the clinic nurse that Olga has diabetes and chronic kidney disease and refuses to take her medications. Instead, Olga likes to take bush medicine.

Questions

1. What are the key social and psychological issues for Olga?
2. What communication techniques or strategies can you use to optimise Olga's understanding?
3. The communication gap between health professionals and Indigenous Australians has a significant impact on health outcomes. How can we close the communication gap and promote a shared understanding between health professionals and remote Indigenous people?
4. How can you optimise cultural safety?

Pharmacy—clinical scenario 5

Themes

Loss and grief | Lifespan development

Scenario

Albie, a 71-year-old regular patient at your pharmacy, has a diagnosis of Alzheimer's disease. Over the past several years, you have seen Albie's Alzheimer's progress from what he described as 'forgetfulness' to profound memory impairment and personality change. Albie's wife, Leonie, also 71 years old, visits the pharmacy distressed. She explains that Albie no longer needs his medication packed weekly from your pharmacy, and that because of Albie's increasing high needs she can no longer care for him in their home. He is now a resident at an aged care facility and his medication will be packed by another pharmacy. Leonie and Albie have been married for nearly 50 years and Leonie says she 'doesn't think I can do life without him'. Leonie explains that while Albie is still alive, at times he no longer recognises her or their three children and that his aggression and psychosis makes the man she loves difficult to recognise.

Questions

1. Describe the grief process as theorised by prominent psychologists.
2. Identify Leonie's losses.
3. What are the key social and psychological issues for Leonie?
4. As a pharmacist, what is your advice and how do you respond to Leonie?
5. What health professionals can you refer Leonie to for further support?

 Occupational therapy

Occupational therapy—clinical scenario 1

Themes

Biopsychosocial model of health | Biopsychosocial model of pain

Scenario

Jayne is a 32-year-old woman who was diagnosed with rheumatoid arthritis (RA) 3 years ago. She gave birth to her first child, a daughter, Ellie, 4 weeks ago. As is often the case, Jayne's RA symptoms

Cont... ▶

improved significantly during her pregnancy and she was able to manage them with regular exercise and minimal medication. Within days of giving birth, Jayne experienced a severe flare-up of her RA. She is in considerable pain; all the joints in both her hands and wrists are affected, as are the metatarsal joints in both feet. She is extremely fatigued and weak. Her rheumatologist has suggested she take an increased dosage of anti-inflammatory medication, but this may present a risk to breastfeeding, which she is not willing to take yet because she wants to breastfeed Ellie for as long as possible. She has been referred to see an occupational therapist for support with joint protection and work simplification. Jayne, her partner Alex and baby Ellie arrive at their appointment with you in distress. Jayne is scared that she won't be able to care for Ellie properly. Alex has been doing most of the care, but he is due back at work in 2 weeks' time. Jayne reports feeling overwhelmed by the responsibility of caring for a new baby and managing the flare-up of her RA. She is exhausted, in considerable pain and unable to do most of the things she needs to do to care for herself, let alone a newborn. Jayne is worried that this flare-up will never settle and can't imagine how she will cope. Alex is worried about Jayne and Ellie. He too is exhausted from worry, sleeplessness associated with caring for a newborn and adjusting to fatherhood.

Questions

1. How would you explain what is going on for Jayne by applying a biopsychosocial model of health?
2. Break down the physical, psychological and social factors that may be impacting on Jayne's presentation and discuss these.
3. Occupational therapists apply an occupational lens to considering health and wellbeing. This means they consider health as a resource to enable engagement in the meaningful occupations that a person needs and wants to do in their daily life. Occupation in this context relates to anything that occupies a person's time.
4. Considering this, how is a biopsychosocial model of health useful when considering occupational engagement?
5. What are the key occupations Jayne needs and wants to be able to do at this time and how are they being impacted on by her current situation?
6. How might the pain Jayne is experiencing be affecting her current situation?
7. Work through the biopsychosocial model of pain and consider how it may help you understand more about what is occurring for Jayne at this difficult time.

Occupational therapy—clinical scenario 2

Themes

Structural determinants of inequity | Social determinants of health | Effective communication | Partnerships in health care

Scenario

Jaime is a 2-year-old boy with developmental delay. He has limited play, fine motor and speech and language skills as well as reduced attention and concentration. He lives with his 20-year-old mother, Emma, in an area of low socioeconomic status in rural South Australia. Emma grew up in a household where her mother struggled to manage her own mental health and her father coped with his recurrent unemployment by drinking alcohol. Neither of her parents completed high school and neither has been able to hold down jobs for longer than a few months at a time. Emma grew up in poverty. She and her three younger brothers were regularly hungry; toys and clothes were usually second-hand and often broken or unclean. Emma's parents frequently fought, and home was not a safe or supportive place for her growing up. She left home at 15 and 'couch-surfed' for the next 2 years while working in a variety of casual jobs. Since becoming pregnant with Jaime when she was 17, Emma has been working at a local fish and chip shop and saving her money. She moved in with Jaime's father, Chris, to have a stable home for Jaime, but she is worried that her relationship with Chris is not a good one. Chris is very immature and, like her father, drinks a lot.

She is trying her best to give Jaime a better childhood than she herself experienced and is worried that something is wrong with him because he is behind in all his developmental milestones. She took him to her GP who then referred him to the community early childhood service for occupational therapy and speech pathology.

Questions

1. Consider what is going on for Jaime and Emma by analysing the structural determinants of health inequities. Specifically consider how income, social class, education, occupation and gender may have impacted on Jaime presenting with a developmental delay.

2. How does considering the social determinants of health help you as an occupational therapist to plan how you will work with Jaime and Emma?

3. What are the risks of working only at the individual and skill development level with Jaime focusing on 'treating' his developmental delay rather than working at a broader social and structural level?

4. What key interpersonal skills would you call on to build a trusting and therapeutic partnership with Emma to facilitate your work with Jaime and Emma? Explain why this is so important.

Occupational therapy—clinical scenario 3

Themes

Transtheoretical model of behaviour change | Pain | Fear avoidance model | 'Noncompliance' | Person-centred practice

Scenario

Matt is a 25-year-old man who badly burned his dominant hand in an accident. He was drunk and messing around with his mates when he tripped and fell into a campfire.

He has been referred to see an occupational therapist for scar management. His injury and the resulting scarring is impacting on all his daily occupations; he is having difficulty dressing himself, using the toilet, eating, writing and cooking. He works as a plumber, recently starting his own business, which is growing.

Matt worries about whether he will be able to work again and how he will manage while he is recovering. He has had to move back in with his parents, and his mother is helping him with all his daily needs. He finds this embarrassing and frustrating.

Matt was very engaged in the initial stages of rehabilitation while he needed to wear a specially constructed splint and undertake gentle stretching exercises and massage. More recently though, you have noticed that his attitude has changed. He isn't doing his exercises regularly or completing his scar management routine and he complains about wearing the splint. He seems despondent, flat and frustrated. He says there is no point and that nothing is working. He complains that everything you ask him to do is too hard and painful, and he thinks the exercises and stretching in particular are making things worse.

He appears very embarrassed as you discuss how he is managing with self-care tasks like dressing and toileting.

Questions

1. Apply the transtheoretical model of behaviour change to this situation to help make sense of what may be going on for Matt.
2. How does the transtheoretical model of behaviour change help reframe Matt's behaviour and allow you as the therapist to maintain an empathetic and therapeutic relationship with Matt rather than become frustrated with his behaviour or label him as noncompliant?
3. Discuss how the concept of 'noncompliance' could apply here and the impact this could have on Matt and his experience of rehabilitation.
4. How may pain and, in particular, the fear avoidance model be impacting on Matt's behaviour and responses in therapy?
5. Consider how applying person-centred practice principles could help build a partnership with Matt and ameliorate his feelings of embarrassment and awkwardness while you are addressing highly personal issues.

Occupational therapy—clinical scenario 4

Themes

Loss | Person-centred practice | Advocacy | Multidisciplinary teamwork

Scenario

Agathe is a 79-year-old woman of Greek heritage. She speaks with heavily accented English. Her husband of 55 years, Con, died 6 months ago and she has been living alone in the family home since that time. She has been hospitalised following a night-time fall when getting up to go to the toilet and fracturing her neck of femur. You are the occupational therapist on the ward and have been asked to assess her and help with planning her discharge.

When you meet with her to conduct your initial assessment, she appears visibly distressed. She is convinced everyone is planning to move her to a nursing home and tells you that she must go home and be with Con. She doesn't seem obviously disoriented but is agitated and distressed. This, combined with her heavily accented English, is making it difficult to understand her. You decide to conduct a functional cognitive screen with her to check her cognitive status. Her performance on this indicates that her cognition is within normal limits. However, she is still adamant that she wants to go home to Con. As you actively listen to Agathe, and explain what you are doing and the reasons why, she starts to open up and expresses that her family home is the place she feels she can remain connected to her dead husband. She is very clear that he has died and isn't actually there but still feels the connection to him and takes great comfort in this. She talks about her daily routine, the things she does in her home and community, and it becomes clear that her home environment is very important to her and is likely to be sustaining her health and wellbeing.

While she is currently still frail, Agathe appears to be recovering well from her surgery. You conduct a self-care assessment, which she manages well. You plan to advocate for Agathe to return home with supports in place at the multidisciplinary discharge planning meeting, but you are overridden by the doctor on the team. The doctor is a much older woman who implies you are too inexperienced. The doctor also says that Agathe was clearly confused when she saw her this morning and kept talking about her dead husband. The discussion is cut short when the doctor gets a phone call and rushes off, saying that the plan needs to be for nursing home placement for Agathe.

Questions

1. How might Worden's four tasks of mourning apply to what Agathe is experiencing?
2. What specific strategies would you put in place when communicating with Agathe to ensure any language and cultural differences are not barriers to communication?
3. What factors might be going on within the multidisciplinary team that could affect client outcomes?
4. How could the occupational therapist address these issues within the team? Discuss the things that you would try and the possible implications.

Occupational therapy—clinical scenario 5

Themes

Cultural safety | Primary health care | Building healthy communities and capacity building

Scenario

Jara is a 4-year-old Aboriginal girl who attends the local community children and family centre in a remote country town. Jara is not yet talking and seems to have trouble understanding. She lives with her mother, father and two younger sisters. She plays well on her own and loves to run and climb and make things. She doesn't join in with any of the song times or group activities at the centre. Her mother, Tara, and auntie, Bette, are worried about how little she talks and how dreamy and vague she always seems, but they know she is a happy child and they love her for who she is.

You are working as an occupational therapist in the centre and your role is to support young children's development by working with the families and communities to create more positive and health-promoting environments.

You gently ask if Jara has ever had her ears or hearing checked because you wonder if maybe the reason she isn't speaking or joining in is that she isn't hearing what is going on around her. You are aware that Aboriginal children have high rates of ear infections and these often get missed.

Tara and Bette say they took her to a hospital in the nearest city last year but the people there didn't listen to them and that it was very rushed. They gave Jara medicine to take but it had to be kept in a fridge. Because it took them more than a day to get there and back, they were worried the medicine 'went off' in the heat. Jara didn't like taking the medicine and Tara and Bette didn't want to force her to take it in case it was off.

You arrange for them to come to the monthly health clinic that runs from the centre and is supported by local Aboriginal health workers. You ensure the doctor and audiologist will be there and support Jara, Tara and Bette through the process, checking that they understand what is going on and explaining things if required.

Jara is diagnosed with bilateral otitis media and prescribed antibiotics. This is followed up within the centre, with Tara receiving regular support to continue giving Jara the medicine. Jara needs two courses of antibiotics to cure the infection. As the infection clears, Jara starts to pay more attention to her surroundings.

The centre starts promoting the benefits of regular ear checks for all families attending and the importance of medicine in fixing these problems. The staff at the centre help the families interpret and build relationships with other healthcare staff through the process.

Cont... ▶

Questions

1. Discuss how this is an example of working with and applying primary healthcare principles.
2. Which aspects of the Ottawa Charter for Health Promotion are being applied here?
3. Applying a cultural safety perspective, how would you explain what happened to Jara and her family when she attended hospital?
4. How can occupational therapists work effectively with Indigenous peoples?
5. What specific communication skills are needed?

Glossary

Acceptance: unconditional positive regard of another person. The active process of recognising the reality of a situation, especially an aversive situation which cannot be changed, without attempting to protest, escape or avoid it.

Acceptance and commitment therapy (ACT): a cognitive behavioural intervention, which uses acceptance, mindfulness and behaviour change strategies to manage self-destructive behaviour. The goal of ACT is not to eradicate uncomfortable feelings, but rather to enable the person to accept and embrace them as unpleasant, but not catastrophic, experiences.

Active listening: a way of engaging with the other person's verbal and non-verbal communication to achieve mutual understanding. It involves using the micro-skills of paraphrasing, clarifying and empathy.

Acute stress: an immediate, short-term physical and psychological response to an actual or anticipated event or experience. It may or may not challenge the person's coping resources.

Adherence: see *compliance*.

Advanced care directives: a legal form that allows people over the age of 18 years to write down their wishes, preferences and instructions for future healthcare, end of life, living arrangements and personal matters and/or appoint one or more substitute decision-makers to make these decisions on their behalf when they are unable to do so themselves.

Advocacy: usually means a professional representing a patient when the professional believes the patient is disempowered or unable to speak for themselves.

Allodynia: pain in response to a non-painful stimulus, such as light touch.

Ambiguous loss: a loss that is unclear, unconfirmed or indeterminate and therefore is often more difficult to deal with.

Antecedents: the stimulus events that trigger a behaviour or response.

Anxiety: an unpleasant physical and emotional reaction to a perceived threat.

Attachment theory: a psychological model that emphasises the strong physical and emotional relationship between a child and a primary caregiver.

Auditability: the process of ensuring rigour in qualitative research by identifying the research process and decision trail.

Authoritarian parenting: parenting that is rejecting or unresponsive while at the same time attempting to control the child and what they do.

Authoritative parenting: parenting that is accepting and responsive while trying to control the child and protect them from mistakes.

Behavioural theory: a school of psychology that views behaviour as being influenced by factors external to the individual, that is, behaviours are learned depending on whether they are rewarded or not, by association with another event or by imitation. It is also called learning theory.

Behavioural model of health: suggests many illnesses result from the interaction between physical factors and the behaviour of individuals, with the responsibility for treatment residing solely with the individual.

Beneficence: an ethical principle that potential benefits outweigh the risks of participating in a research study.

Benzodiazepine: a class of psychoactive drugs that are commonly used in the treatment of anxiety and sleeplessness.

Beta-blockers: medications used to lower blood pressure and reduce heart rate.

Biological age: age in terms of physical health and development.

Biomedical: relates to the biology of the body and medical science with a focus on disease and illness, how it occurs, and how it can be treated or prevented.

Biomedical model of health: a health model holding that ill-health is caused by viruses and germs, injury or structural change, and as such there is one cause and one cure.

Biopsychosocial model of health: this model extends the causes of disease to social disadvantages linked to the environment and the social, cultural and political structures of a society. The biopsychosocial model takes into account the interactions between biological, psychological and social factors in assessing and treating the cause, presentation and outcome of wellness and disease.

Borderline personality disorder: a mental illness in which the person has trouble managing their emotions and impulses, often resulting in self-destructive behaviour.

Burnout: a psychological syndrome characterised by emotional exhaustion, cynicism and a diminished sense of self-efficacy that occurs as a consequence of prolonged chronic workplace stress.

Causal explanations: explanations that provide a single or sometimes multiple causes for why things occur; often formed with the word 'because'.

Central sensitisation: increased responsiveness or sensitivity of nociceptive neurons within the central nervous system (spinal cord and brain).

Cholesteatoma: an abnormal, noncancerous skin growth that can develop in the middle ear, behind the eardrum. It is most commonly caused by repeated middle ear infections.

Chronic conditions: long-term enduring conditions that can occur suddenly or over an extended period of time.

Chronic illness: see above.

Chronic pain: pain that lasts beyond the term of normal healing; pain that lasts for longer than 3 months.

Chronic stress: experienced when stressors continue over a prolonged period of time (months or years). Chronic stress can impair the individual's immune system.

Chronological age: the number of years since someone was born.

Classical conditioning: a simple form of learning by association whereby repeated pairing of a conditioned stimulus with an unconditioned stimulus elicits a conditioned response.

Claustrophobia: an irrational fear of small or confined spaces.

Clinical significance: the extent to which changes observed in a research study, such as reductions in symptoms, are meaningful for the patient and their management.

Code of conduct: a statement of belief about the standard of care a profession should deliver.

Cognitive appraisal: the assessment by the individual of a situation or stressor. It can be either primary (Is the event threatening, neutral or positive?) or secondary (Do I have the personal or other resources to respond to the stressor?)

Cognitive behavioural pain management: the use of cognitive behavioural therapy (see below) to manage pain.

Cognitive behavioural therapies: a range of psychological therapies that focus on challenging and changing cognitions (thoughts) and behaviours in order to change emotions, improve quality of life and influence outcomes.

Cognitive development: the development of mental processes such as knowledge acquisition, language, perception, problem-solving, memory and judgment within the brain's functioning.

Cognitive dissonance: the feeling of discomfort experienced when conflicting beliefs are held simultaneously. It is a technique used in motivational interviewing to bring about behavioural change.

Cognitive theory: a school of psychology that acknowledges the role of perception and thoughts about oneself, one's individual experience and the environment as influences on behaviour.

Collaborative practice: people from different backgrounds (e.g. health professionals and/ or clients and carers) working together to deliver quality care.

Collectivist culture: a culture in which the rights and aspirations of the family or group are greater than those of the individual. The smallest socioeconomic unit is the family and interdependence is valued.

Compliance: when a patient shows the behaviours and follows the treatment regimen a health professional has advised, they are described by many health professionals as 'compliant'. For some time, however, this term has been questioned and it has been suggested that it be replaced by 'adherence'.

Complicated grief: grief that is ongoing and problematic for the bereaved person, often associated with complexities in relationships, lack of preparation for the loss and limited social support.

Concordance: respecting the beliefs, needs and preferences of a person taking prescribed medication.

Concrete operational stage: when a child uses logical forms of reasoning to classify things into groups based on characteristics but only with concrete objects.

Conditioned response: the response elicited by the conditioned stimulus after repeated pairing with the unconditioned stimulus.

Conditioned stimulus: a neutral stimulus that elicits a particular response after repeated pairing with a stimulus that naturally produces the response (unconditioned stimulus).

Consumer (of healthcare): an individual who uses health services.

Consumer (of research): an individual who utilises research evidence to inform work practices, that is, engages in evidence-based practice.

Contextual explanations: explanations that provide situational descriptions of what conditions are present when something happens.

Control group: the group of participants in a randomised control trial that receive either no treatment or a standard treatment.

Coping strategy: the process of responding to and managing demands that the individual perceives as challenging or threatening.

Correlation: the degree of relationship between two or more events or characteristics.

Credibility: a measure of rigour in qualitative research. It establishes whether the results of the research are credible or believable from the perspective of the participant in the study.

CT: computed tomography, a medical imaging technique employing X-rays to examine the body's organs.

Daily hassles: minor stressful events that can have a cumulative effect on health.

Defence mechanism: an unconscious psychological process used to reduce anxiety and protect the conscious mind from threatening feelings and perceptions. Common defence mechanisms are denial, projection, repression and rationalisation.

Dementia: an umbrella term for a number of neurological conditions, of which the major symptom includes a global decline in brain function.

Denial: an unconscious defence mechanism whereby the individual does not acknowledge an impending or actual threat or loss.

Dependent variable: the presumed effect of the independent variable in the study, that is, the outcome that results from the intervention.

Descriptive theories: based on observation and conceptual interpretation rather than empirical research and evidence.

Determinism: a philosophical position that views all events as being predetermined and having a cause. It also proposes that specific causal factors can potentially be known.

Developmental milestones: key events or periods of a child's development; sometimes used as a watershed to predict outcomes if the milestone is met or not met adequately.

Developmental theories: a collection of theories that describe psychological, cognitive, emotional and physical development throughout the lifespan.

Diagnostic and Statistical Manual (DSM) V: a reference work published by the American Psychiatric Association that provides guidelines and criteria for diagnosing and classifying mental disorders.

Dialectical behaviour therapy: a cognitive behavioural intervention to manage self-destructive behaviours exhibited by people diagnosed with borderline personality disorder (BPD) (e.g. self-mutilation and suicidal ideas and actions).

Diathesis-stress hypothesis: a proposition that mental illness results from a combination of a genetic predisposition and environmental stress, and that both must be present for the condition to manifest itself.

Disenfranchised grief: grief that is not or cannot be openly acknowledged, publicly mourned or socially supported. Specific types of relationships, losses, grievers, circumstances and ways of grieving may not be socially recognised.

Disinhibited social engagement disorder: a type of attachment disorder that consists of a pattern of behaviour in which a child actively approaches and interacts with unfamiliar adults.

Dual process model: a particular conceptualisation of grieving that views the grief process as the oscillation between loss-oriented work and restoration-oriented work.

Early intervention: early diagnosis and treatment of illness to minimise the impact of the illness and its consequences.

Eclectic/holistic approach: draws on the theory and research from several paradigms to obtain an overall understanding and/or provide a more comprehensive explanation than would be achieved by using one theoretical model alone.

Emerging adulthood: the transition from adolescence to adulthood.

Empathy: sensing and non-judgmentally verbalising how one senses the other individual's feelings and meanings.

Endogamous marriage: a marriage in which the partners are from the same social, ethnic or cultural group.

Essentialism: explaining behaviour or events in terms of some 'essential' property of the person or object such as 'The tree moved because it possesses magic' or 'All African children like to dance'.

Ethics: moral principles that guide action. In health research ethical research ensures that potential benefits outweigh possible harm and that participants' consent is informed.

Evidence-based healthcare: using research findings to inform and establish sound clinical practices.

Exogamous marriage: a marriage in which the partners are from different groups.

Experimental group: the group of participants in a randomised control trial that receive the treatment or intervention under investigation.

Explanative theories: theories that are only satisfied when a cause or a context is given for why the events happened the way they did; description alone is not enough.

Fear appeal: efforts to increase motivation to change an individual's attitudes and behaviours by inducing fear.

Fear avoidance: the avoidance of physical activity due to a fear of increased pain and/or (re)injury.

Fight or flight mechanism: a response to a perceived threat involving sympathetic and endocrine arousal that prepares the individual to attack or flee.

Flinders model: a cognitive- and behavioural-based intervention for self-management of chronic disease.

Formal operational stage: stage in which abstract thinking is possible and can be used in reasoning and logical processes.

General adaptation syndrome (GAS): a stress response consisting of three phases: arousal, resistance and exhaustion.

Genuineness: genuine people are 'congruent'; their non-verbal behaviour is consistent with their inner thoughts and feelings.

Gestalt psychology: a school of psychology that maintains that psychological investigation must focus on the whole individual and the context in which behaviours occur, and not just on parts of the person or on an isolated behaviour.

Glasgow Coma Scale (GCS): a scale used to rate the level of consciousness of a patient suffering a traumatic injury or illness based on a total of scores for eye, verbal and motor responses. A maximum score of 15 indicates no impairment.

Grey literature: publications that are either unpublished or published in a non-commercial form such as government policies and reports, conference proceedings or theses.

Grief: the emotional response to an actual or anticipated loss.

Grief support and counselling: a therapeutic intervention which aims to assist individuals and groups to cope with the emotional, psychological, spiritual and physical consequences of loss

Grief process: the reactions, behaviours and adaptations that grieving people experience over time in response to a loss. This process has been described using such concepts as stages, phases and tasks.

Grief work: a view of grief first proposed by Sigmund Freud that emphasises the emotional, cognitive, social and behavioural activity and effort involved in coping and making adjustments after a significant loss.

Health: a state of mental, physical, social and spiritual wellbeing; not merely the absence of disease.

Health action process approach: a theory that explains the initiation, adoption and continuation of health behaviours as a process that consists of planning, action and maintenance tasks.

Health behaviour: action by an individual that enhances, maintains or threatens health.

Health belief model: a psychological theory that predicts health behaviours based on the person's perception of the health threat and belief that engaging in a certain behaviour will reduce the health threat.

Health biology: the focus of biology such as the pathological and physiological processes of the body to understand health and disease.

Health education: an educational approach to increase health literacy to assist individuals and communities to make informed decisions and take action regarding their health, particularly in relation to lifestyle.

Health inequities: inequalities in health that stem from differences in social status and are therefore 'socially unjust'.

Health literacy: the skills (cognitive and social) which influence an individual's ability to gain access to, understand and use health information.

Health locus of control: the individual's belief regarding responsibility for their health outcomes, that is, internal (personal), external/powerful others (e.g. doctors) or external/chance (fate).

Health promotion: the process of enabling people to increase control over, and to improve, their health. It can involve a range of educational, political, social and environmental strategies.

Health psychology: a field of study that examines how and why people stay healthy or become ill, and how individuals react when ill.

Healthy ageing: a process that develops and maintains physical, social and mental health to enable older people to participate and enjoy an active role in society.

Healthy Cities: a global movement initiated by the World Health Organization that encourages local governments to engage in health development through political commitment, institutional change, capacity building, partnership-based planning and innovative projects.

Humanistic psychology: a school of psychology that emphasises the development of a concept of self and the striving of the individual towards achieving personal goals and potential.

Hyperalgesia: increased or exaggerated pain in response to a noxious stimulus.

Hypoaesthesia: decreased sensitivity, particularly with regard to touch or pressure.

Illness prevention: strategies that aim to deter the occurrence of illness.

Independent variable: the presumed cause of the outcome (dependent variable) observed.

Indigenous Australian: a person who identifies as being Aboriginal or Torres Strait Islander.

Individualist culture: a culture in which the individual's goals and achievements are valued over those of the family or group. The smallest socioeconomic unit is the individual and independence is valued.

Indulgent (or permissive) parenting: parenting that accepts what a child does and where a parent does not try to control the child.

Informed consent: an ethical principle that requires a researcher to obtain the voluntary participation of subjects after informing them of potential benefits and risks.

Intercultural communication: communication between people that respects, values and understands individuals of different cultural or linguistic origins.

Interdisciplinary: an approach to healthcare practice in which different health disciplines, such as psychology, nursing, social work and other medical and allied health professionals, work collaboratively to achieve common, shared goals (see *multidisciplinary*).

Intermediary determinants: the 'downstream' social factors that maintain, but can also minimise health inequalities that are caused by the structural determinants of health such as education, housing and access to transport.

Intersectoral: an approach whereby different agencies and government departments such as health, housing and transport work collaboratively on a common goal like 'health'.

Kinship: family or blood ties.

Levels of loss: Weenolsen's framework proposing that loss is experienced at five levels: primary, secondary, holistic, self-conceptual and metaphorical.

Lifespan development: changes that occur from birth throughout a person's life.

Locus of control (LOC): the individual's belief regarding responsibility for reinforcement for a particular behaviour and whether the individual believes that reinforcements (outcomes) are controlled by the self (internal LOC) or by the environment (external LOC).

Loss: separation from someone or something that has meaning for the individual and to which they feel strongly connected.

Māori: an indigenous New Zealander.

Marriage: a permanent and legally recognised arrangement between two people that includes both a sexual and an economic relationship with mutual rights and obligations.

Mechanism: a scientific philosophy developed by Descartes that rejects purpose and qualities in favour of what is quantifiable. It proposes that all natural phenomena, including human behaviour, can be explained by physical causes and processes.

Mediational/mediationism: where behaviour or concepts are mediated by something else; we see a tree and walk towards it but this is mediated by the eye and brain and these must be part of our explanation.

Medical model: the view that health and illness (including behavioural and emotional problems) have physical causes and hence are treated with biomedical interventions. It is the predominant model of care delivery in Western healthcare systems.

Metabolic syndrome: the presence of three of more of the following symptoms: central abdominal obesity, hyperglycaemia, hypertension, elevated triglycerides or low levels of high-density lipoprotein cholesterol.

Micro-skills: attending behaviours that are the essence of good communication including eye contact, attentive body language, vocal style and verbal style.

Milestones of adulthood: significant events that occur in adult life.

Mindfullness: The ability to focus on the present moment and to fully embrace the experience, with the goal of reducing anxiety and distress, and increasing feelings of wellbeing. It requires paying active, open attention to the present. Meditation is a tool used to achieve mindfulness.

Modelling: learning by observation (also called vicarious learning).

Monogamous: refers to a relationship in which an individual has only one partner at a time.

Morbidity: the frequency or occurrence of a disease and the degree to which the illness or disability affects the person.

Mortality rate: the number of deaths in a population (from a specific cause).

Motivational interviewing: a client-centred, semi-directed counselling approach that encourages an individual to change a health behaviour by focusing on reasons for and against the change. The resulting cognitive dissonance creates a state of ambivalence for the person and hence an opportunity for the person to initiate change. It is particularly suited to clients with addictive behaviours.

MRI: magnetic resonance imaging, a medical imaging technique employing strong magnetic fields and radiofrequencies to examine the body's organs.

Multidisciplinary team: team composed of health professionals from different disciplines, each with their own specialised knowledge, skills and expertise, who work collaboratively. Also called the interdisciplinary team.

Nature versus nurture: the controversy concerning whether human behaviour is influenced more by genetic inheritance and biology (nature) or by learning and the environment (nurture).

Neglectful (or uninvolved) parenting: parenting that is unaccepting or unresponsive to the child and also does not try to control them.

Neoliberal policy: policy based on the idea that the market will provide what is needed given the opportunity. Health is therefore a commodity and those who need health purchase it.

Nephrogenic systemic fibrosis: a disease found in patients with advanced renal disease exposed to gadolinium characterised by hardening of the skin and connective tissues.

Neuropathic pain: pain arising as a direct consequence of a lesion or disease of the somatosensory nervous system.

New public health: a movement which incorporates social determinants and politics into the traditional biomedical approach of public health.

Nociception: activity in the nervous system generated by a noxious stimulus. Pain is not necessarily implied in nociception.

Nociception: activity in the nervous system generated by a noxious stimulus.

Nociceptive pain: pain arising from actual or threatened damage to non-neural tissue (e.g. soft tissue sprains and strains, bone fractures or appendicitis) and is due to activation of nociceptors.

Nociplastic pain: pain due to altered nociception despite no clear evidence of actual or threatened tissue damage or disease or lesion of the somatosensory system initiating the pain (e.g. chronic widespread pain).

Nociceptor: a high threshold sensory receptor of the peripheral somatosensory nervous system that is preferentially sensitive to noxious stimuli.

Nonfinite loss: the loss associated with experiences such as disability and dementia that unfolds throughout one's lifespan and involves awareness of having lost 'what should have been'.

Noxious stimulus: a stimulus that is actually or potentially damaging to body tissue.

Object permanence: when a child acts as if an object has permanence even when it cannot be seen.

Operant conditioning: a learning process whereby outcomes are controlled by consequences of the behaviour, that is, whether behaviour is rewarded, punished or ignored.

Optimism: the perception and belief that adverse events are a temporary challenge to be addressed and are within the control of the individual.

Pain behaviour: any behaviour that serves to indicate that a person is in pain (e.g. complaining, grimacing, limping, avoiding activity).

Palliative care: an approach to healthcare concerned primarily with attending to physical and emotional comfort, rather than effecting a cure, through responding holistically to symptoms, pain and emotional, social and spiritual needs.

Parenting: taking care of another person (i.e. raising a child by taking responsibility for their care and supporting their development).

Partnership: a relationship between a health professional and the recipient of care in which they both share some degree of responsibility for the treatment decisions, implementation and outcomes.

Person-centred communication: one element of person-centred practice (see below).

Person-centred practice: working in partnership with a person to understand their individual perspective in order to reach a shared understanding that enables a sharing of power, responsibility and decision-making in care.

Peripheral sensitisation: increased responsiveness or sensitivity of nociceptive neurons in the periphery, which occurs in response to a noxious stimulus.

Pessimism: the perception and belief that adverse events are permanent, catastrophic and outside the control of the individual.

Phenomenology: a qualitative research methodology that examines a phenomenon or the 'lived experience' of a phenomenon. It aims to understand either the experience or the meaning of the experience for the participant(s).

Placebo: a substance or treatment which is inert or sham but has a psychobiological effect attributable to the overall therapeutic context, including factors such as beliefs and expectations of both patient and clinician, the patient–clinician interaction and the environment in which the treatment takes place.

Policy: a series of actions by a government that guide present or future courses of action. For example, Medicare is a government policy that provides healthcare for all Australians with funding derived from the taxation base. This enables Medicare to be classified as a universal healthcare policy based on redistribution of taxes between high income earners and lower income groups.

Polyandry: where a woman has more than one husband at the same time.

Polygyny (polygamous marriage): marriage to multiple spouses.

Population-focused approaches: approaches to health promotion that target whole communities (not individuals) who share a common health need (e.g. school students regarding sun protection, people who live in rural areas regarding depression and suicide, and the elderly regarding falls prevention).

Population health: the health of a group of people who are united by a specific factor (e.g. biological, social or geographic). A population health approach is action taken to improve the health of whole populations.

Positivism: the philosophical view that knowledge is limited to facts that are observable or obtained through scientific experiment.

Posttraumatic stress disorder (PTSD): a serious, debilitating mental illness that affects some people who experience or witness an extremely traumatic stressful event that is outside the realm of usual human experience and involves the threat of death or serious injury.

Preoperational stage: when children begin to have words for the things around them and use those words, but this stage is 'pre' operational where 'operational' refers to 'logical' operations.

Primary appraisal: the individual's judgment as to whether a particular event or situation is negative (poses a threat), positive (benign) or neutral (irrelevant).

Primary healthcare: a holistic approach to healthcare that is underpinned by a philosophy of social justice and addresses the social determinants of health in addition to biomedical causative factors for illness.

Primary intervention: the implementation of biomedical, psychosocial, political and environmental strategies that aim to foster wellbeing and prevent the occurrence of illness.

Probability: the likelihood that a research finding occurred by chance (statistical significance).

Professional boundaries: the limits of a relationship between a professional and a client and /or carers which recognises the professional's power and client vulnerability and allows for an appropriate, safe and effective relationship.

Prolonged grief disorder: a particular type of complicated grief characterised by intrusive thoughts related to the deceased, intense separation distress and/or distressingly strong yearnings for the person or thing that is lost, lasting longer than six months and causing significant impairment in functioning.

Protective factors for health: factors that reduce the likelihood that an illness will occur; for example, by being vaccinated, by having access to clean water and by having a supportive family and social network.

Proximity: the distance people place themselves from each other in different interactions such as public, social and personal.

Psychology: the scientific study of behaviour—essentially, but not exclusively, the study of human behaviour.

Psychoanalytic theory: a personality theory that asserts that behaviour is driven by unconscious processes, as well as influenced by childhood/developmental conflicts that either have been resolved or remain unresolved.

Psychological age: an individual's ability to adapt to various circumstances compared with others who might be the same chronological age.

Psychological theories: derived from psychological research and propose explanations for human behaviour.

Psychoneuroimmunology: the multidisciplinary study of the interrelationship between behavioural, neuroendocrine and immunological adaptive processes.

Psychosocial ageing: a focus on changes in the psychological and social aspects of a person as they age.

Public policy: a system of regulatory measures, social laws, or courses of action by governments to enhance community outcomes.

Public health: concerned with the health of individuals, communities and populations and also the identification and modification of environmental factors that impact on health.

Qualitative research: a research paradigm that is interested in questions that involve human consciousness and subjectivity and values humans and their experiences in the research process.

Quantitative research: a process that attempts to find out scientific knowledge by measurement of elements.

Quasi-experimental design: a study design in which random assignment is not used but the independent variable is manipulated and certain mechanisms of control are used.

Randomised control trial (RCT): an experimental study of the effects of a variable (e.g. a drug or treatment) administered to human subjects who are randomly selected from a broad population and assigned randomly to either an experimental or a control group.

Rational non-adherence: a person may not believe that what a health professional suggests is in their best interest and, after considering the facts, may choose not to accept treatment or choose a different therapy.

Recovery: refers to the process of making adaptations to live with an ongoing or chronic illness. The focus is on the individual's strengths, aspirations and enabling them to live a fulfilling life, regardless of any disability.

Recovery-oriented care: working in partnership with a person to support personal autonomy, social identity, a sense of hope and engagement in life despite their symptoms.

Reductionism: a philosophical approach in which concepts are interpreted with reference to simpler processes. The issue under investigation is analysed into simpler parts or organised systems, with a view to explaining or understanding it.

Refereed journal: a journal that requires its articles to have been evaluated or critiqued by expert peers before being accepted for publication.

Reliability: a statistical term for the internal consistency of a test and the extent to which it can be expected to produce the same result on different occasions.

Research consumer: an individual who utilises research evidence to inform work practices, that is, engages in evidence-based practice.

Research ethics: ethical issues that can arise when people are participants in research.

Resilience: the ability to bounce back following adversity and to achieve good outcomes despite challenges and threats.

Rigour: the extent to which research methods are scrupulously and meticulously carried out in order to recognise important influences in the study.

Risk factors for health: increase vulnerability to illness (e.g. social inequities and poor nutrition).

Sample: a group of cases or individuals studied as representatives of the population from which they are drawn.

Secondary appraisal: the individual's assessment of his/her personal (internal) and environmental (external) resources to respond to a particular stressful event or situation.

Secondary intervention: healthcare that is delivered when symptoms, injury or illness are identified. Treatment is initiated as early as possible to restore health.

Secondary source: scholarly material written by someone other than the individual who developed the theory or conducted the research. Most are usually published. Often a secondary source represents a response to or a summary and critique of a theorist's or researcher's work.

Self-actualisation: the achievement of one's potential and the mark of a healthy individual according to Maslow.

Self-disclosure: when one person shares their own personal information or experiences to another.

Self-efficacy: the personal belief that one can achieve certain goals and cope adequately in particular circumstances.

Sensorimotor stage: children at this stage think, as it were, through their senses and their physical movements; children explore and learn just what they physically interact with through their senses.

Settings: a holistic multidisciplinary model of health promotion, which is delivered in the everyday settings of people's lives (e.g. school, work, communities). It is focused on health, rather than illness.

Social age: the social roles and expectations relative to chronological age.

Social construction: an idea, concept or phenomenon that is viewed as real because there is agreement within a social group that they will act as if the construction does exist.

Social determinants of health: the social and economic factors that impact on health outcomes such as socioeconomic status, housing and employment.

Social gradient: the gap between those who are well-off and those who are socially and economically disadvantaged. It is presented as a sloping line moving from low income to high income. It is also present within the workplace between lower paid and higher paid workers.

Social justice: a value base that views fairness and equity as a right for all regardless of social position.

Social learning theory: Bandura's theory of observational learning or modelling.

Social marketing: uses marketing principles and theory from the disciplines of psychology, sociology and communications to identify solutions to social and health problems and to encourage individuals and populations to lead healthy lifestyles.

Social model of health: the health of an individual is a result of their social circumstances and social policies.

Social readjustment rating scale (SRRS): developed by Holmes and Rathe, the SRRS is a tool for measuring the impact of life changes on health and to predict an individual's vulnerability to illness.

Social scaffolding: having social support or help from those around you.

Sociocultural approach: refers to how society and culture contribute to a person's development by influencing how people learn and think.

Sociological theories: explanatory models for human behaviour in which the emphasis shifts from the individual to the broader social forces influencing the person.

Somatosensory nervous system: the part of the nervous system (peripheral and central) that provides conscious perception of sensory information from the skin, musculoskeletal system and viscera.

Spirituality: an individual process of having a sense of connection and purpose to the universe and life formed from personal beliefs.

Statistical significance: the likelihood that the results of a study could have occurred by chance or not (probability).

Stigmatisation: the process of perceiving, describing or responding to a person or groups of people in such a way that they are socially discredited, devalued or isolated.

Stress: a physical, cognitive, emotional and behavioural experience of an individual in response to an event that the individual perceives to be challenging or threatening.

Stress as a process or transaction: a process or transaction between the individual and the environment in response to a stressor.

Stress as a stimulus: refers the stressors in the environment that precipitates a stress reaction in an individual.

Stress as a response: the individual's physical, emotional and psychological reaction to the stressor.

Stressor: the event or experience that challenges or threatens the individual's coping resources.

Structural determinants: the societal factors and components of people's socioeconomic position that generate or reinforce social and political inequalities such as class, gender, ethnicity or access to resources.

Systematic review: a literature review that examines all of the available quality literature on a research question and provides a comprehensive summary of the findings.

Tertiary intervention: healthcare delivered when the disease cannot be cured or the illness process is prolonged. It aims to assist individuals (and their family and carers) to cope with a change in their health status, to limit disability from the health problem and to promote health and quality of life.

The therapeutic triad: the three qualities considered important by Rogers: genuineness, acceptance and empathy.

Thematic analysis: a method of analysis in qualitative research.

Theory of planned behaviour: a psychological theory that proposes that a person's intentions and behaviour can be understood by identifying the person's attitudes to the behaviour, subjective norms about the behaviour and the person's belief regarding their control of the action.

Third force: a term used to describe the school of humanistic psychology.

Thyroid: a gland in the neck, near the base of the throat. The thyroid gland makes hormones that help control many of the body's metabolic processes, such as heart rate, blood pressure, body temperature and weight.

Transtheoretical model: a model of behaviour change that outlines the stages a person goes through when changing a behaviour. The stages are precontemplation, contemplation, preparation, action and maintenance (or relapse).

Triangulation: the use of multiple methods of data collection on the same topic.

Typology: the systematic classification of types, such as losses, that have characteristics or traits in common.

Unconditioned stimulus: a stimulus that regularly and reliably elicits a response such as salivation at the sight of food.

Validity: determination of whether a measurement instrument actually measures what it is purported to measure.

Yerkes-Dodson law: a hypothesis that predicts performance based on the degree to which the individual is aroused. The theory predicts that performance increases with arousal up to a point at which performance deteriorates.

Zone of proximal development: Vygotsky's term for the range of behaviour between what a child can do alone and what a child can do with social scaffolding.

Index

Page numbers followed by 'f' indicate figures 't' indicate tables and 'b' indicate boxes.